THE
EXPERIMENTAL ANALYSIS
OF BEHAVIOR

THE CENTURY PSYCHOLOGY SERIES

Richard M. Elliott, Gardner Lindzey & Kenneth MacCorquodale

Editors

THOM VERHAVE
Arizona State University

THE
EXPERIMENTAL ANALYSIS
OF BEHAVIOR

Selected Readings

 New York

APPLETON-CENTURY-CROFTS
Division of Meredith Publishing Company

To

F. S. KELLER

and

W. N. SCHOENFELD

PREFACE

The main purpose of this collection of papers is to provide materials for students of current research concerning the experimental analysis of behavior.

The book is intended to serve both as a supplementary textbook for students in introductory courses and as a source book for more advanced courses and seminars.

As a supplementary text it is primarily intended to accompany *Principles of Reinforcement* by F. S. Keller and W. N. Schoenfeld and *The Analysis of Behavior* by J. G. Holland and B. F. Skinner.

Rather than use extensive interstitial material for each selection or chapter, I have preferred to write a single introductory chapter which serves, I hope, much the same purpose. It may also increase the possibility that the book can be used by itself.

Editors of books of readings usually find it necessary to rationalize their criteria for selection. In this respect I owe a considerable debt of gratitude to those friends and colleagues who gave their counsel and advice. I hope they will accede to receive my acknowledgment anonymously. In addition to their thoughtful suggestions, however, the personal interests and whims of the editor were involved to an inextricable degree. The final responsibility for better or worse must therefore rest with myself.

Whether the results of my editorial decisions will be found useful and valuable to others, the readers of the *Journal of the Experimental Analysis of Behavior* will, I suspect, be the main judges.

Since it clearly was impossible to reprint all of the volumes of "JEAB" published since 1958 in addition to all relevant articles in *Science* and other journals, many difficult and arbitrary decisions had to be made. And so, to those friends and colleagues who find important articles missing, I let it herewith be known that I will appreciate the receipt of angry letters, so that armed with this constructive and critical feedback, a second volume can in due time correct the present one.

I would like to thank the original authors of the papers here reprinted for their kind permission to plunder the results of their scholarship and experimental skill. In deference to their integrity, I have limited editorial cutting to a minimum. Special acknowledgment is due to Drs. C. B.

Ferster and B. F. Skinner for their generous permission to reproduce the glossary to *Schedules of Reinforcement*.

I also wish to express my gratitude to the original publishers who granted permission to reprint this material. In addition I am especially grateful to those authors who contributed original prints of photographs used in several of the articles.

To Kenneth MacCorquodale goes my sincere appreciation for his careful editorial criticisms. The critical evaluation and suggestions as well as the general support for this endeavor given by Arthur J. Bachrach were also very much appreciated.

In addition I wish to express my thanks to my publisher for the interest in and support of this project. His patience over the last three years is warmly appreciated.

A similar but even more deserved acknowledgment is due to my wife, who has, in addition to her many other activities, found the time to serve as secretary and typist.

The cooperation of Mrs. Jane Little in retyping a last-minute revision of the entire first chapter is gratefully acknowledged.

Finally, I take particular pleasure in gratefully acknowledging the conscientious assistance of Mr. Harold Friedman in the preparation of the manuscript, the reading of the galleys, and his painstaking review of the page proofs.

Thom Verhave

Tempe, Arizona

CONTENTS

CHAPTER V   DISCRIMINATION AND GENERALIZATION   190

CHAPTER VI   RESPONSE DIFFERENTIATION AND INDUCTION   239

CHAPTER VII   CHAINING AND CONDITIONED REINFORCEMENT   272

Chapter I

AN INTRODUCTION TO THE
EXPERIMENTAL ANALYSIS OF BEHAVIOR

It is Nature herself that should be
examined as closely as possible . . .
progress may be slow, but what we
find will be certain.

W. J. 'sGravesande (1688-1742)

INTRODUCTION

Although space limitations force a selective coverage of the subject, it is hoped that this brief survey will be of value to those who are introduced for the first time to the current literature concerning the experimental analysis of behavior. This introduction especially emphasizes material relevant to an understanding of this literature, and the topics discussed have more or less been keyed to the sample articles presented in this volume.

In order to keep the bibliography within reasonable limits, statements are made frequently without citation of many of the relevant publications. The bibliography especially includes those review articles and books in which additional information concerning particular topics can be found.

OPERANT CONDITIONING AND OPERANT BEHAVIOR

In *An Introduction to the Study of Experimental Medicine,* Claude Bernard wrote: "I am convinced that, in experimental sciences that are evolving, and especially in those as complex as biology, discovery of a new tool for observation or experiment is much more useful than any number of systematic or philosophic dissertations. Indeed, a new method or a new means of investigation increases our power and makes discoveries and researches possible which would not have been possible without its help" (Bernard, 1865; 1957 edition, p. 171).

Bernard's point is demonstrated by Pavlov's discovery (1927) of condi-

1

tioning and the subsequent development of conditioning techniques as tools for experimental analysis in physiology, psychology, and pharmacology. Bernard's statement is also illustrated by Skinner's introduction of frequency of responding as a dependent variable in the investigation of the factors controlling operant or voluntary behavior (Skinner, 1930, 1956). Since Skinner's basic experiments are not as well known and are more recent than Pavlov's, one of his early ground-breaking experiments will be described in some detail. In 1932 Skinner first reported the development of an experimental method that, with various modifications by many subsequent workers, has become "a fixture in modern experimental research on behavior" (Keller and Schoenfeld, 1950). His method for studying the conditioning of a "voluntary" act by a white rat required (1) an experimental cage equipped with a device that dispensed a small pellet of food to a hungry rat each time the animal pressed down a small lever at one end of its chamber and (2) a recorder that automatically registered the rate of lever pressing. Today, as in Skinner's original studies, the rate of responding usually is recorded as a cumulative curve on a modified kymograph. A pen moves across a paper tape which is driven by a slowly revolving cylinder. With each response, a ratchet device moves the pen vertically for a short, uniform distance. The resulting sloping line, therefore, is proportional to the rate of responding (Ferster and Skinner, 1957; Skinner, 1938).

Figure 1 illustrates the construction of a cumulative record of behavior. The steplike nature of the record is obvious in this figure because of the excessively large time and response units selected for illustrative purposes.

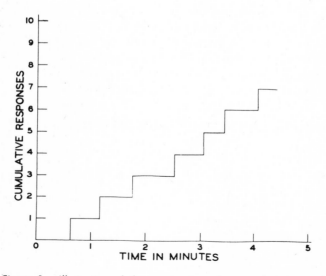

Figure 1. Illustration of the construction of a cumulative record.

In contemporary work involving many different species, appropriate paper speeds and unit steps are chosen so that the rates to be studied give convenient slopes. Figure 2 shows an example of the various slopes obtained with a recorder running with a paper speed of 30 cm. per hour. Each millimeter in the vertical dimension represents eight responses.

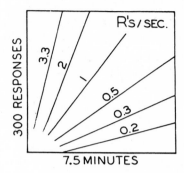

Figure 2. Grid illustrating the various slopes obtained with a cumulative recorder.

Figure 3 is a cumulative record produced by a rat nosing a small plastic disk in a wall of a small cage. Each time the rat pushed with his nose against the disk, a small (0.1 gram) pellet of food was dropped into a cup in the cage. The animal previously had been deprived of food for 22 hours. The outstanding feature of this record is the progressive decrease in the rate of responding as the number of pellets eaten increases.

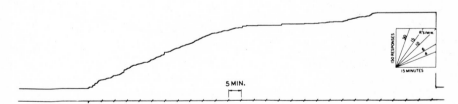

Figure 3. Performance of a rat nosing a low-mounted pigeon key (see Figure 4) on regular reinforcement.

It may be pointed out that the experimenter never intervenes to modify records generated by a cumulative recorder. The cumulative recording data presented in this survey are photographic reproductions of original records made by the animals themselves.

In the experiment illustrated by Figure 3, the response required by the animal was chosen by the experimenter. The responses by a subject in this type of experiment are referred to as *operants,* and the process of teaching the subject the required (operant) behavior is referred to as *operant conditioning.*

In laboratory experiments, selection of a response is based on the following considerations: (1) the response should be objectively measurable; (2) it should be executed easily by the subject; (3) the experimental subject should be able to respond repeatedly without fatigue (Ferster, 1953).

In operant conditioning experiments with pigeons, the birds are trained to peck at a small translucent plastic key or disk mounted at about the height of the beak in one of the walls of a small cage (Figure 4). A bird may make as many as 70,000 pecks during a 4½ hour experimental period. Rates of key pecking may vary between zero and 15 pecks per second.

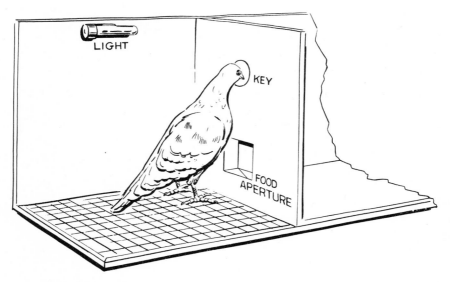

Figure 4. Experimental cage used for operant-conditioning research with pigeons.

Figure 5 shows the cumulative record "drawn" by a rat on a variable-interval schedule of reinforcement (reward). The animal pressed a lever mounted in one of the walls of a small cage. Although the animal was free to press the lever at any time, it was reinforced only occasionally with a food pellet. The pellets were given at irregular (variable) intervals. In this experiment the intervals between payoff ranged from 5 to 120 seconds, and the mean interval was 1 minute. The scale of the record is indicated by the insert in Figure 5 which shows a small set of coordinates containing some representative slopes.

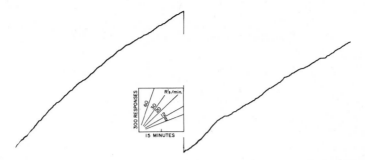

Figure 5.   Performance of a rat under variable-interval reinforcement.

This experiment, as in the case of most contemporary work, was programmed automatically by means of electrical relay circuits. Data were recorded by running-time meters, impulse counters, and a cumulative recorder. A general discussion of some of the basic techniques of operant conditioning can be found in publications of Ferster and Skinner (Ferster, 1953; Ferster and Skinner, 1957).

The phenomena of operant conditioning are not restricted to laboratory animals, nor is elaborate and expensive equipment necessary to demonstrate their basic properties. Anyone in the possession of a watch with a large sweep-second hand can demonstrate to himself the operant conditioning phenomena shown by Skinner's experiments.

A lecturer standing in front of a fairly small audience makes an especially good subject. Many speakers let their eyes wander from person to person. Before conditioning, the experimenter should determine the number of times the speaker looks at him during a given period, e.g., 10 minutes. This allows one to calculate the pre-experimental or control rate of the response involved. This has come to be called the operant level of the behavior in question (Keller and Schoenfeld, 1950). From then on, every time the speaker looks at him, the experimenter should smile or nod, meanwhile keeping a record of the frequency of the speaker's behavior during successive 5 minute intervals. It is not uncommon to triple or even quadruple the frequency of the "looking-at-the-experimenter" behavior within a 20 minute period. The operant conditioning of "verbal behavior" of human subjects has become a favorite topic of research since the pioneering work of Greenspoon (1949, 1955) and Verplanck (1955). A summary of a large number of studies in this area can be found in articles by Krasner (1958, 1962).

The consequences of Skinner's modest and seemingly trivial initial experiments have been staggering. Since 1930, at an acceleration, the end of which is not yet in sight, thousands of rats and pigeons, as well as mice, turtles, chimpanzees, fish, cats, dogs, college students, mentally defective persons, psychotic patients, and naval trainees, have been pushing doors, pressing levers, nosing plastic disks, and pulling all sorts of switches, thereby unwittingly producing cumulative records.

OPERANT BEHAVIOR, REINFORCEMENT, AND FEEDBACK

In all of these experiments, the behavior of the subjects is controlled by its consequences. In the experiment with the rat (see Figure 5) the consequence of pressing the lever was the delivery of an occasional pellet of food. Such consequences of behavior, ranging from water and candy to a pat on the back, are some of the most powerful factors that alter the rate of voluntary behavior. With this type of behavior, the organism acts upon its environment and thereby changes it. Skinner proposed the term "operant behavior" because the organism operates on its environment. These changes in the environment produced by the behavior of the organism subsequently change the organism and affect its future behavior. Because of these feedback effects of what in daily life are usually called rewards and punishment, this area of research may be thought of as a kind of experimental cybernetics (Ashby, 1958, 1960; Weiner, 1948).

Operant behavior, then, is powerfully controlled by the consequences of similar previous behavior. Those events that do control behavior in this way, when they follow or are made contingent upon it, are now called "reinforcers." The principle of reinforcement was formulated by the American psychologist Thorndike (1898, 1911, 1916, 1931, 1932) as the "law of effect," which stated in essence that voluntary behavior may be changed in strength by its past consequences.

RESPONSE VARIABILITY AND DIFFERENTIATION

One of the basic facts of operant behavior, and all biological phenomena, is its variability (Keller and Schoenfeld, 1950). Each individual response that occurs in the experimental situations described above differs slightly from every other. With the key peck of the pigeon, for example, individual responses may differ in various aspects, such as force, speed, and duration. By taking advantage of this response variability and by making use of the principle of reinforcement, the experimenter can produce behavior that otherwise might never have occurred in an organism's repertoire. If he has control of a reinforcer, for instance food, that can be made instantly contingent upon a specific activity of an organism, he can also make the reinforcement contingent upon those responses that meet special requirements. Beginning then with a form of the response already in the animal's repertoire, one can gradually develop increasingly different forms by observing the natural variability of the behavior from instant to instant and shifting the reinforcement in the direction of whatever specific form of the behavior is required. Thus, starting with a rat that initially simply presses a lever far enough to close a microswitch, one may eventually get an animal that presses the lever with a force between 200 and 300 grams. Such an accomplishment depends on the fact that the forces with which individual responses occur vary from instant to instant. If the initial range of force lies between 40 to 50 grams, and the mean force is 45 grams, one can reinforce only those presses that are emitted with a force greater than 47 grams. This value is chosen so that at least some responses are guaranteed to be reinforced so that the behavior will be maintained. If the force criteria are shifted too rapidly, "extinction" (disappearance of the behavior) may occur because of lack of reinforcement. An analogous procedure can be followed with respect to response duration. An early description of the process was given by the English surgeon and biologist Alfred Smee (1850):

> The various images impressed upon the mind of man and animals, according to their pleasurable or painful character, regulate . . . their subsequent operations. By a pleasurable impression the most obdurate beast may, to some extent, be tamed, and led to perform various acts . . .
>
> Pigeons may be readily taught to go through a bolting wire by gently pushing them through a few times and then supplying them with food. Goldfinches, redpolls, and some other species of the charming finch kind, may be taught to draw up their water in a little bucket by accustoming the bird to go to one spot for the water. The water is then placed barely within their reach, and then a trifle beyond it, taking care that they do not perish for want of water before they have learnt the trick.

By successive reinforcements of small gradations in the direction of the required performance, it is possible then to shape the activity of the animal and mold behavior "just as the sculptor shapes his figure from a lump of clay" (Skinner, 1953). This technique is sometimes referred to as the "method of successive approximation" or "shaping," and the process itself has been termed response differentiation.

VOLUNTARY AND INVOLUNTARY BEHAVIOR

The question arises as to what extent the operant conditioning studies, examples of which have been described above, are related to Pavlov's pioneering research on conditioning. In order to clarify this issue, a distinction must be made between two different kinds of behavior. This distinction is closely related to the traditional views on voluntary and involuntary behavior which date back to the early days of the experimental investigation of reflex behavior (Fearing, 1930). Only recently, however, have the relevant distinguishing properties of these two kinds of behavior become clear. One view is that voluntary behavior is accompanied by consciousness, that is subjective phenomena; the occurrence of these subjective phenomena provides the real distinction between reflex and voluntary behavior (Bierens De Haan, 1940). Reflex behavior also has traditionally been defined mainly in negative terms such as involuntary, unlearned, and unconscious. It is, furthermore, frequently stated that voluntary movements are movements which are directed, purposive, and supposedly more variable. In contrast, reflexes are often described as machinelike, simple, and inevitable responses to sensory (incoming) stimuli. A reflex is said to work like a coin in a vending machine. This description of the reflex is true when only the general character of the reaction is considered, but when examined in detail the reflex response usually shows a considerable degree of variability and complexity. No clear-cut distinction can be drawn from such loose and ambiguous criteria. Because of the ambiguity of the terms involved in these traditional discussions concerning the real and apparent differences between voluntary and involuntary behavior, it is not surprising that these concepts have been associated with a long history of scientific dispute. Arguments concerning the interpretation of experimental data go back to the early days of experimental physiology (Fearing, 1930). Because technical terms in science are no better than their clarity of meaning, several investigators have tried to introduce new terms and concepts. The terms operant and respondent behavior have now become well established and will be used throughout the remainder of this survey.

RESPONDENT BEHAVIOR: REFLEXES

One of the classical preparations employed in the experimental analysis of reflex behavior is the scratch reflex of the spinal dog. A spinal dog is an animal in which the spinal cord has been transected below the medulla. In the case of such a preparation the scratch reflex becomes observable within a few months after surgery, after which tickling the skin, pulling lightly on a hair, or stimulation with a weak electric current within a large saddle-shaped area of the rump of the dog elicits scratching movements of the hind leg. These movements consist of rhythmic flexions and extensions of the leg at the ankle, the knee and the hip. The movements recur at a frequency of about four times per second, and they may last several seconds.

On the basis of many detailed experiments and observations of the functional properties of the scratch reflex and other reflexes, several important basic principles of reflex behavior have been formulated. A prominent figure in this field was Sir Charles Sherrington (1906), a British physiologist who summarized and drew together the work of his predecessors and contemporaries.

Movements that function like Sherrington's spinal reflex can be defined in general as reflex behavior. Some of the basic aspects of this behavior are stated below.

1. *The principle of the threshold:* The intensity of the stimulus must exceed a certain critical point in order to produce a response.

2. *The principle of latency:* An interval of time elapses between the onset of the stimulus and the occurrence of the response.

3. *The principle of after-discharge:* The response persists for some time after the cessation of the stimulus.

The above three aspects of reflex behavior, are, of course, general features true of all behavior controlled by stimuli. In addition, however, the following functional relationships hold especially true for reflex behavior.

4. There is a relationship between the intensity of the stimulus and the magnitude of the response. In the case of the knee jerk, for example, the kick of the leg becomes higher as the force of tap on the patellar tendon is increased.

5. The latency and the after-discharge of a reflex are also a function of the intensity of the stimulus. In the case of the scratch reflex of a spinal dog, for example, not only the magnitude, but also the latency and the after-discharge of the response are modified if the intensity of the stimulus (electric shock) is increased (Sherrington, 1906). The latency decreases as a function of stimulus intensity, whereas the magnitude and the after-discharge of the response increase.

6. An increase in duration of the stimulus has the same effect as an increase in the intensity of the stimulus.

7. The repetitive presentation of a stimulus (within certain limits) also has the same effect as increasing the intensity of the stimulus. This phenomenon is referred to as *temporal summation.* The principle of temporal summation implies that it should be possible to use a stimulus of subthreshold intensity, present it several times in rapid succession, and obtain a response. The striking fact here is that a single presentation of the stimulus would not be sufficient to produce the response since its intensity is not high enough. The phenomenon of temporal summation has again been demonstrated in the case of the scratch reflex (Sherrington, 1906).

8. Once a response has occurred, it may be more difficult, if not impossible, to obtain the same response immediately again. However, after a certain amount of time has elapsed, the response can again be produced as easily as before. This phenomenon is referred to as the *refractory phase.* In the case of the eyelid reflex, for example, the chance that a second presentation of a stimulus will elicit a response is reduced by 50 percent if the second presentation follows upon the first within 1 second (Sherrington, 1906).

Different reflexes show large variation in the duration of their refractory phases. In the case of the eye-blink reflex or the knee jerk, for example, it is relatively short as compared to the duration of the refractory phase associated with a sexual reflex such as ejaculation in the male rat (Larsson, 1956).

9. In the case of the refractory phase, the ease of producing a response is decreased if a response occurs only once. Further decreases in the magnitude and after-discharge of the response may occur when it is repeatedly produced in relatively rapid succession. These temporary changes, due to *repeated* successive elicitation, are referred to as *reflex fatigue*.

10. Finally, the measurable aspects of the response, such as its magnitude, latency, and after-discharge, can be changed by the almost simultaneous presentation of another stimulus that does not itself produce the response. If the magnitude of a response increases with the presentation of another stimulus, one speaks of *facilitation;* if it decreases, of *inhibition*. It has been demonstrated that the threshold of certain responses to electric shock is increased if a vibratory stimulus is presented at almost the same time (Vernon, 1953). This study thus provides an example of inhibition. An extensive discussion of inhibition and facilitation can be found in a recent book by Diamond *et al.* (1963).

In the above discussion of some of the basic aspects of reflex behavior, frequent reference has been made to the classic book by Sherrington (1906). A more up-to-date account of our knowledge in this area can be found elsewhere (Ruch *et al.,* 1961).

CONDITIONED RESPONDENT BEHAVIOR: CONDITIONED REFLEXES

The range of application of the concept of the reflex was greatly extended by the concept of the conditioned reflex introduced by Pavlov at the turn of this century (see Koshtoyants, 1964).

In 1796 Erasmus Darwin, Charles Darwin's grandfather, had already observed that:

The flow of saliva into the mouths of hungry animals at the sight or smell of food is seen in dogs standing round a dinner table. The increased actions of the salivary glands have usually been produced by the stimulus of agreeable food on their excretory ducts during the mastication of it; and with this increased action of their excretory ducts the other terminations of those glands in the capillary arteries have been excited into increased action by the mutual association of the ends of the canals; and at the same time the pleasurable ideas, or sensual motions, of the sense of smell and of sight have accompanied this increased secretion of saliva. Hence this chain of motions becomes associated with those visual or olfactory ideas, or with the pleasure, which produces or attends them (Darwin, 1796, Vol. 2, p. 444).

Erasmus Darwin's observations were subsequently made by many famous nineteenth-century physiologists such as Claude Bernard and Johannes Müller (Rosenzweig, 1959). The quotation from Darwin presented above is of general interest since it points up the relationship of Pavlov's concept of conditioning to the ancient notion of the association of ideas which already had been discussed by Plato and Aristotle (Warren, 1921).

A general statement of the principle of the conditioned reflex, based on a systematic experimental analysis, was first clearly formulated, however, by Pavlov. Before Pavlov introduced the term "conditioning," phenomena similar to those already observed and commented on by Erasmus Darwin were referred to as "psychic secretion." It was one of Pavlov's great contributions to show that certain specific events in the life history of the organism were responsible for them. By deliberately building up "psychic secretion" to previously "neutral" stimuli, he was able to show that the activity of the salivary glands could be accounted for in a lawful way. It became superfluous to appeal to the possibility that Darwin's dogs had been "thinking about food" or that Pavlov's dogs had "associated the sound of the bell with the *idea* of food." An interesting historical account of the history of psychic secretion can be found in the article by Rosenzweig (1959) previously cited.

In the process of conditioning as studied by Pavlov (1927), one stimulus, the conditioned stimulus, is said to be substituted for another, the unconditioned stimulus. The implication of the term "substitute" is actually incorrect. Contrary to what is implied by the word "substituted," the unconditioned stimulus usually does not lose its effectiveness to elicit the response during conditioning (Grant, 1964). A previously ineffective stimulus (for instance the sound of a metronome) will elicit salivation only if it has been followed by stimuli (food or mild acid solutions) that are already effective in increasing salivation. Respondent conditioned reflexes are therefore necessarily composed of behavior that is already under reflex control.

Sherrington's laws of the reflex (see previous section) may hold also for Pavlov's conditioned reflexes: they should describe the relationships that are obtained between various characteristics of the conditioned stimulus and the response. The relationship between the intensity of the stimulus and the magnitude of the response, as well as the principle of stimulus summation, for example, also applies to conditioned reflexes (Hull, 1934a; Kupalov and Gantt, 1927).

SOME BASIC BEHAVIORAL PROCESSES

Pavlov and his co-workers studied the properties of conditioned reflexes in great detail. Much of this work stands unchallenged today. Besides the basic principle of conditioning, Pavlov also investigated and named the following phenomena.

1. *Extinction:* The process whereby a conditioned reflex is weakened by withholding the unconditioned stimulus and only presenting the conditioned stimulus.

2. *Spontaneous recovery:* A conditioned reflex is spontaneously and partially reinstated during the first few sessions during which the unconditioned stimulus is withheld (extinction).

3. *Generalization and discrimination:* Pavlov discovered that a change in the strength of a conditioned reflex by reinforcement would frequently also produce similar changes in related reflexes. These induced changes were usually less extensive. As Pavlov pointed out, this phenomenon is due to the possession of common properties by the stimuli employed. The notion that in order for generalization to occur the stimuli involved must possess "common elements" was also suggested by Thorndike (1916).

As a specific example of respondent generalization, or the "irradiation" of a conditioned reflex, the following experiment may be cited (Bass and Hull, 1934). The reflex studied and conditioned was the galvanic skin reaction (a change in the electrical resistance of the skin). This response was conditioned using a weak shock delivered to the wrist of the subject as the unconditioned stimulus. A tactual stimulus was employed as the conditioned stimulus. Four practically silent vibratory stimulators were placed at different points along the left side of the body. After a conditioned reflex had been established to a stimulus on the shoulder, it was found that the other three stimulators also elicited the conditioned response. The magnitude of the conditioned reaction, however, decreased as the distance from the point initially conditioned increased.

Skinner reformulated Pavlov's principle of "irradiation" (generalization) as the "law of induction," which stated that a change in the strength of a reflex may be accompanied by a similar, but not so extensive, change to other stimuli, where the relation is due to the possession of common properties by the stimuli involved (Skinner, 1938).

This general principle does not specify the direction of the change in the strength of the reflex. It can be either an increase in strength as produced by conditioning (reinforcement) or a decrease as produced by extinction (nonreinforcement). This last aspect of generalization was described by Pavlov as "irradiation of inhibition." Bass and Hull (1934) found that if stimulation at all four points of the body had been established as a conditioned stimulus for the galvanic skin reaction, submission of one of the stimuli to extinction produced a decrease in the magnitude of the response to the other three stimuli also.

Because the effects of extinction "irradiate" just as do the effects of reinforcement, it is possible to break down the connections between stimuli and responses that have come about by way of generalization. If the unconditioned stimulus always follows conditioned stimulus *A*, but never conditioned stimulus *B* (extinction), the reflex will eventually be made almost exclusively to stimulus *A*. In a specific experimental demonstration of this statement, the initial strength of the conditioned response with respect to stimulus *B* should, of course, only be due to induction from the reinforcement that always follows the occurrence of stimulus *A*.

Pavlov's way of showing how discriminations are established has been labeled the "method of contrasts." Essentially, discrimination training is a combination of the procedures of reinforcement and extinction. Another important aspect of this procedure of selective reinforcement with respect to stimuli is the more or less random alternation of the stimuli to be discriminated. Too many successive presentations of the reinforced (positive) stimulus or the unreinforced (negative) stimulus will prevent discrimination learning. In respondent conditioning, frequent interchange of positive and negative stimuli is necessary if a discrimination is to be obtained. The formation of a discrimination is, then, a double process. Through generalization, each reinforced presentation of stimulus *A* adds to the eliciting power of stimulus *B;* each nonreinforced presentation of stimulus *B* subtracts from the eliciting power of *A*. Further reinforcements give more strength to *A* than to *B,* and further extinction trials take more from *B* than from *A*. As the stimuli draw apart in strength, the discrimination is formed. The gradual accumulation of differences in the strength of the two reflexes is the core of the discriminative process.

Pavlov dealt almost entirely with salivation, but the scope of conditioned reflex phenomena extends to many aspects of the internal physiology of the organism. Relatively few systematic and precisely controlled observations are available on the formation and properties of conditioned reflexes involving the many organ systems of the mammalian body. It has become clear, however, that a major role is played by many conditioned reflexes, extending to almost every phase of organic functioning. Conditioning has been demonstrated to affect the volume of the arteries, the passage of urine from the kidney to the bladder, the secretion of bile, gastric secretion, heart rate, respiration, intestinal motility, etc. (Airapetyantz and Bykov, 1944; Bykov, 1957). Many aspects of this work have been confirmed by other experimenters.

OPERANT AND RESPONDENT BEHAVIOR: A COMPARISON

We now return to our earlier question concerning the specific nature of the differences between respondent and operant conditioning. Comparison of the examples of operant conditioning, described in the early part of this survey, with Pavlov's conditioning phenomena, leads one to make the following observations.

1. Respondent conditioning involves the formation of new reflexes

starting from initially established reflexes; operant conditioning involves the modification of behavior already in the repertoire.

A reflex such as the knee jerk can from the start be elicited by its proper stimulus, as by a tap on the patellar tendon. In operant conditioning experiments, however, the investigator either has to wait until the desired response occurs, and then reinforce it, or establish the desired behavior by the special process of response differentiation or shaping. Initially, there is no "ready-made" stimulus he can use to produce the desired response.

2. In respondent conditioning, the conditioned stimulus prepares the organism for the unconditioned stimulus that follows later. In Pavlov's salivary conditioning experiments with food or a weak acid solution as the unconditioned stimulus, salivation increases in response to the conditioned stimulus, paving the way, so to speak, for the digestion of the food or the dilution of the acid. Reflex behavior does not usually manipulate the environment. It does, however, frequently change or adjust the internal physiology of the organism and therefore may be said to relate the organism to its internal environment. In the case of operant behavior, however, the behavior characteristically manipulates the external environment; the response may be said to *produce* the reinforcer.

3. Respondent behavior is usually mediated by the autonomic nervous system and involves glands and smooth muscles; operant behavior is mediated mainly by the somatic (central) nervous system and involves striated muscles.

4. Response differentiation is not possible in respondent behavior. Response strength is determined by the intensity of stimulation; apparently one cannot lower or increase the saliva production of a dog by reinforcing it with food whenever the flow rate drops below or increases above a certain value. It is possible, however, to lower the rate of responding of operant behavior by such a technique.

The issues involved here are far from settled. Heart rate, for example, apparently can be controlled to some extent by operant-type reinforcement contingencies (Shearn, 1961).

5. In operant behavior no direct and simple relationship exists between the intensity of a preceding stimulus and the strength of the subsequent response.

Just as in the case of the scratch reflex of a spinal dog the magnitude of the response is a function of the intensity of the stimulus, so in the case of a *conditioned* stimulus the magnitude of the *conditioned* response increases when the intensity of the conditioned stimulus increases. It has been shown, for example, by Kupalov and Gantt (1927) that the magnitude of the conditioned salivary response in dogs varies with the intensity of a conditioned sound stimulus.

In the case of the stimuli that precede the behavior in an operant conditioning situation, however, the importance of their intensity is considerably reduced or nonexistent. In order to clarify this point it will be necessary to describe how, in the case of operant behavior, a stimulus presented before occurrence of the response comes to control the subsequent behavior.

Our first point of comparison between operant and respondent behavior emphasized the fact that, at least initially, there are no "ready-made" stimuli which produce the response. If the response occurs, however, it can be reinforced. If the response occurs with some frequency, "differential reinforcement with respect to stimuli" can be given: When the response occurs in the presence of one stimulus (the positive stimulus), it is reinforced; when it occurs in the presence of another stimulus (the negative stimulus), it is not. In this way the positive and negative stimuli acquire control over the occurrence of the response: They come to function as "stop" and "go" signals. The process described above is usually referred to as the formation of a discrimination and the procedure as discrimination training. The differences between operant discrimination training and Pavlov's method of contrast lie in the basic differences between respondent and operant conditioning described above. The terms positive and negative (conditioned) stimulus are frequently employed in the case of Pavlov's method of contrast in a respondent conditioning situation. In the case of operant discrimination training, however, the stimulus in the presence of which the behavior is reinforced is commonly referred to as the *discriminative stimulus* or S^D (S^{dee}); and the negative stimulus in the presence of which the behavior is extinguished is commonly referred to as the S^Δ (S^{delta}) or "time-out" stimulus (see below).

Let us return now to our statement that in the case of operant behavior no direct and simple relationship exists between the intensity of the preceding stimulus and the strength of the subsequent response. It can now be restated: The relationship that exists between stimulus intensity and response magnitude in the case of respondent behavior does not hold in the case of a discriminative stimulus. An increase in the intensity of a discriminative stimulus does not produce an increase in the frequency, force, duration, amplitude, or latency of the operant which is reinforced in its presence. Suppose that a rat is first taught to press a lever by the process of response differentiation. Next a discrimination is established with respect to two tones which differ only in intensity. Either the higher or the lower intensity of sound could, of course, be used as the discriminative stimulus in the presence of which pressing the lever is reinforced. As the discrimination is formed, responding in the presence of S^Δ is extinguished, whereas responding in the presence of the S^D is maintained.

In terms of the rapidity with which the animal would have learned to discriminate between the two sound intensities, it would have made little or no difference whether the high or the low intensity were used as S^D or S^Δ (Pierrel and Sherman, 1960). If, however, the behavior were dependent on the magnitude of the stimuli, this would not have been the case. More-over, it can be demonstrated that once a stimulus, employed as an S^D in an operant conditioning situation, has acquired control over the response, an increase in its intensity produces no simple increase in any of the many measurable aspects of the response. In the case just described, an increase in the intensity of the tone which was established as the discriminative stimulus or S^D does not produce an increase in either the rate of lever pressing or the forces with which the responses are executed. Nor are there any simple and systematic changes in other measurable aspects of the behavior such as its duration (how *long* the rat holds the lever down), its amplitude (how *far* the rat pushes the lever down), or the speed with which the animal reacts to the stimulus (the latency or reaction time). All of these dimensions of the response, however, are subject to changes in the reinforcement contingencies arranged by the experimenter as shown by the data on response differentiation.

The above discussion of operant and respondent behavior has put great emphasis on the presence or absence of a simple and direct relationship between stimulus intensity and the quantitative dimensions of the response. This emphasis can be further justified by pointing out that the nature of the intensity-magnitude relationship has from the very beginning in the evolutionary development of life played a decisive factor in natural selec-tion (Schneirla, 1959). In the case of primitive organisms, the intensity of a stimulus determines not only the magnitude of the response (Jennings, 1906), but it also determines the direction of the response with respect to the source of stimulation (Fraenkel and Gunn, 1940). Animals which ap-proach a weak source of stimulation may withdraw from a stronger source. In this way stimulus intensity determines what conditions generally affect an organism. As Schneirla (1959) put it: "Doubtless the high road of evolution has been littered with the remains of species that diverged too far from . . . [an] . . . effective adaptive relationship between environ-mental conditions and response" (1964 edition, p. 513).

In the case of those organisms who exhibit behavior which is not sub-ject to a rigid and simple intensity-magnitude relationship, more flexible adaptive mechanisms appear. The feedback relationship between operant behavior and its consequences is a case in point.

Although we owe to Skinner the terms operant and respondent behavior and a clear cut differentiation between the two types of conditioning, the distinction had been anticipated in the writings of many others (Hunter, 1928; Maier and Schneirla, 1935). Miller and Konorski (1928), two Polish investigators, had independently arrived at a closely related dis-tinction.

Many attempts have been made to explain the phenomena of operant conditioning in terms of the principles derived from respondent condi-tioning and vice versa. The distinction itself, as item Number 4 above implies, is an empirical one, however. So far, it has not been demonstrated that operant behavior controlled by its past consequences can be conditioned by means of Pavlov's formula, nor that respondent behavior can be manipulated by differential reinforcement contingencies (Skinner, 1938). A more elaborate discussion of the similarities and differences between operant and respondent conditioning can be found in Kimble's (1961) extensive survey of conditioning and learning and in recent articles by Grant (1964) and Kimble (1964).

Although the characteristics of operant and respondent conditioning can be analyzed separately, these two types of conditioning procedures usually occur simultaneously but involve different responses. Distinctive properties can be discovered only by experiments in which both processes are studied at the same time. In the experiments by Pavlov in which salivary conditioning was employed, the conditioned stimulus preceding the unconditioned stimulus (food) rapidly acquired control of the salivary response. In the process, however, any operant behavior of the dog occurring immediately before food presentation is strengthened according to the law of effect.

Pavlov, however, was mainly interested in the salivary reflex. In an operant type situation, the rat that is reinforced with food pellets when it presses a lever is also subjected to the very conditions that lead to the development of a conditioned salivary reflex. Any repeated and consistent, or possibly even intermittent relationship (Notterman, Schoenfeld, and Bersh, 1952), between the visual, tactual, and proprioceptive stimuli occurring at the time of the lever press and followed almost immediately by the presentation of food would produce conditioned salivation. However, in most of these types of experiments, the salivary aspect is ignored.

Studies have recently been reported, however, of the way in which both kinds of conditioning processes take place simultaneously (Kintsch and Witte, 1962; Shapiro, 1960; Wolf, 1963). In one of such studies, Ellison and Konorski (1964) trained dogs in the following way: first, employing a respondent conditioning procedure, a conditioned response was established to a buzzer as a conditioned stimulus. During this phase of the experiment the buzzer was, after 1 second, followed by an unconditioned stimulus which consisted of a small portion of cooked meat and broth-soaked bread. Next, the animals were trained to perform an operant type of response. A lever was located near the automatic feeder, which, if pressed with the right forepaw, resulted in the onset of the buzzer which, as was the case during the previous phase, was followed by food after 1 second. During the next and third phase of the training program, a third stimulus (a light) was introduced. Pressing the lever was now reinforced with the buzzer-food sequence only in the presence of the light. It was extinguished when the light was not on. The procedure during this phase then involved operant discrimination training with respect to the presence or absence of a light. In this manner the light became a discriminative stimulus for pressing the lever.

During the next and fourth phase of the experiment the following changes were made in the training procedure:

1. The duration of the third stimulus (the light) was increased.
2. The number of lever presses required before the buzzer was turned on was increased from one to nine. (See the discussion of fixed-ratio schedules below.)
3. The time interval between the onset of the buzzer and the presentation of the food was increased from 1 to 8 seconds.

By the time this training phase was completed, the procedure during an experimental session consisted of a series of trials involving two successive segments: First, in the presence of the light, a total of nine lever presses resulted in the termination of the light and, simultaneously, the onset of the buzzer. Second, the buzzer was, after 8 seconds, followed by food. Then, after a certain period of time the entire series of events that constituted a trial was initiated again. Thus, during the first segment of a trial, work was required to produce the second segment which only required waiting for food. The results of the experiment showed that the respondent (salivary) and operant components did *not* occur simultaneously: the discriminative stimulus (the light) set the occasion for the occurrence of nine lever presses to be reinforced with the buzzer-food sequence. However, it did not become a conditioned stimulus for the salivary reflex. No increase in the flow of saliva occurred when the light was presented. The buzzer, however, did function as a conditioned stimulus and as such produced an increase in salivation. It did *not,* however, function as a discriminative stimulus for pressing the lever: no lever pressing occurred while the buzzer sounded, even though no measures were taken either to prevent or discourage such responses. (If they had occurred, they would, of course, within 8 seconds have been reinforced by the presentation of the food.) Data of this kind raise many further questions about the similarities and differences between operant and respondent conditioning and behavior. Ellison and Konorski concluded their account of the experiment as follows: "The present result, in showing a clear difference between the two responses and perhaps the rules governing them, emphasizes the necessity of studying both of them concomitantly in order to obtain a better understanding of learning processes" (1964, p. 1072).

Whereas in the above described situation the respondent and operant components occur more or less independent from each other, in other situations involving different responses this may not be the case. It has been suggested, for example, that interactions between respondent and operant behavior do occur in the case of behavior controlled by aversive or noxious consequences (escape, avoidance, punishment) (Schoenfeld, 1950).

INSTINCTIVE BEHAVIOR

If the above discussion of respondent and operant behavior has stressed their differences, any implication that an absolute and rigid dichotomy exists should be corrected. Many forms of behavior, often called instinctive (Thorpe, 1963), assume in certain aspects an intermediate position between the classical reflex and the typical free operant such as bar pressing or key pecking.

Distinctions between different kinds of behavior such as reflex (respondent), instinctive, and operant are all more or less arbitrary. As Aristotle pointed out in another but related context:

. . . Nature advances little by little from the inanimate to animals, in such a way that owing to the continuity it is impossible to tell to which class the intermediate creatures and those on the borderline belong. After the class of inanimate things comes first the class of plants, and within this class one member differs from another in the degree to which they seem to possess life. The whole class appears living as compared to inanimate matter, but lifeless in comparison with animals. Moreover, the gradation from plants to animals is continuous . . . (Aristotle).

One way in which instinctive reactions are intermediate between reflex and operant behavior is in the complexity of the stimuli that elicit them. For example, provided certain conditions are present (see below), a male three-spined stickleback (a small fish) will attack objects of a certain size, but only if they have a red underside or belly (Tinbergen, 1951). This attack behavior is directed at other males intruding on the attacker's territory. The behavior is identifiable as a specific type of threat posture and only occurs in the spring during the mating season. It is only one item in a complex repertory of behaviors all related to and part of the reproductive pattern of this particular species of 'fish. Its mating pattern, for example, consists of a complex series of responses on the part of both the male and female. Each successive response in the series is elicited or released by a complex stimulus. The entire pattern culminates in the fertilization of the female's eggs. All of the many different responses in the entire reproductive behavior pattern, such as the courtship zigzag dance, mating, fanning the eggs, and attacking intruders, are in addition to their specific releasing stimuli controlled by endocrinological factors (hormones). This is, of course, true for the reproductive behavior patterns of many other animals (Beach, 1948).

All of the above is clearly different from the relatively less complex set of conditions which elicit the spinal scratch reflex. In neither case, however, is a history of discrimination training necessarily involved (Spalding, 1872).

In general one can distinguish between the various broad categories of behavior such as reflexive, instinctive, respondent, and operant in terms of the type and number of conditions (independent variables or parameters) that are involved in producing or controlling them. In general, complexity in terms of controlling variables increases with more advanced evolutionary development (Maier and Schneirla, 1964); to paraphrase Aristotle, the gradation from reflex to operant is continuous.

NEGATIVE AND POSITIVE REINFORCEMENT

As was pointed out earlier, one of the characteristic features of the operant conditioning situation is that the behavior must occur first, after which the reinforcing consequences may or may not follow. It appears that there are two different kinds of consequences. This is, in fact, a feature which reinforcing stimuli have in common with the stimuli which produce reflex or instinctive behavior. Even animals as low on the evolutionary scale as the amoeba show *withdrawal from* one kind of stimulus (such as a hydrochloric acid solution) in contrast to *approach towards* another stimulus (such as contact with a smooth solid object) (Jennings, 1906). In the case of conditioned reflexes, Pavlov (1927) distinguished between the *alimentary* (conditioned) reflex as opposed to the *defense* (conditioned) reflex dependent on whether food or a weak acid solution was used as the unconditioned stimulus. In a discussion of instinctive behavior, Wallace Craig (1918) distinguished between "appetites and aversions as constituents of instincts." In the case of a male dove locating a nesting site, either a nest box, a ready-made nest, or nest-building materials function as "appeted stimuli"; whereas the sight of another male dove near his mate is a "disturbing stimulus." Thorndike (1898), who introduced the puzzle box as a method to study learning, spoke of "satisfiers" and "annoyers"; Tolman (1932), in a systematic account of maze-learning experiments, distinguished between "demands for" and "demands against" certain "environmental presences"; Hull (1943) and Skinner (1938) distinguished between positive and negative reinforcers; and everybody, for countless years, has distinguished between reward and punishment.

The phrases "approach to" and "withdrawal from" imply a movement of the organism with respect to certain specific aspects of the immediate environment. They emphasize the changing spatial relations between an organism and the objects, stimuli, or "environmental presences" towards which it moves or from which it withdraws. In contrast, as Skinner (1963) has pointed out, the response in the operant conditioning situation produces food only in the sense that food merely *follows* the response *in time*. In the case of operant behavior, therefore, it is more appropriate to speak of the response as *initiating* or *terminating* certain events or conditions.

A positive reinforcer may then be tentatively defined as a stimulus towards which an organism approaches or which he will turn on, produce, or initiate. A negative reinforcer may be tentatively defined as a stimulus from which an organism withdraws or which he will get rid of, terminate, or escape from. Following Wallace Craig (1918), we could speak of operant behavior controlled by the feedback from positively reinforcing consequences as "appetites," and we could speak of "aversions" in the case of behavior controlled by the feedback from negatively reinforcing consequences. These terms are not commonly used in this way; one does speak, however, of "aversive control" though not of "appetitive control." In the latter case, the phrase "positive control" has recently come to be used.

ESCAPE AND AVOIDANCE BEHAVIOR

As indicated by the above definition of negative reinforcement, a simple and basic experiment, appropriate as a first step in the experimental analysis of aversive control, would be a situation in which the subject is presented with a stimulus and given the opportunity to terminate it. If he does so, we are dealing, by definition, with a negative reinforcer. Keller (1941), for example, trained rats to turn off a bright light by pressing a lever when the light was turned on. Subsequent research has shown that the strength of the escape behavior depends on the intensity of the light (Kaplan, 1952; Lockard, 1963). In other experiments loud noise has been employed as the aversive stimulus (Barry and Harrison, 1957). Most commonly, however, electric shock is used in research with animals and humans. This practice dates back to the Russian physiologist and psychiatrist Bechterev (1933), a contemporary of Pavlov. Experiments in which rats were trained to press a lever to turn off shock have been reported by Dinsmoor and Hughes (1956).

In the above type of experiments the subject merely escapes from, terminates, or partially reduces (Weiss and Laties, 1959) an aversive stimulus. Other experiments provide a subject with the opportunity to avoid, cancel, or postpone the aversive event before its onset. It is upon this difference that the distinction between escape and avoidance behavior is based (Schoenfeld, 1950). A technique for generating a stable rate of avoidance behavior was first described by Sidman (1953). Rats were given an electric shock through a grid floor at regular intervals unless a lever was depressed by the animal. Each lever depression reset the timer that controlled the shock and thus delayed its occurrence. If, for example, each response reset a 30-second timer, a minimum interval of 30 seconds was insured between avoidance behavior and shock. By continuously pressing the lever within 30-second intervals, the rat could avoid shock completely. The interval by which each response postpones the shock (the response-shock, or RS interval) does not have to be equal to that between shocks (the shock-shock, or SS interval) if no responding occurs at all. As does Skinner's original experiment, Sidman's technique permits use of the rate of responding as a continuous and direct indicator of the effects of experimental manipulations.

A record of the lever-pressing behavior of a rat during an 11-hour session is shown in Figure 6. Neither food nor water was available to the animal during the experimental session. Successive hours are indicated by the numbered vertical arrows. The interval between shocks and the time interval by which each press postponed the shock were each 30 seconds. Since the slope of the curve is the only relevant feature of a cumulative record, white space has been cut out of the original record and the separate segments have been brought closer together to facilitate reproduction. Shocks are indicated by the oblique marks on the record. The cumulative record shows that the number of shocks per hour increases as the session continues. The first 6 to 8 hours, however, show a stability of response as well as shock rate.

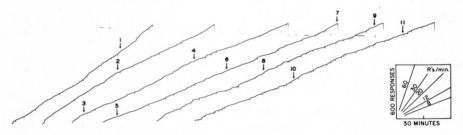

Figure 6.   Performance of a rat avoiding shock by pressing a lever using the procedure developed by Sidman (1953). Successive hours are indicated by the numbered arrows. Shocks are indicated by the oblique marks on the record.

Much higher rates of responding than the one shown by the rat in Figure 6 can be generated by a modification of Sidman's original procedure (Verhave, 1959). Instead of requiring the animal to reset the shock timer by pressing once, one can train it to press several times to postpone the shock. Figure 7 shows the various rates of responding of a rat when eight presses are required to reset the shock timer. The four panels from top to bottom show the rate of responding during four 6-hour sessions when each lever press postponed the shock for 100, 50, 20, and 15 seconds, respectively. Figure 8 is a plot of the rate of responding against the duration of the RS interval. These data demonstrate that, as in Sidman's original procedure, the rate of responding is a decreasing function of the time period by which each response postpones the shock (the RS interval).

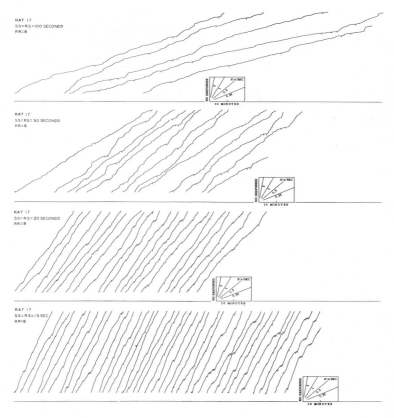

Figure 7. Performance of a rat that avoids shock by pressing a lever under a modified Sidman procedure. The performance during four different sessions is shown.

The avoidance procedure can be used very effectively to limit an animal's repertoire to the almost exclusive emission of a single kind of behavior selected arbitrarily by the experimenter. Williams and Teitelbaum (1956) employed Sidman's procedure to force satiated rats to drink exorbitantly large quantities of water. A similar procedure could be used to make animals overeat. The degree of control exerted by the avoidance schedule discussed here and by operant conditioning techniques in general is remarkable and has important implications for human behavior. The basic contingencies involved, the postponement or reduction of aversive consequences, are common in the daily control of human behavior. Prison practices provide a good example of the various ways in which aversive control can be used in a relatively crude and rule-of-thumb manner (Glaser, 1964). A discussion of the ethical issues generated by the development of a science of behavior and the parallel development of a powerful behavioral technology can be found elsewhere (Skinner, 1953, 1961).

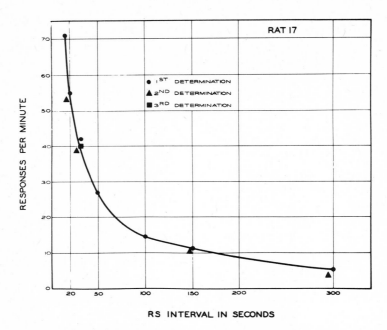

RS INTERVAL IN SECONDS

Figure 8. *Rate of avoidance responding as a function of the time period by which each eighth response postpones electric shock. This response-shock interval is labelled the RS interval (Verhave, 1959).*

The experimental investigation of the control over operant behavior by aversive contingencies has not been limited to animals. Hefferline (1962) in recent ingenious experiments has generated Sidman-type avoidance behavior in human subjects. Fortunately for both the experimenter and the subjects, the aversive stimuli employed were innocuous. The subjects relaxed in semireclining chairs. Recording electrodes were taped to the right hand to pick up thumb twitches which are unobservable with the naked eye. Dummy electrodes were attached to various other parts of the body. The subjects were led to believe that the experimenter was interested in changes in body tension when noise was occasionally superimposed on music. During the experiment, music and noise were fed through earphones. The music consisted of semiclassical selections and the noise was a loud hum generated by a signal tracer. Music alone was played during the first 10 minutes of a session, during which time the experimenter determined the frequency of the thumb twitch before avoidance conditioning. Thereafter the noise was introduced along with the music, and from then on each muscle twitch turned the noise off for 15 seconds. As in Sidman's experiments with animals, responses during the 15-second-noise-free periods reset the 15-second timer, postponing the noise for another 15 seconds. Subjects conditioned rapidly, first escaping from the noise and subsequently avoiding it. Interestingly enough, when the subjects were questioned after the experiments, they showed no evidence of suspecting that they had had any control over the noise. According to Hefferline, the subjects "expressed annoyance at the noise, not only because it was unpleasant in itself, but also because it interrupted the music at times when they were particularly absorbed in it." They reported that "the situation became more tolerable after the experimenter cut down the length of the noise periods" (Hefferline *et al.,* 1959). The subjects were completely unaware of their thumb-twitching behavior! An extensive experimental analysis of escape and avoidance behavior is currently being pursued in many laboratories. No up-to-date review articles of this very active area are available; however, publications by Schoenfeld (1950), Solomon and Brush (1956), and Anger (1963) cover a large part of the territory. Articles which should also be mentioned in this connection are those by Azrin and Holz, Sidman, and Hoffman in W. K. Honig (1966).

All the experiments with operant behavior discussed so far have illustrated two kinds of consequences by means of which such behavior is established and maintained. A person who drops a coin into a soft drink machine demonstrates behavior determined by previous positive reinforcement. The rat that terminates electric shock by pressing a lever demonstrates behavior controlled by a negative reinforcer (Dinsmoor and Hughes, 1956). Another example of the latter is provided by a recent series of experiments in which escape from cold is used to reinforce operant behavior (Weiss and Laties, 1961).

On the basis of the illustrations of operant conditioning experiments given so far, the reader will perhaps understand the more technical definitions of these two kinds of reinforcement. The term "positive reinforcer" is a label for those behavioral consequences that increase or maintain the frequency of behavior when *presented,* that is, when they are made contingent upon a certain bit of behavior. A "negative reinforcer" is a behavioral consequence that also increases or maintains behavior, but only when its *removal* is made contingent upon a particular response. Both reinforce, i.e., they increase or maintain behavior.

A moment's study of the technical definition of a negative reinforcer may lead one to speculate about the effects of a negative reinforcer made contingent upon a specific response. This is exactly what the layman does when he inflicts punishment. The effects of punishment, however, are far from simple, and we shall return to this problem later.

SCHEDULES OF REINFORCEMENT

Skinner not only introduced the concept of operant behavior and a new way to study it, but also in this connection he opened up an entirely new and important field of investigation. In his early experiments Skinner took care that each lever press was reinforced with a pellet. Figure 5 illustrates the fact that operant behavior can be maintained by intermittent reinforcement as well.

Figure 9 is an example of a typical performance of a rat on a fixed-interval schedule of reinforcement. In this experiment the animal was reinforced by the presentation of 0.5 cc. of sweetened condensed milk in a dipper. In the present case, lever pressing was reinforced at intervals of 7 minutes. During reinforcement (at C) the dipper was accessible for a 10-second period, long enough to give the animal a chance to clean out the cup of milk. Each reinforcement was followed by a 2-minute blackout period during which all lights in the cage were turned off and pressing the lever was completely ineffective. At the end of this break, a light came on above the lever and the 5-minute fixed-interval timer was started again. Figure 9 shows only a sample portion of the cumulative record obtained during a session after a considerable amount of training. The animal had been exposed previously to the schedule for more than 100 hours over a period of several weeks.

Figure 9.   Performance of a rat on a 5-minute fixed-interval schedule. A 2-minute black out period follows each reinforcement.

In this experiment the cumulative recorder pen automatically reset to the bottom of the recorder at the end of each 2-minute blackout period after reinforcement, indicated by small oblique marks on the record (see arrow C). In the short sample of the performance shown in Figure 9, the light above the lever came on at A. The first reinforcement was not given until 5 minutes later. It can be seen that the animal began responding at a very low rate. The onset of responding during each 5-minute period is indicated by a D. As time passed, responding accelerated into a fairly stable terminal rate seen at B and was maintained until reinforcement occurred. During the 2-minute blackout periods the animal did not respond at all, as indicated by the flat horizontal stretch of record after each reinforcement. During the subsequent 5-minute fixed-interval periods, responding did not start until a few minutes after the light came on again above the lever, which coincided with the return of the pen to the baseline at E. Now and then, pauses occurred (F) after the animal had started to respond. A smooth gradual acceleration with an occasional pause may be seen at G. The overall characteristic pattern of performance shows fairly gradual, positively accelerated scallops in each fixed-interval period. Characteristic performances when the intervals between reinforcement are not fixed are shown in Figures 5 and 11. Note that the present situation generates a performance typical of a 5-minute FI schedule, even though reinforcements are scheduled 7 minutes apart. This is due to the 2-minute blackout after each reinforcement. The animal discriminates between the blackout and "light-on-above-lever" conditions. The light above the lever "sets the occasion for" and "triggers" the FI performance.

The differences in performance due to particular schedules of reinforcement are not limited to a certain species or a certain type of reward. Similar results have been obtained with many different species and with other reinforcers. Under special conditions the general features can also be reproduced with human subjects (Holland, 1958).

The effects of piecework schedules have also been extensively investigated. Figure 10 shows the cumulative response record of a monkey

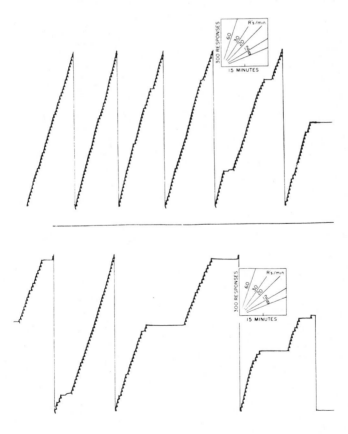

Figure 10.   Typical performance by a monkey under fixed-ratio reinforcement. Reinforcements occurred at the vertical marks on the record.

pressing a lever, with water used as a reinforcer. The monkey is on piece-work in the sense that it has to perform a certain amount of "work" (in the present case 20 responses) to obtain reinforcement. Such a schedule is called a fixed-ratio (FR20) schedule of reinforcement, since the ratio of responses to reinforcements is fixed.

Comparison of the curves of Figures 5 and 10 brings out some interest-ing differences. Whereas the rat of Figure 5 works steadily at a fairly constant rate, the monkey works in spurts. An animal on a fixed-ratio schedule often pauses briefly, after reinforcement. The record of Figure 10 shows a relatively high and steady rate of responding. During the first half of the experimental session there are about five clearly noticeable pauses, four of which occur immediately after a reinforcement has been received (see top half of Figure 10). As the session continues and the number of water reinforcements the animal has received becomes larger, the fre-quency of occurrence of the post-reinforcement pauses also increases. Towards the end of the session several are of considerable duration (see bottom half of Figure 10). These changes in the frequency and duration of the post-reinforcement pauses are due to satiation. Similar data have been reported previously (Sidman and Stebbins, 1954; Verhave, 1963).

Satiation records of animals working on variable-interval schedules of reinforcement look quite different. Figure 11 shows the cumulative record of a rat pressing a lever on a 1-minute variable-interval schedule, with water used as a reinforcement. In this case the curve is negatively ac-celerated and levels off smoothly.

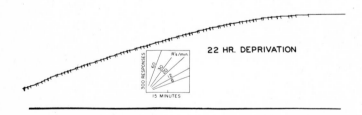

Figure 11. Performance of a rat under variable-interval reinforcement and low deprivation.

Behavior characteristic of different schedules can be generated, of course, in the same organism. Figure 12 shows the performance of a rat on a fixed-ratio as well as on a fixed-interval schedule of reinforcement. A different stimulus indicates which schedule is in effect. Such a reinforce-ment program is called a multiple schedule of reinforcement. In the present case the fixed-ratio component required 20 responses per reinforcement, whereas the fixed-intervals of the other component were 2 minutes long (Mult. FR20 FI2'). Each experimental session began with 11 reinforcements on fixed-ratio followed by 11 reinforcements on fixed-interval, after which the same sequence was repeated once more. Reinforcement consisted of sweetened condensed milk.

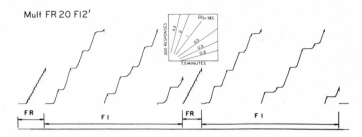

Figure 12. Performance of a rat on a multiple fixed-ratio, fixed-interval schedule.

The performance patterns characteristic of each schedule are clearly demonstrated (compare Figure 12 with Figures 9 and 10).

The behavior shown by the rat of Figure 12 takes, of course, a certain amount of time to develop. Among others, the subject has to learn to discriminate between the stimuli which indicate which particular schedule is in effect.

It was mentioned that the pauses after reinforcement were characteristic of behavior maintained by fixed-ratio schedules. In addition to satiation, the length of the schedule also increases the duration and frequency of these post-reinforcement pauses. As the number of required responses per reinforcement is increased beyond a certain point (which differs for different animals), the organism may stop working entirely (Hodos, 1961). A fixed-ratio performance characterized by frequent and relatively long pauses after reinforcement has been dubbed a "strained" performance. Straining is not muscle fatigue; were the latter present, all behavior employing the fatigued muscles would be equally depressed. Rather, the long and frequent pauses occur only when the "too-long" fixed-ratio schedule is in effect. A reduction in the length of the schedule may produce an almost instantaneous disappearance of the straining. The same effect can be achieved by an increase in the amount of reinforcement. When a larger amount of food or water is given per reinforcement, for example, straining can be considerably reduced almost instantly without the FR requirement being lowered.

The fact that straining is a phenomenon partially produced by a complex interaction of uniquely behavioral variables can be demonstrated further by means of the more complex multiple schedule of reinforcement. By using a multiple schedule consisting of two FR components, one a short and the other a long FR, it can be demonstrated that straining occurs only during the stimulus associated with the long FR schedule. One can also program a multiple schedule with fixed-ratio components of equal length. However, each component is associated with a different amount of reinforcement. In this case, straining is most severe in the presence of the stimulus associated with the smallest amount of reinforcement (Verhave, unpublished data). This phenomenon may be comparable to the case of a student who is too "tired" to read assigned material after several hours of study but who can still easily spend several more hours reading an absorbing novel.

STIMULUS GENERALIZATION AND OPERANT BEHAVIOR

Like respondent behavior, operant behavior is under the control of stimuli, and, like conditioned respondents, it shows the phenomena of stimulus generalization.

Generalization of operant behavior can be demonstrated by the following type of experiment. A pigeon trained to peck a plastic key of a certain color can be shown to peck also when the key is slightly changed in color, but it then pecks at a reduced rate. The bird has, of course, at no time during the experiment been reinforced for pecking at the slightly changed color. Experimenters usually use a variable-interval schedule of reinforcement during the period when the bird is pecking at the initial training color. Other colors are used only for short periods between reinforcements so that any drop-off in rate cannot be attributed to the effect of nonreinforcement (extinction) itself. (Eventually the bird would extinguish with respect to any but the initial color, because it is never reinforced for pecking at other colors.) The data obtained in such experiments consist of changes in rate of responding as a function of the "distance away" from an original training stimulus, and are usually referred to as generalization gradients (Guttman and Kalish, 1958). Generalization is a well established empirical phenomenon of considerable importance for an understanding of human behavior. It inevitably occurs whenever respondent or operant conditioning takes place. It is shown by the adult who mistakenly waves at strangers as well as by the young child who, after he has just learned to pronounce the name of his pet dog, for a while calls all dogs by the same name. Generalization may show itself in unexpected emotional reactions to situations which are similar to incidents that frightened us many years before, or it may be seen in our aesthetic appreciation of works of art. Razran (1938) has demonstrated that preferences for modern music could be increased by playing the music while the subjects were eating a free meal.

Leonhard Adam (1949), an Australian ethnologist, has observed, "It seems as though a complete enjoyment of beauty is possible only when we are confronted with a work of art which either belongs to our own kind of culture, or is at least superficially related to our own ideals of artistic beauty. The combination of form and colour evolved by foreign civilizations may have many attractions, but they remain shrouded in an uncanny mysterious atmosphere which is entirely alien to us."

The topic of generalization is a large one and no up-to-date review of findings is available. Two reviews of a restricted part of the literature have been published by Mednick and Freedman (1960) and Razran (1949).

PUNISHMENT

It has been pointed out that a distinction has been made between positive and negative reinforcers. Both types of reinforcers increase the frequency of operant behavior. Positive reinforcers do so when they are presented; negative reinforcers, when they are terminated or removed.

When the effects of punishment are to be studied, the presentation of the punishment can either be made contingent upon the occurrence of a specific response or it may be made to occur in a nonspecific fashion. In the latter case the punishment would occur irrespective of the nature of the on-going behavior. This type of arrangement was first studied by Skinner (1941) and Estes and Skinner (1941).

In the situation where the punishment is contingent upon the occurrence of a specific type of behavior, the punishment can be made to follow: (1) Unconditioned or instinctive behavior (Adler and Hogan, 1963). (2) Previously established operant behavior emitted in extinction. This means that in addition to the presentation of a negative reinforcer, positive reinforcement previously available is withheld (Estes, 1944). (3) Previously established operant behavior which continues to be positively reinforced (Azrin, 1956; Estes, 1944). In this case the punishment is added as an additional response-reinforcement contingency.

As an illustration of the last type of situation, we may refer to an experiment by Azrin (1959). Pigeons trained to peck a key were reinforced with food on a fixed-ratio schedule. However, each peck was immediately followed by a brief shock delivered through electrodes permanently. implanted in the skin near the pubic bone of the bird. Azrin found that if the punishment (shock) contingency was introduced after previous stabilization of the rate of pecking on the FR schedule, the initial effect of punishment was an increase in pausing after reinforcement. There was no reduction in the response rate once the animal started pecking. More important, he found that unless extremely high shock levels were used, progressive recovery of the performance occurred, even with continued exposure to the punishment contingency. Similar results are obtained when intense noise is used instead of shock.

Other experiments have shown that moderately severe punishment only serves to postpone the emission of punished behavior. If punishment is discontinued, but positive reinforcement continued, the previously punished behavior reappears. The effects of punishment on a repertoire maintained by other positive reinforcers is therefore more correctly described as temporary response suppression than as response elimination (Azrin, 1960).

The reasons for various effects of punishment are far from simple. There is an abundance of data in support of the notion that punishment, if effective in suppressing behavior, only does so because it strengthens competing avoidance behavior (Dinsmoor, 1954, 1955).

The general topic of punishment is a large one and the problems are complex. Because of limitations of space, the issues involved cannot be further discussed here. Reviews of experimental work can be found in papers by Church (1963), Dinsmoor (1954, 1955), Solomon (1964), and Azrin and Holz (1966).

THE REINFORCING FUNCTION OF A TIME-OUT

A little reflection concerning the technical definition of a positive reinforcer gives rise to the following question: What happens when the removal of a positive reinforcer (such as money) is made contingent upon behavior (as in the case of a fine)? Ferster has investigated this situation in experiments with chimpanzees and pigeons. He demonstrated that the removal of a positive reinforcer has effects similar to those that can be obtained by the presentation of a negative reinforcer (punishment) (Ferster, 1957, 1958).

In one of these experiments (1957), chimpanzees were trained to press a telegraph key that occasionally, on a variable-interval schedule, produced food. The key would pay off, however, only when an overhead light was turned on. Since responding in the absence of the light was never reinforced, the apes soon stopped pressing the key in its absence. They were trained in such a manner that by turning the light on or off, the experimenter could start or stop the responding of the animal. After this preliminary training, a red light, called the "pre-time-out" or "pre-aversive" stimulus, was installed next to the key. This light came on every 15 minutes for 2½ to 3 minutes. If during the last 20 seconds of the pre-time-out period the animal pressed the key, a 1-hour time-out from the variable-interval schedule followed, as indicated by the absence of the overhead light. However, if the animal did not respond during the final 20 seconds of the pre-time-out warning period, no time-out would occur. The next threat of a long 1 hour "layoff" would come again in 15 minutes, when the red light came on again. The results of this and similar experiments by Ferster show that the threat of a period of nonreinforcement (time-out) is functionally equivalent to the threat of the presentation of negative reinforcement: The animals learned to avoid the time-out by not responding during the 20-second pre-time-out warning period.

The resulting performance looked very much like the one from another experiment illustrated in Figure 13, which is the cumulative record of the behavior of a rat on a 1-minute variable-interval schedule, pressing a lever with water used as reinforcement. Every 10 minutes a tone came on for 5 minutes, as indicated by the dip in the record (see arrow). An electric shock was administered to the animal unless it did not press the lever during the last 30 seconds of the 5-minute warning period. It is obvious from the flattening out of the cumulative record that the animal hardly responded towards the end of these warning periods.

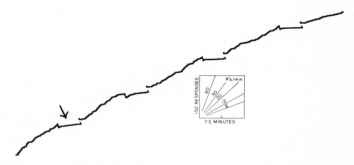

Figure 13. Suppression of lever-pressing behavior of a rat during a warning stimulus. The pen of the recorder is deflected downwards during the warning period (see arrow).

Ferster therefore concluded from his experiments that "the suppression of the baseline behavior by the stimulus preceding the time-out from the variable-interval schedule of reinforcement establishes the time-out as an aversive event having properties similar to those of electric shock. The time-out as an aversive event can be extrapolated to most aversive control in human behavior, where noxious stimuli such as corporal punishment or electric shock are rarely used" (1957).

It may be mentioned at this point that if the reinforcement contingencies in the last two experiments were changed in such a way that the animal had been required to *increase* its rate of responding by a certain amount to avoid the time-out, the experimental situation would have generated a form of avoidance behavior almost analogous to the behavior produced by the conditions that confront the driver of a car at an intersection controlled by traffic lights. The amber traffic light which is followed after a few seconds by a red light during which the driver has to stop his car has the same function as Ferster's pre-time-out stimulus. It is doubtful whether anybody would care to argue that the red light is not aversive. The amber pre-time-out and the red time-out lights are occasionally superimposed upon the intermittently positively reinforced behavior of driving a car. Similar to Ferster's chimpanzees, many drivers have a strong tendency to increase their rate of movement by stepping on the gas pedal if they are close to an intersection when the yellow light appears.

There is an interesting opposite to the control of behavior by a stimulus associated with "time-out from positive reinforcement." Sidman and Verhave have investigated a situation in which a response is conditioned and maintained by a time-out from a stimulus associated with the avoidance schedules described previously (Sidman, 1962; Verhave, 1962). It follows from the definition of a negative reinforcer that its removal should be rewarding.

In one of these experiments (Verhave, 1962) a certain arbitrary stimulus, for example a 433 cycle/sec. tone, is made aversive to a rat by always being associated with a Sidman-type avoidance schedule. During several 6-hour experimental sessions, given every other day, the animal was first taught to discriminate between tone-on and tone-off periods, which alternated every 10 minutes. During the 10-minute tone-off period (S^D), the avoidance schedule was in effect. During the tone-on period (S^Δ), the animal was released from the avoidance schedule; when the rat did not respond, it did not get shocked. Within a few sessions under these conditions, the animals learned the discrimination. They did not respond during the time-out, but went back to work immediately when the tone went off again. A typical performance of a rat is shown in Figure 14. During the first 10 minutes of the session, while the tone is off, the animal responds in a manner characteristic of the Sidman-type avoidance schedule (compare with Figure 6). The rate of responding during the S^Δ periods (tone-on) is negligible; a few responses occur during the first time-out period only. In the next phase of the experiment the rat is given control over the occurrence of the time-out periods. Pressing a second lever now produced the 10-minute time-out from the shock-avoidance schedule (S^Δ). Since the second lever looks exactly like the one the animal has been trained to work on already, it is almost guaranteed that the rat will press the second lever within a short time after its introduction. When he does so, the tone goes on indicating the beginning of a 10-minute long time-out period free from the possibility of being shocked. As a consequence, the animal very quickly learns to respond on the second lever, producing another time-out as soon as the previous one ends. Figure 15 shows the performance of the same rat whose performance was shown in Figure 14. This record was obtained three sessions after the second lever was introduced. The animal produces one time-out after another, spending hardly any time in the stimulus associated with the avoidance schedule.

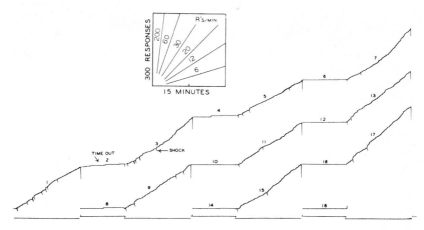

Figue 14. Performance of a rat in an avoidance procedure involving a discrimination between tone-on and tone-off periods. Tone-on periods, correlated with a time-out from the avoidance schedule, occurred during the even-numbered flat stretches in the cumulative record. The event pen (bottom line) was deflected upwards during the s^Δ periods.

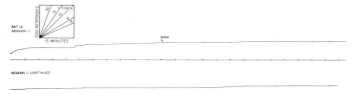

Figure 15. Performance of a rat on the avoidance lever in a procedure identical with that described for Figure 14 except that the rat can produce the time-out from the avoidance schedule by pressing a second lever in its cage. The event pen (bottom line) was deflected downwards during the time-out periods.

CONDITIONED REINFORCEMENT

The experiment described immediately above, as well as the time-out experiment by Ferster described before, demonstrates another general principle of operant behavior. It was shown that stimuli associated with certain kinds of reinforcement schedules could become reinforcing in their own right. It was also implied that conditions associated with or followed by negative reinforcers became negative reinforcers, whereas circumstances paired with positive reinforcing events became positive reinforcers. There are many names used for stimuli that owe their capacity to reinforce to a previous history of association with other reinforcers. The most prevalent one today is the term "conditioned reinforcers." Others are "secondary reinforcers," "token reward," and "symbolic reward."

Conditioned reinforcers appear capable of functioning like any other reinforcer, such as food and electric shock. A stimulus associated with an avoidance schedule, for example, can not only maintain escape behavior, which terminates it, but can also be used to suppress other behavior in progress when regularly preceded by a pre-aversive stimulus in the manner of Ferster's chimpanzee experiments.

The most straightforward way to study the strength of a conditioned reinforcer is by exploitation of its capacity to reinforce, i.e., generate or maintain operant behavior. In a recent series of experiments, Kelleher has studied the strength of conditioned reinforcers by means of a special type of reinforcement schedule, a chained schedule (Kelleher, 1957a, 1957b, 1957c). Chimpanzees were trained to obtain food by inserting poker chips through a slot in a Plexiglas window in their experimental cage. They subsequently were taught to discriminate between a red light and no illumination behind the Plexiglas window; insertion of a poker chip produced food only when the red light was on. During the third part of the training program the animals were taught to press a lever for poker chips in the presence of an overhead light only. From this point on, the animal had to do two different things before being reinforced with food. First, in the presence of the overhead light, the pressing of a lever produced a poker chip. Next, in the presence of the red light behind the Plexiglas window, the insertion of the poker chip through the slot was reinforced with food. During the next stage various schedules of reinforcement were programmed for both the conditioned (poker chips) and unconditioned (food) reinforcers. During a typical sequence of an experimental session the ape might be reinforced (for pressing the lever) by poker chips on a fixed-interval schedule. At occasional intervals, however, the red light behind the Plexiglas window would turn on and the animal could then exchange the poker chips for food. From studies of this type and others, it has become possible to evaluate the importance of many factors that determine the relative strength of conditioned reinforcers. Kelleher has suggested, for example, that in his experiments with poker chips the effects of "inflating this coin of the realm" could be studied by requiring the subject to insert more than one poker chip to obtain one piece of food. Two reviews of the experimental literature on conditioned reinforcement have recently been published (Kelleher and Gollub, 1962; Myers, 1958).

CHAINING

So far our account has stressed the reinforcing function of the immediate consequences of behavior. These same consequences, however, serve also as cues. They function as important signals for the next movement to be made. Dramatic demonstrations of this type of stimulus control have been made by means of special techniques which delay the auditory or visual feedback from such common and usually well-established behaviors as speaking and drawing (Lee, 1950; Smith, *et al.,* 1960; Yates, 1963).

The experiments by Kelleher with a chained schedule (described in the previous section) were a continuation of some widely publicized experiments on token rewards pioneered in the mid-thirties by Cowles (1937) and Wolfe (1936). All of these experiments also illustrate the fact that one operant may produce the cue, signal, or S^D for another. Although in the laboratory attention may be focused on only one particular aspect of an organism's behavior, no response, of course, occurs in a vacuum. All responses are not only preceded and followed by other behavior, but other behaviors may go on concurrently.

In well-established skills, such as tying one's shoe laces, the responses blend into one another so smoothly that it practically is impossible to identify the individual cues and responses. The experiments with chained schedules of reinforcement, as exemplified by the research on conditioned reinforcement, point up the fact that complex sequences of operant behavior consist of trains of cues and responses in which each cue in the series functions as a positive signal for the next operant response and simultaneously as the reinforcement for the preceding one.

A more elaborate discussion of chaining can be found elsewhere (Keller and Schoenfeld, 1950; Findley, 1962). The preceding discussion of operant chains is historically related to the argument of Watson, the founder of early behaviorism, that the performances involved in rote memorization and complex labyrinths (mazes) consisted in no more than chains of conditioned reflexes (Watson, 1919). At the time of his writing, the experimental analysis of behavior had only just started and an experimentally founded distinction between reflex and voluntary behavior was not to emerge for almost two decades.

MOTIVATION: DEPRIVATION AND SATIATION

The meaning of the term "motivation" is far from agreed on. Recent books which include this term as part of the title discuss pretty much the same material discussed in books on learning or behavior theory. Their bibliographies are almost identical. In terms of the broadest possible usage the materials discussed under the heading of motivation have something to do with certain aspects of the operation and process of reinforcement. One way to make the meaning of motivation more specific is to restrict it to refer to the processes of deprivation and satiation.

These terms refer to the basic fact that the frequency of occurrence of many behaviors may be changed by means other than the operation of presenting or removing stimuli (cues) and the operation of reinforcement. There are certain reinforcers that an organism may be deprived of. When such reinforcers are withheld for a certain period of time, the frequency of certain behaviors increases. In other cases some dimension of behavior other than its frequency, such as amplitude or latency, changes. The rate of eating, for example, is a function of food deprivation, that is, the time since the last meal. In a similar way breathing is dependent on oxygen-deprivation (actually carbon dioxide excess in the blood). Other reinforcers of which mammals can be deprived with similar consequences are liquids, sexual reinforcement, sleep, and activity.

Once an organism has been deprived to a certain degree, he can then be reinforced with the reinforcer that has been withheld. As the number of reinforcements obtained during a period of observation increases, the organism is said to satiate. Satiation, then, is the opposite of deprivation. Notice that one and the same event, for example consuming a pellet of food, may satiate as well as reinforce. Other events, such as turning on a heat lamp while in the cold, only reinforce. The two processes must always be carefully distinguished; satiation momentarily reduces the frequency of behavior; reinforcement increases its likelihood of occurrence in the future.

It was stated above that when certain reinforcers are withheld the strength of certain behaviors increases. Clearly not all behaviors that together make up an organism's repertoire increase in strength with any one kind of deprivation. The effects of deprivation and satiation are specific to those behaviors which in the past life history of the organism have been reinforced by the reinforcers that have been withheld. Because of the inevitable complexity of the reinforcement history of most organisms, there is likely to be a considerable number of more or less alternative responses or behavior sequences all of which at one time or another have received the same kind of reinforcement. Such a set of related or equivalent responses (Hunter, 1928) has been referred to as a "habit-family hierarchy" (Hull, 1934b). As deprivation increases, all behaviors that make up the food-reinforced habit-family hierarchy increase in strength. The complex relationships between the behaviors of the same or related hierarchies are far from having been fully analyzed. A recent discussion of such problems can be found in a text by Staats and Staats (1964).

PREFERENCE

For nine degrees of pleasure, less by nine degrees of pain, are equal to nothing; but nine degrees of one, less by three degrees of the other, give six of the former net and true . . . the excess gives the true quantity of pleasure and pain. . . .

W. Wollaston (1659–1724)

It may be argued that if the meaning of "motivation" is restricted to deprivation and satiation, many other so-called motivational concepts are arbitrarily excluded. The concept of *preference* is one of these, if one adheres to the prevalent broad usage of the term motivation. Other closely related concepts are *choice* and *decision*. All of them are related to the concepts of reinforcement and habit-family hierarchy.

To make a decision is to choose between two (or more) mutually exclusive routes toward a single goal, or between similar routes leading to different goals. Decision making, then, is a matter of choice between alternatives, of selecting one path or an outcome (reinforcement) in preference to another. In the case of an option between two alternatives leading to the same reinforcer, one deals, of course, with two items in the same habit-family hierarchy (see above). The word "decision" literally means "cutting off" and implies that the decision is made at the moment that the subject cuts himself off from one of the possible alternatives in a choice situation. Whenever there is an opportunity to make more than one response, and if the various response alternatives are incompatible with each other in the sense that they cannot occur at the same time, the possibility of studying choice as a behavioral process exists.

The close relationship of the concepts of choice, decision, and preference to the notion of reinforcement becomes clear when we inquire further into the meaning of the word "preference."

Statements concerning preferences are usually based on behavior as it occurs in choice situations. It is more important that such propositions can usually be translated into statements concerning the relative value of the different reinforcers contingent upon the alternative behaviors.

The many variables that determine which particular response-alternative occurs can be put into three categories: (1) The immediately present stimulus conditions, (2) the history of deprivation of the relevant reinforcers, and (3) the reinforcement history of the organism with respect to each of the response alternatives. Suppose an animal is taught to press one lever for food in the presence of a tone and another lever for water in the presence of a light. Which lever will be pressed in such a case depends on the presence of the appropriate discriminative stimulus and the lengths of the periods of deprivation of food and water. Such a situation involves a choice between alternatives leading to two different reinforcers. Other experimental situations can be constructed in which two different response alternatives are both reinforced by food. In that case, since we are dealing with responses belonging to the same habit-family hierarchy, the length of food deprivation no longer determines the choice. The immediate stimulus conditions and the reinforcement history of the response alternatives remain as the important "determiners of behavior at the choice-point" (Tolman, 1938). As an example of the importance of the reinforcement history we may cite an experiment by Hull (1939). Rats were trained to press two different levers, one lever had to be pressed downwards, the other had to be pushed sideways. Both responses were reinforced with food. During the training phase of the experiment each response was established separately by presenting only one lever at a time. One response received a larger number of reinforcements than the other. When subsequently both levers were presented simultaneously, it was found that the animals initially performed the response which had received the larger number of previous reinforcements.

Whereas the above experiment demonstrates the importance of differences in the previous number of reinforcements for the response alternatives in a choice situation, other more recent experiments have explored the importance of different schedules of reinforcement (Herrnstein, 1961; Verhave, 1961). In the experiment by Herrnstein, pigeons were reinforced with food for pecking at either of two keys. Each key was associated with a different frequency of reinforcement. It was found that the *relative* frequency of responding on a given key closely approximated the *relative* frequency of reinforcement on that key: The more often responding on a given key is reinforced relative to the frequency of payoff on the other key, the higher the rate of responding on the more favorable key.

In all of the above experiments the subject finds himself in a choice situation in which he can execute each response alternative immediately. In more complex experiments, the subject has to produce one of the alternatives himself (Findley, 1962; Verhave, 1963). The experimental situation employed in a recent study (Verhave, 1963) was as follows: The subject had access to two manipulanda or keys. Only one of these keys, designated the main key, eventually reinforced the animal with food on an intermittent basis. This key could assume either of two colors. Each color was associated with a different condition (e.g., a fixed-ratio schedule vs. a variable-interval schedule) for obtaining reinforcement. These two different schedules (or other conditions such as duration or kind of reinforcement) of the main key were the two alternatives between which the bird was permitted to choose. In the research here described the two ways to obtain food reinforcement through the main key were fixed-ratio (FR) schedules of different lengths, a relatively long one and a shorter one. The function of the second key in the experimental situation was to permit the animal to switch the key color, and thus to switch from the long fixed-ratio schedule to the shorter schedule. For this reason the second key is designated the choice or switching key. The long fixed-ratio schedule is designated the imposed condition, because each time the bird obtained food reinforcement, the long FR schedule was put back into effect on the main key. Only by responding on the choice key could the bird switch from the imposed long schedule to the shorter, alternative schedule of the main key.

If the difference between the fixed-ratio schedules of the main key is large enough, a preference for the shorter schedule is clearly demonstrable. The animal will not work on the long imposed schedule, but after each reinforcement obtained through the short schedule it will immediately return to the choice key and again switch back to the shorter alternative schedule. A measure of the degree of preference for the alternative schedule is obtained in the following manner.

Each time the animal switches to the shorter schedule of the main key, the number of pecks required to produce the *next* switch is automatically increased. In this way the "ante" on the choice key is progressively increased. In the present experiment the animal's preference for the alternative condition is assessed by the number of responses he will emit on the choice key to produce a switch in the main key schedules. As the ante on the choice key increases it becomes gradually less worthwhile to work on the choice key, since the effective difference between the two ways to get food decreases. Suppose the long schedule required 400 responses, and the short schedule 100, if the choice-key schedule has gradually been raised to 300 responses, any difference in favor of the choice-key route has decreased to zero.

The gradual steplike decrease in the difference between the two routes to food shows up in the animal's behavior in two ways: (1) there is an increase in the number of times per session that the bird works through the long imposed schedule; (2) after each food reinforcement, when the bird is again exposed to the choice situation, it takes longer and longer before the bird starts to respond again on the choice key. This is the fixed-ratio straining effect discussed previously.

It is this last effect which is made use of to "titrate" the bird's preference for the shorter schedule. If, at some point, it does not produce the next change in the main-key schedules within some fixed arbitrary length of time (as measured from the moment the choice situation is reintroduced after food reinforcement), the progressively increasing ratio schedule of the choice key is *decreased*. The bird therefore has a way to bring the choice key schedule gradually down again. This additional contingency makes the schedule in effect on the choice key an adjusting schedule (Ferster and Skinner, 1957).

In this manner the experimenter "haggles" with the animal, via the continuously changing schedule of the choice key, about the "value" of the shorter schedule. A specific value, in terms of a rather specific number of responses the bird is willing to make on the choice key, is arrived at.

Such experiments outline a basic paradigm for determining the relative strength of reinforcers. It is possible to use the experimental situation as a psychological Wheatstone bridge to determine the value of unknown reinforcers relative to any set of arbitrary standard conditions, as is done in calorimetry.

It has been shown that if the imposed and alternative conditions on the main key consist of two different ratio schedules, a definite stable value of an adjusting schedule can be found on the choice key (Verhave, 1963). One can substitute, however, some other imposed condition (another schedule, for example) for the one originally used. One can then empirically determine the specific value at which the new imposed condition produces the same stable equilibrium value as the previous one under otherwise identical circumstances. The above indicated line of research suggests an approach toward the experimental analysis of more complex motivational problems.

CODA

This concludes our bird's eye view presentation of basic facts, concepts, and principles derived from the experimental analysis of behavior. Even as an introductory survey it has been far from complete; however, an attempt has been made to include that material which is prerequisite to an understanding of original research reports in the current literature. If the concepts and terminology introduced in this chapter have become part of the readers' fund of knowledge, further readings in the selections from the literature collected in this book should hopefully present no major problem. For those who desire exposure to other brief introductions to this experimental literature, the accounts of Keller (1954) and Mednick (1964) are highly recommended.

REFERENCES

ADAM, L. *Primitive art.* New York: Penguin, 1949.

ADLER, M., and HOGAN, J. A. Classical conditioning and punishment of an instinctive response in Betta Splendens. *Anim. Behav.,* 1963, *11,* 351–354.

AIRAPETYANTZ, E., and BYKOV, K. Physiological experiments and the psychology of the subconscious. *Philos. Phenomenal. Res.,* 1944, *5,* 577–593.

ANGER, D. The role of temporal discrimination in the reinforcement of Sidman avoidance behavior. *J. exp. Anal. Behav.,* 1963, *6,* 477–506.

ASHBY, W. R. *An introduction to cybernetics.* New York: Wiley, 1958.

ASHBY, W. R. *Design for a brain.* (2nd ed.) New York: Wiley, 1960.

AZRIN, N. H. Some effects of two intermittent schedules of immediate and non-immediate punishment. *J. Psychol.,* 1956, *42,* 3–21.

AZRIN, N. H. Punishment and recovery during fixed-ratio performance. *J. exp. Anal. Behav.,* 1959, *2,* 301–305.

AZRIN, N. H., and HOLZ, W. C. Punishment. In W. K. Honig (Ed.), *Operant behavior.* New York: Appleton-Century-Crofts, 1966.

BARRY, J. J., and HARRISON, J. M. Relation between stimulus intensity and strength of escape responding. *Psychol. Rep.,* 1957, *3,* 3–8.

BASS, M. J., and HULL, C. L. The irradiation of a tactile conditioned reflex in man. *J. comp. Psychol.,* 1934, *17,* 47–65.

BEACH, F. A. *Hormones and behavior.* New York: Hoeber-Harper, 1948.

BECHTEREV, V. M. *General principles of human reflexology.* London: Jarrolds Publishers, Ltd., 1933.

BERNARD, C. *An introduction to the study of experimental medicine.* New York: Dover, 1957 (originally published in French, 1865).

BIERENS DE HAAN, J. A. *Die Tierischen Instinkte und ihr Umbau durch Erfahrung.* Leiden: Brill, 1940.

BYKOV, K. M. *The cerebral cortex and the internal organs.* (Translated and edited by W. H. Gantt.) New York: Chemical Publishing, 1957.

CHURCH, R. M. The varied effects of punishment. *Psychol. Rev.,* 1963, *70,* 369–402.

COWLES, J. T. Food tokens as incentives for learning by chimpanzees. *Comp. psychol. Monogr.,* 1937, *14,* 1–96.

CRAIG, W. Appetites and aversions as constituents of instincts. *Biol. Bull.,* 1918, *34,* 91–107.

DARWIN, E. *Zoonomia; or the Laws of Organic Life.* London: Johnson, 1794–1796. 2 vols.

DIAMOND, S., BALVIN, R. S., and DIAMOND, F. R. *Inhibition and choice.* New York: Harper & Row, 1963.

DINSMOOR, J. A. Punishment: I. The avoidance hypothesis. *Psychol. Rev.,* 1954, *61,* 34–46.

DINSMOOR, J. A. Punishment: II. An interpretation of empirical findings. *Psychol. Rev.,* 1955, *62,* 96–105.

DINSMOOR, J. A., and HUGHES, L. H. Training rats to press a bar to turn off shock. *J. comp. physiol. Psychol.,* 1956, *49,* 235–238.

ELLISON, G. D., and KONORSKI, J. Separation of the salivary and motor responses in instrumental conditioning. *Science,* 1964, *146,* 1071–1072.

ESTES, W. K., and SKINNER, B. F. Some quantitative properties of anxiety. *J. exp. Psychol.,* 1941, *29,* 390–400.

ESTES, W. K. An experimental study of punishment. *Psychol. Monogr.,* 1944, *57,* 1–40, No. 263.

FEARING, F. *Reflex action: A study in the history of physiological psychology.* Baltimore: Williams & Wilkins, 1930. (Reprinted by Hafner, New York, 1964.)

FERSTER, C. B. The use of the free operant in the analysis of behavior. *Psychol. Bull.,* 1953, *50,* 263–274.

FERSTER, C. B. Withdrawal of positive reinforcement as punishment. *Science,* 1957, *126,* 509.

FERSTER, C. B. Control of behavior in chimpanzees and pigeons by time out from positive reinforcement. *Psychol. Monogr.,* 1958, *72,* 1–38, No. 461.

FERSTER, C. B., and SKINNER, B. F. *Schedules of reinforcement.* New York: Appleton-Century-Crofts, 1957.

FINDLEY, J. D. An experimental outline for building and exploring multi-operant behavior repertoires. *J. exp. Anal. Behav.,* 1962, *5,* 113–166.

FRAENKEL, G., and GUNN, D. L. *The orientation of animals.* London: Oxford University Press, 1940. (Reprinted by Dover, New York, 1961.)

GLASER, D. *The effectiveness of a prison and parole system.* Indianapolis: Bobbs-Merrill, 1964.

GRANT, D. A. Classical and operant conditioning. In A. W. Melton (Ed.), *Categories of human learning.* New York: Academic Press, 1964.

GREENSPOON, J. The effect of a verbal stimulus as a reinforcement. *Proc. Indiana Acad. Sci.,* 1949, *59,* 287.

GREENSPOON, J. The reinforcing effect of two spoken sounds on the frequency of two responses. *Amer. J. Psychol.,* 1955, *68,* 409–416.

GUTTMAN, M., and KALISH, H. I. Experiments in discrimination. *Sci. Amer.,* 1958, *198,* 72–82.

HEFFERLINE, R. F. Learning theory and clinical psychology—an eventual symbiosis? In A. J. Bachrach (Ed.), *Experimental foundations of clinical psychology.* New York: Basic Books, 1962.

HEFFERLINE, R. F., KEENAN, B., and HARFORD, R. A. Escape and avoidance conditioning in human subjects without their observation of the response. *Science,* 1959, *130,* 1338–1339.

HERRNSTEIN, R. J. Relative and absolute strength of response as a function of frequency of reinforcement. *J. exp. Anal. Behav.,* 1961, *4,* 267–272.

HODOS, W. Progressive ratio as a measure of reward strength. *Science,* 1961, *134,* 943–944.

HOLLAND, J. G. Human vigilance. *Science,* 1958, *128,* 61–67.

HONIG, W. K. (Ed.), *Operant behavior.* New York: Appleton-Century-Crofts, 1966.

HULL, C. L. Learning: The factor of the conditioned reflex. In C. Murchison (Ed.), *Handbook of general experimental psychology.* Worcester, Mass.: Clark University Press, 1934. (a)

HULL, C. L. The concept of the habit-family hierarchy and maze learning. Part I. *Psychol. Rev.,* 1934, *41,* 33–54. (b)

HULL, C. L. Simple trial-and-error learning—an empirical investigation. *J. comp. Psychol.,* 1939, *27,* 233–258.

HULL, C. L. *Principles of behavior.* New York: Appleton-Century-Crofts, 1943.

HUNTER, W. S. *Human behavior.* (Rev. ed.) Chicago: University of Chicago Press, 1928.

JENNINGS, H. S. *Behavior of the lower organisms.* New York: Columbia University Press, 1906. (Reprinted by Indiana University Press, Bloomington, 1962.)

KAPLAN, M. The effects of noxious stimulus intensity and duration during intermittent reinforcement of escape behavior. *J. comp. physiol. Psychol.,* 1952, *45,* 538–549.

KELLEHER, R. T. A comparison of conditioned and food reinforcement on a fixed-ratio schedule in chimpanzees. *Psychol. Newsltr.,* 1957, *8,* 88–93. (a)

KELLEHER, R. T. A multiple schedule of conditioned reinforcement with chimpanzees. *Psychol. Rep.,* 1957, *3,* 485–491. (b)

KELLEHER, R. T. Conditioned reinforcement in chimpanzees. *J. comp. physiol. Psychol.,* 1957, *50,* 571–575. (c)

KELLEHER, R. T., and GOLLUB, L. R. A review of positive conditioned reinforcement. *J. exp. Anal. Behav.,* 1962, *5,* 543–597.

KELLER, F. S. Light aversion in the white rat. *Psychol. Rec.,* 1941, *4,* 235–250.

KELLER, F. S. *Learning.* New York: Random House, 1954.

KELLER, F. S., and SCHOENFELD, W. N. *Principles of psychology.* New York: Appleton-Century-Crofts, 1950.

KIMBLE, G. A. *Hilgard and Marquis' conditioning and learning.* (2nd ed.) New York: Appleton-Century-Crofts, 1961.

KIMBLE, G. A. Categories of learning and the problem of definition. In A. W. Melton (Ed.), *Categories of human learning.* New York: Academic Press, 1964.

KINTSCH, W., and WITTE, R. S. Concurrent conditioning of bar press and salivation responses. *J. comp. physiol. Psychol.*, 1962, *55*, 963–968.

KOSHTOYANTS, Kh. S. *Essays on the history of physiology in Russia.* Washington, D. C.: American Institute of Biological Sciences, 1964.

KRASNER, L. Studies of the conditioning of verbal behavior. *Psychol. Bull.*, 1958, *55*, 148–170.

KRASNER, L. The therapist as a social reinforcement machine. In H. Strupp and L. Luborsky (Eds.), *Research in psychotherapy.* Washington: American Psychological Association, 1962.

KUPALOV, P. S., and GANTT, W. H. The relationship between the strength of the intensity of tone stimuli and the size of the resulting conditioned reflexes. *Brain,* 1927, *54*, 85–98.

LARSSON, K. *Conditioning and sexual behavior in the male albino rat.* Stockholm: Almqvist and Wiksell, 1956.

LEE, B. S. Effects of delayed speech feedback. *J. acoust. Soc. Amer.,* 1950, *22*, 824–826.

LOCKARD, R. B. Some effects of light upon the behavior of rodents. *Psychol. Bull.,* 1963, *60*, 509–529.

MAIER, N. R. F., and SCHNEIRLA, T. C. *Principles of animal psychology.* New York: McGraw-Hill, 1935. (Enlarged ed., Dover, New York, 1964.)

MEDNICK, S. A. *Learning.* Englewood Cliffs, N.J.: Prentice-Hall, 1964.

MEDNICK, S. A., and FREEDMAN, J. L. Stimulus generalization. *Psychol. Bull.,* 1960, *57*, 169–200.

MILLER, S., and KONORSKI, J. Sur une forme particulière des réflexes conditionnels. *C. R. Soc. Biol.,* 1928, *99*, 1155–1157.

MYERS, J. L. Secondary reinforcement: A review of recent experimentation. *Psychol. Bull.,* 1958, *55*, 284–301.

NOTTERMAN, J. M., SCHOENFELD, W. N., and BERSH, P. J. Partial reinforcement and conditioned heart rate response in human subjects. *Science,* 1952, *115*, 77–79.

PAVLOV, I. P. *Conditioned reflexes: An investigation of the physiological activity of the cerebral cortex.* (Translated and edited by G. V. Anrep.) London: Oxford University Press, 1927. (Reprinted by Dover, New York, 1960.)

PIERREL, R., and SHERMAN, J. G. Generalization of auditory intensity following generalization training. *J. exp. Anal. Behav.,* 1960, *3*, 313–322.

RAZRAN, G. H. S. Music, art, and the conditioned response. Paper read at Eastern Psychological Association, April 1–2, 1938.

RAZRAN, G. H. S. Stimulus generalization of conditioned responses. *Psychol. Bull.,* 1949, *46*, 337–365.

ROZENZWEIG, M. R. Salivary conditioning before Pavlov. *Amer. J. Psychol.,* 1959, *72*, 628–633.

RUCH, T. C., PATTON, M. D., WOODBURY, J. W., and TOWE, A. L. *Neurophysiology.* Philadelphia: Saunders, 1961.

SCHNEIRLA, T. C. An evolutionary and developmental theory of biphasic processes underlying approach and withdrawal. In M. R. Jones (Ed.), *Nebraska symposium on motivation.* Lincoln: University of Nebraska Press, 1959.

SCHOENFELD, W. N. An experimental approach to anxiety, escape, and avoidance behavior. In P. J. Hoch and J. Zubin (Eds.), *Anxiety.* New York: Grune & Stratton, 1950.

SHAPIRO, M. M. Respondent salivary conditioning during operant lever pressing in dogs. *Science,* 1960, *132,* 619–620.

SHEARN, D. Does the heart learn? *Psychol. Bull.,* 1961, *58,* 452–458.

SHERRINGTON, C. S. *The integrative action of the nervous system.* New Haven, Conn.: Yale University Press, 1906. (Reprinted, 1961.)

SIDMAN, M. Avoidance conditioning with brief shock and no exteroceptive warning signal. *Science,* 1953, *118,* 157–158.

SIDMAN, M. Time out from avoidance as a reinforcer: A study of response interaction. *J. exp. Anal. Behav.,* 1962, *5,* 423–434.

SIDMAN, M., and STEBBINS, W. C. Satiation effects under fixed-ratio schedules of reinforcement. *J. comp. physiol. Psychol.,* 1954, *47,* 114–116.

SKINNER, B. F. On the conditions of elicitation of certain eating reflexes. *Proc. Nat. Acad. Sci.,* 1930, *16,* 433–438.

SKINNER, B. F. On the rate of formation of a conditioned reflex. *J. gen. Psychol.,* 1932, *7,* 274–285.

SKINNER, B. F. *The behavior of organisms.* New York: Appleton-Century-Crofts, 1938.

SKINNER, B. F. Some quantitative properties of anxiety. *Psychol. Bull.,* 1941, *38,* 539.

SKINNER, B. F. Some contributions of an experimental analysis of behavior to psychology as a whole. *Amer. Psychol.,* 1953, *8,* 69–78.

SKINNER, B. F. A case history in scientific method. *Amer. Psychol.,* 1956, *11,* 221–233.

SKINNER, B. F. *Cumulative record.* (Enlarged ed.) New York: Appleton-Century-Crofts, 1961.

SKINNER, B. F. Operant behavior. *Amer. Psychol.,* 1963, *18,* 503–515.

SMEE, A. *Instinct and reason.* London: Reeve, Benham, and Reeve, 1850.

SMITH, W. M., McCRARY, J. W., and SMITH, K. U. Delayed visual feedback and behavior. *Science,* 1960, *132,* 1013–1014.

SOLOMAN, R. L. Punishment. *Amer. Psychol.,* 1964, *19,* 239–253.

SOLOMAN, R. L., and BRUSH, E. S. Experimentally derived conceptions of anxiety and aversion. In M. R. Jones (Ed.), *Nebraska symposium on motivation.* Lincoln: University of Nebraska Press, 1956.

SPALDING, D. A. On instinct. *Nature,* 1872, *6,* 485–486.

STAATS, A. W., and STAATS, C. K. *Complex human behavior.* New York: Holt, Rinehart and Winston, 1964.

THORNDIKE, E. L. Animal intelligence: An experimental study of the associative processes in animals. *Psychol. Rev. Monogr. Supp.,* 1898, *2,* No. 4 (Whole No. 8).

THORNDIKE, E. L. *Animal intelligence.* New York: Macmillan, 1911.

THORNDIKE, E. L. *Educational psychology.* New York: Columbia, 1916.

THORNDIKE, E. L. *Human learning.* New York: Appleton-Century-Crofts, 1931.

THORNDIKE, E. L. *Fundamentals of learning.* New York: Teachers College, Columbia University, 1932.

THORPE, W. H. *Learning and instinct in animals.* (2nd ed.) London: Methuen, 1963.

TINBERGEN, M. *The study of instinct.* London: Oxford, 1951.

TOLMAN, E. C. *Purposive behavior in animals and man.* New York: Appleton-

Century-Crofts, 1932. (Reprinted by University of California Press, Berkeley, 1949.)

TOLMAN, E. C. The determiners of behavior at a choice point. *Psychol. Rev.*, 1938, *45*, 1–41.

VERHAVE, T. Technique for the differential reinforcement of the rate of avoidance responding. *Science*, 1959, *129*, 959–960.

VERHAVE, T. Some observations concerning prepotency and probability of postponing shock with a two-lever avoidance procedure. *J. exp. Anal. Behav.*, 1961, *4*, 187–192.

VERHAVE, T. The functional properties of a time out from an avoidance schedule. *J. exp. Anal. Behav.*, 1962, *5*, 391–422.

VERHAVE, T. Towards an empirical calculus of reinforcement value. *J. exp. Anal Behav.*, 1963, *6*, 525–536.

VERNON, J. A. Cutaneous interaction resulting from simultaneous electrical and mechanical vibratory stimulation. *J. exp. Psychol.*, 1953, *45*, 283–287.

VERPLANCK, W. S. The control of the content of conversation: Reinforcement of statements of opinion. *J. abnorm. soc. Psychol.*, 1955, *51*, 668–676.

WARREN, H. C. *A history of the association psychology.* New York: Scribner, 1921.

WATSON, J. B. *Psychology from the standpoint of a behaviorist.* Philadelphia: Lippincott, 1919.

WEINER, N. *Cybernetics or control and communication in the animal and the machine.* New York: Wiley, 1948.

WEISS, B., and LATIES, V. G. Titration behavior on various fractional escape programs. *J. exp. Anal. Behav.*, 1959, *2*, 227–248.

WEISS, B., and LATIES, V. G. Behavioral thermoregulation. *Science*, 1961, *133*, 1338–1344.

WILLIAMS, D. R., and TEITELBAUM, P. Control of drinking behavior by means of an operant-conditioning technique. *Science*, 1956, *124*, 1294–1296.

WOLF, K. Properties of multiple conditioned reflex type II activity. *Acta Biol. Exp.* (Warsaw), 1963, *23*, 133–150.

WOLFE, J. B. Effectiveness of token-rewards for chimpanzees. *Comp. psychol. Monogr.*, 1936, *12*, 1–72.

YATES, A. J. Delayed auditory feedback. *Psychol. Bull.*, 1963, *60*, 213–232.

SUGGESTED READINGS

KELLER, F. S. *Learning: reinforcement theory.* New York: Random House, 1954.

KELLER, F. S., and SCHOENFELD, W. N. *Principles of psychology.* New York: Appleton-Century-Crofts, 1950.

STAATS, A. W., and STAATS, C. K. *Complex human behavior.* New York: Holt, Rinehart and Winston, 1963.

WOODWORTH, R. S., and SCHLOSBERG, H. *Experimental psychology.* (Rev. ed.) New York: Holt, Rinehart and Winston, 1954.

Chapter II

REFLEX, INSTINCT, AND RESPONDENT
BEHAVIOR

The papers reprinted in this chapter serve mainly to set the stage for the material of the chapters that follow.

The data or observations to be analyzed in a scientific study of behavior may come from a variety of sources. Just as human behavior may be studied in a naturalistic setting by the clinical psychologist or cultural anthropologist, animal behavior can also be studied in a naturalistic as well as a laboratory setting. A naturalistic setting need not prevent the imaginative observer from performing instructive experiments, as evidenced by the type of study currently identified with the ethological approach. In the present chapter it is represented by the articles of Wallace Craig and Niko Tinbergen and his associates. Craig's historic paper presents a lucid discussion of many of the basic phenomena and concepts subsequently more extensively explored by both the experimental psychologist and the ethologist. The article is of particular interest since it demonstrates the unity of the subject matter which is the common interest of both approaches. At the time the paper was written (1918), the two approaches were as yet neither distinct, nor identified with different professional organizations or with separate journals in which research was published. The content of the paper shows clearly that the subsequent divergence and separation of experimental psychology and ethology was largely a historical and geographical accident. There can be little rational or theoretical basis for a distinction between two disciplines which deal with the same subject matter. Recent developments which indicate a "remerger" of concepts and techniques attest to the truth of this view. The common core of interest, the development of an understanding of behavior by the objective methods characteristic of natural science, is not only shown by Craig and the learning theorist whom he most directly influenced, Edward C. Tolman (1932), but also by the ethologists who claim him as their intellectual ancestor, Niko Tinbergen (1951) and Eckhard H. Hess (1962).

For those to whom the ethological approach is new and unfamiliar, the papers by Craig and Tinbergen's group offer a good introduction. The latter paper illustrates many of the features that are identified with the ethological approach: the objective, and if possible, experimental study of behavior in a naturalistic setting, a concern with the evolutionary origin and survival value of the behavior investigated, and the selection for study of behavior as it is normally performed by an animal rather than behavior which does not naturally occur and has to be specially taught by various conditioning techniques.

B. F. Skinner, the author of the second selection of this chapter, needs no further introduction after the discussion of his work in the previous chapter. The discussion of the reflex by Skinner as well as by Craig illustrates the historical importance of the concept of the reflex in the development of contemporary learning and behavior theory.

REFERENCES

HESS, E. H. *Ethology: An approach toward the complete analysis of behavior in new directions in psychology.* New York: Holt, Rinehart and Winston, 1962.

TINBERGEN, N. *The study of instinct.* London: Oxford University Press, 1951.

TOLMAN, E. C. *Purposive behavior in animals and men.* New York: Appleton-Century-Crofts, 1932. (Reprinted by University of California Press, Berkeley, 1949.)

1

Appetites and Aversions as Constituents of Instincts

Wallace Craig

GENERAL ACCOUNT OF APPETITE AND AVERSION

The overt behavior of adult animals occurs largely in rather definite chains and cycles, and it has been held that these are merely chain reflexes. Many years of study of the behavior of animals—studies especially of the blond ring-dove (*Turtur risorius*) and other pigeons—have convinced me

Adapted from *Biological Bull. of the Marine Biol. Lab.*, Woods Hole, Mass., 1918, XXXIV, 91–107. With permission of the publisher.

that instinctive behavior does not consist of mere chain reflexes; it involves other factors which it is the purpose of this article to describe. I do not deny that innate chain reflexes constitute a considerable part of the instinctive equipment of doves. Indeed, I think it probable that some of the dove's instincts include an element which is even a tropism as described by Loeb. But with few if any exceptions among the instincts of doves, this reflex action constitutes only a part of each instinct in which it is present. Each instinct involves an element of appetite, or aversion, or both.

An appetite (or appetence, if this term may be used with purely behavioristic meaning), so far as externally observable, is a state of agitation which continues so long as a certain stimulus, which may be called the appeted stimulus, is absent. When the appeted stimulus is at length received it stimulates a consummatory reaction, after which the appetitive behavior ceases and is succeeded by a state of relative rest.

An aversion (example 7, page 57) is a state of agitation which continues so long as a certain stimulus, referred to as the disturbing stimulus, is present; but which ceases, being replaced by a state of relative rest, when that stimulus has ceased to act on the sense-organs.

The state of agitation, in either appetite or aversion, is exhibited externally by increased muscular tension; by static and phasic contractions of many skeletal and dermal muscles, giving rise to bodily attitudes and gestures which are easily recognized signs or "expressions" of appetite or of aversion; by restlessness; by activity, in extreme cases violent activity; and by "varied effort" (Lloyd Morgan, 1896; Stout, 1907).

In the theoretically simplest case, which I think we may observe in doves to some extent, these states bring about the appeted situation in a simple mechanical manner. The organism is disturbed, actively moving, in one situation, but quiet and inactive in another; hence it tends to move out of the first situation and to remain in the second, obeying essentially the same law as is seen in the physical laboratory when sand or lycopodium powder on a sounding body leaves the antinodes and comes to rest in the nodes.

But pigeons seldom are guided in so simple a manner. Their behavior involves other factors which must be described in connection with appetite and aversion.

An appetite is accompanied by a certain *readiness to act*. When most fully predetermined, this has the form of a chain reflex. But in the case of most supposedly innate chain reflexes, the reactions of the beginning or middle part of the series are not innate, or not completely innate, but must be learned by trial. The end action of the series, the consummatory action, is always innate. One evidence of this is the fact that in the first [1]

[1] To see the appetitive nature of an instinct, it is necessary in some cases to observe an individual animal carefully during its first performance of the act in question. But the performance may be so quick that the observer is quite unable to analyze it.

manifestation (also, in some cases, in later performances) of many instincts, the animal begins with an *incipient consummatory action,* although the appeted stimulus, which is the adequate stimulus of that consummatory action, has not yet been received. I speak of an incipient "action" rather than "reaction" because it seems clearly wrong to speak of a "reaction" to a stimulus which has not yet been received. The stimulus in question is obtained only after a course of appetitive, trial-and-error behavior. When at last this stimulus is obtained, the consummatory reaction takes place completely, no longer incipiently. Then the appetitive behavior ceases; in common speech we say the animal is "satisfied."

One may observe all gradations between a true reflex and a mere readiness to act, mere facilitation. Thus, in the dove, a stimulus from food in the crop may cause the parent to vomit the food or to feed it to young: there are all gradations from an immediate crop-reflex, in which the food is vomited upon the ground, through intermediate cases in which the parent is much disturbed by the food in his crop, but appetitively seeks the young and induces them to take the food; to other cases in which the parent is only ready to feed the young if importuned by them; and finally to cases in which the stimulus from the crop does not even cause facilitation, and the parent does not disgorge the food at all, even if importuned by the young.

While an appetite is accompanied by readiness for certain actions, it may be accompanied by a distinct *unreadiness* for certain other actions, and this is an important factor in some forms of behavior. It is altogether probable that this unreadiness is due in some cases to the fact that the activity of certain neurones *inhibits* the activity of certain other neurones. It is now well known, too, that unreadiness may be due to the condition of the internal secretions. And the mutual exclusion of certain forms of instinctive behavior is inevitable, due to the incompatibility (Washburn, 1916) of their motor components.

Unreadiness may be accompanied by aversion, and vice versa; but either of these may occur without the evident presence of the other. An

---

Analysis may be aided by preventing the animal from attaining the consummatory situation for a time, so that the appetitive phase is prolonged, as it were magnified. My cripple dove (example 5, page 56) afforded just this aid to analysis. The literature is full of reports of instinctive behavior which might well be further analyzed. Consider for example the case of the young moorhen cited by Lloyd Morgan (1896) which had never previously dived, but on being suddenly frightened by a puppy, dived like a flash. That act was too quick for us to analyze it. But if we could successfully impede the diving of a young moorhen so as to prolong the phases of the act, I think it probable that we should find an appetite for the consummatory situation (that of being under water) and a restless striving until it is attained; and that some details in the series of actions, details which in a normal dive are very sure to be hit upon by accident, are not innately predetermined. When one sees the first performance of an instinctive act take place very quickly and with apparent perfection, this does not prove that there is an innate chain reflex determining every detail of the act.

aversion is sometimes accompanied by an innately determined reaction adapted to getting rid of the disturbing stimulus, or—this point is of special interest—by two alternative reactions which are tried and interchanged repeatedly until the disturbing stimulus is got rid of (see example 7, page 57).

The escape from a disturbing situation or the attainment of an appeted one is accomplished, in case of some instincts, far more surely and more rapidly after one or more experiences. In the first performance of an appetitive action, the bird makes a first trial; if this fails to bring the appeted stimulus he remains agitated and active, and makes a second trial, which differs more or less from the first; if this fails to bring the appeted stimulus he remains still active and makes a third trial; and so on until at last the appeted stimulus is received, the consummatory reaction follows, and then the bird comes to rest. In later experience with the same situation, the modes of behavior which were followed immediately by the appeted stimulus and consummatory reaction are repeated; those which were not so followed tend to drop out.

If a young bird be kept experimentally where it cannot obtain the normal stimulus of a certain consummatory reaction, it may vent that reaction upon an abnormal or inadequate stimulus, and show some satisfaction in doing so; but if the bird be allowed at first, or even later, to obtain the normal stimulus, it will be thereafter very unwilling to accept the abnormal stimulus. That this is true of the sex instinct has been shown in a former article (Craig, 1914). It is true also of the appetite for a nest. Thus a female dove which has never had a nest, nor material to build one, lays eggs readily on the floor; but a dove that has had long experience with nests will withhold her egg if no nest is obtainable. The male dove similarly, if he has never had a nest, goes through the brooding behavior on the floor; but an experienced male is unwilling to do so, and shows extreme anxiety to find a nest. These examples illustrate the fact that the bird must *learn* to obtain the adequate stimulus for a complete consummatory reaction, and thus to satisfy its own appetites.

There is often a struggle between two appetites, as when a bird hesitates, and it may hesitate for a long time, between going on the nest to incubate and going away to join the flock, eat, etc. By watching the bird one can predict which line of behavior it will follow, for each appetite is distinguished by its own expressive signs (consisting partly of the incipient consummatory action), and one can see which appetite is gaining control of the organism.

These outward expressions of appetite are signs of physiological states which are but little known. Since my own observations have been on external behavior only, I say little about the internal states. They are probably exceedingly complex and numerous and similar to the physiological states which in the human organism are concomitants of appetites,[2] emotions, desires. They doubtless include stimulations from interoceptors and proprioceptors; perhaps automatic action of nerve centers; perhaps readiness or unreadiness of neurones to conduct. It is known that some of the periodic appetites are coincident with profound physiological changes. Thus Gerhartz (1914) found that during the incubation period in the domestic fowl the metabolism of the body as a whole is at a low ebb. In some cases a stimulus from the environment is the immediate excitant of an appetite; especially, stimulation of a distance-receptor may arouse appetite for a contact stimulus, as when the sight of food arouses appetite for the taste of it. But probably in every case appetite is dependent upon physiological factors. And in many cases the rise of appetite is due to internal causes which are highly independent of environmental conditions, and even extremely resistant to environmental interference.

Appetitive behavior in vertebrates is evidently a higher development of what Jennings (1906) calls the positive reaction in lower organisms; aversive behavior in vertebrates corresponds to what Jennings calls negative reactions.

The attempt to distinguish between instinct and appetite, as in Baldwin's Dictionary (1901), is not justified by the facts of behavior. Baldwin says: "Appetite is distinguished from instinct in that it shows itself at first in connection with the life of the organism itself, and does not wait for an external stimulus, but appears and craves satisfaction." These characteristics, here ascribed to appetite, are the very ones which I have observed in the instinctive behavior of pigeons. The instincts of pigeons satisfy Baldwin's further description of appetite in that each appears first as a "state of vague unrest" involving especially the "organs by which the gratification is to be secured"; and "a complex state of tension of all the motor . . . elements whenever the appetite is aroused either (a) by the direct organic condition of need, or (b) indirectly through the presence or memory of the object." This last point is illustrated, e.g., by doves learning to drink (example 1, page 54), in whom the sight of the water-dish at a distance aroused the drinking actions by associative memory. I have observed appetitive behavior as Baldwin describes it in nearly all the instinctive activities of doves, and I think that sufficient observation will reveal it in all their instincts.

The most thorough attempt to distinguish instincts from appetites and to show the logical consequences of such distinction, in all the literature to which I have access, is in an old article by Professor Bowen (1846).

---

[2] Hunger furnishes a typical case of appetitive behavior (Carlson, 1916; Ellis, 1910). Carlson makes a distinction between hunger and appetite. The distinction he finds is certainly real, but the use of words is unfortunate, for hunger is clearly one kind of appetite.

This article is still worth study, to suggest the conclusions to which one is logically led if he denies that instincts contain any element of appetite. These conclusions, taken almost literally from Bowen, may be summarized as follows: (1) "If the name of instinct be denied to these original and simple preferences [appetites] and aversions, there will appear good reason to doubt whether man is ever governed by instinct, whether all his actions are not reducible to passion, appetite, and reason." The "passions" of man cannot be concomitants of instinct. (2) "Instinct is not a free and conscious power of the animal itself. It is, if we may so speak, a foreign agency, which enters not into the individuality of the brute." Instinct "has no effect on the rest of their conduct, which is governed by their own individuality." (3) Bowen contends with logical consistency that if instinct contains no appetitive factor, the ends toward which instincts work, as seen by an observer, are not ends for the agent; that therefore the agent has no power to make the instinctive behavior more effective. In short, instinctive behavior is not susceptible of improvement by intelligence. (4) Bowen concludes that the intellect and the "passions" of man are not products of evolution. (5) It may be added that even Bowen, strive as he did to separate appetite from instinct, was compelled to admit that the attempt at such separation leads one into difficulties and disputed cases. In contravention of Bowen's conclusions I contend: (1) That much of human behavior is instinctive. (2) That Bowen's description of instinct as "a foreign agency, which enters not into the individuality" is true of reflex action, such as coughing or sneezing, but is not true of instinctive behavior, which is extremely different from such mere reflexes. (For a fuller statement on this point, see below, page 61. See also Hobhouse, 1915.) (3) That, of the useful results toward which instincts tend, some, not all, are ends for the agent. For they are the objects of appetites, and the animal strives and learns to attain them. (4) That human conative behavior evolved from the instinctive appetitive behavior of lower animals.

EXAMPLES

1. The case of doves learning to drink, as described in detail in a former article (Craig, 1912), illustrates appetite. The observed appetitive behavior was aroused by stimulation of distance-receptors, such as the sight of the water-dish being brought to the cage, and of the man bringing it; these acted as appetizers. Each dove, as soon as it had learned to associate such stimuli with the drinking situation, responded to these stimuli by making drinking movements (incipient consummatory action) at once without going to the water-dish. The first drinking movements failing to bring water, the dove repeated these movements again and again, sometimes walking a few steps, sometimes turning round, until after many trials and many errors it did get its bill into the water, received the stimulus

from water in the mouth (appeted stimulus), whereupon the drinking movements (consummatory reaction) were made not incipiently but completely, the water being swallowed, after which the bird rested and appeared satisfied.

2. A good example of appetitive behavior is seen in the way in which a young male dove locates a nesting site for the first time. The first thing the observer sees is that the dove, while standing on his perch, spontaneously assumes the nest-calling attitude, his body tilted forward, head down, as if his neck and breast were already touching the hollow of a nest (incipient consummatory action), and in this attitude he sounds the nest-call. But he shows dissatisfaction, as if the bare perch were not a comfortable situation for this nest-dedicating attitude. He shifts about until he finds a corner which more or less fits his body while in the tilted posture; he is seldom satisfied with his first corner, but tries another and another. If now an appropriate nest-box or a ready-made nest is put into his cage, this inexperienced dove does not recognize it as a nest, but sooner or later he tries it, as he has tried all other places, for nest-calling, and in such trial the nest evidently gives him a strong and satisfying stimulation (the appeted stimulus) which no other situation has given him. In the nest his attitude becomes extreme; he abandons himself to an orgy of nest-calling (complete consummatory action), turning now this way and now that in the hollow, palpating the straws with his feet, wings, breast, neck, and beak, and rioting in the wealth of new, luxurious stimuli. He no longer wanders restlessly in search of new nesting situations, but remains satisfied with his present highly stimulating nest.

3. Fetching straws to the nest is apparently due to an appetite for building them into the nest. The dove has an innate tendency to pick up straws, and an innate tendency to build them into the nest (consummatory reaction); but it has apparently no innate tendency to carry a straw to the nest, no innate "chain" of reflexes. When an experienced bird finds a straw he seizes it repeatedly and toys with it, sometimes making movements resembling those by which he would build the straw into the nest. He seems thus to get up an appetite for building the straw in, and when this appetite is sufficiently aroused he flies to the nest, guided by associative memory, and performs the consummatory reaction completely. A young female, No. 70, which I observed picking up a straw for the first (?) time, on her 54th day, showed the lack of a "chain reflex." For she continued toying with the straw an excessively long time, not carrying it at all, though she happened to be very near the nest. This was the more remarkable as she had a well-formed habit of going to the nest on all occasions. At length she did go to the nest with her straw, and made well-ordered movements to build it in.

4. The male and the female dove take regular turns in sitting on the eggs. The male is seized by the appetite for brooding about 8 or 9 A.M., and the

female about 5 P.M., the state evidently being brought on in each case by physiological causes which are part of the daily physiological rhythm. When either one, e.g., the female, comes to the side of the nest prepared to enter and sit, she already has somewhat the attitude of the sitting bird, the body sunk down on the legs and the feathers fluffed out (incipient consummatory action). If her sitting appetite be thwarted, as by her mate refusing to budge from his position, she shows restlessness and makes intelligent efforts to obtain possession of the nest. When at last her mate yields his place, she steps exultingly into the center of the nest and settles herself on the eggs with many movements indicative of satisfying emotion (complete consummatory reaction).

A broody hen of course illustrates the same principle.

5. It is an interesting fact, exhibited in a variety of instincts, that a young bird may make feints of performing actions which it has never yet performed. Thus the young dove makes feints of flying before it has ever flown. This was illustrated in a peculiarly instructive manner by one of my young doves, No. 46, which developed cripple wings and was unable to fly. When placed in a box with sides $3\frac{1}{2}$ inches high, it was just able to jump on the edge. Nevertheless, when its roosting instinct developed, it endeavored strenuously every evening to fly to the perch which was some inches above its head. It looked at the perch and aimed at it with perfect definiteness, opening its wings and making feints of flying. In the evolution of birds, there can be no doubt, flying developed gradually from jumping. The new movements of flying were gradually intercalated into the interval between the initial action, leaping from the ground, and the final action, landing again upon the feet. The young dove to this day shows *first* the incipient end action, aiming at the perch to be alighted on, and only after it has launched itself toward this end situation does the "chain" of flight reactions take place.

6. In the pigeons the order of activities culminating in the sexual act is, first display, second billing, third copulation, with numerous details each finding a place in the succession. Yet the sexual tendency is manifestly present from the beginning of the "chain," and the preliminary steps are directed, with much guidance by experience, toward securing the stimulation required for discharging the sexual reflex. In absence of the normal stimulus to the consummatory reaction, the instinct manifests itself in marked appetitive behavior, and, especially in inexperienced birds (Craig, 1914), in those imperfect consummatory reactions known as perversions and auto-erotic phenomena. The behavior of the sexual appetite is now so well known that it may be cited as the type of appetitive behavior; and to readers who are familiar with modern analyses of the sex instinct I may make my whole article clearest by saying that all the appetitive mechanisms I have mentioned, and I believe all the instincts of the dove, behave in the

same manner as that of sex, in regard to appetitive manifestations and anticipation of the consummatory reaction.

7. I shall take space to describe only one example of aversion—the so-called jealousy of the male dove, which is manifested especially in the early days of the brood cycle before the eggs are laid. At this time the male has an aversion to seeing his mate in proximity to any other dove. The sight of another dove near his mate is an "original annoyer" (Thorndike, 1913). If the male sees another dove near his mate, he follows *either of two* courses of action; namely: (*a*) attacking the intruder, with real pugnacity; (*b*) driving his mate, gently, not pugnaciously, away from the intruder. When he has succeeded either in conquering the stranger and getting rid of him, or in driving his mate away from the stranger, so that he has got rid of the disturbing sight of another dove in presence of his mate, his agitation ceases. If we prevent him from being successful with either of these methods, as, by confining the pair of doves in one cage and the third dove in plain sight in a contiguous cage, then he will continue indefinitely to try both methods. If we leave all three doves free in one pen, the mated male will try the mettle of the intruder and conquer him if he can; if he fails, he will turn all his energies into an effort to drive his mate away from the intruder. Or if in former experiences he has learned to gage this individual intruder, if he conquered him before he will promptly attack him now, but if defeated by him before he will now choose the alternative of driving his mate away. In sum, the instinctive aversion impels the dove to thoroughly intelligent efforts to get rid of the disturbing situation.

8. In some cases the seeking of a certain situation involves both appetences and aversions in considerable number. Thus, when the day draws to a close, each dove seeks as its roosting-place a perch that is high up, with free space both below it and above it, with no enemies near, with friendly companions by its side, but these companions not too close, not touching (except in certain cases of mate, nest-mate, or parent). The endeavor to achieve this complex situation, to secure the appeted stimuli and to avoid the disturbing ones, keeps the birds busy every evening, often for an hour or more.

CYCLES

Instinctive activity runs in cycles. The type cycle, as it were a composite photograph representing all such cycles, would show four phases, as follows:

Phase I—Absence of a certain stimulus. Physiological state of appetite for that stimulus. Restlessness, varied movements, effort, search. Incipient consummatory action.

Phase II—Reception of the appeted stimulus. Consummatory reaction in response to that stimulus. State of satisfaction. No restlessness nor search.

Phase III—Surfeit of the said stimulus, which has now become a disturbing stimulus. State of aversion. Restlessness, trial, effort, directed toward getting rid of the stimulus.

Phase IV—Freedom from the said stimulus. Physiological state of rest. Inactivity of the tendencies which were active in Phases I, II, III.

Some forms of behavior show all four phases clearly. The following are examples.

Sex—(Phase I) The dove, either the male or the female, shows sexual appetite and invites the mate to sexual activity. Gradually they lead up to (Phase II) the consummatory sexual act. (Phase III) After the sexual act, in some cases one bird shows marked aversion, e.g., by striking at the mate. Either the male or the female may show aversion. In some species, signs of aversion after the sexual act seem to be a normal and regular occurrence. In other species they are shown only by a bird whose mate, having failed of satisfaction, invites to further sexual activity. (Phase IV) The pair usually become sexually indifferent for a considerable time after each copulation.

Brooding—(Phase I) The dove shows the brooding appetence, goes to the nest, and, if need be, struggles to obtain possession of it. (Phase II) It sits throughout its customary period, during which it often resists efforts of the mate to relieve it. (Phase III) At the end of this period, in contrast, it comes off at a slight sign from the mate, runs about, flaps its wings, and thus shows its joy in being off. This may be interpreted as a sort of mild aversion for the nest. (Phase IV) It goes away and becomes temporarily indifferent to the nest.

In other cases, one or another of the phases is not clearly present, so that there are various sorts of incomplete cycles, such as the following.

(*a*) When the bird shows appetitive behavior but fails to obtain the appeted stimulus, the appetite sometimes disappears, due to fatigue or to drainage of energy into other channels; in which case, Phase II is not attained.

But many instinctive appetites are so persistent that if they do not attain the normal appeted stimulus they make connection with some abnormal stimulus (see page 52); to this the consummatory reaction takes place, the tension of the appetite is relieved, its energy discharged, and the organism shows satisfaction. This is of course *compensation,* in the sense in which that word is used in psychiatry. But the abnormal stimulus is usually inadequate or incomplete, the relief or discharge is imperfect, the satisfaction is marred by the fact that some of the constituent elements of the appetite, failing to receive their appeted stimuli, are still in Phase I and abnormally active, while at the same time other elements have already reached Phase III, aversion.

(b) Some forms of behavior consist of appetite and satisfaction which are not, in ordinary cases, followed by any distinct aversion. For example, the drinking cycle shows clearly: (Phase I) appetite for water; (Phase II) the drinking reaction, with expression of satisfaction; (Phase IV) indifference. The dove when it finishes drinking shows no distinct sign of aversion (Phase III) except withdrawing the bill from the water. But if the observer takes this dove then gently in the hand and resubmerges its bill in the water, it shows marked aversion, struggling to withdraw the bill and to shake the water out of it.

(c) On the other hand it may seem that there are some forms of behavior, e.g., fear, in which Phases I and II are lacking; that there is no appetite for the fear stimuli and no satisfaction in them; that when the slightest of these stimuli is received it at once arouses (Phase III) aversive behavior. Yet it is an interesting fact that even in these cases a slight degree of appetite and satisfaction may be present. Children seek and enjoy a little fear. A dove, when it hears the alarm cry from other doves, at once endeavors to see the alarming object. Even pain is (in man) to some degree, sought and enjoyed.

In actual life the cycles and phases of cycles are multiplied and overlapped in very complex ways.

For example, when a certain satisfaction has been attained, this, instead of leading at once to a state of surfeit and aversion, may lead to further appetite, which leads to a second satisfaction, and so on. Thus Phase I and Phase II continue to alternate, constituting a "circular reaction" (Baldwin). I have seen a pair of house sparrows copulate thirteen times in immediate succession, and know by the sound of their voices that I did not see the beginning of the series. In many cases such circular reaction serves to rouse the organism to a high state of appetite and readiness for action.

Smaller cycles are superposed upon larger ones. For example, when a female bird is building a nest, so long as she is in the nest she is in a certain nest-building attitude, a high state of satisfaction, which constitutes the consummatory reaction (Phase II) of a large cycle. But each time she reaches for a straw, seizes it, and tucks it into the nest, she exhibits thus a little cycle containing a little appetence followed by its own satisfaction.

The time occupied by a cycle varies extremely, from cycles measured in seconds to those that occupy a year or even longer. The relative duration of the phases also is extremely variable. In some cases the appeted situation is attained without delay, and Phase I thus passes so rapidly as to be overlooked by the observer. In other cases the bird strives hard to overcome great obstacles which stand in the way of the attainment of the appeted stimulus, consequently Phase I is of long duration. Phase II may last, in the case of drinking, about one second; in the case of incubation, about three weeks.

It should be stated, too, that the phases are not sharply separated; each passes more or less gradually into the next. Thus, from Phase IV of one cycle in a series to Phase I of the succeeding cycle, there is often a gradual rise of appetite; active search for satisfaction does not commence until a certain intensity of appetite is attained. This is what is known in pedagogical literature as "warming up." This gradual rise of the energy of appetite is followed (Phase II-III, or II-IV) by its sudden or gradual discharge. This rise and discharge are named by Ellis (1903), in the case of the sex instinct, "tumescence" and "detumescence." They are important phases in the psychology of art, in which sphere they are named by Hirn (1900) "enhancement" and "relief." The discharge (Phase II) is also exemplified in "catharsis" in art and in psychiatry.

The cycles in the behavior of birds are fundamentally the same phenomenon as the cycles in human behavior. Human cycles are enriched by an intelligence far surpassing that of doves, but this is a difference of degree only. If the dove's cycles are determined largely by instinct, habit, physiological conditions, and not intelligence, so are some human cycles, as those of sleeping, eating, drinking, sex. F. H. Herrick (1910) emphasizes the fact that a bird may scamp one cycle in order to begin another. Thus, birds may abandon young which are not yet weaned, because their appetence for a new brood has set in. But the same principle works, though not quite so crudely, in human life: as in the case of a mother who grows indifferent or even somewhat hostile toward her older children each time a new child is born. Herrick emphasizes also the fact that when anything disturbs the bird in the progress of a cycle, she very often gives up that cycle and begins a new one. Thus, a cedarbird who has just completed her nest one day finds a man examining it; she forthwith abandons that nest and begins to build another. But, again, the same phenomenon appears in human behavior. A man begins to build a house; when he has progressed far with the building he meets some horrible experience in it which "turns him against" it, and nothing will induce him to proceed with that house; he abandons it and begins to build elsewhere. The cedarbird has had a, to her, horrible experience which has turned her against her nest; that nest has lost its *value* for her; the sight of it now, instead of arousing her appetence, arouses aversion.

C. J. Herrick (1915) says that many of these cyclical activities of birds are "simply complex chain reflexes." The reason he gives for this statement is that "each step in the cycle is a necessary antecedent to the next, and if the series is interrupted it is often necessary for the birds to go back to the beginning of the cycle. They cannot make an intelligent adjustment midway of the series." But all this, in some degree, is true of the behavior of human beings toward their mates, their nests, and their young. This has been illustrated in the preceding paragraph, and a few illustrations are here added. As to mates: When the cordial relation between a husband and wife is, by some mischance, broken, the pair may make an "intelligent adjustment" if the difficulty is not too great. But birds also make such adjustments constantly, when the difficulty is not too great. And with human beings, as with birds, the difficulty may be insurmountable; in which case, the husband and wife separate for a week, a month, or a year, after which period of rest (Phase IV), they can commence a new cycle with Phase I, courtship. As to their nests: The fact of homesickness proves that the behavior of a human being toward his or her home runs in a series which conforms to Herrick's statements. As to behavior toward the young: The inability of human parents to make "an intelligent adjustment midway of the series" is shown by the fact that they cannot arouse the fullest degree of parental behavior toward an adopted child unless they adopt the child in its infancy. These facts do not prove that the human behavior in question consists of mere chain reflexes. Neither do the similar facts as to avian cycles prove that the avian behavior consists of mere chain reflexes.

The birds in their cycles exhibit attention (using this and all the following terms in a strictly behavioristic sense), intelligence, memory, intensely emotional behavior, conflict of tendencies, hesitation, deliberation (of course an elementary sort of deliberation), rise, maintenance, and decline of appetences, behavior comformable to certain laws of valuation. All these forms of behavior function in bringing about the consummatory situations of the cycles. Thus the instinctive behavior of birds, so far from consisting of mere chain reflexes, and having no relation to "individuality" (Bowen, *vide ut supra,* p. 54), is in reality very highly integrated, and is the very core of the bird's individuality.

All human behavior runs in cycles which are of the same fundamental character as the cycles of avian behavior. These appear in consciousness as cycles of attention, of feeling, and of valuation.

This description is true not only of our behavior toward objects specifically sought by instinct, such as food, mate, and young, but also of our behavior toward the objects of our highest and most sophisticated impulses. Consider, for example, the course of a music-lover's feelings and attention in the case of a symphony concert. Before the concert, if his internal state is favorable (Phase I), he is all eagerness, desire, interest. He goes to the concert-hall, chooses a good seat for hearing, and in every way shows appetitive behavior. (Phase II) The music begins, he pays close attention, and feels satisfaction. (Phase III) If the concert continues too long, he is surfeited, his pleasure diminishes, he even feels some unpleasantness, and his attention turns away, which is of course a form of aversion. (Phase IV) When the music at length ceases, he feels restfulness, relief, and his attention goes elsewhere. This cycle of the whole concert is overlaid by a complex system of epicycles, each extending through one symphony, one movement, or a smaller division, down to the measure and the beat. This is only one illustration of the fact that the entire behavior of the human being is, like that of the bird, a vast system of cycles and epicycles, the longest cycle extending through life, the shortest ones being measured in seconds. This view helps us to understand the laws of attention; for example, the law that attention cannot be held continuously upon a faint, simple stimulus. For as soon as such a stimulus is brought to maximum clearness, which constitutes the consummatory situation, the appetite for it is quickly discharged and its cycle comes to an end. This familiar fact shows that we, like the birds, are but little able to alter the course of our behavior cycles.

REFERENCES

BALDWIN, J. M. Appetite. *Dictionary of philosophy and psychology.* New York: Macmillan, 1901.

BOWEN, F. Instinct and intellect. *N. Amer. Rev.,* 1846, *63,* 91–118.

CARLSON, A. J. *The control of hunger in health and disease.* Chicago: University of Chicago Press, 1916.

CRAIG, W. Observations on doves learning to drink. *J. Anim. Behav.,* 1912, *2,* 273–279.

CRAIG, W. Male doves reared in isolation. *J. Anim. Behav.,* 1914, *4,* 121–133.

ELLIS, H. Analysis of the sexual impulse. *Studies in the psychology of sex.* Vol. 3. Philadelphia: Davis, 1903.

ELLIS, H. Sex in relation to society. *Studies in the psychology of sex.* Vol. 6. Philadelphia: Davis, 1910.

GERHARTZ, H. Ueber die zum aufbau der Eizelle notwendige energie (Transformations-energie). *Pflüger's Arch.,* 1914, *156,* 1–224.

HERRICK, C. J. *An introduction to neurology.* Philadelphia: Saunders, 1915.

HERRICK, F. H. Instinct and intelligence in birds. *Popular Sci. mon.,* 1910, *76,* 532–556; *77,* 82–97, 122–141.

HIRN, Y. *The origins of art.* London: Macmillan, 1900.

HOBHOUSE, L. T. *Mind in evolution.* (2nd ed.) London: Macmillan, 1915.

JENNINGS, H. S. *Behavior of the lower organisms.* New York: Columbia University Press, 1906.

MORGAN, C. L. *Habit and instinct.* London: E. Arnold, 1896.

STOUT, G. F. *A manual of psychology.* (2nd ed.) London: University Tutorial Press, 1907.

THORNDIKE, E. L. *The original nature of man.* New York: Teachers College, Columbia University, 1913.

WASHBURN, M. F. *Movement and mental imagery.* Boston: Houghton Mifflin, 1916.

2

The Concept of the Reflex in the Description of Behavior

B. F. Skinner

INTRODUCTORY NOTE

The extension of the concept of the reflex to the description of the behavior of intact organisms is a common practice in modern theorizing. Nevertheless, we owe most of our knowledge of the reflex to investigators who have dealt only with "preparations," and who have never held themselves to be concerned with anything but a subsidiary function of the central nervous system. Doubtless, there is ample justification for the use of relatively simple systems in an early investigation. But it is true, nevertheless, that the concept of the reflex has not emerged unmarked by such a circumstance of its development. In its extension to the behavior of intact organisms, that is to say, the historical definition finds itself encumbered with what now appear to be superfluous interpretations.

The present paper examines the concept of the reflex and attempts to evaluate the historical definition. It undertakes eventually to frame an alternative definition, which is not wholly in despite of the historical usage. The reader will recognize a method of criticism first formulated with respect to scientific concepts by Ernst Mach (1883, 1886) and perhaps better stated by Henri Poincaré (1903, 1908). To the works of these men and to Bridgman's excellent application of the method (1927) the reader is referred for any discussion of the method *qua* method. Probably the chief advantage, first exploited in this respect by Mach, lies in the use of a historical approach. But the reader should understand that in the present case no attempt is made to give an exhaustive account of the history of the reflex. Certain historical facts are considered for two reasons: to discover the nature of the observations upon which the concept has been

Adapted from *J. gen. Psychol.*, 1931, 5, 427–458. With permission of the author and The Journal Press.

based, and to indicate the source of the incidental interpretations with which we are concerned.

I

It was Descartes [1] who first proposed a mechanism by which the characteristics of the living organism could plausibly be produced. He came very near describing its action as the true mode of operation of the animal body, but the criticism of his contemporary, Nicolas Stensen, probably expressed his intention correctly. "Descartes," said Stensen, "was too clever in exposing the errors of current treatises on man to undertake the task of expounding the true structure of man. Therefore in his essay on Man he does not attempt such a delineation, but is content to describe a machine capable of performing all the functions of which man is capable." This interpretation is borne out by the text of the *Traité*, where, although parts of the anatomy are again and again pointed out as suitable for the functions of the mechanism, and the machine and body are, indeed, almost identified, the reader is, nevertheless, invited only to suppose the truth of the details. Descartes' interest lay primarily in furthering his philosophical notions, and the invention which is usually taken as the earliest expression of the reflex was little more than an instrument of persuasion.

In designing a convincing model of the living organism Descartes faced a peculiar difficulty. Movement in itself was easily enough obtained, for there were many mechanisms available as sources of energy. There was, for example, the current explanation of muscular contraction upon a hydraulic analogy, which, in fact, Descartes adopted. But if the energy itself was conveniently accounted for, the direction and order of its release were, on the contrary, critical. In meeting this difficulty Descartes introduced a novel device—the mechanism of the stimulus, by means of which external forces released the movements of the machine. The stimulus distinguished the model of *la bête machine* from that of a mere activated doll. It enabled the model to simulate the appropriateness and the apparent spontaneity of the movements of the living organism. So far as Descartes' purpose was concerned, it was successful in supplanting certain metaphysical concepts as causal agents leading to movement. Heretofore, the supposition had been that an animal moved because of the action of, let us say, a "soul." Descartes proposed that the body be regarded as a system of stored energy, and he pointed to minute, hitherto unobserved forces which acted upon the organism in such a way as to serve as releasing mechanisms.

[1] Descartes' account is to be found in the *Traité de l'homme* (1662), which differs in many respects from the earlier *Passions de l'âme* (1649) in its representation of the action of the nervous system.

A convenient account of Descartes as physiologist is given by Sir Michael Foster (1924). The quotations from Nicolas Stensen and the translations from Descartes are taken from this work.

The principle of the stimulus was, of course, little more than a guess. With an enthusiasm for the new physics, Descartes contended that the movements of an organism were functions of the forces acting upon it, but he could in practice point to only the roughest demonstration of this relationship. Subsequent investigation of the reflex has revealed the extraordinary difficulty of identifying the stimulating forces correlated with particular movements. The information available in Descartes' time was so scant, and the principle so far-reaching, that one is tempted to regard the discovery of the stimulus simply as another example of the insight with which Descartes anticipated later thought. But this would be to overlook the influence of an unusual analogy.

Descartes sought a mechanical model of the living organism for the support of an argument. For other reasons, namely, for the sake of the entertainment which they afforded, suitable models (utilizing the action of a stimulus as a source of spontaneity and appropriateness) had already been constructed by the engineers of the royal fountains in France. Descartes describes two of these fountain figures and the action of their releasing mechanisms, which are operated unwittingly by the observers.

For in entering they necessarily tread on certain tiles or plates, which are so disposed that if they approach a bathing Diana, they cause her to hide in the rose-bushes, and if they try to follow her, they cause a Neptune to come forward to meet them threatening them with his trident. Or if they pass in another direction they occasion the springing forward of a marine monster who spouts water into their faces or things of a like sort according to the caprice of the engineers who constructed them.

A contemporary engineer, Salomon de Caus,[2] published an account of the operation of similar figures, although he did not describe the two groups referred to by Descartes. The mechanical principles are few in number, but among them can be found all of those used by Descartes in his "reflex arc." In Descartes' proposed model the organ of sense is set in motion "even ever so little" by the external object and pulls upon a thread, which in turn, acting like a bell rope, opens a valve at a central reservoir, letting the contained fluid flow outward along a pipeline into the muscles, which it activates. With a plate or lever substituted for the organ of sense and a waterwheel or similar device for the muscles, the description applies as well to the fountain figures. So slightly does Descartes depart from the details of the fountain mechanism that its position as the prototype of his model seems unquestionable.

It was the accident of a convenient analogy which led Descartes to the

[2] De Caus, *Les raisons des forces mouvantes avec diverse machines . . . de grottes et de fontaines.* The date (1624) is considerably earlier than that of the *Traité,* and the examples treated by de Caus are, in general, simpler than those described by Descartes.

discovery of an important principle, and so great a mutation was it in the evolution of human thought that it proved lethal. In spite of frequent assertions to the contrary, Descartes seems to have exerted no influence upon the development of the reflex. Instead, the discovery of the stimulus was made again, with great difficulty, as the culmination of a century of experimentation, and another century and a half had elapsed before the principle had again been comparably extended to the behavior of the total organism. This lack of historical influence may be variously explained. Descartes was, as Foster has said, a "retrograde" physiologist, who accepted the more convenient theory, as against the more accurate, for the sake of a broader consistency. His interest was ultimately philosophical, even in his physiological explanations, and he did not attempt to discover the true action of the nervous system.

Descartes is important to an understanding of the reflex, not because of an organic connection with subsequent history, but as a symbol. The stimulus is an essential part of a mechanistic theory of behavior, whether the notion is arrived at through observation, as it was with Marshall Hall (1833), for example, or argued from physical necessity or mechanical analogy, as it was with Descartes. Furthermore, the analysis of behavior which is accomplished in the mere descriptive phrase, "withdrawing the foot from fire," became a critical part of later method. But a further characteristic of Descartes' position must be noted: although he substituted the stimulus for a metaphysical concept in his description of the animal, Descartes could not eliminate metaphysical concepts from his description of man. Here he regarded the mechanical principles as at work, but under the control of the soul, which might suspend the physical necessities much as the engineer might modify the activity of the fountain figures.

Descartes reserved a field of action for the concept of soul, not because the physical facts were any more lacking in the case of man than elsewhere, but because of the pressure of certain metaphysical notions. Fragments of similar reservations still prevail. But the history of the reflex can almost be told by describing the progressive encroachment of the stimulus upon them. The line which Descartes drew between the fields of action of his physical and metaphysical concepts was a temporal one only. A movement might follow at one time the action of a stimulus and at another the action of soul. The later distinction which was first definitely established by Marshall Hall set in part an anatomical boundary. But both lines were drawn for the same purpose, namely, to resolve, by compromise, the conflict between an *observed necessity* and *preconceptions of freedom* in the behavior of organisms. In one form or another, this compromise accounts almost wholly for the aspects of the historical definition of the reflex which we are attempting to reconsider.

VI

We may summarize this much of the argument in the following way. A reflex is defined as an observed correlation of two events, a stimulus and a response. A survey of the history discloses no other characteristic upon which a definition can legitimately be based. The physiological investigation does not question the correlative nature of the reflex, for its data and its concepts deal essentially with the conditions of a correlation; but heterogeneous instances of correlations which would be embraced by the definition, read literally, are excluded by the physiological refinements of usage. It now remains for us to deal more specifically with the reflex in the description of behavior. What is the description of behavior, and how does the reflex, as a correlation, enter into it? Here (the reader may again be warned) we shall be concerned not so much with the validity or the adequacy of the concept as with its nature and the method peculiar to it.

Lacking some arbitrary distinction, the term *behavior* must include the total activity of the organism—the functioning of all its parts. Obviously, its proper application is much less general, but it is difficult to reach any clear distinction. The definition of the subject matter of any science, however, is determined largely by the interest of the scientist, and this will be our safest rule here. We are interested primarily in the movement of an organism in some frame of reference. We are interested in any internal change which has an observable and significant effect upon this movement. In special cases we are directly interested in glandular activity, but this will usually concern us only secondarily in its effect upon movement. The unity and internal consistency of this subject matter is historical: we are interested, that is to say, in what the organism *does*.

But the description of behavior, if it is to be either scientific or satisfying, must go further. As a scientific discipline, it must describe the event not only for itself but in its relation to other events; and, in point of satisfaction, it must *explain*. These are essentially identical activities. In the brief survey at the beginning of this paper it was occasionally necessary to regard the stimulus as a newly discovered cause of movement for which various conceptual causes had previously been designed. In this way we represented a real aspect of the history of the reflex. But we may now take that more humble view of explanation and causation which seems to have been first suggested by Mach and is now a common characteristic of scientific thought, wherein, in a word, explanation is reduced to description and the notion of function substituted for that of causation. The full description of an event is taken to include a description of its functional relationship with antecedent events. In the description of behavior we are interested in the relationships within a regressive series of events extending from the behavior itself to those energy changes at the periphery which we designate as stimuli. We stop here in the regression only because further steps are beyond the field of behavior. The two end events, the behavior and the stimulus, have, moreover, a particular importance, because they alone are directly observable in an intact organism, and because they limit the series. With the relationship of these two end terms the description of behavior is chiefly concerned.

The reflex is important in the description of behavior because it is by definition a statement of the *necessity* of this relationship. The demonstration of the necessity is ultimately a matter of observation: a given response is observed invariably to follow a given stimulus, or exceptions to this rule may be independently described. In its extension to total behavior the principle generalizes the statement of the necessity observed in a particular reflex, the form of the expression remaining essentially the same. That is to say, the hypothesis that "the behavior of an organism is an exact, if involved, function of the forces acting upon the organism" states the correlation of a stimulus and a response, both of which remain wholly undifferentiated. It is, in this sense, the broadest possible statement of a reflex, but it is not an observed correlation and is therefore a hypothesis only.

It is, nevertheless, solely the fault of our method that we cannot deal directly with this single correlation between behavior as a whole and all the forces acting upon the organism stated in the hypothesis. Quantitative statements of both stimulus and response and a statistical demonstration of the correlation are theoretically possible but would be wholly unmanageable. We are led, for lack of a better approach, to investigate the correlation of parts of the stimulus with parts of the response. For the sake of a greater facility (and in this case the very possibility) of description, we turn to analysis.

Originally, the use of analysis was quite accidental and unrecognized, but it has, nevertheless, always been necessary. The early observations were possible only after it had been achieved in some form or other. This is not difficult to understand if we remember that the correlation which we call a reflex rests ultimately upon observation. In an intact newt, to return to Hall's experiment, it would have been very nearly impossible to observe a correlation between the movement of the tail and the application of a probing needle, because the movement of the tail was also correlated with other stimuli and the action of the probing needle with other movements. *In the isolated tail,* however, one kind of movement followed a given stimulus and was absent in the absence of the stimulus. The correlation was obvious and therefore observed.

Marshall Hall and his few predecessors divided the behavior of an organism into parts by the expedient method of dividing the organism. This became, in general, the method of reflex physiology, although, for obvious reasons, the division of the nervous system supplanted the division of the whole organism. The best-known group of reflexes to be studied in surgical isolation are those surviving in the body of the organism after section of the cord just below the bulb. This is the "spinal" preparation, which has been the basis for the greater part of physiological investigation, notably that of Sherrington (1906). Other common reflex systems are the decerebrate, in which the medulla and the cerebellum remain intact, and the various mid-brain and thalamic preparations, as, for example, those of Magnus (1924). A further extension of the method involves the surgical or physiological exclusion of end-organs, as by extirpation or anaesthetization (for example, of the labyrinth), or by section of afferent nerves. The common object of these procedures is to permit the investigation of a particular response in relation to a controlled variable, independent of other variables also related to that response.

But the same result may be obtained in another way. The experiment may be so designed that the undesired variables do not vary. The distinction between the two methods will appear in the following example from the work of Magnus (1924). Certain postural effects in a mid-brain animal are correlated partly with the position of the labyrinths relative to the earth and partly with the condition of flexion or extension of the muscles of the neck. The correlation between the posture and the state of the neck muscles can be studied alone if the labyrinths are cocainized or extirpated. But Magnus was also able to obtain the isolation by designing his experiments in such a way that the position of the labyrinths relative to the earth did not change. Perhaps the best examples of this method, however, are to be found in the work of Pavlov (1927). Here the organism is intact and the very active receptors of the head segments fully functional. By controlling light, sound, odor, and other conditions in the experimental chamber, it is possible to observe in isolation the correlation between a given response and a selected stimulus. Placing an animal in a dark room, that is to say, is equivalent for purposes of isolation to blinding it, to sectioning the optic tracts, or to destroying the visual projection areas in the cortex, and has the great advantage over these surgical methods of being relatively free from unknown artifacts.

The practical merits of both these methods are obvious; but we are concerned with a broader aspect of analysis. For the physiologist, the isolation of a reflex is a preliminary matter of method and is relatively insignificant. In the description of behavior it is of first importance. How legitimate, then, is the process of analysis, and what is the nature of its product?

Let us deal entirely with the flexion reflex in the spinal dog, as a familiar and convenient example. We have already analyzed, of course, when we have once named, so that we must go back for a moment to the behavior as a whole. Without regard to its correlation with stimulating forces, behavior, as we have seen, is simply part of the total functioning of the organism. The problem of analysis at this level is common to physiology and anatomy. We shall not need to solve it, but shall assume that for purposes of description the body of an organism may be divided into parts (that we may speak, for example, of a leg), and that the functioning of a particular part may be described in isolation (that we may speak, for example, of the flexion of a leg). Moreover, we shall assume that the forces acting upon the organism may be analyzed and described in the manner common to the physical sciences. Our own problem lies beyond these assumptions.

In the flexion reflex our first experimental datum is the nearly simultaneous occurrence of the flexion of a leg and, let us say, the electrical stimulation of the skin of the foot. If we measure both events very carefully and repeat the stimulation, we obtain a second flexion which closely resembles the first, and we find that we may corroborate the observation, within limits, as often as we like. We call the observed correlation a reflex and, for convenience of reference, give it a special name, the flexion reflex.

The question then arises: *what is the flexion reflex?* If we try to answer by describing in detail a stimulus and a response, we meet embarrassing difficulties. We find that the exact degree and direction of flexion may vary with many factors. We find, for example, that it was very important for our original measurements that the torso of the animal had a particular position, that the contralateral leg was, say, unsupported, and so on. But we cannot specify these incidental conditions in our description without destroying its generality. Thereupon we shall probably resort to surgical methods. Theoretically, at least, we may pare down the structures underlying the flexion reflex until the collateral variables are no longer effective. But we can never be sure that the reflex which we have thus carved out of the behavior of the organism would not have been grossly otherwise if our operative procedure had been different. We are not sure, that is to say, that what turns up at the end of our process of isolation is the flexion reflex. There is another method open to us. In the flexion reflex we are dealing essentially with a group of correlations showing many characteristics in common. They involve the same effectors acting roughly in the same way and stimuli which resemble each other at least in their gross anatomical reference. We may, therefore, if we wish, *construct* a flexion reflex by a statistical treatment of many of these separate correlations. We may, in other words, determine and state a correlation between the characteristics common to all our observed responses and the characteristics common to all our observed stimuli, and we may name this construct the flexion reflex. But the resulting description of this statistical entity will likewise depend upon our choice of observations and upon our method of analysis.

We have been proceeding, of course, upon an unnecessary assumption, namely, that there *is* a flexion reflex, which exists independently of our observations, and which our observations approximate. Such an assumption is wholly gratuitous, but it is remarkably insistent. It arises in part from the nature of the reflex. If we remain at the level of our observations, we must recognize a reflex as a correlation. But the immediate uncritical reaction to a definition on that basis is that a correlation, in point of satisfaction, is not enough. There is an urge toward solidification, clearly evident throughout the history. We turn instantly to the reflex arc for material support. Although our knowledge of the critical part of the arc is, as we have seen, derived wholly from the observation of a correlation, we much prefer to regard the characteristics of the correlation as properties of the synapse rather than to retain them as characteristics of a correlation. Under the same pressure, then, but with less justification, we are led to assume that there are isolated reflexes concealed in the behavior of an organism, which by proper investigatory methods we may discover, and in the description of behavior to state the corollary of this proposition, namely, that behavior is the sum or the integration of these units.

Here we are touching upon the subject of a widespread current controversy, but we may, by virtue of what we have already said, dispose of the matter briefly. Let us phrase two typical questions. Is a reflex a unitary mechanism? Is behavior a sum of such mechanisms? Then, if by reflex we mean a hypothetical entity which exists apart from our observations but which our observations are assumed to approach, the questions are academic and need not detain us; if, on the other hand, we define a reflex as a given observed correlation or as a statistical treatment of observed correlations, the questions are meaningless, for they ignore the process of analysis implied in the definition. A reflex, that is to say, has no scientific meaning apart from its definition in terms of such experimental operations as we have examined, and, so defined, it cannot be the subject of questions of this sort.

There is a certain practical advantage, it is true, in regarding a reflex as a unitary mechanism—an advantage, as Mach might have said, which may have given rise to the practice. It is only when we misconstrue a purely practical device and take it to be an integral part of our definition that the possibility of theoretical misunderstanding arises. Our sample questions deal necessarily with the reflex defined in terms which we have seen to be well beyond any observational justification. As Poincaré has said of a similar issue, *"ces questions ne sont pas seulement insolubles, elles sont illusoires et dépourvues de sens"* (Poincaré, 1903). A common mistake in the present case has been to suppose that, because an answer is lacking, the principle of the reflex is somehow impeached. As we have repeatedly noted, the validity of the reflex as a scientific concept is not here in question. The reflex remains, as it has always been, an observed correlation of stimulus and response.

VII

It remains for us to consider how a reflex as a correlation is dealt with experimentally. The first step, as we have seen, is the isolation of a response and the identification of its correlated stimulus. In practice, the demonstration of the correlation is usually left at an elementary level. It is based upon the appearance of the two events together and their failure to appear separately. As an experimental datum of this sort, a reflex may be given the expression

$$R = f(S) \tag{1}$$

where R is a response and S a stimulus. Theoretically, the exact nature of the function is determinable, although for any present purpose corresponding values of S and R are obtainable by observation only. Choosing convenient measures of both stimulus and response, we may vary the strength of S and observe variations in the strength of R. This is common practice, although very little has been done toward determining how a given R varies with its corresponding S. One characteristic of the relationship is the threshold: for values below a given value of S, $R = O$. There are also temporal aspects of the function, which have been investigated under the headings of latency and after-discharge.

Threshold, latency, after-discharge, and the order of variation of S and R are thus descriptions of the correlation we call a reflex. They may be investigated with only one elicitation of the reflex or, at most, with a single set of corresponding values of S and R. There is a second field of investigation, however, which is concerned with variations in any aspect of a correlation, as they may appear in the comparison of successive elicitations. If, for example, we select a value of S and repeat the elicitation of the reflex at a given rate, we shall observe a progressive decrease in the value of R. Or, again, if the interval between two successive elicitations be made brief enough, the second R may be of greatly reduced magnitude or wholly lacking. Here are significant variations in the value of the terms in Equation 1. They do not challenge the necessity of the relationship expressed therein (as they might well do if they were less orderly), but they do require that, in the description of a reflex, account be taken of *third variables*. We may indicate the required change by rewriting our equation as

$$R = f(S,A) \tag{2}$$

where A is a variable designed to account for any given observed change in the value of R.

As it appears in such an experiment, A is properly either time or the number of elicitations at a given rate. The inference is commonly made that it represents a factor of another sort, which varies with time or the number of elicitations in the same way. In the first example noted above the phenomenon has been called reflex fatigue, which is regarded as a synaptic change—as the exhaustion of a substance or state, or as an increase in resistance, according to one's preference in synaptic theory. But in the description of behavior, where we are only secondarily interested in these physiological inferences, reflex fatigue is nothing more than an orderly change in some measured aspect of a given correlation. A law describing the course of that change, where the independent variable is time or the number of elicitations or some other condition of the experiment, is peculiarly a law of behavior. It may become a law of the synapse, by virtue of certain physiological inferences, but it has by that time passed beyond the scope of the description of behavior.

Nevertheless, if we are to follow current usage, a definition of reflex fatigue as an observed variation in *one* aspect of a correlation is too narrow, for we know from observation that, when such a change has taken place, the other aspects of the correlation have also changed. If we have observed, for example, a change in the ratio of a particular R and S, we may expect to find all other ratios, as well as the threshold, latency, and after-discharge of the reflex, likewise changed. It is usual, therefore, to regard the particular change which we chance to observe as a sample of a greater process. Occasionally, where a change in one aspect of a correlation is alone important (as in summation, which is chiefly a matter of threshold), the characteristic may possibly be defined in terms of a single change. But such a characteristic as reflex fatigue, or the refractory phase, or facilitation, is by intention a description of a group of concurrent changes.

If we are to speak in terms of these group changes, it is almost necessary to have a term describing the *state* of a correlation at any given time with respect to all its aspects. The physiologist, of course, may use the synapse for this purpose. When he has once described reflex fatigue as the exhaustion of a synaptic substance, for example, he may attribute a change in *any* aspect of a correlation to that exhaustion. Although he may observe and measure at one time a change in after-discharge and at another a change in the magnitude of R, he may reasonably consider himself to be dealing with the same process in both cases. Fortunately, there is also a term serving the same purpose at the level of behavior. If, in a given reflex, the threshold is low, the latency short, the after-discharge prolonged, and the ratio R/S large, the reflex is ordinarily said to be strong. If, on the other hand, the threshold is high, the latency long, the after-discharge short, and the ratio R/S small, the reflex is said to be weak. An attribute of *strength* is imputed to the reflex. The strength of the response, of course, is not meant; a weak response may indicate a strong reflex if it be elicitable with a very weak stimulus.

"Reflex strength" expresses in a very general way the state of a given correlation at a given time with respect to many of its characteristics. It is a useful term, for it permits us to deal with reflex fatigue, for example, as a *change in reflex strength*, without stopping to specify the particular changes which compose it. Nevertheless, its usefulness does not extend beyond this qualitative level. The concept is subject to a major objection, which holds as well for the parallel use of the synaptic state. We do not know, since it has never been determined, whether the changes which compose such a characteristic as reflex fatigue all proceed at the same rate. If the threshold, let us say, and the magnitude of R do not vary in precisely the same way, we are not justified in taking either as a measure of a supposed common variable, nor, indeed, in continuing to regard reflex fatigue as a unitary process.

The study of the reflex, then, leads to the formulation of two kinds of law. The first are laws describing correlations of stimulus and response. A reflex, as we have defined it, is itself a law, and of this sort. It has a considerable generality in spite of the specificity of its terms, but it must be supplemented by other laws describing the exact conditions of a correlation. Secondly, there are laws describing changes in any aspect of these primary relationships as functions of third variables, where the third variable in any given case is a condition of the experiment. These secondary laws may be dealt with in groups, according as they involve the same experimental third variable, and they may be spoken of, for convenience, as describing changes in reflex strength. In the behavior of intact organisms the apparent variability of specific stimulus-response relationships emphasizes the importance of laws of the second sort. Conditioning, "emotion," and "drive," so far as they concern behavior, are essentially to be regarded as changes in reflex strength, and their quantitative investigation may be expected to lead to the determination of laws describing the course of such changes, that is, to laws of the second sort.[3]

It is difficult to discover any aspect of the behavior of organisms which may not be described with a law of one or the other of these forms. From the point of view of scientific method, at least, the description of behavior is adequately embraced by the principle of the reflex.

SUMMARY

The present analysis of the reflex as a concept in the description of behavior follows the method first formulated with respect to scientific concepts by Mach and Poincaré. It examines the source of the historical definition and points out the incidental nature of most of its criteria. Eventually, it offers an alternative definition and considers in detail some of the questions which arise from the nature of the concept so defined.

[3] The second half of my thesis, of which this paper was the first half, describes experiments on "hunger drive" from this point of view.

I. Descartes "discovered the stimulus" and designed a mechanism which could account for animal movement upon the basis of the appropriate release of stored energy. But he was interested less in describing the action of the nervous system than in supporting metaphysical contentions of the automaticity of animals. He advanced the stimulus as a substitute for soul, but only within a field which omitted the greater part of the activity of man.

II. The notion of the reflex developed, independently of Descartes, from the investigation of "irritability." The action of a stimulus was implicit in the concept of irritability, which also assigned an autonomy of function to the parts of an organism. The concept of the reflex arose quite naturally when a stimulus and its related response were to be spatially distinguished. Robert Whytt made the first historically effective observations.

III. It remained for Marshall Hall to clear the concept of psychical counterparts. This he did by setting up a distinction between reflex and voluntary action, which resulted eventually in the unfortunate historical definition of the reflex as a form of movement unconscious, involuntary, and unlearned. Volition, in Hall's sense, was essentially the hypothetical antecedent of movement for which no corresponding stimulus could be observed, a definition which served to identify the reflex with scientific necessity and volition with unpredictability.

IV. The history of the reflex has known only one positive characteristic by which the concept may be defined: the observed correlation of two events, a stimulus and a response. The negative characteristics, on the other hand, which describe the reflex as involuntary, unconscious, and unlearned, have proceeded from unscientific presuppositions concerning the behavior of organisms. The reflex is tentatively defined herein as an observed correlation of stimulus and response.

V. Reflex physiology undertakes to describe the events which intervene between a stimulus and a response. The physiological usage does not question the definition of a reflex as a correlation, for the synapse is only a conceptual expression for the "reduced" characteristics of a given correlation.

VI. The essence of the description of behavior is held to be the determination of functional laws describing the relationship between the forces acting upon, and the movement of, a given system. The reflex is, by definition, the precise instrument for this description. Its analytical nature is discussed, and existing methods of analysis are examined. Current objections to analysis are held to have no scientific meaning.

VII. The experimental study of the reflex may be divided into two parts. There is, first, the investigation of the characteristics of a correlation—latency, threshold, after-discharge, and the order of variation of S and R. Secondly, there is the investigation of variations in these characteristics as functions of third variables. The notion of reflex strength is useful in dealing with this second group. The question of third variables is of extreme importance in the description of the behavior of intact organisms.

From the point of view of scientific method, any law describing the behavior of organisms must be reducible to one of the forms herein discussed. The description of behavior, that is to say, is adequately embraced by the principle of the reflex.

REFERENCES

BRIDGMAN, P. W. *The logic of modern physics.* New York: Macmillan, 1927. (Reprinted, 1960.)

DE CAUS. *Les raisons des forces mouvantes avec diverse machines . . . de grottes et de fontaines.* 1624.

DESCARTES, R. *Traité de l'homme.* Paris, 1662. In *Oeuvres complètes.* Vol. 11. Adam and Tannery edition, Paris: L. Cerf, 1897–1910 (12 volumes).

DESCARTES, R. *Passions de l'âme.* Paris and Amsterdam, 1649. Translated by E. S. Haldane and G. R. T. Ross as *The passions of the soul.* In *The philosophical works of Descartes.* 1931. (Reprinted by Dover, New York, 1955, Vol. 1. pp. 331–427.)

FOSTER, M. S. *Lectures on the history of physiology during the 16th, 17th and 18th centuries.* Cambridge: Cambridge University Press, 1924.

HALL, M. On the reflex function of the medulla oblongata and medulla spinalis. *Phil. Trans. Roy. Soc.* (London), 1833, *123,* 635–665.

MACH, E. *Die Mechanik in ihrer Entwicklung historischkritisch dargestellt.* 1883. *The science of mechanics, a critical and historical account of its development.* (Translated by T. J. McCormack.) LaSalle, Ill.: Open Court, 1960.

MACH, E. *Beiträge zur Analyze der Empfindungen.* 1886. *The analysis of sensations and the relation of the physical to the psychical.* (Translated by C. M. Williams. Revised and supplemented from the 5th German edition by S. Waterlow.) New York: Dover, 1959.

MAGNUS, R. *Körperstellung. Experimentell-physiologische Untersuchungen über die einzelnen bei der Körperstellung in Tätigkeit tretenden Reflexe, über ihr Zusammenwirken und ihre Storungen.* Berlin: Springer, 1924.

PAVLOV, I. P. *Conditioned reflexes: An investigation of the physiological activity of the cerebral cortex.* (Translated and edited by G. V. Anrep.) London: Oxford University Press, 1927. (Reprinted by Dover, New York, 1960.)

POINCARÉ, H. *La science et l'hypothese.* Paris: Flammarion, 1903. (Reprinted by Dover, New York, 1952.)

POINCARÉ, H. *Science et methode.* Paris: Flammarion, 1908. (Reprinted by Dover, New York, 1952.)

SHERRINGTON, C. S. *The integrative action of the nervous system.* New Haven, Conn.: Yale University Press, 1906. (Reprinted, 1961.)

3

Egg Shell Removal by the Black-Headed Gull, *Larus ridibundus* L.; A Behaviour Component of Camouflage

N. Tinbergen, G. J. Broekhuysen, F. Feekes,
J. C. W. Houghton, H. Kruuk, and E. Szulc

I. INTRODUCTION

Many birds dispose in one way or another of the empty egg shell after the chick has hatched. A shell may be built in or trampled down; it may be broken up and eaten; or, more usually, it is picked up, carried away, and dropped at some distance from the nest. C. and D. Nethersole Thompson (1942), who have given a detailed summary of our knowledge of egg shell disposal in birds, emphasise the inter- and even intra-specific variability of the responses involved. Since, in addition, the actual response is often over in a few seconds, and happens only once or twice for each egg, it is not surprising that our knowledge is still fragmentary. On the whole, the presence or absence of the response and its particular form seems to be typical of species or groups of species; for instance, it seems to be absent or nearly so in Anseres and in Gallinaceous birds; Accipitres often break up and eat the shell; Snipe are said to be "particularly lax" (Nethersole Thompson); Avocets, *Recurvirostra avosetta* L., remove discarded eggs shells anywhere in the colony (Makkink, 1936). In the many species which carry the egg shell away, the response, occurring as it does just after hatching, when the young birds need warmth and protection from predators, must be supposed to have considerable survival value.

Adapted from *Behaviour*, 1962, XIX, 74–117. With permission of the authors and E. J. Brill, Ltd.

The Black-headed Gull invariably removes the egg shell in a matter of hours after hatching (Figure 1); it is extremely rare to find an egg shell in the nest once the chicks have dried. We have only a few direct observations on the time lapse between hatching and carrying in undisturbed gulls, but the 10 records we have (1', 1', 15', 55', 60', 105', 109', 192', 206', 225') suggest that the response is usually not very prompt. The carrying is done by the parent actually engaged at the nest, never (as far as we know) by the non-brooding partner which may be standing on the territory, even when it stands next to the sitting bird. At nest relief either the leaving partner, or, more often, the reliever carries the shell. Often however it is the sitting bird who starts looking at the shell, stretches its neck towards it, takes it in its bill and nibbles it (sometimes breaking off fragments while doing so, which then are swallowed), and finally rises and then either walks or flies away with the shell in its bill. The shell is dropped anywhere between a few inches and a hundred yards from the nest. We have also observed birds which flew off with the shell, made a wide loop in the air, and descended again at the nest with the shell still in their bill which they then either dropped on the nest or carried effectively straight away. There is no special place to which the shell is carried, though there may be a slight tendency to fly against the wind, or over an updraught, or where the carrier is less likely to be harassed by other gulls; almost always the shell lands well beyond the territory's boundary. On rare occasions a shell may land in a neighbour's nest—where the latter then treats it as one of its own shells, i.e., removes it.

II. STATEMENT OF THE PROBLEMS

During our studies of the biology and the behaviour of gulls this response gradually began to intrigue us for a variety of reasons. (1) The shell does not differ strikingly from an egg, since it is only the small "lid" at the obtuse end which comes off during hatching; yet it is treated very differently from an egg, and eggs are never carried away. This raised the question of the stimuli by which the gulls recognise the shell. Systematic tests with egg shell dummies could provide the answer. (2) What could be the survival value of the response? (a) Would the sharp edges of the shell be likely to injure the chicks? Nethersole Thompson raises this possibility, adding that poultry breeders know this danger well. (b) Would the shell tend to slip over an unhatched egg, thus trapping the chick in a double shell? (c) Would the shells interfere in some way with brooding? (d) Would the moist organic material left behind in the shell provide a breeding ground for bacteria or moulds? (e) Would egg shells, if left near the nest, perhaps attract the attention of predators and so endanger the brood?

The following facts, obtained earlier by our co-workers, seemed to give some clues.

(A) Beer (1960) found that Black-headed Gulls do not merely carry shells but a great variety of other objects as well if they happen to be found in the nest. Some of these objects are shown in Figure 2. It seemed that the best characterisation of this class of objects would be: "Any object—perhaps below a certain size—which does not resemble an egg, or a chick, or nest material, or food"; in short: "any strange object." The very wide range of objects responded to suggests that the birds respond to very few sign stimuli; it might be that the response was adapted to deal with a much wider range of objects than just the egg shell.

(B) Beer (1960), testing the gulls' readiness to show this response at different times of the season, offered standard egg shell dummies (halved ping-pong balls painted egg shell colour outside, Figure 2) to a large number of gulls once every day from the moment nest scrapes were formed (which is up to about 3 weeks before the laying of the first egg) till well beyond the hatching of the chicks. He found that under these conditions of standard (and near-optimal) stimulation the response could be elicited from at least 20 days before laying till 3 weeks after hatching. In this respect the response behaves rather like typical incubation responses such as sitting and egg retrieving which also develop gradually in the pre-egg period (Beer, 1960). In view of the heavy predation to which eggs are subjected (see below), and of the fact that the eggs are otherwise carefully guarded, this fact suggests that the response is important throughout the incubation period, and not merely during the few days when the chicks hatch.

(C) Finally, Cullen (1957) found that the Kittiwake, *Rissa tridactyla* L., never carries the egg shell. The shells are just left in the nest until they are accidentally kicked off. It is true that this often happens in the first few days after hatching, but shells occasionally stay in the nest or on the rim for weeks, and at any rate they remain in or on the nest much longer than is the case with the Black-headed Gull. The Sandwich Tern, *Sterna sandvicensis* Lath., does not remove the egg shells either (Cullen, 1960).

These observations combined suggest that neither the avoidance of injury, nor of parasitic infection, nor of interference with brooding are the main functions of eggs shell removal—if this were so, then the Kittiwake as the most nidicolous species of gull would not lack the response. The most likely function seemed to be the maintenance of the camouflage of the brood—neither Kittiwake nor Sandwich Tern can be said to go in for camouflage to the extent of the other gulls and terns.

Thus these observations naturally led to an investigation into the function of the response and to a study of the stimuli eliciting it. In the following we shall deal with the problem of survival value first.

Figure 1. Black-headed Gull about to remove the empty egg shell.

Figure 2. A sample collection of various objects which Black-headed Gulls remove from the nest. Top center: Beer's standard model (a halved ping pong ball); bottom right: real egg shell. After C. Beer, 1960.

Figure 4.   A small angle presented on a nest's rim.

Figure 5.   Some of the dummies used. Left, top to bottom: large angle, small angle, halved ping pong ball; center, top to bottom: khaki hen's shell, gull's egg shell, black egg; right, top to bottom: large ring, small ring.

Figure 10.   Some of the small angles of Experiment 8, together with a gull's egg shell.
Top to bottom: "all egg," "cam," "sage green," and "shell."

Figure 11.   Black-headed Gull trying to swallow rectangle measuring ½ × 18 cm.

III. THE SURVIVAL VALUE OF EGG SHELL REMOVAL

The assumption that egg shell removal would serve to maintain the camouflage of the brood presupposes that the brood is protected by camouflage. This basic assumption, usually taken for granted but—as far as we know—never really tested, was investigated in the following way.

First, we collected whatever observations we could about predation in the colony. While these observations are largely qualitative, they show convincingly that predation is severe throughout the season.

Very many eggs disappear in the course of spring. We did not make systematic counts but can give the following qualitative data. In the Ravenglass colony Carrion Crows, *Corvos corone* L., did not account for many egg losses, because, as we could observe time and again, they are easily chased away by the mass attack of the Black-headed Gulls. In fact we never saw a Crow alight in the colony. However, attacks by one, two, or three gulls (which often occurred in our tests) did not deter Crows, and we must assume that nests on the fringe of the colony, and the dozens of nests we regularly find outside the colony and which do not survive, often fall victims to the Crows.

Egg predation within the colony was due to the following predators. Three pairs of Herring Gulls, *Larus argentatus* Pont., which bred in the gullery levied a constant toll of eggs, and later of chicks. Although the Black-headed Gulls attacked them, they could not altogether stop them from snatching eggs and chicks. We observed hundreds of occasions on which non-breeding Herring Gulls and Lesser Black-backed Gulls, *Larus fuscus* L. (many of them immature), passed near or over the colony or over our tests. On only one occasion did we see any of these taking an egg; they usually were totally uninterested in the colony.

Black-headed Gulls prey on each other's eggs to a certain extent. Most of those who visited our experiments did not attack an undamaged egg (the few exceptions are mentioned in our tables) but finished an egg once it had been broken by other predators. Later in the season individual Black-headed Gulls specialised on a diet of newly hatched chicks (see Section VI).

Foxes, *Vulpes vulpes* L., which regularly visited the colony, and killed large numbers of adults early in the season and many half or fully grown chicks towards the end, did visit the gullery in the egg season, but we have no direct evidence of the amount of damage done by them in this part of the year. The gulls were greatly disturbed whenever a Fox entered the colony, but they did not attack him as fiercely as they attacked Herring Gulls and Crows. They flew over the Fox in a dense flock, calling the alarm, and made occasional swoops at it.

Stoats, *Mustela erminea* L., and Hedgehogs, *Erinaceus europaeus* L., visited the gullery and probably accounted for some losses. The gulls hovered over them in a low, dense flock but did not quite succeed in deterring them. In spite of several thousands of man-hours spent in hides in the gullery by us and by our colleagues Dr. Beer and Dr. Manley we never saw either a Fox, a Stoat, or a Hedgehog actually taking an egg; they stayed in the dense cover, and though we have been able to read a great deal from their tracks whenever they had moved over bare sand, this method is of no avail in the egg season since the gulls' nests are situated in vegetation.

Surprisingly, the Peregrine Falcons, *Falco peregrinus* L., which were often seen near or over the gulleries left the Black-headed Gulls in peace, though they regularly took waders and carrier pigeons. The gulls panicked however when a Peregrine flew past.

In order to eliminate the effect of the gulls' social nest defense we put out eggs, singly and widely scattered (20 yards apart) in two wide valleys outside the gullery proper. These valleys had a close vegetation of grasses, sedges, and other plants not exceeding 10 cm. in height. Each egg was laid out in a small depression roughly the size of a Black-headed Gull's nest. Two categories of eggs were arranged in alternate pattern, and in successive tests exchanged position. While predators, particularly Carrion Crows, showed remarkable and quick conditioning to the general areas where we presented eggs, there was no indication that the exact spots where eggs had been found were remembered, and in any case such retention, if it would occur, would tend to reduce rather than enhance differential predation. We assumed (erroneously) that it might well be days before the first predator would discover the eggs, and in our first tests we therefore did not keep a continuous watch. We soon discovered however that the first eggs were taken within one or a few hours after laying out the test, and from then on we usually watched the test area from a hide put up in a commanding position, allowing a view of the entire valley. The tests were usually broken off as soon as approximately half the eggs had been taken.

Experiment 1

Not wishing to take eggs of the Black-headed Gulls themselves (the colony is protected) we did our first test with hens' eggs, half of which were painted a matt white, the other half painted roughly like gulls' eggs. To the human eye the latter, though not quite similar to gulls' eggs, were relatively well camouflaged. It soon became clear that we had underrated the eye-sight of the predators, for the "artificially camouflaged" eggs were readily found. In 9 sessions, lasting from 20 minutes to 7½ hours, we saw

TABLE 1

Numbers of artificially camouflaged hens' eggs ("Artif. Cam.") and white hens' eggs ("White") taken and not taken by predators.

	Artif. Cam.		White	
	taken	not taken	taken	not taken
Carrion Crows	16		18	
Herring Gulls	0		1 (+3)	
Total	16	36	19 (+3)	33 (−3)

N presentations: 2 × 52. Difference between "Artif. Cam." and "White" not significant.[1]

Carrion Crows and Herring Gulls take the numbers of eggs (out of a total presented of 104) given in Table 1.

We were astonished to see how easily particularly the Carrion Crows found even our "camouflaged" eggs. Each test area was usually visited every few hours by a pair of Crows.[2] They would fly in at a height of about 20 feet, looking down. Their sudden stalling and subsequent alighting near an egg were unmistakable signs that they had seen it; they usually discovered even camouflaged eggs from well over 10 metres distance. Often the Crows would discover every single egg, whether white or camouflaged, in the area over which they happened to fly. They either carried an egg away in their bills without damaging it to eat it elsewhere, or opened it on the spot and ate part of the contents, or (usually after they had first eaten four or five eggs) they carried it away and buried it. In some cases we saw Crows uncover these buried eggs one or more days after they had been cached.

---

[1] The P-Values given in the tables were calculated by the χ^2-method, except where stated otherwise.

[2] We have good reasons to believe that each of our two test areas were visited by one pair.

Of the numerous Herring Gulls and Lesser Black-backed Gulls living in the general area, many of which flew over our test area every day, interest in eggs was shown only by three resident pairs of Herring Gulls. Their eyesight was undoubtedly less keen than that of the Crows (as expressed in the scores in Table 1, and particularly Table 2); further they were remarkably timid. For instance in Experiment 1 we were certain on three separate occasions that a Herring Gull had discovered a white egg but did not dare approach it (the "3" in brackets in Table 1 refers to these occasions). Yet as soon as Crows began to search the area, Herring Gulls would appear and attack them. Often Crows and Gulls attacked each other mutually, swooping down on their opponents from the air, for minutes before either of them alighted near an egg. Usually the Gulls succeeded in claiming an egg first. There were also occasions on which the Crows had the area to themselves.

It seemed obvious that our "camouflage" was not effective at all. Now the artificially camouflaged eggs differed from real gulls' eggs in four respects: (1) the ground colour, though to the human eye matching the overall colour of the rather brownish background very well, was slightly different from the ground colour of most of the gulls' eggs; (2) the dark grey dots which we painted on the eggs were more uniform in size and distribution than those on the real gulls' eggs; (3) unlike the natural dots they were all of one hue; and (4) hens' eggs are considerably larger than Black-headed Gulls' eggs, and hence probably more conspicuous.

Experiment 2

Therefore, we next tested real, unchanged Black-headed Gulls' eggs against Black-headed Gulls' eggs painted a matt white. The tests were conducted in the same way as the previous ones. The results, obtained in 12 sessions lasting from 20 minutes to 4 hours, in which 137 eggs were presented, are summarised in Table 2.

TABLE 2

Numbers of normal Black-headed Gulls' eggs ("Natural") and Black-headed Gulls' eggs painted white ("White") taken and not taken by predators.

	Natural		White	
	taken	not taken	taken	not taken
Carrion Crows	8		14	
Herring Gulls	1		19	
Black-headed Gulls	2		7	
Unknown	2		3	
Total	13	55	43	26

N presentations: 68 + 69: Difference between "Natural" and "White" significant at .1% level.

Experiment 3

In order to get an impression of the parts played by size and by the nature of our "artificial camouflage," we painted Black-headed Gulls' eggs in the same way as the "camouflaged" hens' eggs, and compared their vulnerability with that of Black-headed Gulls' eggs painted white. The results of this test, to which we devoted only 5 sessions of from 1 to 3 hours, and in which 48 eggs were presented, are given in Table 3.

TABLE 3

Numbers of artificially camouflaged Black-headed Gulls' eggs ("Artif. Cam.") and Black-headed Gulls' eggs painted white ("White") taken and not taken by predators.

	Artif. Cam.		White	
	taken	not taken	taken	not taken
Carrion Crows	4		5	
Herring Gulls	4		8	
Black-headed Gulls	1		1	
Total	9	15	14	10

N presentations: 24 + 24. Difference between "Artif. Cam." and "White" not significant ($20\% < p < 30\%$).

From these experiments, and particularly from Experiment 2, we conclude that the natural egg colour of the Black-headed Gulls' eggs makes them less vulnerable to attack by predators hunting by sight than they would be if they were white; in other words that their colour acts as camouflage. The difference between the results of Experiments 1 and 3 on the one hand and Experiment 2 on the other indicates that we had underrated the eyesight of the predators, and also that their reactions to the different aspects of camouflage deserve a closer study: the parts played by overall colour, by pattern and hue of the dotting, perhaps even by the texture of the eggs' surface we hope to investigate later—it was a pleasant surprise to discover that large scale experiments are possible. For our present purpose we consider it sufficient to know that painting the eggs white makes them more vulnerable.

Experiment 4

We can now turn to the question whether or not the presence of an egg shell endangers an egg or a chick it is near. For obvious reasons we chose to investigate this for eggs rather than for chicks. The principle of this experiment was the same as that of the previous ones. We laid out, again avoiding site-conditioning in the predators, equal numbers of single Black-headed Gulls' eggs with and without an empty egg shell beside them. The shells used were such from which a chick had actually hatched the year before and which we had dried in the shade and kept in closed tins. The shells were put at about 5 cm. from the eggs which were again put in nest-shaped pits. Predators were watched during 5 sessions lasting from 45 minutes to 4½ hours. Sixty eggs were used. The results are given in Table 4.

TABLE 4

Numbers of Black-headed Gulls' "Eggs-with-Shell" and "Eggs-without-Shell" taken and not taken by predators. Eggs not concealed.

	Eggs-with-Shell		Eggs-without-Shell	
	taken	not taken	taken	not taken
Carrion Crows	6		7	
Herring Gulls	9		7	
Total	15	15	14	16

N presentations: 30 + 30. Difference between "Eggs-with-Shell" and "Eggs-without-Shell" not significant.

We did not consider this result conclusive because the circumstances of the experiment differed from the natural situation in two respects. (1) Although a nest in which a chick has recently hatched may contain un-hatched eggs, there are chicks equally or rather more often; and chicks, apart from having a less conspicuous shape than eggs, do at a quite early stage show a tendency to crouch at least half concealed in the vegetation when the parent gulls call the alarm. The Crows and Gulls might have less difficulty finding eggs than seeing chicks. (2) Both predators were always vigorously attacked by many Black-headed Gulls whenever they came in or near the gullery. In avoiding these attacks their attention is taken up for the greater part of the time (as judged by their head movements and evading action) by keeping an eye on the attackers; in the natural situation they never have the opportunity to look and search at their leisure. And to predators searching for camouflaged prey leisure means time for random scanning and opportunity for undivided attention—both probably factors enhancing discovery, i.e., fixation of non-conspicuous objects. In other words our experiment had probably made things too easy for the predators, even though in the colony the nests themselves are often visible from a distance.

Experiment 5

We therefore decided to repeat this experiment with slightly concealed eggs. This was done by covering each egg (whether or not accompanied by an egg shell) with two or three straws of dead Marram Grass, a very slight change which nevertheless made the situation far more similar to that offered by crouching chicks. Most tests of this experiment were done without watching from a hide; we knew by now who the main predators were, and for our main problem it was not really relevant to know the agent. In 8 tests, lasting from 2 hours 40 minutes to 4 hours 40 minutes, 120 eggs were offered, of which 60 with a shell at 5 cm. distance. The results are given in Table 5.

TABLE 5

Number of Black-headed Gulls' "Eggs-with-Shell" and "Eggs-without-Shell" taken and not taken by predators. Eggs slightly concealed.

Eggs-with-Shell		Eggs-without-Shell	
taken	not taken	taken	not taken
39	21	13	47

N presentations: $60 + 60$. Difference between "Eggs-with-Shell" and "Eggs-without-Shell": $p < .1\%$.

The conclusion must be that the near presence of an egg shell helps Carrion Crows and Herring Gulls in finding a more or less concealed, camouflaged prey, and that therefore egg shells would endanger the brood if they were not carried away.

Experiment 6

This was a series of pilot tests designed to examine whether the Carrion Crows would be readily conditioned to shells once they had found eggs near shells, and whether, if they would find shells without eggs, they would lose interest in the shells. These tests began on April 21, 1960, after the Crows operating in the valley had already gained experience with white and camouflaged eggs, and, since they had broken many of those while eating them, could have learned that egg shells meant food. In the very first test, egg shells were laid out in the Western area of the valley, where in previous tests with whole eggs the Crows had never been seen to alight. At their first visit the Crows alighted near these shells, pecked at them, and searched in the neighbourhood. They left after a few minutes whereupon we took the shells away. A few hours later we again laid out egg shells without eggs, this time scattered over the whole valley. When the Crows next returned they flew round over the valley, looking down as usual, but they did not alight. Next morning semi-concealed eggs were laid out over the whole valley, each with an egg shell at the usual distance of 5 cm. This time the Crows did alight and took a number of the eggs. A few hours later we once more laid out shells only, scattered over the valley, and at the next visit the Crows came down near several of them and searched. The morning after this we laid out just shells, this time in the Eastern part of the valley. This time the Crows did not alight. When next, between this and their next visit we gave each shell an egg at 5 cm., the Crows alighted again when they returned and took several eggs. Later that same day just shells were given in the Western part, which could not induce the Crows to alight. Such tests were continued until April 30, and while they did not give sufficient information, they strongly suggest: (1) that one experience with shells-without-eggs was sufficient to keep the Crows from alighting near shells the next time; and (2) that renewed presentation of eggs with the shells attracted them again. Further, we had the impression (3) that the Crows later learned that egg shells in a part of the valley where shells only had been presented several times meant no food—in other words that they associated "shells only" with the locality. The full record of these experiments is given in Table 6.

TABLE 6

Record of "conditioning test" explained in text.

Es + = eggs + shells offered, eggs taken; Es − = eggs + shells offered, eggs not taken; S + = shells alone offered, crows alighted and searched; S − = shells alone offered, crows did not alight.

	21	21	22	22	23	23	23	24	24	25	25
Eastern area					S −	Es +		Es +			
Entire valley		S −	Es +	S +							S −
Western area	S +						S −		S −	S −	
Date (April)	21	21	22	22	23	23	23	24	24	25	25

	25	26	26	27	27	28	28	28	29	29	30
Eastern area	Es +	Es +			Es −	Es −	Es +		Es +		
Entire valley										S +	
Western area			S −	S −				S −			S +
Date (April)	25	26	26	27	27	28	28	28	29	29	30

Experiment 7

We next investigate the effect of distance between egg and shell. This was done in a mass test without direct observation from the hide, and in the same valley where we had regularly seen Crows and Herring Gulls take eggs. Half concealed gulls' eggs were laid out; one-third of them had a shell at 15 cm. distance, one-third at 100 cm., and one-third at 200 cm. A total of 450 eggs were presented in 15 tests, with the following results (Table 7).

TABLE 7

Number of eggs taken out of the 450 offered with a shell 15, 100, and 200 cm. away.

15 cm.		100 cm.		200 cm.	
taken	not taken	taken	not taken	taken	not taken
63	87	48	102	32	118

N presentations: 3×150. Difference between 15 cm. and 200 cm. significant at .1% level. Significance of the total result: $p < 1\%$.

Part of each group of eggs may of course have been found without the aid of the shell (and this may explain why so many eggs were found even of the 200 cm. group), but the figures show that the "betrayal effect" is reduced with increased distance.

A second, similar test was taken with the shells at 15 cm. and 200 cm.; altogether 60 eggs were presented in 3 tests; the results are given in Table 8 and show a similar result.

TABLE 8

Number of "Eggs-plus-Shell" taken/not taken for different distances (in cm.) between egg and shell. 60 eggs were offered.

15 cm.		200 cm.	
taken	not taken	taken	not taken
13	17	4	26

N presentations: 2×30. Difference between 15 cm. and 200 cm. significant at 2.5% level.

The following test, to be mentioned only briefly because it did not contribute to our results, was in fact done before any of the tests mentioned so far in an attempt to short-circuit our procedure. We put out 50 hens' eggs painted in what we then hoped would be a good camouflaged pattern (see above), and gave each egg an egg shell dummy at 15 cm. distance. These dummies were metal cylinders made by bending a strip of metal sheet measuring 2×10 cm. as used in our later tests with Black-headed Gulls, see Experiments 11, 17, and 18 (Figure 5). Half of these were painted like the eggs, inside and outside (they were in fact satisfactorily cryptic to the human eye); the other half were painted white. We assumed that predators would be slow to come, and that in the beginning one check per day would be sufficient. Upon our first check, about 24 hours after we laid out the eggs, we found that all 50 eggs had disappeared. Our first conclusion was that a whole horde of predators, such as a flock of Herring Gulls, had raided the valley, but we later saw that this valley was searched mainly by one pair of Carrion Crows and one, two, or sometimes three pairs of Herring Gulls. During the following weeks we discovered that the Crows kept digging up these eggs which they must have buried on the first day.

This failure forced us to check the effectiveness of our "camouflage" paint first (see Experiments 1-3) and to test the effect of the natural egg shell (Experiments 4-7); by the time these questions had been settled we had to start our tests on the stimuli eliciting egg shell removal in the Black-headed Gulls themselves, and so had to abandon for the moment any tests on the effect of the colour of the egg shell on the predators. However, the method having now been worked out, it is hoped to investigate this more fully.

The conclusion of this part of our study must therefore be that the eggs of the Black-headed Gulls are subject to predation; that in tests outside the colony the number of eggs found by Carrion Crows and Herring Gulls is lower than it would be if the eggs were white; that the proximity of an egg shell endangers the brood; and that this effect decreases with increasing distance. While it will now be worth investigating the predators' responsiveness to eggs and shells in more detail, the facts reported leave little room for doubt about the survival value of egg shell removal as an anti-predator device. Whether or not the response has other functions is of course left undecided.

IV. THE STIMULI ELICITING EGG SHELL REMOVAL

Beer's demonstration that a great variety of objects can elicit the response naturally led to the question whether all these objects did so to exactly the same extent. This was investigated by presenting dummies of different types, one at a time at each nest, to hundreds of nests, and checking after

	a	b	c	d	e	f	g	h
A	1	8	2	7	3	6	4	5
B	2	1	3	8	4	7	5	6
C	3	2	4	1	5	8	6	7
D	4	3	5	2	6	1	7	8
E	5	4	6	3	7	2	8	1
F	6	5	7	4	8	3	1	2
G	7	6	8	5	1	4	2	3
H	8	7	1	6	2	5	3	4

Figure 3.   A latin square experiment sequence, in which eight models (1-8) were offered in eight successive tests (a-h) to eight groups of nests (A-H).

a certain period (constant for each experiment but varying for different experiments according to the overall stimulating value of the dummies compared) whether or not the dummy had been removed. Nests were marked with numbered wooden pegs, and, unless otherwise mentioned, each nest was used for only one experiment. Each experiment was arranged according to the latin square method, as set out in Figure 3. The nests were divided in as many equal groups as there were dummies, and each nest was offered each dummy once; the sequence of presentation to each group was arranged in such a way that each dummy was presented equally often in the first, second, third, etc. position in the sequence.

Since each experiment involved repeated presentation of dummies, even though no nest had the same dummy twice in one latin square experiment, the problem of waning of the response was important. As will be discussed in detail in Section V the waning within the time limits of one latin square was so slight as to be negligible, but with repetition of entire experiments with the same group of birds there was definite waning from one experiment to the next.

The dummies were put down in a uniform way on the nest's rim, namely approximately 12 cm. from the centre of the nest (in 80 nests measured the average outside diameter was 27 cm., the average inside diameter 13 cm.) (Figure 4). Their orientation was likewise standardised as much as possible. Watch was kept from a hide nearby in a number of cases. From these direct observations we know that both male and female remove egg shells; we also know that egg shell dummies were not moved by the wind (quite strong gales had no effect even on some of our lightest models if they were lightly anchored on the nest's rim; yet for other reasons we avoided testing in rough weather). Small movements of the dummies might be the result of the bird accidentally kicking it; this meant that very slight changes in the position of the dummies could not be interpreted with certainty; this category however was small and we tried to score them in a uniform way, displacement over more than 1 inch away from the nest being taken as evidence of carrying.

Because both sexes carried the egg shell, and because intervals between nest reliefs varied widely, it was impossible to keep records of individual birds, at least in the mass tests. This is an inaccuracy which, while probably not very important, has to be borne in mind in judging the results.

Since we had reasons to concentrate on the antipredator aspects of the response and particularly on camouflage, the question of visual conspicuousness, and therefore of the effect of different colours, was taken up first.

The effect of colour was tested by offering rectangles of flat sheet metal bent at right angles in the middle ("small angles," Figure 5). In 1959 these rectangles measured 1 × 2 inches; in 1960, when we compared some of the angles with cylindrical rings of the same diameter as Black-headed Gulls' eggs, our angles were either made of strips of the same surface area as the rings, or half that size; the "small angles" measured 2 × 5 cm.; the "large angles" 2 × 10 cm. Within each colour experiment the size of the angles was of course uniform. As colours we used Bergermaster Magicote (matt) in 1959, and Rowny Fixed Powder Colours mixed with water or, for other dummies, Du-Lite emulsion paint. All paints gave a uniform matt surface. The reflected colours within the visible spectrum were measured with a Keuffel and Esser "Colorimeter," Model E; Figures 6 to 9 incl. show the reflection graphs. Any interpretation of the results obtained with such models must depend on knowledge of the sensitivity of the Black-headed Gulls' eye to light of various wave lengths. Although no data are available of this species, all species of birds examined so far are sensitive to the same spectral range as human beings; there are indications of a slightly

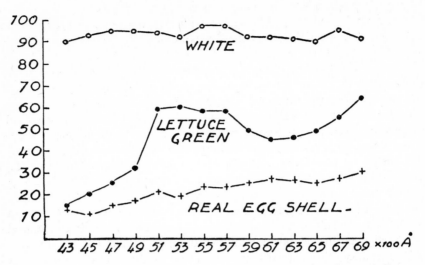

Figure 6.   Reflection graphs of white, lettuce green and real egg shell.

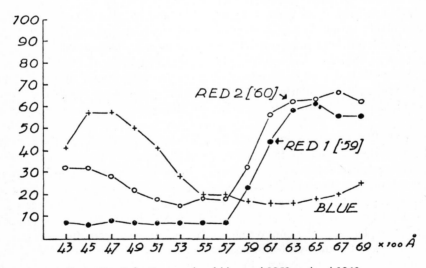

Figure 7.   Reflection graphs of blue, red 1959 and red 1960.

reduced sensitivity to blue in day birds, and owls are less sensitive to red than we are, but no bird so far investigated sees infrared or ultraviolet (for a recent summary, see Schwartzkopff, 1960). Several species have been shown to distinguish well between the main colours. Weidmann (in litt.) analysing the begging response of the Black-headed Gull chick, obtained scores for a variety of colours which are not compatible with colour blindness. We will assume that reflected colours which are similar to us are

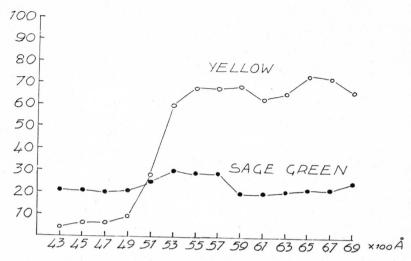

Figure 8.   Reflection graphs of yellow and sage green.

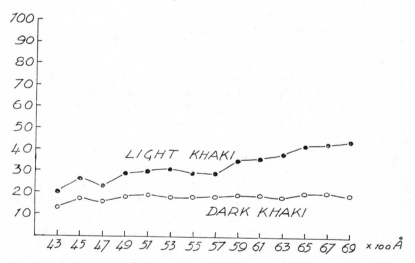

Figure 9.   Reflection graphs of light khaki and dark khaki.

so to Black-headed Gulls as well, a conclusion substantiated by our own
results.

Experiment 8

In our first experiment, done in 1959, the following colours were used:
"shine" (blank, shiny metal), white, red, black, "shell" white inside, out-

side sage green with dark grey dotting), sage green, "all egg" (sage green with dark grey dotting both inside and outside), and "cam" (sage green with dark grey irregular striping inside and outside) (Figure 10). Shine was taken because, while its overall appearance was a rather dull grey (much darker than white) when seen from certain angles it reflected the sun and thus appeared much brighter than white. Since a bird, when moving about and when sitting on the nest, would be exposed to the bright flash far less often than to the overall greyish colour of the model, its score might help us find out when the stimulus eliciting shell removal had to be received: acting on the hypothesis (which proved correct) that white would have a high score, shine should have a lower score than white if the stimulus had to be received by the sitting bird (since the chances were then that it would usually see it as a grey angle), but if shine would have a high score, this would mean that it stimulated the bird particularly strongly whenever the bright reflection was briefly visible. White was chosen because to the human eye it was very conspicuous, and because real egg shells, particularly those which have dried for a little while, often show white patches on the rim where the pigmented shell has broken off and the egg membranes were showing (the inside of the shell is rarely white; also, most of it is in the shade). Red was chosen because there were indications in other gulls (see Tinbergen, 1953) that red objects in the nest are pecked at more often than objects of other colours. Black was originally chosen in order to check whether, if white would have a high score, this was due to whiteness or to contrast with the environment. However, it was remarkable how cryptic black really was on the nest rim; even the deep black of our dummies blended easily with the shadows of the nest rim, and as soon as one or two straws blew over a dummy or were kicked over it by the bird, a black model blended with the shades. Sage green was chosen because it was, of the available standard colours, the one most similar to the ground colour of at least some of the gulls' eggs. As is well known, the eggs of all gulls and terns show considerable variation in colour; this, in combination with the fact that the Herring Gull (and according to some of our own pilot tests, the Black-headed Gull) respond by egg rolling and by incubation to egg dummies of an extremely wide range of colours (Tinbergen, 1953, but see also Baerends, 1959) made us confident that sage green was near enough to the natural egg colour to justify its use as such—later experiments showed us how wrong we were.

This experiment was done with 96 nests, and was repeated three times with the same group. The results are given in Table 9.

Applying the Mann-Whitney test to the whole range of the individual trial scores (Siegel, 1956) we find the following p-values for what are clearly borderline cases: Shell-red: 15%; Shine-red: 2%; White-red:

TABLE 9

Number of small angles of different colours (Experiment 8) carried and not carried in three successive latin square tests. (In all tables, successive tests with the same group of birds will be indicated by Roman numerals I, II, III; tests taken with different groups of birds will be indicated by capitals A, B, etc.)

	I carried	II carried	III carried	Total carried	not carried
Shine	38	34	21	93	195
White	44	25	20	89	199
Shell	38	25	18	81	207
Red	32	23	16	71	217
Black	25	24	14	63	225
All egg	27	19	12	58	230
Cam	28	13	13	54	234
Green	23	14	8	45	243

N presentations: $3 \times 8 \times 96$. Significance of differences discussed in text.

11%; Shell-black: 8%; White-black: 4%; White-all egg: 1%; Cam-green: 23%; Black-green: 3%.

We conclude that "shine," "white," and "shell" elicit more responses than red and black, and that these have a higher valence than "all egg," "cam," and "green." This suggested that the contrast in brightness between the dummy and its background entirely determined its releasing value. Because, as mentioned above, there is a considerable colour variation in the eggs of the gulls, and because previous experiments on egg-recognition in Herring Gulls had shown colour to play a relatively minor part, we considered that sage green was probably similar enough to the colour of real eggs to justify the conclusion that brightness was the only colour character which controlled egg shell removal, and that the colour of the outside was not specifically responded to. The intermediate position of red and black seemed to support this, for red was physically less bright than white (Figures 6 and 7) and black was, to the human eye, remarkably cryptic. Experiments 11, 12, and 13 showed that this conclusion was incorrect. However, before discussing them, two experiments must be mentioned which were intended to examine the possible effect of contrast between the white and darker parts of the egg shell.

Experiment 9

The fact that "shell" was not treated differently from either white or shine suggested that contrast between parts of one dummy did not play a part. In order to test this, we made a series of angles of which one "wing" was white inside and outside, and the other wing was coloured on both sides. The additional advantage of this type of dummy compared with those of the previous experiment was that the bird would always see both colours, wherever it was; the old shell models were all white when seen from the inside, all egg when seen from the outside. We used white/white, shine/white, shell/white, sage green/white and red/white. In this experiment, 80 nests were used, and the experiment was repeated three times with these birds. Table 10 gives the results.

TABLE 10

Numbers of small angles of different colours (Experiment 9) carried and not carried in three successive latin square tests.

	I carried	II carried	III carried	Total carried	not carried
Shine/white	41	32	30	103	137
Red/white	34	30	22	86	154
White/white	33	30	19	82	158
Shell/white	34	26	19	79	161
Green/white	32	29	13	74	166

N presentations: $3 \times 5 \times 80$. Differences discussed in the text.

The Mann-Whitney test gave the following results: Shine/white—shell/white: $2.5\% < p < 5\%$; shine/white—green/white: $1\% < p < 2.5\%$; shine/white—white/white $p > 5\%$; red/white—green/white $p > 5\%$.

Since in Table 9 "shine" received a higher score than "shell," and red had a higher score than green, the results of Table 10 are consistent with the conclusion reached in the previous experiment, and there is no reason to assume that contrast within the shell-dummy plays a part. The high score of "shell" in Experiment 8 must therefore have been due to its white surface alone.

Experiment 10

Before we did the previous experiment, we had subjected 80 birds to one experiment with slightly different dummies. Two colours were used on each dummy as in Experiment 9, but while colour A was on the inside of one wing, it was on the outside of the other: this ensured that both colours were always visible to the bird sitting on the nest. The combinations used were red/white, green/white, shine/white, and shell/white. The scores, which we will not give in detail, are again similar except for shine/white which is a little higher than the others. Since shine had the highest score in all three experiments, it seems likely that this is a real effect; it seems most probable that this is due to its greater brightness when seen in such a way that the sun is directly reflected by it. Since this must be supposed to happen only during a very brief fraction of the time in which the bird sees the model, and in very different positions for the different birds, this again suggests that a very brief stimulus is sufficient to make the bird carry the shell away.

Experiment 11

The first indication that our interpretation had been in part incorrect came from the results of this experiment, which was taken mainly for the purpose of investigating characters of shape. We had already found (see below, Experiment 16) that white angles were far less stimulating than real egg shells, and that the halved ping-pong balls which Beer had used received a score halfway between real shell and white angle. We suspected that the rounded shape of the shells had to do with this, and we therefore made cylindrical rings by bending sheet metal strips measuring 2 × 10 cm. The rings were not quite closed but had a gap of about 1 cm. between the two ends (Figure 5). Because we had, after the 1959 season, compared the colour "sage green" more carefully with the colours of real eggs and had seen that even the greener eggs were rather different from sage green, we had decided to use a new colour in 1960. This colour was mixed so that to the human eye it exactly matched the ground color of the majority of eggs, which corresponds to "OOY, 11, 4°" in Villabolos and Villabolos (1947). This colour was called "khaki." As substitutes for real egg shells we used hen's egg shells with the "lid" broken off. The models used in this experiment were: hens' egg shells painted khaki outside and left white inside; small rings painted khaki inside and outside, white small rings, and white angles. The results of this test, taken with two groups of nests (group A, consisting of 80 nests, was tested twice; group B, also of 80 nests, was subjected to one experiment) are given in Table 11.

TABLE 11

Numbers of four models (Experiment 11) carried and not carried in three tests with two groups of birds.

	A_I	A_{II}	B	Total carried	Total not carried
Hen's shell khaki outside	59	45	53	157	83
All white ring	36	30	44	110	130
All khaki ring	49	22	37	108	132
White angle	31	19	28	78	162

N presentations: 3 × 4 × 80. Difference between khaki shell and all rings: $p <$ .1%. Difference between khaki ring and angle: $p < 1\%$.

The relevance of this test for the question of response to shape will be discussed below, but here the scores for khaki rings and white rings must be considered. They are not significantly different and in fact almost equal. If khaki represented no better "egg colour" than sage green, there was a contradiction between this and the previous experiments. It became likely that the birds responded not only to white but also specifically to the exact colour of the eggs.

Experiment 12

We therefore decided to compare the effects of khaki and sage green in one experiment. Khaki angles were compared with green angles in 120 nests. The results are given in Table 12.

TABLE 12

Numbers of small angles of different colours (Experiment 12) carried and not carried in one test.

	Carried	Not Carried
Khaki angles	52	68
Sage green angles	29	91

N presentations: 2 × 120.

Our suspicion was strikingly confirmed: sage green received a much lower score ($p < .5\%$). This result raised two points: (1) how would khaki compare with the other colours? Perhaps it would turn out to be equally effective as white because it was similar to the real ground colour of the eggs; and (2) why was green so low—in Experiment 8 it had received a decidedly lower score than either red or black. We thought that this was due to sage green being inconspicuous, but khaki was, if anything, less conspicuous on the nest's rim. We decided to run an entirely new and more comprehensive colour test.

Experiment 13

Because their dotting makes the overall colour of gulls' eggs darker than their ground colour, we prepared two khaki colours, one resembling the ground colour, the other, made by mixing this with some black, a darker shade of the same colour, roughly matching the overall colour of eggs seen from a distance. Unfortunately, although we had prepared a large quantity of the standard khaki colour, much of this was accidentally spilled, and we had to mix a new khaki. This was again done in such a way as to match the natural eggs' ground colour, but although we used the same ingredients our new khaki was not exactly the same as the original khaki. We do not think it likely, however, that this very slight difference has affected our results significantly but experiments using the "new khaki" are mentioned separately. Apart from dark and light khaki our other colours were:

yellow, white, a very bright yellowish green ("lettuce green"), sage green, blue, and red. We used small angles of 2 × 5 cm. The reflection graphs of these colours are given in Figures 6 to 9 incl. Table 13 gives the results obtained in one experiment with 240 nests; Table 14 gives the figures of an experiment with four of these colours, run with 80 new nests.

TABLE 13

Numbers of small angles of different colours (Experiment 13) carried and not carried in one test.

	Carried	Not Carried
Dark khaki	92	148
White	85	155
Light khaki	77	163
Yellow	73	167
Blue	62	178
Red	57	183
Sage green	45	195
Lettuce green	19	221

N presentations: 8 × 240.

TABLE 14

Numbers of small angles of different colours (Experiment 13) carried and not carried in one test.

	Carried	Not Carried
Dark khaki	35	45
White	35	45
Yellow	28	52
Blue	22	58

N presentations: 4 × 80.

The Mann-Whitney test gave the following p's: dark khaki-light khaki: 5%; white-yellow: 35%; dark khaki-yellow: $1\% < p < 5\%$; yellow-blue: 5%.

Together with the results obtained in 1959 these facts point to the following conclusion: angles of any colour, however bright and unnatural, are carried to a certain extent. There are peaks for white and for khaki. Since khaki is, on the nest rim which is made of dead grass mainly, by far the most cryptic of all, and since dark khaki is carried more often than light khaki; since further the very light and conspicuous lettuce green received a very low score, the light khaki's lightness cannot be responsible for its high score, and this must be due to its special colour. In other words the birds responded to wavelength rather than brightness. Yellow has, among the bright colours with intermediate scores, the highest position, undoubtedly due to the fact that in mixing the khaki a very large amount of just this yellow had to be used; red and blue have intermediate scores, and sage green and particularly lettuce green are exceptionally low.

It thus seems that the gulls' responsiveness to colours of egg shells fits the demands very well: the two colours of the natural egg shell, khaki and white, are most stimulating, while the gulls respond least to green, the colour of the vegetation in the immediate surroundings of the nests—it would be not only wasteful, but decidedly harmful to keep carrying away the leaves of the cover round the nests.

Experiment 14

This experiment was done with small rings instead of angles. We used four colour combinations: (new) khaki inside and outside, white inside and outside, (new) khaki outside, white inside, and blank, shiny metal. The first three models were taken in order to investigate once more the possible effect of contrast within the dummy; the fourth model was added in the hope that we might find a "supernormal" stimulus (Tinbergen, 1951). The results, with 80 nests, are given in Table 15.

TABLE 15

Numbers of four models (Experiment 14) carried and not carried in one test.

	Carried	Not Carried
Khaki ring	37	43
White ring	39	41
Khaki/white ring	42	38
Shiny ring	40	40

N presentation: 4×80. No significant differences.

This again confirms that contrasts within the egg shell dummy have no discernible effect (Experiments 8, 9, and 10). The shiny rings, while in parts brighter than white, did not give a higher score than white. New khaki and white have again approximately the same score.

Experiment 15

In this experiment, done before we began to use new khaki, old khaki, which was a little darker than new khaki, was compared, on angles, with white. Table 16, of two successive tests with 80 nests, gives a higher score for white.

TABLE 16

Numbers of small angles of different colour (Experiment 15) carried and not carried in two successive tests.

	I carried	II carried	Total carried	Total not carried
White angle	36	36	72	88
Khaki angle	25	18	43	117

N presentations: $2 \times 2 \times 80$. Difference is significant at the .5% level.

In this admittedly small scale test the superiority of white over khaki, slight in Experiments 13 and 14, is more pronounced. We do not know why this is so.

Experiment 16

Both in 1959 and 1960 we compared some of our models with real gulls' shells in order to get an impression of the overall valence of the dummies used. In the experiment mentioned here done in 1959, real gulls' shells were compared with halved ping-pong balls: still ignorant of the intricacies of responsiveness to colour discussed above, we painted them sage green with dark grey dots—roughly the same pattern as that used for "all egg" and "shell" angles of Experiment 8. We further used white small angles of 1×2 inches, and flat paper rectangles as used in Experiment 19 reported on below. These paper strips measured $2 \times 4\frac{1}{2}$ cm. and were a pale buff. Table 17, obtained in one experiment with 160 nests, summarises the results.

TABLE 17

Numbers of four models (Experiment 16) carried and not carried in one test.

	Carried	Not Carried
Real shell	155	5
Halved ping-pong balls	120	40
White angle	91	69
Paper rectangle	53	107

N presentations: 4×160. All differences are significant at the .1% level.

White angles therefore, while better than the buff flat strips, were clearly inferior to the halved ping-pong balls (in spite of the latters' inferior colour); and these received a lower score than real shells. This however could at least in part be due to the sage green colour of the halved ping-pong balls.

Experiment 17

Hens' shells of which the blunt end was broken off so that they resembled gulls' eggs in shape while being a little larger, were painted all
white, and these were compared with hens' shells painted (old) khaki outside and white inside, with real gulls' shells, and with all white small rings.
This experiment differed from all others, for although each model was
presented to 40 nests, each group of 40 nests received the same model on
all four occasions (this was done to gain an impression of the degree of
waning which will be discussed later). The results are in Table 18.

TABLE 18

Numbers of four models (Experiment 17) carried and not carried in four
successive tests. No latin square arrangement; each nest received the same
model throughout.

	I	II	III	IV	Total carried	not carried
White hens' shell	34	29	28	32	123	37
Khaki hens' shell	35	34	34	33	136	24
Real gulls' shell	36	35	35	33	139	21
White ring	29	28	22	28	107	53

N presentations: $4 \times 4 \times 40$.

There is no significant difference between real shell and khaki hens'
shell; white hens' shell received a score significantly lower than real gulls'
shells at the 5% level; the difference between the white ring and the
white hens' shell was almost significant (p just above 5%), and that
between white ring and the other shells was thoroughly significant
($p < .1\%$).

The conclusions to be drawn from the two last experiments are that
khaki hens' shells are not inferior to real gulls' shells; that white shells are
superior to white rings; and that shells are considerably superior to angles.
We have already seen (Experiment 11) that rings are superior to angles,
and (Experiment 16) that halved ping-pong balls are superior to angles.
Although the colour of the paper strips was slightly different from khaki,
there seems little doubt that such flat rectangles are inferior to angles.

Our next task was now to examine whether the size difference between
angles and rings (which were made of metal strips twice the size of the
angles) could be responsible for their different effects.

Experiment 18

We presented the following four models, all painted all-khaki (new):
small ring (bent strips measuring 2×10 cm.), large ring (made of a strip of

aluminium sheet measuring 4 × 20 cm.; its weight was 16 grams, that of the small ring was 10 grams); the small angle made of a strip of 2 × 5 cm., and "large angles" made of the same strips as small rings but folded at right angles in the middle (Figure 5). Three groups of birds were used: group A of 80 nests, group B of 80 nests, and group C of 160 nests; each group was subjected to one complete latin square. The results are in Table 19.

TABLE 19

Numbers of four models (Experiment 18) carried and not carried by three groups of birds.

	A	B	C	Total carried	not carried
Large ring	34	30	56	120	200
Small ring	38	40	74	152	167
Large angle	34	20	47	101	219
Small angle	31	24	52	107	212

N presentations: 4 × 3 × 320 (−2).

As expected, the small rings were carried more than small angles ($p < .1\%$). Small rings were carried more than large rings ($p < 2.5\%$); small rings were significantly superior to large angles ($p < .1\%$), but there was no significant difference between the two angles.

The relatively low score of the large rings was rather unexpected because we knew from past experience (Tinbergen, 1951, 1953; Baerends, 1959) that the egg retrieving response of gulls responds better to outsize eggs than to normal eggs. However, since we also knew that the responses to such large eggs were a combination of retrieving and avoidance (which often kept the birds away from the nest in the beginning of a test), we suspected that we might have to do with a similarly ambivalent response towards the large rings, which might, either in part or even entirely, be responsible for the difference in removal scores between large rings and small rings.

We therefore observed from a hide the responses of ten individual birds to small rings and to large rings. Six of these birds received the small ring first, the large second; one bird was presented the large ring first, the small second; and three birds had the small ring first, then the large ring, then the small ring once more. Their fear responses, expressed by delay in returning to the nest, alarm calls, stretching of the neck, repeated withdrawal after initial approach, were roughly classified as: no signs of fear (0), and a scale of four intensities (1, 2, 3, 4) of avoidance behaviour, 4 being the highest score. Each test lasted until the birds settled on the eggs. Table 20 summarises the results of this admittedly crude assessment.

TABLE 20

Fear responses shown by ten birds presented with either a large ring or a small ring on the nest's rim.

Bird No.	Small Ring	Large Ring	Small Ring
1	0	0	
2	0	0	
3	1	1	
4	1	4	
5		3	1
6	2	3	
7	0	3	0
8	0	0	
9	0	4	0
10	0	4	0

On 9 occasions the fear score for the large ring was higher than for the small ring; it was the same (either 0 or 1) on 4 occasions, while the small ring never elicited a higher score.

The lower score of these large rings is therefore in part due to the interference by another response (fear, or avoidance) with the removal response. This was the first indication of a fact which became increasingly clear as the work proceeded, viz. that we were not measuring the direct expression of the "releasing mechanism" of just the removal response, but rather the effect of the interaction of this response with, or its dominance over, a variety of other responses. Applied to the present experiment, it might be that the large ring does stimulate the removal response as strongly as or even more strongly than the small ring. Our scores, in other words, could be said to indicate the "resultant removal tendency."

Experiment 19

This was done in 1959 with the special aim of investigating how the gulls distinguished between egg shells and nest material. The immediate impetus to this was given by Beer's observations, illustrated in Figure 2, which had shown (1) that some objects were very similar to objects which the gulls were sometimes seen to carry to their nests while building; and (2) that a bird would sometimes actually alternate between carrying an object to the nest and carrying it away. Further, some of our "small angles" were found at the end of a test in the nest rim in such a position that it seemed as if the birds had made "sideways building" movements with them. From a comparison of the classes of objects carried away and those found built into the nests, the main criterion of objects eliciting nest building movements seemed to be the elongate shape. This led to the use of four flat models which differed only in their proportions. Flat rectangles of thin cardboard were used of the following dimensions: 3×3 cm. (model 1); $2 \times 4\frac{1}{2}$ cm. (2); 1×9 cm. (3); and $\frac{1}{2} \times 18$ cm. (4). The surface area of all these models was the same. They were painted a buff colour rather similar to light khaki. Direct observations, and checks in which models found moved at the end of a test were classified according to the direction of the wind, proved that even these light models were not blown away, not even on days with winds up to about Beaufort force 8. However, to prevent confusion through birds taking up models in their bills and dropping them, which would expose them to the wind, we decided to be on the safe side and did not run tests when the wind was stronger than about force 5.

In the first series of tests 40 nests (group A) were offered the models in a latin square arrangement four times in succession; in a second series, another group (B), also consisting of 40 nests, was subjected to three consecutive latin square tests. These tests were repeated so often because the absolute level of the score was low—this was no doubt due to the fact (see Table 17) that important characters of shape were missing in all four models. Table 21 summarises the results.

TABLE 21

Numbers of four models (Experiment 19) carried and not carried in seven tests with 2 groups of birds.

	A_I	A_{II}	A_{III}	A_{IV}	B_I	B_{II}	B_{III}	Total carried	Total not carried
1 (3×3 cm.)	11	5	11	7	14	7	11	66	214
2 ($2 \times 4\frac{1}{2}$ cm.)	8	5	10	8	15	5	7	58	222
3 (1×9 cm.)	15	11	12	12	14	9	9	82	198
4 ($\frac{1}{2} \times 18$ cm.)	12	9	12	7	10	10	6	66	214

N presentations: $4 \times 7 \times 40$.

While there is no significant difference between the scores for models 1, 2, and 4, model 3 was carried significantly more often than model 2 ($p < 2.5\%$). This was a rather unexpected result, because model 3 could not be said to approach the dimensions of the egg shell most closely; both 2 and 1 would seem to conform better. We believe that the clue to this problem was provided by the fact that on many occasions where one of these flat models had not been removed it was found in the nest, partly covered by nest material. Table 22 shows how often a model of each category which was not carried was found in this position.

TABLE 22

Numbers of models found in nest after Experiment 19 compared with numbers not carried ("minus responses").

1 (3×3 cm.)	52 out of 214	"minus responses"	24%
2 ($2 \times 4\frac{1}{2}$ cm.)	62	228	27%
3 (1×9 cm.)	59	198	30%
4 ($\frac{1}{2} \times 18$ cm.)	94	206	46%

The differences between 1 and 4 and between 2 and 4 are significant at the .1% level; that between 3 and 4 at the .5% level.

At first we thought that the birds had in such cases invariably treated the model as nest material and had performed sideways building movements with it. However, when we decided to check this by direct observations from a hide, the situation appeared to be even more complicated. We found that a model could land among the material of the nest either because it was taken up and dropped (which often made the impression of an incomplete carrying response), when it could subsequently be covered by the scraping and egg shifting movements of the bird; or because the bird performed actual nest building movements with it. Further, as Table 23 shows, a third response was involved as well: some of the models elicited feeding (Figure 11). It is true that in all but one of the observations (when a model 4 was fully swallowed) the bird did not succeed in actually eating the model, but attempts at swallowing were unmistakable.

TABLE 23

Direct observations of responses to the four models of Experiment 19.

	No Notice	Carried	Attempts at Swallowing	Built in	Total Obs.
1 (3× 3 cm.)	22	5	0	1	28
2 (2 × 4½ cm.)	16	4	1	2	23
3 (1 × 9 cm.)	10	7	2	4	23
4 (½ × 18 cm.)	8	7	4	5	24

It is no doubt significant that all three responses (removing, swallowing, and building) started off with the same movement: taking the model in the bill. It was further revealing that on more than one occasion we saw a bird alternate between attempts at swallowing, incomplete building movements, and incomplete carrying movements (standing up with the model in its bill, stretching the neck, but then settling down again). What happened was therefore something like this: a model might be picked up because it provided stimuli for either of the three responses. Once the bird "found itself" with the model in its bill, this stimulus might set off either the same response as was started by the visual stimulus which elicited picking-up, or one of the two other responses. Since feeding and nest building are obviously more readily elicited by the longer models, particularly model 4, their "carrying score" might have become higher than expected if merely egg shell removal were aroused. Model 3 might have given the highest score because it elicited more initial feeding and building responses than 2 and 3, and because it was still less exclusively eliciting feeding and nest building than the extremely long model 4. A further reason for its high score could have been that it proved more difficult to use as building material than 4, and that the response was therefore more often continued into carrying.

Whatever the exact explanation, however, the observations once more reveal the fact that the carrying score as obtained in the mass experiments reflects, not the functioning of the carrying response alone, but its preponderance over other responses, with which it interacts.

Experiment 20

We had found (Experiment 7) that the "betrayal effect" of shells decreased rapidly with increased distance between shell and egg. It was therefore of interest to test the effect of distance on the gulls' response as well. We offered hens' shells painted khaki outside at four distances from the centre of the nest: on the rim (appr. 10 cm. from the centre), and at 15, 25, and 35 cm. distance from the centre. This was done with 80 nests: the results are given in Table 24.

TABLE 24

Numbers of hens' eggs painted khaki outside, carried and not carried when offered at different distances from nest (Experiment 20).

	Carried	Not Carried
10 cm.	64	16
15 cm.	54	26
25 cm.	27	53
35 cm.	11	69

N presentations: 4×80. Difference between 10 and 15 cm. not significant; that between 15 and 25 cm. significant at .1% level; that between 25 and 35 cm. significant at 1% level. Significance of the total result: $p < 1\%$.

It is obvious that the response decreases very rapidly with increased distance. The sharpest drop is just outside the nest's rim, between 15 and 25 cm. It is regrettable that we did not use the same scale of distances in the predation tests. It looks from the predation tests as if it might "pay" the gulls to show a better response to shells further than 15 cm. from the nest, but as we shall see later there are good reasons to believe that here again another response interferes with shell removal: the need of covering the brood.

Experiment 21

When we compared the results obtained so far in analyses of stimulus situations which specifically release a single response (Tinbergen, 1951; Magnus, 1958; Weidmann in litt.) we were puzzled by the fact that, while on the one hand shell removal could be elicited by a very wide range of objects (neither shape, nor size, nor colour being strikingly specific) yet there were these two rather sharply defined peaks for khaki and white, and the very specific trough for green. We wondered to what extent this response was normally conditioned, and to what extent the selective responsiveness was independent of previous experience with eggs or egg shells. One effect of experience will be discussed below: having carried a shell slightly reduces the likelihood of carrying one again.

The present experiment was a gamble, and was done on a small scale; but the rather striking results justified it.

We knew from Weidmann's work (1956) that Black-headed Gulls could be prevented from laying by offering them eggs on the empty scrape well before the first egg was due. We therefore laid out a black wooden egg in each of a number of scrapes in early April, some weeks before the majority of birds laid. As it turned out, some of these nests were abandoned; others were occupied by birds which did not sit on the black egg dummies but built nests on top of them; in others again eggs were laid soon after we gave the black eggs. However, fourteen pairs accepted our black eggs, began to incubate on them and were thereby stopped from laying eggs of their own. When these birds began to incubate, we added two more black eggs to each clutch so as to ensure the best possible situation, and these fourteen pairs were allowed to incubate these black clutches for approximately 5 weeks (well beyond the normal incubation period, which according to Beer, 1960, and Ytreberg, 1956, is on the average about 24 days). We then presented to these birds, in the normal latin square arrangement, black angles and khaki angles. Though we had never compared the effects of these two colours directly, Experiment 8 had shown that black has a low valence compared with white, shine, and shell, and was about equal to red. Nevertheless we selected fourteen normal pairs as controls, which had been sitting on their own eggs, and ran this experiment with them simultaneously. The results of seven latin squares in succession, run over 5 consecutive days, are given in Table 25.

TABLE 25

Numbers of small angles of different colours carried and not carried by birds which had been sitting on black eggs ("experimentals") and birds which had been sitting on normal eggs ("controls") (Experiment 21).

	Black Angle		Khaki Angle	
	carried	not carried	carried	not carried
Experimentals	12	37	13	36
Controls	3	46	12	37

N presentations: $2 \times 7 \times 14$. The difference between Experimentals and Controls in their scores for black angles is significant at the 2.5% level.

The conclusion must be that having incubated black eggs increases the response to black egg shell dummies. We do not know the age of these birds, and hence cannot say whether they may have had experience with normal eggs in a previous season; in inexperienced birds the effect may well be still more pronounced. It is worth pointing out that these birds had had no experience with carrying black egg shells; the experience they had was with another response: incubating black eggs.

There is of course the possibility that this is not the result of a learning process at all, but that the birds at the moment of carrying matched the colour of egg shell dummy and egg: we hope to follow this question up next year.

Experiment 22

In Experiment 17 we had compared real gulls' shells with hens' shells painted either khaki or white, and had been surprised to see that the scores for these three models were about equal. We thought it possible that they were not really equally effective but that even the least effective of them was still near-optimal and thus sufficient to give, under the conditions of our tests, a near 100 percent score. The response to shells was usually so prompt that the birds who carried at all did so immediately upon alighting on the nest. Shortening the duration of the tests was therefore hardly feasible, and we decided, after having found that the effect of a shell decreased with increasing distance, to run an experiment with several highly effective models at a greater distance from the nest. The following dummies were therefore presented at 15 cm. from the centre of the nest: real gull shells; all white hens' shells; all (old) khaki hens' shells; and all lettuce green hens' shells. The result, obtained in one latin square with 160 nests, are set out in Table 26.

TABLE 26

Numbers of four different types of egg shell offered at 15 cm. from nest (Experiment 22) carried and not carried in one test.

	Carried	Not Carried
Real gulls' shell	114	46
White hens' shell	80	80
Khaki hens' shell	36	124
Lettuce hens' shell	31	129

N presentations: 4×160. The difference between real shell and white is significant ($p < .1\%$); as is the difference between white and khaki ($p < .1\%$); khaki and lettuce are not significantly different.

While, according to expectation, real gulls' shells were removed from more nests than any of the other models, the khaki shells were not carried more than the lettuce shells, and considerably less than white shells.[3] White was superior to khaki in our previous tests too, though usually not to this extent, but in the angle tests khaki had been far superior to lettuce green. The only suggestion we can offer is that with increasing distance from the nest the khaki shells, because of their strikingly cryptic colour, failed to attract the birds' attention; while a khaki model on the nest's rim cannot be missed, its inconspicuousness might have effect at greater distances, but it is certainly puzzling that this should already be noticeable at 15 cm.

V. CHANGES IN RESPONSIVENESS IN TIME

As mentioned in Section II Beer (1960) had found that Black-headed Gulls are ready to remove an egg shell throughout the incubation period and even well before the first egg is laid. Our experiments were done at different times in the breeding season, and although our conclusions are not based on inter-test comparisons, it is of interest to know as precisely as possible how the overall readiness behaves in the course of time. Dr. Beer has kindly allowed us to publish the details of the tests he did to this purpose in 1958 and on which his general conclusion was based. A large number of nests were offered a halved ping-pong ball painted egg shell colour outside once every day, from 20 days before egg laying occurred till 13 days after hatching. The models were left at the nest for 6 hours, at the end of which a check was made, as in our experiments, and the models still present removed. Table 27 summarises the results.

TABLE 27

Summary of C. Beer's results with a standard dummy (halved ping-pong ball) offered once daily throughout the breeding season. Eo: day on which first egg was laid; Ho: day on which first chick hatched. Data lumped for periods of different lengths.

	E−20/−10	E−9/−1	Eo	E1	E2	E3
Shell carried	174	584	97	88	91	90
Not carried	92	210	12	13	12	9
Total tests	266	794	109	101	103	99
% carried	65.4	73.7	89.0	87.1	88.3	91.0

	E4/10	E11/17	E18/25	Ho/6	H7/13	H14/25
Shell carried	437	222	230	187	111	105
Not carried	47	22	29	51	80	76
Total tests	484	244	259	238	191	181
% carried	90.3	91.0	88.8	78.5	58.1	58.0

[3] It should be noted however that in Experiment 17 we offered hens' shells which were khaki outside but white inside whereas the present "khaki hens' shells" were khaki on both surfaces.

The number of pairs tested during the first few days is naturally low since at this stage birds may still abandon their scrapes. The score for days E—20/—10 is significantly lower than that for days E—9/—1 ($p < 2.5\%$). During laying the score rises still more (p diff. E—/—1 and Eo $< .5\%$). From then on it stays practically constant until the time when the chicks begin to hatch (p diff. between E18/25 and Ho/6 $< .5\%$), when it begins to drop.

Before we can accept this as a fully reliable index of the readiness to carry at different times, we must consider the possibility that the responsiveness changes as a result of repeated presentation; it could wane, increase, stay constant, or fluctuate in a complicated way. While we have not run systematic tests with the same models throughout the season and using new birds for each test (which would have monopolised the entire colony just for this experiment alone), we have two sets of data which throw some light on this question.

First, our experiments give some information of waning under the conditions of our experiments. Table 28 gives the scores for consecutive tests within a latin square sequence for the first four presentations of each of 14 latin squares, with specification of the experiments of which the total scores have been given already.

In judging these figures it should be remembered that in each of these experiments every nest received a new model on every occasion, i.e., a model that had some but not all of the characteristics of the preceding model. Whatever stimulus-specific revival of the response (Hinde, 1954) there might be therefore would tend to counteract the waning of the scores. The differences between the models compared in the experiments however varied greatly: in some experiments some models scored much better than others; in others the various models used had approximately the same valence. It is therefore impossible to say more than that a certain degree of stimulus-specific change might, but must not, be reflected in these figures, and that this differs from one experiment to the other. It might be rewarding to plot waning against the degree of newness of each model as expressed through differences in absolute scores, but since we intend to continue this work we think it advisable to await more results. For our present purpose it is sufficient to point out that there is some evidence of waning, but this intra-experiment waning is at best slight.

Second, we can present some figures about waning with repeated presentation of exactly the same model, since on various occasions we repeated full latin squares one or more times with the same birds. This was done with seven groups of birds, and the total carrying scores of each latin square are given in Table 29.

The table shows convincingly that repeated presentation of the same models does reduce the score. In some experiments this reduction is marked even when pauses of 8-10 days were given between two experiments,

TABLE 28

Scores of four successive tests in one latin square each, for 14 latin squares.

Table	Test 1	Test 2	Test 3	Test 4	N nests
9-1	43	35	36	28	96
10-1	46	39	33	27	80
X^4	53	35	38	39	80
11-A	46	45	43	41	80
11-B	39	43	39	41	80
13	93	62	69	68	240
14	35	28	27	30	80
15	44	36	37	41	80
17	99	114	105	101	160
26	71	66	60	64	160
18	134	126	119	126	160
19C	59	61	60	49	320
19A	39	36	29	33	320
19B	34	21	27	32	320
Totals	835	747	722	720	

whereas in one of the series with (low-valence) cardboard rectangles the pause was followed by a revival. It is further perhaps significant that the figures of Experiment 17 obtained with high-valence objects (mainly egg

TABLE 29

Positive scores in seven series of successive latin squares with the same sets of models. A double vertical line indicates an interval of 8–10 days; all other repeats were run without interruption.

Experiment	I	II	III	IV	N presentations	Models Used
8	255	177 ||	122		2304	angles diff. colours
9	174	147	103		1200	angles diff. colours
11	175 ||	116			640	shell, rings, angle
15	61	54			320	angles diff. colours
17	134	126	119	126	640	shells and ring
19A	46	25 ||	45	34	640	cardboard rectangles
19B	53	31 ||	33		480	cardboard rectangles

shells) hardly drop at all after the first test, and show no significant fluctuation through the next three repeats.

Judging from these admittedly inadequate figures, repeated presentation of the same model must be supposed to cause some waning. This effect may have been relatively slight in Beer's work because he left the models

---

[4] This concerns an experiment not mentioned in the text.

at the nests for 6 hours—much longer than in our tests, which varied from 30 minutes to 4 hours—and because his standard model had a relatively high valence.

A second set of relevant data is given in Table 30.

On various occasions the same model was given at different times of the season to different groups of new birds, and the scores therefore reflect their valence at different times without interference by waning. Because the duration of exposure to the models varied from one experiment to another comparison is possible only between tests of the same exposure time, that is, between figures in the same horizontal row. Further, the tests are arranged according to calendar date. While the colony as a whole is relatively well synchronised (most birds laying their first egg between April 12 and early May, with a peak in the last week of April—Beer, 1960), late birds do come in, and birds which have lost their first clutch do relay; this blurs the colony's calendar; yet on the average an arrangement of experiments according to calendar dates roughly reflects a classification according to age of eggs. In each horizontal row of Table 30 the highest score is marked 1 and the next lower score is marked 2; it will be seen that while in two rows 1 precedes 2 in time, in the two others 2 precedes 1. Whatever differences in responsiveness there are between the different groups of birds within one horizontal series, they do not seem to be correlated with age of eggs; this, as far as it goes, is in accordance with Beer's findings.

It seems most likely therefore that the readiness to remove egg shells remains roughly constant through the incubation period, with perhaps a slight tendency to increase with time, which in Beer's figures might just have been offset by whatever slight waning may have occurred. Another possibility is that waning occurs only in the first few repeats, after which the response stays at a slightly lower but further constant level. If this were so, Beer's figures would mean that the build-up before egg laying is slightly steeper than apparent, and that the lack of increase in his figures after egg laying is real.

VI. THE LACK OF PROMPTNESS OF THE RESPONSE

The predator tests reported in Section III demonstrated the intense pressure exerted at least by Carrion Crows and Herring Gulls against leaving the egg shell near the nest. Admittedly our observations refer to only one colony (which however contains a sizeable part of the British breeding population), but Carrion Crows are practically omnipresent and are notorious egg robbers. One should therefore expect that the Black-headed Gull would have developed a very prompt response and would remove the shell immediately after the chick has hatched. Yet, as we have

TABLE 30

Four series of scores obtained with the same models with different groups of birds at different times.

Models	28 IV/2 V	5 V	2-7 V	6 V	7-10 V	10-11 V	11-13 V	14-17 V	17-18 V	19 V	21-23 V
Khaki angles 30 mins.		1 61% N = 80		2 46% N = 80						2 46% N = 80	
White angles 120 mins.						1 45% N = 160		2 35% N = 240			29% N = 120
White angles 240 mins.							2 41% N = 80		1 57% N = 160		
Cardboard rectangles 240 mins.	2 48% N = 96		2 48% N = 160		1 54% N = 160						

116

seen, this is not usual. We cannot believe that the species has not been able to achieve promptness—egg shell removal is so widespread taxonomically that it must be an old response. The most likely reason is that there is a counteracting selection pressure—that too prompt removal is in some way penalised. At first we thought that the risk of carrying the chick with the shell before it had hatched completely might be responsible, but this risk is the same for gulls and other species. Yet we have observations (admittedly few in number) which show that Oystercatchers and Ringed Plovers carry the shell with far less delay—in spite of the fact that their chicks stay in the nest for a mere couple of hours, and shell removal therefore must be less urgent. In the course of 1959 and 1960 the reason for the delay became gradually clear: in both years there were a number of Black-headed Gulls in the colony which preyed selectively on nearly hatched eggs and on wet chicks. Although we are certain that not all gulls engage in this "cannibalism," this type of predation is very common, particularly towards the end of the season. In fact many of our efforts to observe the development of the behaviour during the first few hours of a chick's life (which were usually done late in the season) were time and again frustrated by the wet chicks being snatched away by such robber gulls immediately after hatching. We have not made systematic notes on this, but twenty is a conservative estimate of the number of occasions on which we actually observed such chicks being taken in front of the hide, while dry chicks only hours older (equally or even more available) were left alone. The number of occasions on which we lost wet chicks without actually seeing it happen is much higher still. On only three occasions did we observe a Black-headed Gull trying to swallow a dry chick. While a wet chick is usually swallowed in a few seconds (often even in flight) dry chicks of less than a day old took approximately 10 minutes to swallow. There can be no doubt that chicks are practically safe from predation by neighbours (though not from Herring Gulls) as soon as their plumage becomes dry and fluffy.

It is interesting to see the behaviour of parent gulls sitting on hatching chicks while there are robber gulls about. The parents are aware of the latters' intentions; they show signs of increased hostility whenever the robber comes near, and they are extremely loath to leave the nest. As soon as the gulls are disturbed by other predators or fly up for human visitors robbers snatch up the wet chicks in a fraction of a second. We had the impression that the robber gulls kept an eye on many nests and knew where chicks were hatching. On one occasion we saw a still wet chick being taken during the few seconds when the parent carried away the shell.

We feel justified therefore to ascribe the lack of promptness of the response to this tendency of some members of the colony to prey on wet chicks.

DISCUSSION

Removal of an egg shell lasts a few seconds. It is normally done three times in a year. Nothing would seem to be more trivial than this response, which at first glance might seem to be no more than fussy "tidying-up" by a "house proud" bird. Yet we have seen that it has considerable survival value, and that the behavioural organisation is complicated, and well adapted to the needs. In addition, our study has given us some insight in some more general problems of an ecological and evolutionary nature. The following discussion owes much to the stimulating studies of E. Cullen (1956) and J. M. Cullen (1960).

Territory

In 1956, N. Tinbergen listed the alleged functions of territory in gulls as follows. One component, site attachment, assists in pair formation, in homing to the nest site, and in providing known shelter for the chicks. Inter-pair hostility, the other aspect of territoriality, prevents interference with pair formation, and, by forcing breeding pairs and thus nests apart, renders mass slaughter by predators less likely (see also Tinbergen, 1952b). We believe that the facts mentioned in this paper show a hitherto unrecognised function of territorial hostility in the Black-headed Gull: reducing the likelihood of predation by neighbouring gulls. We distinguish this effect from the effect of spacing-out on inter-specific predation for the following reason. Tinbergen (1960) has shown that some predatory birds can be guided for shorter or longer periods, by a "searching image": they can, through an unknown process, concentrate their attention on one particular type of prey while being less responsive to other types. The stability of this state of narrowed responsiveness seems to be controlled in part by the density of the prey species: a series of successes in a short time seems to strengthen or at least to maintain specialisation, but lack of success tends to widen their responsiveness again. This property of predators, which may well be wide-spread, puts a premium on spacing-out of potential prey animals, because it increases searching time between successes. In this connection it is distance which counts.

We suggest that predation by neighbouring Black-headed Gulls is reduced by another aspect of territoriality. Each gull learns, during the prolonged period of territorial fighting in the early part of the season, not to intrude into the territories of its neighbours. The factor which reduces predation in this case is the existence of barriers, irrespective of distances between the broods (density).

Of course the inhibition of trespassing as a consequence of acquired knowledge of the boundaries does not totally prevent predation, but the fact that gulls do not trespass except very briefly and on rare moments (such as during a general alarm caused by another predator, e.g., Man or Fox which require adult gulls to leave the ground) obviously reduces the amount of intra-species predation considerably.

The Compromise Character of Colony Density

As we have seen, the mass attack by Black-headed Gulls discourages at least one predator, the Carrion Crow, from penetrating into the colony. This demonstrates the advantage of colonial nesting—Crows were not deterred by attacks of one, two, or even three Black-headed Gulls. On the other hand, spacing-out of breeding pairs within the colony and the establishment of knowledge of boundaries, both achieved by territorial hostility, have also distinct advantages. Thus the density of a Black-headed Gull colony has the character of a compromise between at least these two opposing demands. As E. Cullen (1957) and J. M. Cullen (1960) have shown, a study of the anti-predator devices of other species might help in elucidating the adaptedness of inter-specific differences in colony density.

Synchronisation of the Breeding Calendar

Some of our data strengthen the conclusion that predator pressure may be an ultimate factor in the synchronisation of breeding. Beer's data (1960) show that the scatter in time of the appearance of fledged young on the beach does not differ strikingly from the scatter of egg laying. Yet there are every season a large number of late broods, partly those of birds arriving later than the main body, partly repeat clutches of birds who have lost their first clutch. Our observations show that at least intra-specific predation of wet chicks is particularly severe towards the end of the season, and it is striking how many of the late broods disappear. It is clear that most of the successful broods come from pairs which arrive early and which have not been forced to relay; failure to synchronize is heavily penalised.

The Anti-Predator System as a Whole

At this stage of our studies it seems worthwhile to review what is now known of the ways in which the Black-headed Gull protects itself against predators. Some of these devices protect the individual—for brevity's sake we will call these "egoistic" devices, even though they may at the same time protect others. Others protect the brood, often at the cost of danger to the individual, and such devices we will call "altruistic." Naturally these terms refer to the function, not to motivation.

The most obvious, and seemingly trivial response is escape. Even this however takes different forms, dependent on the nature of the predator and on the age of the bird. A gull can simply fly away, as it does at the approach of a human being. The response to a Peregrine Falcon, which we have observed in detail several times, is different: the gulls fly up, form dense flocks and fly at great speed low over the ground or the water, executing quick zigzag manoeuvres. We believe that "erratic flights," in which individuals gulls separate themselves from the flock and fly away, often downwards, at great speed and with very quick and sharp turns, are likely to be elicited by a Peregrine approaching gulls that are flying high. Chicks, in response to the alarmed behaviour of the adults in a colony, crouch, at first on the spot, but already after one day and occasionally even earlier they walk a little distance away from the nest and towards the surrounding vegetation. Each chick becomes soon conditioned to one or more individual hiding places; this conditioning allows them to reach safety more quickly than they would if they had to search for suitable cover.

Outside the breeding season Black-headed Gulls select wide open spaces: marshy meadows, open seashores, or water. This no doubt allows them to see an approaching predator in time.

In flocks of adult birds there operates at least one signaling system: the alarm call alerts other individuals.

The "altruistic" habitat selection in the breeding season shows signs of anti-predator adaptedness: in the open sand dunes gulls avoid nesting on the bare sand, even though males may start by taking up a pairing territory there. Once paired, however, they select a nest site in moderately dense vegetation. Black-headed Gulls breeding on inland lakes usually select islands; either large ones which accommodate large numbers, or smaller islands such as individual *Molinia* bushes which offer space for one nest only. Where Black-headed Gulls nest on tidal saltings, this inclination to select islands can be the undoing of their broods in high spring tides (Tinbergen, 1952a).

Several other behaviour patterns appear in the breeding season which, while endangering or at least not protecting the lives of the parents, do contribute to the safety of the brood. First, the scattering of the broods, which provides a certain degree of protection both from inter- and from intra-specific predation, is effected by the balanced attack-escape system, with its components of actual attack, withdrawal, and agonistic displays (Tinbergen, 1959; Manley, 1960). Further, unlike camouflaged species such as ducks, curlews and several other waders, and pheasants, the incubating gull leaves the camouflaged brood at the first sign of danger. The camouflage of the eggs depends on a specialised pigmentation system in the upper reaches of the oviduct.

Parent gulls attack predators; the fierceness of the attack, and the degree to which it is counteracted by escape tendencies depends on the type of predator and the resultant seems highly adaptive. From the moment the first egg is laid, at least one parent stays on the territory and guards the brood. As we have seen, egg shell removal is also effective as an anti-predator device. There can finally be little doubt that the chick's plumage protects its bearer by being camouflaged.

Thus the picture that emerges is one of great complexity and beautiful adaptedness. It has further become clear that at least some of the different means of defence are not fully compatible with each other, and that the total system has the character of a compromise between various, in part directly conflicting demands. These conflicts are of different types. First, the safety requirements of the parents may differ from those of the brood. Thus the parent endangers itself by attacking predators. This is suggested by the fact that Foxes succeed in killing large numbers of adults in the colony. Though we have never seen a Fox killing an adult, their tracks in the sand cannot be misinterpreted. Often they kill many more birds than they eat. Some of these birds were "egg-bound" females (Manley, 1958), but in 1960, when we sexed 32 gulls killed by Foxes we found that 21 of these were males. Many of these gulls have their tails torn off and/or their legs broken. We believe that a Fox sometimes kills such birds by jumping at them when they "swoop." All this suggests that a certain balance between the tendency to attack a Fox and the tendency to flee from it is selected for.

The conflict between "egoistic" and "altruistic" behaviour is also very obvious in the time when the winter preference for wide, open spaces changes into the preference for the breeding habitat which, as we have just seen, is dangerous to the adults. The switch towards the breeding habitat selection is not sudden; there is a long period in which the birds show that they are afraid of it; even when, after long hesitation, they settle in the colony, there are frequent "dreads" when the birds suddenly fly off in panic; these dreads gradually subside (see also Tinbergen, 1953 and Cullen, 1956). Towards the end of the breeding season the adults begin to desert the colony in the evening to roost on the beach, leaving the chicks at the mercy of nocturnal predators.

Second, there are conflicts between two "altruistic" modes of defence, each of which has its advantages. Crowding, advantageous because it allows social attacks which are effective against Crows, has to compromise with spacing-out which also benefits the broods.

Finally there may be conflicts between the optimal ways of dealing with different predators. Herring Gulls and Crows might be prevented entirely from taking eggs and chicks if the gulls stayed on the nests, but this would expose them to the Foxes. While Herring Gulls and Crows exert pressure towards quick egg shell removal, neighbouring gulls exert an opposite pressure; the timing of the response is a compromise.

We cannot claim to have done more than demonstrate that egg shell disposal is a component of a larger system, nor are we forgetting that much in our functional interpretation requires further confirmation. It seems likely however that a more detailed study of all the elements of anti-predator systems of this and other species, and of the ways they are functionally interrelated, would throw light on the manifold ways in which natural selection has contributed towards inter-specific diversity.

VIII. SUMMARY

The Black-headed Gull removes the empty egg shell shortly after the chick has hatched. The present paper describes some experiments on the function of this response, and on the stimuli eliciting it. Carrion Crows and Herring Gulls find white eggs more readily than normal gulls' eggs; it is concluded that the natural colours of the eggs afford a certain degree of cryptic protection. When normal eggs are given an egg shell at 15 cm. distance their vulnerability is greatly increased; this "betrayal effect" decreases rapidly with increased distance between egg and shell. We therefore conclude that egg shell removal helps to protect the brood from predators.

As reported by Beer (1960) the Black-headed Gull removes a surprisingly wide range of objects from the nest. Large scale tests with egg shell dummies in which colour, shape, size, and distance from the nest were varied showed that objects of all colours are carried but that "khaki" (the normal ground colour of the egg) and white are particularly stimulating, while green elicits very few responses. Egg shells elicit more responses than cylindrical rings of the same colour, and these are responded to better than "angles." Size can be varied within wide limits; very large rings elicit fear which interferes with removal. Various other indications are mentioned which show that the score as obtained in the mass tests does not accurately reflect the responsiveness of the reaction itself but rather the result of its interaction with other behaviour tendencies. The eliciting effect decreases rapidly with increasing distance.

On the whole, the gulls' response is very well adapted to its main function of selectively removing the empty shell, but the relatively high scores for objects which have very little resemblance to egg shells suggest that it is adapted to the removal of any object which might make the brood more conspicuous.

A pilot test showed that gulls which have incubated black eggs respond better to black egg shell dummies than normal gulls.

The lack of promptness of the response as compared with non-colonial waders (Ringed Plover and Oystercatcher) is adaptive, since it tends to reduce predation by other Black-headed Gulls, which are shown to prey selectively on wet chicks. A hitherto unrecognised function of territory is suggested.

In a discussion of the entire anti-predator system of the Black-headed Gull its complexity and its compromise character are stressed: the safety demands of the individual clash with those of the brood; there are conflicts between the several safety devices which each benefit the brood; and there are clashes between the ideal safety measures required by each type of predator.

REFERENCES

BAERENDS, G. P. The ethological concept 'Releasing Mechanism' illustrated by a study of the stimuli eliciting egg-retrieving in the Herring Gull. *Anatom. Rec.*, 1957, *128*, 518–519.

BAERENDS, G. P. The ethological analysis of incubation behaviour. *Ibis*, 1959, *101*, 357–368.

BEER, C. Incubation and nest-building by the Black-headed Gull. D. Phil. Thesis, Oxford, 1960.

CULLEN, E. Adaptations in the Kittiwake to cliff-nesting. *Ibis*, 1957, *99*, 275–302.

CULLEN, J. M. A study of the behaviour of the Arctic Tern, *Sterna paradisea*. D. Phil. Thesis, Oxford, 1956.

CULLEN, J. M. Some adaptations in the nesting behaviour of terns. 1960, *Proc. 12th inter. Ornithol. Congr. Helsinki, 1958.*

HINDE, R. A. Factors governing the changes in strength of a partially inborn response, as shown by the mobbing behaviour of the Chaffinch (*Fringilla coelebs*). II. The waning of the response. *Proc. Royal Soc.*, B., 1954, *142*, 331–358.

MAGNUS, D. Experimentelle Untersuchungen zur Bionomie und Ethologie des Kaisermantels, *Argynnis paphia* L. (Lep. Nymph.). I. *Zs. Tierspsychol.*, 1958, *15*, 397–426.

MAKKINK, G. F. An attempt at an ethogram of the European Avocet (*Recurvirostra avosetta* L.) with ethological and psychological remarks. *Ardea*, 1936, *25*, 1–62.

MANLEY, G. H. Unconscious Black-headed Gulls. *Bird Study*, 1957, *4*, 171–172.

MANLEY, G. H. The agonistic behaviour of the Black-headed Gull. D. Phil. Thesis, Oxford, 1960.

NETHERSOLE-THOMPSON, C., and NETHERSOLE-THOMPSON, D. Egg-shell disposal by birds. *British Birds*, 1942, *35*, 162–169, 190–200, 214–223, 241–250.

SCHWARTZKOPF, J. Physiologie der höheren Sinne bei Säugern und Vögeln. *J. Ornithol.*, 1960, *101*, 61–92.

SIEGEL, S. *Non-parametric statistics for the behavioral sciences*. New York: McGraw-Hill, 1956.

TINBERGEN, L. The natural control of insects in pine woods. I. Factors influencing the intensity of predation by songbirds. *Arch. néerl. Zool.*, 1960, *13*, 265–336.

TINBERGEN, N. *The study of instinct*. Oxford: Clarendon Press, 1951.

TINBERGEN, N. When instinct fails. *Country Life*, Feb. 15, 1952, 412–414. (a)

TINBERGEN, N. On the significance of territory in the Herring Gull. *Ibis*, 1952, *94*, 158–159. (b)

TINBERGEN, N. *The Herring Gull's World*. New York: Collins, 1953.

TINBERGEN, N. On the functions of territory in gulls. *Ibis*, 1956, *98*, 408–411.

TINBERGEN, N. Comparative studies of the behaviour of gulls (Laridae); a progress report. *Behaviour*, 1959, *15*, 1–70.

VILLABOLOS, C., and VILLABOLOS, J. *Colour Atlas*. Buenos Aires, 1947.

WEIDMANN, U. Observations and experiments on egg-laying in the Black-headed Gull (*Larus ridibundus* L.). *Brit. J. Anim. Behav.*, 1956, *4*, 150–162.

YTREBERG, N. J. Contribution to the breeding biology of the Black-headed Gull (*Laris ridibundus* L.) in Norway. *Nytt Mag. Zoologi*, 1956, *4*, 5–106.

SUGGESTED READINGS

JENNINGS, H. S. *Behavior of the lower organisms*. New York: Columbia University Press, 1906. (Reprinted by Indiana University Press, Bloomington, 1962.)

SHERRINGTON, C. S. *The integrative action of the nervous system*. New Haven, Conn.: Yale University Press, 1906. (Reprinted, 1961.)

THORPE, W. H. *Learning and instinct in animals*. (2nd ed.) London: Methuen, 1963.

TINBERGEN, N. *The study of instinct*. London: Oxford University Press, 1951.

Chapter III

RESPONDENT CONDITIONING

The selections of this chapter all concern the respondent conditioning or conditioned reflex type of experiments first introduced by I. P. Pavlov. In the first selection Pavlov himself gives a description of the area of research which was responsible for his subsequent influence on experimental psychology and physiology. The paper reproduced here is a relatively early one. It was first published in 1904 before Pavlov had developed the special terminology which is still largely in use today.

The next selection, by E. S. Airapetyantz and K. M. Bykov, describes some of the research conducted by a subsequent generation of Russian investigators. Bykov, a pupil of Pavlov, for many years directed an extensive research program concerned with the ways in which conditioning is involved in the functioning of the internal physiology of the organism (Bykov, 1957).

The experiment reported by J. M. Notterman, W. N. Schoenfeld, and P. J. Bersh was part of a research program investigating the conditioning of cardiac changes in human subjects. The experiment is a demonstration of the partial reinforcement effect in the case of respondent conditioning. It shows that intermittent reinforcement produces an increased resistance to extinction, a finding which is now generally well established for a wide range of responses, respondent as well as operant.

In the United States the experimental investigation of respondent conditioning has been a relatively neglected area. There are signs, however, of a revival of interest (Prokasy, 1965).

REFERENCES

BYKOV, K. M. *The cerebral cortex and the internal organs.* (Translated and edited by W. H. Gantt.) New York: Chemical Publishing, 1957.
PROKASY, W. F. *Classical conditioning: A symposium.* New York: Appleton-Century-Crofts, 1965.

4

The Psychical Secretion of the Salivary Glands (Complex Nervous Phenomena in the Work of the Salivary Glands)

Ivan Petrovitch Pavlov

Recently the physiology of the salivary glands has brought into the limelight special phenomena of their activity, usually called psychical.

The latest investigations of the work of the salivary glands by Glinsky (1895), Wolfson (1898), Henri and Malloizel (1902), and Borisov (1903) have demonstrated the beautiful adaptation of these glands to external stimulations, as had already been foreseen by Claude Bernard. Under the influence of hard, dry food introduced into the mouth, the salivary glands secrete a large quantity of saliva, and this makes possible the manifestation of the chemical properties of the food when in solution, and helps in its mechanical preparation, thus favouring its passage along the oesophagus into the stomach. On the other hand, the saliva is produced in much smaller quantity when the food contains much free water, and the more water, the less saliva. With milk, it is true, a great amount of saliva is secreted, but it must be taken into consideration that the addition of mucous saliva to milk prevents the formation of large curds in the stomach owing to strands of mucus; the saliva in this way aids the digestive effect of gastric juice on the milk. With water or with a physiological saline solution (i.e., 0.9 percent of table salt), there is no trace of saliva secreted; for with them saliva would be useless. To all strong chemical excitants introduced into the mouth, saliva is secreted in an amount strictly conditioned by the stimulating strength of these substances. In such a case saliva makes these substances more dilute, and rinses and cleanses the mouth. With food substances the mucous salivary glands secrete a saliva rich in mucus. With inedible, or chemical substances, there flows, on the

Adapted from *Lectures on Conditioned Reflexes,* Vol. I, Chap. II, 1928, pp. 61–75. By permission of International Publishers Co., Inc.

contrary, a thin, watery saliva, containing little or no mucin. In the first instance the saliva serves as a lubricant for the passage of food into the stomach and to effect certain changes in it; in the second case, only as a cleansing agent. Pure sea- or river-sand introduced into the mouth calls forth a secretion of saliva; for it can be removed only by a flow of fluid. Clean quartz pebbles are simply ejected from the mouth without any salivary secretion; for their removal liquid is unnecessary and useless.

In all the foregoing cases special reflexes are involved which, thanks to the specific irritability of the peripheral endings of the centripetal nerves of the mouth (through various mechanical and chemical stimuli), condition the difference in the activity of the glands in their response to these stimuli.

The same relations are observed between the above mentioned stimuli and the activity of the salivary glands when these stimuli are not in contact with the mouth, but are at some distance from the dog. They need only attract the attention of the animal.

Now arose a question of great importance: how may these latter relations be investigated? Having tried several methods, we decided to persist in studying them objectively. This means that the experimenter, completely ignoring the imaginary and subjective state of the animal, must concentrate all his attention on those exact external conditions which might have an influence on the activity of the salivary glands.

The starting point for this investigation was the idea that the so-called psychical salivary secretion is fundamentally a specific reflex just like the secretion originating from stimuli in the oral cavity, but with this difference only, that the psychical reflex originates from stimuli acting on the other receptor surfaces, and that it is a temporary and conditioned reflex.[1] Thus the purpose of further investigations consisted in the study of the conditions under which these specific reflexes appear. The first experiments of this sort in our laboratory were performed by Dr. Tolochinov (1902).

His experiments showed convincingly, I think, that our subject can actually be investigated along these lines with great success. The following constant relations were established. The aforementioned reflexes with food substances as well as with those the dog refused, which excited the salivary glands from a distance, entirely disappear if the experiment is repeated several times at short intervals. But their effect can be easily restored under the following conditions. If for example meat powder is held in front of the dog without feeding it, and if this is repeated a number of times at short intervals, then the action of this stimulus from a distance gradually diminishes and finally vanishes entirely. But it is only necessary to give some of this powder to the dog to eat in order to restore its action from a

---

[1] Here the conditioned reflex is first spoken of as a temporary connection (Translator).

distance. The same result may be obtained if, instead of feeding the dog with the meat powder, some acid is put into his mouth.

When the acid after some repetitions has lost its ability to call forth saliva when presented from a distance, then it is possible to restore the reflex from a distance by another method analogous to the aforementioned one (putting acid into the mouth or feeding with the meat powder); and this is by showing the dog meat which is moistened with acid. It should be mentioned that meat alone, as it is a watery food, produces only a weak salivary secretion, and often none at all from the parotid gland.

In the case of the food substances, their effect from a distance is markedly influenced by the state of hunger of the animal. When the animal is satiated the reaction is much less than it is in hunger, and on repetition of the stimulation by the food substances at a distance the reaction disappears much more quickly. The individual properties of a substance acting separately from a distance have a much weaker effect when one of these properties acts alone than when the substance with all of its properties and attributes acts; for example, a sniff alone of the meat powder produces less salivary secretion than if the meat powder stimulates not only the nose but also the eyes of the animal. One sees the same thing when the experiment on the distant action of the substance is repeated—the effect of the isolated action of the individual properties disappears more quickly than that of the object with all its attributes.

The conditioned reflex (reflex from a distance) can by certain means be quickly destroyed. If immediately after the production of a strong salivary secretion (by using dry bread at a distance), the dog is shown raw meat, then the secretion is instantaneously arrested. If a hungry dog is shown dry bread, and at the same time a neighbouring dog is given the bread to eat, the salivary secretion which had already begun in the first dog may suddenly stop. A dog which has never been used for such an experiment will give a reaction to the bread when the dog is on the floor, but it is only necessary to remove the animal to the stand on the table and the reaction ceases. The same phenomenon can be reproduced by every substance which acts from a distance.

If acid which is coloured black with India ink is put into the dog's mouth several times, then only showing the dog water similarly coloured produces exactly the same effect. Now this connection between the coloured liquid and the secretion of saliva we can cause to disappear by putting repeatedly into the dog's mouth coloured (black) water, and then, we are able to restore it again by the introduction of coloured acid.

If some odour having no exciting local action on the nasal mucous membrane and issuing from a substance which the dog has never before met, acts on the dog, then this odour is entirely without effect on the salivary glands. But once this substance has been put into the dog's mouth and has produced a flow of saliva, its odour alone will suffice to evoke the secretion.

In the preceding chapter,[2] I endeavoured to draw general conclusions of a scientific nature from all the investigations which had been published concerning the new type of reflexes in the work of the salivary glands, systematising our facts from a purely physiological point of view.

From this point of view, to understand thoroughly the basis of the new aspects of physiological investigation of the activity of the salivary glands, it is necessary to distinguish in the objects of the external world acting on the living organism, two series of properties: the essential properties, which determine absolutely a certain reaction in that or another organ; and the unessential properties, which act only temporarily and conditionally. Take, for instance, a solution of acid. Its action, as that of a definite chemical agent on the mouth cavity, is expressed among other things always by the flow of saliva, which, in neutralising, diluting, and removing the acid, is of prime importance for the welfare of the organism. The other properties of this solution, its appearance, colour, and odour, have no intrinsic relation to the saliva, or, vice versa, the saliva to them. But it is impossible not to be struck with a fact of great importance for the living organism—that the unessential properties of a substance become stimuli of a given organ (in our case of the salivary glands) only when the action of these properties on the sensory receptor surfaces of the organism have coincided with the action of their essential properties. If, on the contrary, the unessential properties act repeatedly alone (without interference of the essential), and if this continues for a long time or always, then they either lose their importance for the given organ, or never attain such importance. The physiological mechanism of this relation can be explained in the following way: suppose that the action in the oral cavity of those properties of the object essential for salivary secretion, i.e., the stimulation of the lower lying salivary centre, coincides with the action of the unessential properties of the object on other receptor surfaces, or coincides with the influence of many phenomena of the external world (stimulation of the eye, nose, etc.); in this event the stimulation of the corresponding centre of the higher parts of the brain will have to choose between countless and different paths which are open to them, or, such of them as lead to the active reflex salivary centre. One is compelled to suppose that this latter centre, being in a state of high excitation, in some way attracts to itself the stimulations from other less strongly excited centres. This may be the general mechanism of all our observed phenomena of psychical stimulation of the salivary glands.

The fact that the salivary reaction to the appearance of bread at a distance decreases in intensity at the sight of another dog's being fed could be explained by the transference of the stimulation to another centre, the motor centre, which, as we may conclude in this case from the extreme increase of the energy of the animal's movements, is strongly excited.

[2] I. P. Pavlov. Experimental Psychology and Psycho-Pathology in Animals. *Lectures on Conditioned Reflexes*, Vol. I, Chap. I (Ed.).

The influence of the state of hunger or satiety on the result of the action of food at a distance may be explained by the changes in the irritability of the salivary centre, which in turn depends upon the different chemical composition of the blood in these two states.

Considering these phenomena from this point of view, the physiologist is hardly inclined to designate them as "psychical"; but in order to distinguish them from the nervous phenomena which until the present time have been analysed physiologically, he may classify them as "complex nervous phenomena."

Reviewing the above facts and results, the reader may say that everything which has been described here as "complex nervous phenomena" is comprehensible from the subjective point of view, and that in the physiological description of these facts there is nothing new. In this assertion there is a grain of truth. But by our physiological scheme, we intend to provide a basis for the collection and exposition of additional facts along this new path of investigation.

In the preceding chapter, I expressed the hope that the enumerated facts might be further studied with complete success. This hope, thanks to the further investigations in my laboratory, has been fully realised.

Dr. Babkin has added much to our knowledge of the disappearance [3] and restoration of new reflexes. Here I give a typical experiment:

Stimulus: Sight of Meat Powder
Duration of Action: One Minute

Time	Quantity of Saliva (cc.)
2:04	0.4
2:49	0.3
2:52	0.2
2:55	0.1
2:58	0.05
3:01	0.05
3:04	0.0

This vanishing of the reflex as a result of repetition takes place with exact regularity only when the conditions remain absolutely the same, i.e., when the stimulation is produced by the same method, by the same person, and when this person makes the same movements and uses the same object (i.e., the same vessel and the same contents). Consequently, this identity of the conditions relates especially to everything which is connected in one way or another with the act of eating, or with the introduction into the dog's mouth of inedible substances. Fluctuations of other conditions, if they do not call out any additional reactions from the animal, have no significance.

[3] Prof. Pavlov purposely uses here an expression only describing the fact, without suggesting its explanation. This phenomenon was later called *extinction* of the conditioned reflex . . . (Translator).

The speed with which the reflex disappears, occurring as a result of repetition, is undoubtedly connected with the length of the interval which separates the consecutive stimulations. The shorter the interval, the more quickly the reflex disappears, and vice versa. Here is an example. The stimulation is again produced by showing the meat powder exactly once every minute. If the stimulation is given every 2 minutes, the reflex disappears after 15 minutes. If an interval of 4 minutes between repetitions of the showing of the meat powder is used, the reflex vanishes after 20 minutes; with an 8-minute interval the reflex disappears after 54 minutes; and with a 16-minute interval the reflex does not disappear even after 2 hours. Again with the stimulation given every 2 minutes, the reflex vanishes after 18 minutes.

Once the stimulation has disappeared spontaneously, unless special measures are applied it sometimes does not return in less than 2 hours.

Every change in the details of the conditioned stimulus immediately augments or restores the salivary reaction. If the dog is stimulated by holding meat powder in the hand and raising and lowering the hand constantly during the stimulation, it is only necessary to stop moving the hand in order that the salivary secretion, which, owing to the repetition of the stimulation had already considerably decreased or even entirely ceased, be markedly increased. If a given stimulus ceases to act on repetition, when performed by a certain person, it immediately becomes active again if it is done by someone else.

Reasoning from this fact, it may be foreseen that if a certain conditioned reflex has temporarily ceased to act, owing to repetition, this will not hinder the manifestation of another conditioned reflex. The following example illustrates this:

Duration of Action: One Minute

Time	Quantity of Saliva (cc.)
Stimulus: Sight of a Glass of Extract of Quassia	
1:10	0.8
1:13	0.3
1:16	0.15
1:19	0.0
1:22	0.05
1:25	0.0
Stimulus: Sight of Meat Powder	
1:28	0.7
1:31	0.3
1:34	0.1
1:37	0.05
1:40	0.0

As has been shown in the experiments of Dr. Tolochinov, a conditioned reflex which has disappeared due to repetition, may at any time be restored. If a conditioned reflex, for example, meat powder at a distance, has lost its effect owing to repetition, it is necessary only to use the unconditioned reflex on the same meat powder or on some other food, or indeed on any inedible substance, in order to restore the lost conditioned reflex, i.e., with meat powder at a distance. And even more. Other conditioned reflex stimuli whose effects have been lost by repetition, may restore the action of the lost reflex if the newly applied stimuli have considerable strength.

The restoring effect of these interposed reflexes (unconditioned as well as conditioned reflexes) is the greater and surer, the larger the salivary secretion provoked by them (i.e., by the interposed reflexes). Here is an experiment illustrative of this:

Stimulus: Sight of Meat Powder
Duration of Action: One Minute

Time	Quantity of Saliva (cc.)
11:34	0.7
11:37	0.4
11:40	0.2
11:43	0.05
11:46	0.0
Total	1.35

At 11:49 the stimulation of acid at a distance (conditioned reflex) acting for one minute produces 1.2 cc. of saliva. Then the experiment with meat powder is immediately continued:

Time	Quantity of Saliva (cc.)
11:52	0.1
11:55	0.0
Total	0.1

At 11:58 the acid is introduced into the mouth of the dog (unconditioned reflex), and produces 3.5 cc. of saliva. The experiment with meat powder is resumed as follows:

Time	Quantity of Saliva (cc.)
12:02	0.4
12:05	0.3
12:08	0.1
12:11	0.0
Total	0.8

At 12:14 a stronger solution of acid is put into the dog's mouth. It produces 8.0 cc. of saliva. The experiment with meat powder follows:

Time	Quantity of Saliva (cc.)
12:20	0.7
12:23	0.4
12:26	0.2
12:29	0.15
12:32	0.05
12:35	0.0
12:38	0.0
Total	1.5

The restoring effect of the interposed reflexes was strongest immediately after their application. The greater the interval between the interposed reflex and the first trial of the conditioned reflex, the weaker was the restoring effect.

The restoring effect of one and the same unconditioned reflex becomes smaller and smaller and finally disappears if it is often repeated. In this case the replacing of one unconditioned reflex by another unconditioned reflex will result in the new unconditioned reflex again restoring the conditioned reflex. In the following example this relation is seen: the dog is given meat powder to eat, and 4.0 cc. of saliva is obtained.

Stimulus: Sight of Meat Powder
Duration of Action: One Minute

Time	Quantity of Saliva (cc.)
11:48	0.8
11:51	0.7
11:54	0.5
11:57	0.3
12:00	0.2
12:03	0.1
12:06	0.0
12:09	0.0
Total	2.6

At 12:10 the dog is given meat powder, and 3.4 cc. is obtained, after which the experiment with the conditioned reflex is continued:

Time	Quantity of Saliva (cc.)
12:14	0.6
12:17	0.4
12:20	0.1
12:23	0.0
12:26	0.05
12:29	0.0
Total	1.15

At 12:30 the meat powder is again fed to the dog, and 3.6 cc. of saliva is obtained. The experiment continues:

Time	Quantity of Saliva (cc.)
12:34	0.3
12:37	0.2
12:40	0.0
12:43	0.0
Total	0.5

At 12:44 the dog is given meat powder, and 4.0 cc. of saliva is secreted: the experiment proceeds as follows:

Time	Quantity of Saliva (cc.)
12:48	0.0
12:51	0.0
Total	0.0

At 12:52, acid is put into the dog's mouth, and 4.9 cc. of saliva is secreted, and the experiment continues thus:

Time	Quantity of Saliva (cc.)
12:56	0.7
12:59	0.4
1:2	0.2
1:5	0.1
1:8	0.05
1:11	0.0
Total	1.45

But the procedure of using again and again a new unconditioned reflex as a means of restoring the conditioned reflex lost in consequence of repetition, has its limits; a moment comes when further changes of the unconditioned reflex fail to bring about a restoration of the vanished conditioned reflex.

The material given so far comprises only a part of that which has been investigated by Dr. Babkin (1904); we are indebted to him also for experiments demonstrating the rapid disappearance of conditioned reflexes. Previously the experiments of Tolochinov (1902) had brought out the fact that during some considerable motor stimulation of the dog, the conditioned reflex becomes weaker or disappears entirely. A general motor stimulation of the dog was produced in the experiments of Babkin (1904) either through strong irritation of the eye or of the ear (loud knocking on the door of the dog's experiment room, or an instantaneous flash of bright light into the previously darkened room), or by some entirely new and unusual irritation (playing of a gramophone). For example, one uses the conditioned reflex on meat powder. It displays its full strength. Now one tries on the dog the effect of the above described stimulations. Immediately after these stimulations, the conditioned reflex is without any effect. In the earlier tests as well as in the present, the conditioned reflex is purposely always accompanied by the unconditioned, i.e., after the exhibition of the meat powder, it is given to the dog to eat, in order not to weaken the conditioned reflex. In the second trial after these strong stimulations, there is during the conditioned irritation a certain salivary secretion which is still small, and only with further trials does it begin to grow and gradually reach its normal size.

In this category must be mentioned the following curious fact. In especially greedy dogs having a strong motor reaction at the sight of meat powder, there is often no flow of saliva from the parotid, whereas in less greedy and quieter ones, saliva flows. In the former animals, the secretion of saliva may start from the beginning of the stimulation with the meat powder, at its presentation, but afterwards, with the setting in and increase of the motor reaction, the salivary activity may cease.

The facts of this material are not detached and disconnected, but they form an introduction to the systematic study, the investigation and explanation of the new and complex phenomena which interest us. This new subject is very complicated, and its problems pile high one upon another; but such a complexity does not hinder an exact and ever deeper research. The experiments can be easily systematised. The laboratory results obtained by one worker have been readily confirmed by others on different dogs. It was evident that the way chosen for the study of the complex nervous phenomena was a fortunate one. At every turn one is convinced of the advantages of the objective way. The rapidity with which exact facts have been collected, and the ease of understanding them, presents a striking contrast to the uncertain and contestable facts of the subjective method. In order to make this difference clearer, let us take some examples.

In repeated stimulations by meat powder acting from a distance and not followed by feeding, there is soon a disappearance of the reflex. Why? Thinking subjectively, one would answer thus: the dog becomes convinced of the uselessness of its efforts to obtain the meat powder, and therefore ceases to give it attention. But let us consider the following experiment of Dr. Babkin (1904). When meat powder acting from a distance has lost its effect in consequence of repetitions, the dog is given water to drink. It drinks, but as mentioned above, saliva does not flow. From the subjective point of view, what could one expect regarding the vanished conditioned reflex on meat powder? It might seem that the dog, having received water from the experimenter, would have reason to think that the powder would follow, and that the dog would concentrate his attention on this hope. In reality, however, the reaction on the meat powder remains nil. But now bring the acid before the dog. The acid calls out a salivary secretion, and afterwards meat powder from a distance will again be effective. How can these facts be explained?

From the subjective standpoint it would indeed be difficult.

Showing the dog acid alone, could hardly awaken his hope of getting the meat. The objective observer is content to state the real and concrete relations existing between the phenomena he observes. Consequently, he notices without especial difficulty that everything which produces in more or less degree a salivary secretion, forms the essential condition for the restoration of the vanished reflex.

Yet another example. The conditioned reflex disappears owing to repetition, and is restored of itself only after a considerable lapse of time. Why? From the subjective point of view one can say that the dog has forgotten the deception, owing to the large number of stimulations impinging upon it during this time. One can, however, during this interim, subject the dog to many different influences and stimuli, and the time necessary for restoring the lost conditioned reflex will not be shortened. You need only to bring before the dog some stimulus which calls forth saliva, and the animal immediately forgets the deception.

In this way, the objective investigation of those biological phenomena of the animal commonly called psychical, becomes a direct continuation and widening of physiological experimentation on the living organism, and the facts thus gathered and systematised must be treated from the physiological standpoint exclusively, if they are to form the basis for our conception of the properties and relations between the different parts of the nervous system. And by varying and repeating our experiments in which one or another part of the nervous system is excluded—now the central, now the peripheral—this conception will correspond closer and closer to reality.

Concerning this last experimental method, I shall give an example. On the basis of the facts given above, it is necessary to admit that every conditioned reflex arises because of the presence of an unconditioned one. A conditioned reflex forms even though the conditioned stimulus and the unconditioned stimulus have coincided in their time of action only once, and it disappears if this coincidence does not occur for a long time. The justification of such a relation for old and firmly established conditioned reflexes is of great interest, and has been made a subject of investigation in my laboratory by Dr. Zelheim (1904). These experiments were performed by Dr. Snarsky (1902) before but they were not then sufficiently analysed. In Zelheim's experiments a series of conditioned and unconditioned reflexes to both food and non-food substances were formed, first in a normal dog. The lingual and glossopharyngeal nerves were then cut on both sides. When the animal had entirely recovered from the operation, all the elaborated reflexes were repeated. On the first trials there seemed to be no difference from the normal state; the salivary reaction had almost the same strength as formerly, on both the presentation of objects from a distance, and their introduction into the dog's mouth. With the repetition of these experiments, however, we noticed that the reflexes to certain substances, such as an extract of quassia and saccharine, as well as a dilute solution of hydrochloric acid and sodium chloride, became gradually weaker. As the unconditioned reflex is characterised by its constancy on repetition, we are forced to the conclusion that for certain stimuli, the unconditioned reflex disappeared, and that the effect which remained after the operation was dependent upon the conditioned reflex, the more so because now the secretory effect of both stimuli was almost equal, no matter whether they were applied from a distance or brought into the mouth of the dog. On the repetition of these experiments after two weeks, the reflex to bitter substances entirely disappeared in both forms (its action from a distance and in the mouth), but the reflex to saccharine, acid, and salt remained, though they were much weaker. It is plain that these last substances excited not only the special chemical fibres which were cut through, but other centripetal nerves responsible for the conduction of the remaining unconditioned reflexes.

Of great interest is the following question: what is the essential unconditioned stimulus of the food substances? The facts hitherto collected are not sufficient for the solution of this problem. In acute experiments by Dr. Heimann in my laboratory, it was shown that in animals which had been poisoned and immediately operated on, the chemical properties of the food substances, when they are brought into the mouth cavity, are entirely without effect on the salivary secretion. In these experiments, much more than in any other acute experiments, numerous defects were found in the acute experiment as an experimental method, and therefore the work of Dr. Heimann must be repeated and controlled. Dr. Zelheim (1904), in his above-mentioned experiments with permanent salivary fistulae, could not note any difference in the salivary secretion during the feeding of the animal before and after operation.

Now that I have explained this new material relating to the physiology of the salivary glands, it may not be superfluous if I revert to a most important point in the physiological significance of these phenomena. Surely these phenomena are much more complicated than we have described them here. But thanks to our new scheme, we are enabled to go forward in the exploration of our subject. This then is the meaning and justification of our plan.

The designation of "reflex" which we have given to these "complex nervous phenomena" is entirely logical. The phenomena are always the result of the stimulation of the peripheral endings of various centripetal nerves, and this stimulation spreads through the centrifugal nerves to the salivary glands.

These reflexes are, as are all natural reflexes, strictly specific (and therefore unlike the artificial reactions which are often produced in the laboratory by artificial stimulation), and they are the expression of a definite reaction of the organism, or of one or another of its organs, to a certain stimulus.

These new reflexes are the function of the highest structure of the nervous system of the animal, and they must be explained on the following basis. First, they represent the most complicated phenomena among nervous functions, and consequently they must be connected with the highest parts of the nervous system. Reasoning further from animal experiments with various poisonings or with total or partial extirpation of the cerebral hemispheres, we can conclude that the conditioned reflex demands for its formation the assistance of the hemispheres.

The reflexes are temporary and conditional, and these qualities characterise and separate them from the old simple reflexes with which physiology has concerned itself in the past. Their temporary character manifests itself in two ways: they can be formed when they did not previously exist, and they may disappear again forever; besides this, when they exist, they often fluctuate in degree even to vanishing, either for a short time, or under certain circumstances, permanently. As we have seen, their formation and extinction are determined by (one or several) coincidences in time of stimulation of the lower lying reflex centres, which govern some functioning organ, with the stimulation of different points of the cerebral hemispheres through the corresponding centripetal nerves. If the stimulation of these two centres coincides many times, then the paths leading from the higher to the lower centres become more and more passable, and the conduction of the excitations along them becomes easier and easier. When these coincidences occur more rarely, or cease altogether, the paths again become less permeable, and finally impassable.

What physiological explanation can be given for the rapid, and unfailing, though temporary, disappearance of a conditioned reflex, when it is repeated alone for several times at short intervals without the support of the unconditioned stimulus with which it was formed? Certain facts indicate, I think, that this event belongs to the category of exhaustion phenomena. First, the vanished conditioned reflex, if left alone without any stimulation from the experimenter, reappears after a certain time. Secondly, the disappearance of the conditioned reflex due to repetition occurs the more quickly, the smaller the interval between repetitions, and vice versa. Such an explanation would agree with the generally accepted opinion concerning the rapid exhaustion of the higher nervous centres brought about by repetition of monotonous stimulations.

The possibility of restoring a conditioned reflex, which has disappeared owing to repetition, and which is determined by the application of the corresponding unconditioned or other conditioned reflex of sufficient strength can be thus explained: that, in spite of a certain degree of exhaustion in the higher nervous centre, its stimulation again penetrates to the lower lying salivary centre, and from that very moment the paths leading to this centre become especially permeable owing to the recent and especially strong stimulation. In favour of this explanation we may cite the above-mentioned experiments on the restoration of the vanished conditioned reflex by means of repeated feedings, though these feedings finally, however, lose their effect.

At the end of that experiment we had a fact which revealed the mechanism of this process as a very complicated one. When the repetition of feeding had lost its efficacy as a means of restoring the reflex, the introduction of acid into the mouth of the dog to assist this restoration was accompanied by a positive effect. Therefore we must bring new elements into our scheme of explanation. If, however, these experiments are continued, there finally comes a moment, whether or not the unconditioned reflexes are varied, when neither of these stimuli is effective, and when the conditioned reflex is restored *per se* only at the cost of a great interval of time.

It is evident that for a full decision of the suggested problems, further investigations are required.

In conclusion, we must count it an incontestable fact that the physiology of the highest parts of the central nervous system of higher animals can not be successfully studied, unless one utterly renounces the indefinite presentations of psychology, and stands upon a purely objective ground. What interest, for example, can there be for physiological analysis in the statements of some authors, that after extirpation of certain parts of the cerebral hemispheres, the animals become now fiercer, now gentler, less intelligent, etc., when these terms themselves represent very complicated conceptions requiring an exact scientific analysis?

REFERENCES

BABKIN, B. P. A systematic investigation of the higher nervous (psychic) functions in the dog. Thesis, St. Petersburg, 1904.

BORISOV, P. *Russian Physician*. 1903, p. 869.

GLINSKY, D. L. *Annals of the Society of Russian Physicians*. St. Petersburg, 1895.

HENRI ET MALLOIZEL. *Comptes rendus de la Société de biologie*. Paris, 1902.

SNARSKY, A. T. Analysis of the normal conditions of functioning of the salivary glands in the dog. Dissertation, St. Petersburg, 1902.

TOLOCHINOV, I. E. Contribution à l'étude de la physiologie des glandes salivaires. *Comptes rendus du Congres des naturalistes et médecins du Nord à Helsingfors*. 1902.

WOLFSON, S. G. The function of the salivary glands. Dissertation, St. Petersburg, 1898.

ZELHEIM, A. P. The function of the salivary glands before and after the cutting of the glosso-pharyngeal and lingual nerves. Dissertation, St. Petersburg, 1904.

5

Physiological Experiments and the Psychology of the Subconscious

E. Airapetyantz and K. Bykov

In the second half of the nineteenth century, the tremendous upheaval in science brought about by Charles Darwin shed a new light on all fields of knowledge. The consistent materialistic picture of the law of evolution of the organic world had such general significance that Engels ranged this

Translated from the original Russian in *Pod Znamenen Marksizma,* 1943, nos. 4–5, 68–78, by Henry F. Mins, Jr. Special acknowledgment is due to the Russian Translation Project of the American Council of Learned Societies for cooperation in the translation of this article. The article is reprinted here as published in *Philosophy and Phenomenological Research,* 1945, V, No. 4, 577–593. With permission of the International Phenomenological Society.

discovery with Marx's discovery of the law of evolution of human history. But the reorganization of science in the spirit of Darwinism began late, and against great inertia and opposition; many representatives of science tried to hush up science and declared war on the evolutionary theory because of its crushing blow at idealism and metaphysics.

Even so swiftly developing an experimental science as physiology, in which just at that time a great number of genuinely scientific discoveries were being made, was still dominated by the static conception of functions. It was a long time after this that the historical, evolutionary principle was applied to the analysis of physiological research. The same is true in especial degree of psychology which stubbornly persisted in its unscientific, pre-Darwinian positions. More than any other science, psychology was in an idealistic impasse.

It is the historical merit of Russian science that the main line of its development was not in the direction of metaphysical speculation, but preeminently toward a real, materialistic knowledge of nature, and that it raised physiology, a science just being born, to the rôle of leader in the fight for a new, scientific psychology. This was the mission fulfilled by the great representatives of our nation's science, I. M. Sechenov and I. P. Pavlov.

Pavlov's theory of conditioned reflexes marked a turning point in both physiology and psychology. Pavlov, a thorough-going Darwinian, introduced the evolutionary principle into physiology at the same time that he directed his method and his principles of research at setting psychology on its feet and giving it a materialist scientific support.

It is well known that the central theme of the extensive researches on higher nervous activity in Pavlov's school was his general biological *principle of temporary connections,* known in its concrete expression as the principle of the formation and dynamics of the *conditioned reflex.* The object of study was the infinite and diverse nervous fund of the organism, along with the newly acquired mechanisms of reflex connections, arising in the cerebral cortex in the course of the life of the individual animal.

The method of conditioned connections enabled us to determine accurately the *cause* of the genesis of physiological behavioral acts, and to elucidate the *essence* of these new reflex connections. It was established that: (1) the reflex newly formed in the central nervous system is strictly dependent on the conditions in which the impulse coming from the milieu is synchronized with the innate unconditioned (alimentary or defensive, etc.) action of the organism; (2) any disturbance in the milieu coincident with the innate reaction inevitably becomes a conditioned stimulus. It remains a question only whether this conditioned connection is actually operative, or whether, by virtue of definite causes, it is still latent. The infinite number of optic, acoustic, olfactory, taste, cutaneous stimuli which previously had nothing in common with an innate activity (alimentary, for example) are transformed by the method of conditioned connections into special alimentary agents. Lapse of time, or the intentional omission of any given external agent, also proved to be conditioned stimuli.

It is of interest to us, in this connection, to take note that under identical circumstances even pain is no exception to the general rule of the formation of a conditioned reflex. The pain caused by the current from an induction coil, if repeatedly reinforced by eating, can serve as the signal for salivation and therefore of a readiness and disposition of the animal to take food.

Conditioned reflexes are easily formed too between the cerebral cortex and external stimuli by way of humoral paths (viz., through the blood stream). The injection of morphine under a dog's skin acts through the blood stream on the nerve centers, and consequently evokes strong salivation, vomiting, and finally sleep. V. A. Krylov showed that after several repetitions of the morphine injection separate elements of the injection procedure (the sight of the syringe, the experimental situation, etc.) became special agents evoking in the dog all the complex of symptoms, up to and including sleep, although the dog did not actually receive morphine.

The formation and development of a conditioned reflex are not connected only with the excitation process, but, as in any reflex act, it involves an inhibitory process. The *act* of inhibition is naturally and organically included in the concept of the conditioned reflex mechanism. In every case the process of inhibition appears as a coordinating agent in the work of the cerebral cortex. By means of inhibition, the conditional reflex plays the part of a delicate and precise analyzer of the environment, and becomes an initiatory factor in the analysis of the external and internal world of the animal. If an agent previously connected with food ceases to elicit a secretory reaction, then the signal loses its positive significance, or else the new condition must transform itself into a special signal which gives notice of the absence of food. In either case, secretion is biologically quite unjustified; thus there arises in the relevant parts of the cerebral cortex a new regulatory mechanism—a process of inhibition, restraining the excitation response.

On the basis of an enormous quantity of factual material, the school of Pavlov showed the existence of various forms of inhibition: extinguishing inhibition, conditioned inhibition, retarded and differential inhibition. In all these cases, the *absence* of reinforcement of the unconditioned reaction creates foci of inhibition in the cortex.[1] The cerebral cortex, which is concerned with the diverse conditions of positive or negative signals, is thus a complex dynamical mosaic of points of excitation and points of inhibition. These processes are constantly shifting within the cortical mass by irradia-

[1] Technical terms in the text are explained in Pavlov (1928).

tion and concentration, strengthening or weakening reactions of excitation and inhibition by reciprocal induction.[2]

By the method of conditioned connections, the school of Pavlov discovered surprising cases of delicate analysis by animals of the external environment. For example, the mechanism of discrimination of sound waves is so refined in dogs that a dog will react by salivation to a metronome set at 100 beats to the minute in the presence of alimentary reinforcement, and will not give a drop of saliva if the beat is 96 to the minute, if the latter stimulus has never been associated with food. Or another instance of the delicacy of the Pavlovian method: L. A. Andreev got a conditional reflex in dogs with tones so high that they are inaudible to the human ear. In response to an acoustic "something," beyond the limits of human perception of sound, the trained animal is aroused, pricks up its ears, expects food: the salivary glands give forth saliva; but to a sound several tones lower, not especially reinforced, the cerebral cortex of the dog responds by a definite inhibition.

Higher analysis in the cerebral cortex is carried on by means of a system of special analyzers, consisting of: (1) the peripheral receptor (perceptive) apparatus in immediate contact with the environment; (2) the nerve conducting the impulses from the receptor to the center; (3) the relevant cells of the brain, where these impulses arrive. The more complex the connections of the animal with the environment, that is, the higher the animal in its evolutionary development, the richer and more varied, and at the same time the more accurate and differentiated, will be the functions of analysis and synthetic perception of the elements of the surrounding world. The receptors, which receive stimuli, are thus the stage in the total analytic mechanism where the degree and the delicacy of the reaction signify the degree and delicacy of the information given the cortex about those events with which, in the given situation, the reaction of the animal is connected. However, the receptors are not merely complex physical apparatuses which register external changes of the environment, but strictly, in their receptor function, reflect both the state of the nervous system at the given moment and the history of the organism as a whole. For example, the structure of the eye in two animals, and the physical environment in which they live, may be identical, yet identical variations of the environment will serve as a signal for aggression to one animal, and call forth a defensive reaction in the other.

The cerebral cortex, which is continually informed of the events of the surrounding situation by means of the receptor apparatus, serves the entire

[2] Pavlov defines reciprocal induction as follows: "An excitation arising in a certain place causes an inhibitory process around this region and owing to this the spread of the original excitation becomes limited. On the other hand, the inhibitory process induces an excitatory process, and this in turn checks the spread of the inhibition. Thus the whole cortical area is partitioned off into excited and inhibited points" (Pavlov, 1928, p. 333. See also pp. 322–325 [Translator]).

organism as an organ of adaptation to the demands of the environment. But the cortex also has the power of altering the functional state of the receptor, and accordingly of altering the relation of the organism to the environment. In this case the cortex reflects a new state of development of the whole organism, and enters into contact with the surrounding world as an initiatory and independent *adaptor of the environment to the demands of the organism*. This process is radically historical. The qualitative preponderance of this aspect of cortical activity played an essential rôle in the history of animal evolution, and was one of the decisive factors in the struggle for existence.

A higher animal whose cortex has been removed loses all the experience which he has acquired and stored up during his individual life. He loses distant-receptor connection with the world and is condemned to die of hunger although adequate food may lie within five centimetres of him. The elimination or deterioration of the signal system transforms the animal into an invalid, who has permanently lost the ability to react actively to the external environment and to maintain his existence for any considerable time. The form of the animal's action and his activity in his interrelations with the environment vary quantitatively and qualitatively in the ascending phylogenetic line. The formation of the cortical layer, and the first beginnings of conditioned reflex connections with the environment constitute the first stage, during which the total adaptive mechanism of the nervous system serves to reflect not merely the conditions of the external environment, but also the mastery and cognition of the elements of the environment.

The experimental results relating to the physiology of the cerebral cortex, obtained by Pavlov's school, provide the physiological substratum of the varied psychic reactions of the animal.

Pavlov enunciated the principle that any variation of the external or internal environment of the animal which is associated with an unconditioned activity, may become a conditioned reflex, i.e., a means of knowing the environment and shaping behavior. This enables us to see the identity in principle of the salivary secretion and the activity of any other internal organ, with regard to the formation of temporary, conditioned reflexes. We were thus led to study the rôle of the cerebral cortex in the origin, the course, and the dynamics of the processes which take place in internal organs.

Dozens of studies carried out along these lines in our laboratories have not only shown the dependence of the conditioned reflex on cortical activity, but also their dependence on the functional rôle of the internal organ and of the organism as a whole. For it was found possible to trace the path of the connection formed between the internal organs and the external environment.

Some examples may be cited. If the introduction of water into the stomach or the rectum is accompanied by some unrelated stimulus, for instance a bell, then thereafter the isolated action of the bell—the conditioned signal—will, without the introduction of water, evoke increased salivation in the same quantities as when water was employed.

These initial experiments of ours were repeated and confirmed in similar experiments by other workers of the laboratory.

V. Balakshina established a conditioned connection of the cortex with the process of excretion of urine, even when all neural connections of the kidney were eliminated by previous denervation of one kidney, and when consequently only a humoral path of connection existed between the kidney and the brain. Under such conditions, the cerebral cortex carried out the analysis of the acoustic signals: inhibitory conditioned factors (not previously reinforced) restrained and diminished the secretion of urine, and conversely, positive factors (for example, a whistle) set the kidney mechanism in motion, calling forth increased diuresis. All these humoral connections with the cortex of the cerebral hemispheres were broken off abruptly upon elimination of the pituitary body. The kidney with intact innervation remained under the influence of the cortex and there was nothing abnormal: the other kidney, denervated yet recently in possession of a humoral connection with the brain, now, after elimination of the pituitary became a simple physical filter apparatus. This kidney had lost its contact with the brain, and therefore lost contact with the external environment: all conditioned reflexes were permanently lost to this kidney.

E. Ivanov introduced a solution of hydrochloric acid into the stomach by means of a sound,[3] and obtained an increased secretion of bile. After several repetitions the mere manipulation of the probe, without the introduction of the acid into the stomach, evoked heightened secretion of bile.

A. Rikkl showed the presence of a direct connection of the cerebral cortex with bile secretion. The introduction of bile substances directly into a dog's blood stream evoked a corresponding bile secretion by an unconditioned mechanism. Upon combining the injection with a sound stimulus, the latter, after several repetitions, became a conditioned stimulus. The conditioned stimulus acting alone now produced increased bile secretion. It was shown that the qualitative composition of the bile is quite uniform, whether it is called forth by direct stimulation by the chemical agent, or whether the whole mechanism is set in motion by the signal system of the cerebral cortex.

K. Bykov and Gorshkov established the influence of the cortex on the

[3] The term "fistula" is probably what is meant here (Ed.).

motor function of the spleen. Spleen introduced under the skin reacts, in every case, by a motion in response to a slight pain stimulus of the skin.[4] If a whistle is associated with this act, the whistle by a conditioned reflex will cause the spleen to contract.

R. Olnyanskaya connected muscular work with a sound stimulus, for instance, the beats of a metronome, and then by the mere sound of the metronome without actual performance of work, caused a change in the gas exchanges; heightening of oxidation processes in the muscle tissue and increased consumption of oxygen. Once experienced and arbitrarily connected, the reflex signal sufficed to speed up the complex neuro-muscular and neuro-humoral reactions, and to put the whole organism on a different level of activity.

The further course of our researches quite naturally brought up the following questions: Do internal organs possess sensitivity? What status do the impulses arising in internal organs have in the cerebral hemispheres? Is the principle of temporary connections applicable in the analysis of the interrelations between the receptive field of the internal organ and the higher portions of the brain? The answer to these questions should in the end explain the importance and the place of the very complex internal world of the animal in the animal's physiological, and perhaps its psychical, acts of behavior.

The solution of this problem requires an investigation of the origin of unexplained phenomena which lie at the root of certain aspects of the human psyche. Our discussion will be concerned with the physiologists' evaluation of their experimental facts (in particular those relating to the field of interoception) as mechanisms useful in the study of the psychology of the unconscious.

In considering this question, we cannot overlook the inspired utterances of great biologists, who, despite the impossibility of experimental verification, prophetically envisaged the nature of these mechanisms. Darwin, for example, wrote with amazing confidence of the significance which the processes taking place in the internal organs have for psychic behavior. In the alimentary apparatus, especially in the stomach, he said, "there are located intellect, consciousness, temperament and the senses." Even earlier, in 1826, the celebrated clinician Charles Bell, dissecting the muscular

[4] This experiment is more clearly described by Bykov (1957) as follows: "Stimulating splenic contraction through cortical action, by using the method of conditional reflexes, seemed to us possible.

"In 1930, M. A. Gorshkov and I established that a conditional stimulus whose action preceded that of a slight, painful stimulation (pricking the paw), after seven or eight combinations produced the contraction of the splenic musculature, which was similar to that caused by the pain stimulus. . . . We succeeded in showing this on a dog whose spleen had been surgically externalized and fixed under the skin while the normal blood supply and innervation of the organ had been fully preserved" (p. 90) (Ed.).

apparatus wrote: "A neural link exists between the brain and the muscles. . . ."

A special importance attaches to the statement of the author of *Reflexes of the Brain* (Sechenov) who, analyzing the complex psychical act, charged future physiologists with the explanation of subconscious stimulation. Sechenov says on this subject:

The phenomena of self-consciousness include those indefinite "obscure sensations" which accompany activities in the organs of the thoracic and abdominal cavities. Who does not know the feelings of hunger, of satisfaction, of distention of the stomach? An insignificant disturbance of the heart action entails an alteration of character; the nervousness and irritability of women is due, nine times out of ten, to an abnormal condition of the uterus. Facts of this sort, of which human pathology is full, point to an association of these "obscure sensations" with the sensations furnished by the sense organs. Unfortunately, these matters are extraordinarily difficult to elaborate, and a satisfactory solution of them belongs to the future. But that solution would be highly important, since the sensations in question are always present in man, are repeated perhaps more often than any others, and thus constitute one of the most powerful moving forces in psychical development.

From the appearance of the *Reflexes of the Brain* to the last decade, that is, over a period of seventy years, our knowledge in the field of the subconscious, or as Sechenov called them, "obscure sensations," has changed very little. Although we must recognize this "neglect" as a necessary historical stage, during which the Pavlovian interest aimed, by perfecting a research method, at probing psychic reactions, we are still backward in the objective discovery of the neuro-psychic elements of the milieu internal to the animal. This must be stressed all the more since psychology has not yet resolved the question of the unconscious by its own methods.

The theory of higher neural activity and the work of Sechenov and Pavlov furnished a complete basis for beginning research by the method of physiological experiments. It is upon this path we embarked. An immediate indication of the competence and the timeliness of investigation in this field, by an analysis of the interoceptor mechanisms, was given by L. A. Orbeli, an outstanding representative of the Pavlovian school. In the *Lectures on the Physiology of the Nervous System* he gives the following characterization of interoception in general and the state of our science on this question in particular.

It may be that, by analogy with other organs, e.g., with the upper parts of the alimentary canal, these parts of our body [other internal organs] send their fibers to the brain, and perhaps even have cortical representation. . . . Moreover, we know subjective states of indefinite character, which we refer to various parts of our body, for instance the abdominal cavity, the thoracic cavity, the region of the liver, the lungs.

He adds:

It is possible, that this is testimony which emanates from the interoceptive system—the sense system of our internal organs and the internal parts of our body. But it is not possible to say this with assurance.

During the last ten or eleven years the collaborators of the Leningrad University Laboratory (V. Balakshina, N. Vasilevskaya, O. Ivanova, A. Perelman, S. Pyshina) succeeded in accumulating factual material on the physiology of interoceptive conditioned reflexes, which fill the gap in our knowledge to some extent.

The research set-up was simple: Some stimulus acts only on their internal organ under conditions which completely exclude the possibility of simultaneous stimulation of the exteroceptors. Simultaneously another stimulus is applied which evokes some unconditioned reflex. It is clear that if the stimulus which acts on the internal organ calls forth a conditioned reflex, this shows, first, that interoceptors exist within the given internal organ, and second, that the impulses from the interoceptors can reach the brain, resulting in the formation of a temporary connection. Here is a typical experiment, where the indicator of the formation of the function is the classic object of the Pavlovian method—the salivary gland of the dog.

An animal, placed in the customary isolated chamber, is equipped with gastric and salivary fistulae. From another room the experimenter, by means of suitable apparatus, irrigates the mucous lining of the stomach with water. The introduction of the water into the stomach is reinforced by food—a meat-sugar powder—from a trough automatically supplied. The salivary secretion is registered on a salivary scale. The water continues to irrigate the interior of the stomach so long as the dog eats from the trough, and the irrigation ceases when there is no more food in the cups. By means of several such associations it was found that if we now set the water flowing and delay for twenty seconds the reinforcement by food, then in answer to this impulse the dog begins to lick its chops and turn its head in the direction of the trough, while saliva is copiously secreted from the salivary glands. What is this? A typical conditioned reflex. In other words, the impulses from the receptor surface of the stomach reach the cerebral cortex, combine with cortical representatives of the digestive center, and become a signal for putting into operation the mechanism of salivation.

Or here is a variant of the same experiment. The mucous lining of the stomach is stimulated by a stream of air, rather than water, and this stimulus is associated with a motor-defensive reflex: at the moment the air is injected into the stomach, a feeble electric current is transmitted to the dog's paw. The dog, of course, lifts his paw. After several such associations, the mere current of air, in entering the stomach, evokes a general uneasiness, whining, and quick withdrawal of the paw, although the electric current is in reality non-existent. Moreover, in response to a rhythmically interrupted current of air into the stomach, the paw of the dog responds by a corresponding rhythmic lifting. It is in place here to note the very characteristic general behavior of the animal, which recalls the behavior of a dog who is accustomed to blows and therefore assumes a defensive-humble posture at the menacing signal. As soon as the conditioned stimulus is removed, the dog shakes itself, wags its tail, and barks loudly. All this results, we repeat, from a signal which comes from an internal organ, with stimuli from the external environment rigorously excluded.

It proved to be possible to form positive conditioned connections of the stomach with the secretion of urine, with morphine poisoning, and in relation to certain pathological reactions. A brief description of these experiments can be given. The ureters of a dog are tapped from the outside. A controlled quantity of diuresis is ascertained over a definite period of time. If by means of a gastric fistula we introduce, say 200 cc. of water, a sharp increase of urine secretion is observed. After twenty to twenty-five such associations, water is admitted into the stomach only for a few seconds, and is immediately withdrawn. It is quite clear that during this period there has been no increase of the water content of the body, but yet the quantity of urine secretion increases sharply. Further, it is known from the work of Krylov, mentioned above, that after several injections of morphine, the mere sight of the syringe, or the prick of the needle in the skin, evokes the whole complex of symptoms which are associated with the introduction of these drugs into the organism.

Is it possible to set up a system of signals from the cortex and thus to activate such vital mechanisms (salivation, nausea, vomiting, gradual switching-off of the cortex, sharp interruption of motor coordination, finally sleep) by means of stimuli which act on the mucous lining of the stomach alone? Such an experiment was in fact set up. First we excluded the influence of exteroceptor stimuli connected with the injection of the morphine: painful tactile, optical (apparatus, sight of the syringe, of the experimenter, etc.). With this end in view, the dog in a chamber received pricks in various places from the same person, while a physiological solution was injected in place of morphine. At last, the animal did not react in any way to the repeated situation and the repeated manipulation plus injection. Now the air-current admitted into the stomach is associated with the injection of morphine. And this is the result: after four associations, unaccompanied by morphine,[5] it was possible to observe that when the current of air began there was uneasiness, licking of chops, copious salivation, frothing at the mouth, and in the successive stages of the experiment the same phenomena occurred, ending with vomiting and sleep.

[5] The term "accompanied" is probably what is intended here (Ed.).

The executive mechanism of the cerebral cortex which is set in action by impulses emanating from an internal organ proved to be efficacious in relation to certain pathological reactions as well. If we temporarily connect a stream of air entering the stomach with an intentionally-elicited complex neurotic state in the dog, later on the mere action of the stream of air in the stomach, in isolation, will elicit the whole complex of symptoms, completely recalling the similar neurotic state. In response to the very first release of air to the stomach cavity, the animal literally "breaks from its chains": a sharp and continuous yelping commences, with squatting on its hind legs, thereafter going over into a general agitation with copious salivation, with twitches of the whole body, and finally convulsions.

Let us confine ourselves for the moment to these experiments. We were quite right to call these conditioned reflexes *interoceptive,* for they were acquired by the organism as a result of reflex reactions occasioned by impulses arising from interoceptive fields. The basic theoretical problem, therefore, was solved. Like extero- and proprioceptors, receptors of internal organs stand in direct connection with the cerebral cortex, with that organ which gives structure to the physiological and biological behavior. In other words, the cortex is accurately and distinctly informed as to the states of the internal milieu of the animal.

It is extremely important in this connection to observe the orienting reactions which occur during the formation of interoceptive reflexes. The new stimulus, binding the cortex with the receptor of the internal organ, calls forth a characteristic exploratory reflex. The animal may be said to "search for" the new, as yet undefined signal, and these seekings are expressed either as a general uneasiness or as a kind of exploratory alertness, with the head turning to one side and then to the other.

A more complicated problem was investigated: Are impulses arising from internal organs subject to higher analysis on the part of the cerebral cortex, as are the impulses arriving from the external environment? For example: does the cerebral cortex differentiate stimuli reaching the receptors of internal organs? Issues of this order must have a most essential significance for describing the interoceptive conditioned reflexes and for explaining the nature of subconscious analysis. It appears to us that with the aid of Pavlov's method a definite and precise answer has been given to this question too. Here are two experimental proofs.

The mucous lining of the stomach is in one case irrigated by water at a temperature of 38°, and this stimulus is reinforced by food. In another case this irrigation is by water at 28°, and is not associated with food by a conditioned reflex. Consequently, a test of differentiation [6] is given in accordance with the difference in temperature. It was shown that in the first case, as might have been expected, there is a distinct salivation under the isolated action of the irrigating water. In the second case this action

[6] The term "discrimination" would be used in contemporary literature (Ed.).

is lacking: there is no saliva. The differentiation is obvious: the cerebral cortex accurately distinguishes the two temperature stimuli. The differential interoceptive stimulus later proved able to expand the inhibitor process, irradiating the inhibition over all the cortical surface. The dog not only is drowsy, but begins to fall asleep in response to a series of stimuli by water at a temperature of 26°.

A second experiment: By means of a rubber balloon, water at a temperature of 6–7° is admitted, in one case, into the intestinal loop, opened according to the method of Tiri-Vella, and reinforced by an electrical current administered to the paw. In the other case, water was admitted to the balloon at a temperature of 28°, but without association with an electric current. As a consequence of such a combination of stimuli in the receptors of the intestinal mucus, the dog reacted by raising his paw to the cold water only. But the dog did not react at all to the warm water; it continued to stand quietly and showed no special motor reaction. Here too the differentiation is clear.

The conclusion is obvious. The facts adduced, and others analogous to them, show the accuracy and delicacy with which the cortex analyzes the impulses arising from internal organs; and they also show the possibility of all the different kinds of internal inhibitions [7] that we find in exteroceptive conditioned connections. The same series of experiments clearly exhibited the cortical processes of excitation and inhibition elicited by interoceptive conditioned stimuli. The regularity of reciprocal induction was also demonstrated. And this means that sensations from internal organs, under conditions of normal life, are uninterruptedly subject to higher analysis, which analyzes what takes place in the "internal economy" of the organism; and that these sensations are not different in their properties from exteroceptive conditioned connections.

But is it not possible to suppose that temporary connections, the higher analyses, are carried out by the cerebral cortex for the internal and external milieus separately, independently of each other; that these two kinds of stimulation from different sources deploy in the cortex without influence on each other; and that the character of their influence on behavior varies only with their perseverance, intensity, and fixed significance for the organism? The facts contradict these suppositions. On the contrary, the whole picture of the processes which take place in the cortex on the occasion of these two stimulations speaks of their close interrelation and constant interaction.

We give some experimental evidence. A dog has alimentary extero-conditioned reflexes—metronome, bell—and an interoceptive conditioned

---

[7] "Internal inhibition develops when the conditioned stimulus is not attended by the unconditioned . . ." (Pavlov, 1928, p. 308). "Internal inhibition" takes different forms: extinction, retardation, conditioned inhibition, and differential inhibition (pp. 297–299 [Translator]).

reflex—irrigation of the wall of the stomach with water. The conditioned reflexes are uniform in strength: 20–21 gradations on the scale. Now these two stimuli conflict: the metronome and the irrigation of the stomach act at the same time. As a result, the reflex diminished, the latent period of reaction was lengthened, and the conditioned salivation was sharply lowered and inhibited. The same result is obtained in the case of a collision of extero- and intero-conditioned *defensive* motor reflexes. The motor reaction is inhibited. The paws are not drawn back, but still the dog whines, barks, yelps, almost squats on its hind legs, and spasmodically presses them against the base of the apparatus. These two signals from diverse sources create a state of conflict in the cortex, and the animal loses correct coordination in its concrete behavior. It sufficed merely to stop the flow of air [*sic;* water?] into the stomach for the dog to reestablish the previous relations to the stimulus from the external milieu.

But the collision of impulses is not yet a conflict. In particular, the collision of the processes of excitation brought about by interoceptor and exteroceptor stimulation does not always result in inhibition. Other patterns of interrelation in the cerebral cortex may be observed when these stimuli meet. Everything depends on which agent has prepared the ground for this or the other reaction, on which points and foci of excitation in the cortex are operative and succeed in determining the given reaction. The question was not at all whether the external agents were strong or whether the impulses reaching the cortex from internal receptors were weak. The preponderance of one stimulation or the other is the consequence of many factors, primarily of the functional condition of the address to which the signals are sent.

We adduce evidence for these results too. A dog has an exteroceptive conditioned reflex to a bell and an interoceptive one to the irrigation by water of the mucus of the stomach wall. If we first irrigate the stomach with water and sound the bell after 15 seconds, salivation is increased; in the reverse combination, with the bell first, followed by irrigation, salivation is concomitantly inhibited. That is, the stimulus coming from the external milieu in one case reinforces the impulses coming from the stomach, while in the other case it is inhibited by the interoceptive stimulus which follows.

Or take another experiment. A dog has two kinds of conditioned reflexes. One is interoceptive-motor: excitation of the mucous lining of the intestinal loop, along with electric-epidermal reinforcement on the paw. The other is a salivary conditioned reflex with a bell. The interoceptive reflex is put into play first: naturally, the dog's paw is sharply and violently raised in defense and then lowered, but within 7 seconds a bell is associated, and in reply to it the motion of the paw is stopped and salivation takes place. As a result of this unexpected juxtaposition, the dog as it were "freezes" in the pose he has reached; he listens intently to the sound, and saliva drips from the salivary fistula. But this is what is particularly interesting about this case: the isolated action of the bell by itself never produced such tension of the musculature, nor so distinct an alimentary conditioned reaction, i.e., salivation. Consequently, here too, not only is the inhibition of signals from the intestines repressed, but this repression heightens the alimentary excitation to the conditioned signal. We thus have before us a mechanism of concomitant reactions occasioned by interoceptive signals. A characteristic example of such interoceptive excitation is the familiar experiment of Academician A. A. Ukhtomsky, on the basis of which he established the principle of the dominant. The essence of this experiment is as follows:

Upon stimulating the motor areas of a dog's cerebral cortex, Ukhtomsky noticed that the reactions of the fore limbs unexpectedly ceased in response to this stimulation, but motions of the tail appeared instead, that is, a reaction which neither *anatomically* nor *physiologically* has immediate connection with the stimulated points of the cortex. The greater the intensity of the stimulation, the more the extremities were inhibited and the more frequent became the movements of the tail. Immediately thereafter there came a moment when the contents of the rectum were ejected with great force. And only after this did the fore limbs begin to react "normally" once more in response to irritation of the motor-areas of the cerebral cortex.

Intercentral relations of just this sort, though under different conditions, were obtained by us in a prolonged experiment with the intact brain. In particular, we were able to obtain inhibition of the spontaneous and conditioned secretion of urine. The bladder of a dog was removed, the ureters were tapped to the outside, and a conditioned reflex on the secretion of urine was formed. One of the kidneys was deprived of its nerves, and thus the only connection with the cerebral cortex was by way of the blood stream. It turned out that inclinations to defecate call forth an inhibition in the cortex, and correspondingly the excretion of urine is repressed in both kidneys: in the kidney with neural connections intact as well as in the kidney deprived of these neural connections.

Impulses and signals from interoceptive fields become in time so strong, persistent, and importunate, owing to the functional purpose of the organ, that they finally become a dominating focus of excitation of the type of a "dominant," subordinating to its interests the current reaction of the animal to the external milieu. The results are surprising too in the case of total exclusion of the internal organ.

Two observations: A dog with its bladder totally eliminated continued for a long time to stand in the posture of urination, even though direct interoceptive causes were permanently excluded: there was no bladder. But there remained circuits in the cerebral cortex which constituted a single complex or stereotype with stimuli from the external milieu. The dog need only set this stereotype in action towards a urination, through tactile or optical receptors, for the interrupted anatomic line of interoceptive stimulation to be restored by the cortical apparatus.

A dog without a bladder assumed the posture of urination at the sight and odor of the urine of other dogs. And if it is not artificially rescued from its fruitless expectation, the animal will try over and over again to return to the tragic illusion of urination.

A second observation relates to human clinical practice. In the case of an invalid in whose lateral abdominal wall an artificial excretory opening had been made, and therefore the ordinary human act of defecation had become impossible, inclinations to defecate arose every time the protruded portion of the intestine was washed. At the moment that the nurse removed the contents of the rectum through the opening of the fistula, the invalid experienced unendurable stimuli to normal defecation. He complained that he had a disagreeable feeling of constipation, that he involuntarily felt inclinations to intestinal tension of the abdominal and anal musculature, that just ahead lay the opening of the "formerly normal" end of the rectum. All this continued so long as the nurse manipulated in the opening of the fistula. After the conclusion of the procedure of washing and cleaning the artificial end of the rectum, the invalid relaxed and experienced the sensation of a completed act of defecation. Thus, impulses from the upper end of the anal portion of the rectum are transmitted to the spinal centers, from which they are in turn sent back to the remaining isolated bit of the normal discharge end of the rectum; now from here the impulses, once converted into conditioned impulses, inform the cortex with regard to the act of defecation being prepared. This state may be called an imaginary readiness to defecate. The cortex reproduces in its entirety all the conditioned-reflex mechanism whether as a painful feeling of constipation, or as a feeling of having completed an act of defecation, accompanied by a feeling of relaxation. We see here the action of the natural biological mechanism of interoceptive conditioned connections.

In conclusion, we must mention, even though in very abbreviated form, one more of our experiments, carried out on a human subject in the winter of 1941–1942, in one of the Leningrad evacuation hospitals. During the treatment of the invalid, Comrade F., a temporary fistula was attached in the middle region of the small intestine. The experiment was as follows: Through the fistula a small rubber balloon was inserted into the bowels, filled in one case with cold water, in another case with warm. These thermal factors play the rôle of interoceptive unconditioned stimuli. The rôle of the conditioned stimulus is played by visual perceptions: the flashing of a red or blue electric light. It goes without saying that here, just as in the previously described experiments, the method and procedure were of a nature to exclude any intrusion of epidermal or acoustic components, while the visual stimuli were restricted to those intended.

It was found, first, that the cold and warm interoceptive impulses evoked sensations in F. which he perceived with full adequacy, and it was significant that F. was aware of peristaltic movements of the bowels. In the second place, all these feelings could easily be reproduced by way of conditioned reflexes, in consequence of several associations of light signals with them. The isolated action of the red lamp (without the balloon!) after a certain latent period elicited in F. a current of emotive reactions, corresponding, for example, to the contact of the cold-water balloon with the mucous lining of the intestine.

What is before us is the complex mechanism of paths of interconnection between the interoceptive fields of man, and the higher analysis carried out by the cerebral cortex, which is manifested by adequate sensations.

We may rest on the factual material given. The essence of the matter is clear without further ado. We now turn to some conclusions.

The facts clearly indicate that impulses arising from the internal organs can, under certain circumstances, become signals for the higher neural activity. By comparison with the action of stimuli coming to the nervous system from the external milieu, these impulses must be regarded as subliminal, yet they can be *quantitatively* detected and *registered* with great accuracy. The cerebral cortex not merely exhibits these impulses, but also carries out what Pavlov called higher analysis. Consequently, the innumerable stimulations to which the animal is subjected dispatch continual information to the cortex about the events taking place in internal and other organs.

On the basis of factual data, it must be recognized that: (1) impulses arising in internal organs play an essential rôle in the formation of acts of higher neural activity; (2) in the cerebral cortex these impulses are in constant interaction with stimuli arriving from the external milieu. Thus, any final behavioral reaction is an integrated act, into which interoceptive stimulation enters in visible or masked form.

Weak interoceptive impulses, which, as we have seen, are subliminal, accumulating at the end of a prolonged period, may become so intensive and insistent that they are able completely to subordinate to themselves the current acts of behavior. Interoception is of especial significance for the cerebral cortex when exteroceptive influences are excluded. This can be distinctly observed in sleep, for example (as when the stomach is filled with indigestible food, or the bladder is full, during heart conditions, liver ailments, etc.). Such is the physiological side of interoceptive temporary connections, which constitute one of the essential elements of higher nervous activity. It is hard not to see the significance of these physiological results for the understanding of what, in psychology, is called the subconscious. However, we must warn that none of us imagines that the physiological basis of the subconscious can be exhausted by the study of interoceptive mechanisms. We are equally far from the notion of reducing the complex subconscious psychic phenomena to stimulations emanating only from the receptors of internal organs, or to the level of results obtained from the study of dogs. We are convinced of only one thing, that the results given above, the physiological laws discovered in the process, the relations and place of interoceptive conditioned connections in higher nervous activity, can explain important aspects of the subconscious, giving this phenomenon a rigorously scientific foundation.

We can now say with full justification that the cerebral cortex, as the material basis of psychic phenomena, functions as a single system, depending on the impulses of the external and the internal world. Reception is one in essence, and this physiological unity is to a great extent realized in virtue of the fact that impulses arising from interoceptors and exteroceptors are inseparably interconnected, and reflect a single dynamic complex and synthetic temporary connections. These complicated integral connections, no doubt, may serve as the occasion for the formation of temporary connections of second and higher orders. Consequently the so-called subconscious (which in our cases is related to the internal organs) ceases to be a riddle *in the nature of its origin and in the locus in which this psychic reaction takes place.*

It is from this point of view, we think, that we should consider the single physiological mechanism of the origin of those phenomena, diverse in physiological character, which are termed "conscious" and "subconscious." Subconscious stimulation is a real process, accomplished in the cerebral cortex, which may become perceptible and present, depending on the character of the intercentral relations in the given current behavioral act. Any stimulus from the internal and external milieu, depending on its physiological and biological intent and the functional state of its address, may become subconscious or be immediately transformed into a conscious one.

The view that the real external world and the internal state of the organism are reflected in consciousness by means of the system of analyzers, provides the material basis of complex psychical functions. This view also increases our power to eliminate the gap which exists between phenomena which are objectively observed and facts which are subjectively experienced.

In a speech prepared for a projected conference of psychiatrists, neurologists, and psychologists, Ivan Petrovich Pavlov thus described the place and significance of physiological researches for psychology:

I see and I bow before the efforts of thought in the work of psychologists old and new, but at the same time it seems to me, and this can hardly be disputed, that this work is done in a frightfully uneconomical way, and I have the conviction that the pure physiology of the animal brain will greatly facilitate, even more—will make fruitful the extraordinary and momentous work of those who have devoted and are devoting themselves to the science of man's subjective states.

We may say with confidence that the facts discovered by Pavlov's method increase the power of science as a tool in deciphering those elements of man's internal world which up to recently were hidden to genuine science.

REFERENCES

BYKOV, K. M. *The cerebral cortex and the internal organs.* (Translated and edited by W. H. Gantt.) New York: Chemical Publishing, 1957.

PAVLOV, I. P. *Lectures on conditioned reflexes.* Vol. 1. (Translated and edited by W. H. Gantt.) New York: International Publishers, 1928. (Reprinted, 1965.)

SECHENOV, I. Reflexes of the brain (1863). In K. Koshtoyants (Ed.), *I. Sechenov: Selected physiological and psychological works.* Moscow: Foreign Languages Pub. House. (Reprinted by M.I.T. Press, Cambridge, Mass., 1965.)

6

Partial Reinforcement and Conditioned Heart Rate Response in Human Subjects

J. M. Notterman, W. N. Schoenfeld, and P. J. Bersh

In a recent review of the experimental literature concerned with partial reinforcement, Jenkins and Stanley (1950) state that "Most of the research in this area has involved responses of the skeletal musculature rather than behavior innervated by the autonomic nervous system." The present

Adapted from *Science*, 1952, *115*, 2978, 77–79. With permission of the authors and the American Association for the Advancement of Science.

note deals with the latter case, in particular with the use of a partial reinforcement schedule for conditioning changes in the human heart rate. It has been shown that changes in heart rate are successfully conditioned by means of a regular reinforcement schedule (Notterman, Schoenfeld, and Bersh, 1952). In the later study, it was reported that a previously neutral stimulus acquires the power of exercising a depressant effect upon the heart rate, following the regular pairing by the trace conditioning technique of that stimulus with electric shock to the hand. Curves of conditioned response strength were obtained for successive trials during conditioning, extinction, spontaneous recovery, reconditioning, and further extinction.

A survey of the literature reveals that several other researchers, beginning with Sherrington (1900), have observed conditioned changes in heart rate when some noxious agent was used as the unconditioned stimulus. Some of these investigators report conditioned cardiac decelerations (Kosupkin and Olmsted, 1943; Sherrington, 1900), others report accelerations (Anderson and Parmenter, 1941; Dykman and Gantt, 1951; Gantt, 1941), and still others report both (Peters and Gantt, 1951; Robinson and Gantt, 1946). Although these cases all involve the use of an aversive stimulus as the reinforcing agent, it is difficult to determine whether there is anything else in common among them, or, on the other hand, if there are any systematic operational differences that might account for the disparate results. This difficulty exists principally for two reasons: (a) Some of the publications are in the form of abstracts and so contain few procedural details (e.g., intensity of noxious stimulus; temporal relations between CS and US; use of simultaneous, trace, or delay techniques; number of trials, etc.). (b) None of the human studies available contains any readily quantifiable data bearing upon the actual acquisition, extinction, spontaneous recovery, and reconditioning processes.

Complete details of the apparatus used in the present experiment are reported by Notterman, Schoenfeld, and Bersh (1952). In the main, the apparatus consisted of a cardiograph, shock circuit, and tone-oscillator circuit. The shock was 30 v.a.c. and was administered by means of two electrodes strapped to the palmar and dorsal sides of the left hand. The subject received a 750 cps tone, approximately 20 db, through a headset. The tone was of 1 second and the shock of 6 seconds' duration. On trials during which shock followed tone, a 6-second interval separated the paired stimuli. There were six phases to the experiment, occurring in the following order: (1) determination of basal (preconditioning) heart rate response to the tone; (2) conditioning; (3) Extinction I; (4) spontaneous recovery; (5) reconditioning; and (6) Extinction II. The first three phases were administered in one session of approximately $1\frac{3}{4}$ hours' total duration; the remaining three phases, in one session of about $1\frac{1}{4}$ hours, some 24 hours later. The basal, Extinction I, spontaneous recovery, and Extinction II phases consisted of 20, 11, 10, and 11 tone-alone presentations, respectively, and were identical with similar phases for the previously reported regular reinforcement group (Notterman, Schoenfeld, and Bersh, 1952). The conditioning phase consisted of 18 trials, of which 11 were tone-shock pairings, and 7 were tone-alone trials. The reinforcement schedule of these 18 trials was as follows: the first 5 in the series were tone-shock, the remaining 13 were randomly presented tone-shock trials (6) and tone-alone trials (7). The randomization of reinforced and unreinforced trials was not begun with the first trial, because it has been found that responses become conditioned more readily under partial reinforcement schedules if some response strength is built up initially with regular reinforcement (Jenkins and Stanley, 1950). The reconditioning phase likewise consisted of 11 tone-shock and 7 tone-alone trials, but randomization of reinforcement was begun after a single tone-shock presentation. The number of tone-shock combinations given during conditioning and reconditioning in the present experiment was precisely the same as that given the subjects of the regularly reinforced group reported by Notterman, Schoenfeld, and Bersh (1952). Hence, the sole difference in experimental conditions between the partial and regular groups lay in the presence of the seven randomized tone-alone trials during conditioning and during reconditioning.

All trials were separated by 1 to 2 minutes, and each subject's cardiogram was taken continuously from about 30 seconds before the tone to about 30 seconds after the shock, or normal time for shock, on each trial. Heart rate measures were taken by determining the period of the last two cycles immediately preceding onset of tone, and the period of the last two cycles in the 6-second interval following tone (and, therefore, immediately preceding shock on the tone-shock trials). These measures, called the "pre-tone" and "post-tone" heart rate, respectively, were then converted to beats per minute.

The data of this experiment are concerned with two principal questions: Does an originally ineffective stimulus come to initiate a characteristic heart rate response as a result of irregular pairing of that stimulus with shock? If so, how does the response strength acquired under these conditions compare with that acquired under regular reinforcement?

The data in Table 1 relate to the first question. These data are the mean pre-tone and mean post-tone heart rate values in beats per minute for the ten subjects used, over each phase of the experiment. The table shows, for example, that Subject No. 1 had a mean pre-tone heart rate during conditioning of 77.0 beats per minute (b/m), this figure being based on 18 trials. The mean post-tone heart rate for the same individual was 70.3 b/m. The *group* mean pre-tone value for all subjects during conditioning, 77.0, was obtained from the individual means shown in the pre-tone subcolumn. In all phases except basal, the individual means shown are for

TABLE 1

Mean pre-tone and mean post-tone heart rate (in beats per minute) during successive phases of the experiment.

Subjects	Basal		Conditioning		Extinction I		Spontaneous Recovery		Reconditioning		Extinction II	
	Pre	Post	Pre	Post	Pre	Post	Pre	Post	Pre	Post	Pre	Post
1	73.2	73.3	77.0	70.3	78.5	63.2	88.3	73.3	81.6	71.6	84.7	72.4
2	87.1	87.3	87.9	85.2	88.8	83.9	80.7	78.5	82.1	79.7	85.8	79.5
3	67.2	67.5	67.2	65.0	70.6	68.1	61.5	60.4	61.7	58.2	63.3	60.9
4	92.7	87.2	92.6	86.5	88.9	84.5	99.1	92.8	92.9	86.6	90.2	84.4
5	90.2	88.4	84.4	78.7	82.9	74.7	95.0	80.4	89.0	77.6	88.1	75.4
6	90.4	92.2	88.7	82.1	86.0	80.4	83.1	82.1	81.3	78.4	81.7	78.2
7	54.0	52.7	54.6	47.7	53.9	46.5	54.0	50.3	52.5	48.1	49.2	44.6
8	74.2	71.8	70.5	66.0	68.7	65.3	69.4	64.1	67.1	65.2	67.4	64.9
9	74.3	76.9	74.8	68.0	68.4	65.1	78.7	76.1	71.1	65.6	65.1	62.0
10	66.6	70.1	72.2	66.0	69.2	62.6	76.7	67.6	73.6	70.3	76.3	69.4
Group mean	77.0	76.7	77.0	71.6	75.6	69.4	78.7	72.5	75.3	70.1	75.2	69.1
Level of confidence	P > .05		P < .001		P < .001		P < .001		P < .001		P < .001	

Note: The levels of confidence shown are for group mean pre-tone minus group mean post-tone differences within each phase. The basal means are for basal trials 11–20; the means for the other phases are for all trials within each phase.

160

the total number of trials given during each phase. For basal, the individual means are for the last 11 of the 20 trials given, these latter trials being used because they are a more stable estimate of preconditioning heart rate (Notterman, Schoenfeld, and Bersh, 1952).

Pitman's variation (1948) of a nonparametric test by Fisher was used to determine whether the distributions of the individual mean pre-tone minus mean post-tone differences for each phase are significantly different from chance. (Nonparametric tests were used throughout the treatment of these data, because in some comparisons variance was heterogeneous, and distributions did not appear to be normal.) This test shows that the basal changes in heart rate are not different from those to be expected on the basis of random variation, whereas for each of the other phases the probability that chance variation accounts for the heart rate changes is slight ($P < .001$). It is thus apparent that a schedule of irregular or partial reinforcement can be used to establish a characteristic conditioned depression in heart rate.

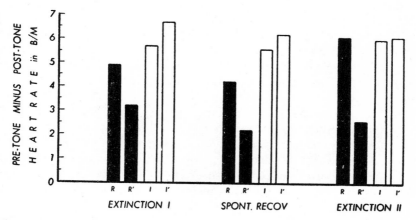

Figure 1.   Resistance to extinction of regularly and irregularly reinforced groups. Response strength of the first five trials (labeled R or I) is compared with response strength of the last five trials (R' or I') for the indicated phases.

Regarding the second question, several trends are indicated in the data:

1. *Acquisition:* The difference in conditioned response strength produced by regular vs. irregular schedules of reinforcement is slight. Table 1 shows that, for conditioning (acquisition), the magnitude of the acquired heart rate depression in the present instance is 5.4 b/m (group mean pre-tone minus group mean post-tone heart rates). This value is quite similar to the 5.6 b/m drop reported by Notterman, Schoenfeld, and Bersh (1952) for a regularly reinforced group. It may be noted parenthetically that, in view of reports by some previous investigators of conditioned cardiac acceleration under aversive stimulation, the present authors were interested

in determining whether the *immediate* effect of the tone was to induce a heart rate speed-up, whereas the deceleration was simply a later effect. For this reason, heart rate measurements based on the first two cycles immediately following the tone were also taken during acquisition in the case of the regularly reinforced group. The data indicate a nonsignificant drop of 0.2 b/m compared to the pre-tone heart rate. Moreover, the heart rate appears to drop progressively throughout the 6-second interval separating tone and shock.

2. *Reconditioning:* Here, too, the difference in conditioned response strength produced by the two separate methods of reinforcement is only minor. Table 1 indicates that the reconditioning drop for irregular subjects is 5.2 b/m; for the previously reported regular group, the drop was 6.8 b/m. The difference between these drops is not significant [$P > .05$ by Pitman's (1948) spread test, based on rank-ordered data].

3. *Extinction:* The most striking effect is found in terms of resistance to extinction; the irregularly reinforced subjects show a significantly greater perseveration of the conditioned response than do regularly reinforced subjects. Figure 1 compares the resistance to extinction of the regularly and irregularly reinforced groups during Extinction I, spontaneous recovery, and Extinction II. Two pairs of columns are shown for each phase; the first pair (solid columns) depicts data of the regular group; the second pair, data of the irregular group. The first member of each pair of columns (marked *R* for regular, or *I* for irregular) gives the group mean pre-tone minus group mean post-tone heart rate for the first five trials of each respective phase. The second member of each pair (marked *R'* or *I'*) gives the corresponding change in heart rate for the last five trials of each phase. By comparing each group's level of conditioned heart rate response for the first five and the last five trials of each phase, differences in the perseverative tendency of the response may be noted. Thus for Extinction I, there is a marked drop in the conditioned heart rate effect for the regular group, but a slight rise for the irregular group. In general, a diminution of conditioned response strength during the tone-alone trials is characteristic for the regular group; the irregular groups show either a slight rise, or no difference.

TABLE 2

Probability values for tests of significance based upon comparisons of extinction effects following schedules of regular and irregular reinforcement.

	R vs I	R' vs I'	R vs R'	I vs I'
Extinction I	$P > .05$	$.05 > P > .02$	$0.2 > P > .01$	$P > .05$
Spontaneous recovery	$P > .05$	$P > .05$	$P > .05$	$P > .05$
Extinction II	$P > .05$	$.05 > P > .02$	$0.3 > P > .02$	$P > .05$

Table 2 gives a summary of the results of statistical comparisons made for the data illustrated in Figure 1 (Pitman's nonparametric tests for correlated or uncorrelated items were used throughout, as appropriate). The probability values shown here, together with the data of Table 1, provide the basis for the following conclusions: (1) Heart rate changes may be conditioned in human beings by means of a schedule of irregular reinforcement. The fact that this autonomic response can be conditioned by such a technique meets a research need indicated by others (Jenkins and Stanley, 1950). (2) The most conspicuous difference between the irregularly and regularly reinforced groups in the present research is in terms of the former's much greater resistance to extinction. It is noteworthy that this difference is obtained with an autonomically mediated response, inasmuch as the same effect has been almost universally observed with respect to motor responses (Jenkins and Stanley, 1950).

REFERENCES

ANDERSON, O. D., and PARMENTER, R. A long-term study of the experimental neurosis in the sheep and the dog. *Psychosom. med. Monogr.*, 1941, *2*, 1–150.

DYKMAN, R. A., and GANTT, W. H. A comparative study of cardiac conditioned responses and motor conditioned responses in controlled "stress" situations. *Am. Psychologist*, 1951, *6*, 263–264.

GANTT, W. H. Cardiac conditional reflexes to time. *Trans. Am. neurol. Assoc.*, 1946, *72*, 166.

JENKINS, W. O., and STANLEY, J. C. JR. Partial reinforcement: A review and critique. *Psychol. Bull.*, 1950, *47*, 193–234.

KOSUPKIN, J. M., and OLMSTED, J. M. D. Slowing of the heart rate as a conditioned reflex in the rabbit. *Am. J. Physiol.*, 1943, *139*, 550–552.

NOTTERMAN, J. M., SCHOENFELD, W. N., and BERSH, P. J. Conditioned heart rate response in human beings during experimental anxiety. *J. comp. physiol. Psychol.*, 1952, *45*, 1–8.

PETERS, J. E., and GANTT, W. H. Conditioning of human heart rate to graded degrees of muscular tension. *Federation Proc.*, 1951, *10*, 104.

PITMAN, E. J. G. *Notes on non-parametric statistical inference.* New York: Dept. Math. Statistics, Columbia Univ., 1948.

ROBINSON, J., and GANTT, W. H. The cardiac component of the orienting reflex. *Federation Proc.*, 1946, *5*, 87–88.

SHERRINGTON, C. S. Experiments on the value of the vascular and visceral factors for the genesis of emotion. *Proc. Roy. Soc.* (London), 1900, *66*, 390–403.

SUGGESTED READINGS

BYKOV, K. M. *The cerebral cortex and the internal organs.* (Translated and edited by W. H. Gantt.) New York: Chemical Publishing, 1957.

HULL, C. L. Learning II. The factor of the conditioned reflex. In C. Murchison (Ed.), *Handbook of general experimental psychology*. Worcester, Mass.: Clark University Press, 1934, 382–455.

PAVLOV, I. P. *Conditioned reflexes*. (Translated and edited by G. V. Anrep.) London: Oxford University Press, 1927. (Reprinted by Dover, New York, 1960.)

PROKASY, W. F. *Classical conditioning: A symposium*. New York: Appleton-Century-Crofts, 1965.

RAZRAN, G. The observable unconscious and the inferable conscious in current Soviet psychophysiology: Interoceptive conditioning, semantic conditioning, and the orienting reflex. *Psychol. Rev.*, 1961, *68*, 81–147.

Chapter IV

OPERANT BEHAVIOR:
THE BASIC PARADIGMS

The papers reproduced in this chapter provide examples of four basic ways in which the relationship between a response and its immediate consequences may be arranged by the experimenter. The research by H. Lane describes an experimental situation in which the occurrence of a response is followed by the presentation of a positively reinforcing stimulus; in other words this is the type of response-reinforcement contingency ordinarily known as "reward." D. M. Baer's paper describes an experiment in which the effect of the removal of a positively reinforcing state of affairs is investigated. The study by J. A. Dinsmoor and L. H. Hughes involves an example of escape behavior. In this case the response terminates the presence of a negative reinforcer or an aversive stimulus. It is followed by the opposite case, which traditionally goes by the name of punishment: N. H. Azrin describes the results produced by the presentation of a negative reinforcer immediately following the occurrence of a response.

7

Control of Vocal Responding
in Chickens

Harlan Lane

The appropriate conditioning procedures for modifying subhuman vocalizing have, until recently, been little studied and poorly understood; some anecdotal information has been available, however (Mowrer, 1950). It has not been clear whether respondent or operant conditioning techniques, or both, are suitable for the control of this behavior. Skinner has suggested that "vocal behavior below the human level is especially refractory" to operant conditioning (Skinner, 1957). The studies reported here show that the rate of chirping by a hungry chicken can be controlled by schedules of presentation of food. The temporal patterns of vocal responding thus obtained are similar to those found with other operants under schedules of reinforcement, for example, key pecking in the pigeon and bar pressing in the rat, and a wide variety of human motor responses.

The subjects for these experiments were two Bantam chickens which were run individually at 80 percent of their ad libitum body weight in sessions that lasted from 30 minutes to 6 hours. The chicks were 5 weeks old at the start of this research. After 5 months there was a marked change in topography and decline in rate of chirping in the home cage and the experiments were discontinued. Because the chicks were growing during this 5-month interval, continued maintenance of 80 percent of their ad libitum body weight, as initially determined, would have resulted in starvation. Therefore, every month the birds were given free access to food in their home cage for 2 days and a revised "running weight" was computed.

The experimental space consisted of an 8-inch, cubical, sound-insulated compartment. An opening in one wall provided access to a food tray whose

Adapted from *Science*, 1960, *132*, 3418, 37–38. With permission of the author. Copyright 1960 by the American Association for the Advancement of Science.

presentation was scheduled automatically. A microphone mounted in the ceiling of the compartment controlled a voice-operated relay which reacted to about 95 percent of the audible chirp responses by sending pulses to programming and recording equipment.

The rate of vocal responding was observed under two experimental and five control conditions. Figure 1 summarizes the data obtained from one bird; a second bird gave similar results. The first two studies were con-

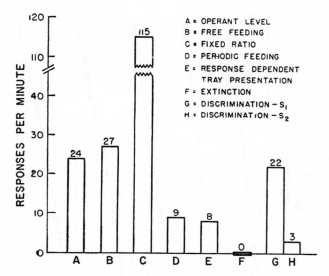

Figure 1. *Rates of chirping obtained under control and experimental conditions with one Bantam chicken.*

trols in which the rate of chirping was observed under conditions of no presentation of food ("operant level") and continuous presentation of food ("free-feeding"). The stabilized rate of responding under each of these two control conditions is shown in Figure 1. Because chirping decelerated in the early stages of the operant-level session, it may be inferred that an average rate lower than 24 responses per minute would have been obtained for this condition if the session had been extended beyond its half-hour duration. The average rate during a 1-hour free-feeding session was 27 responses per minute. The chickens chirped both while pecking at the grain in the tray and while not eating.

In a third experiment the presentation of food was contingent on responding; a fixed-ratio 20 schedule of reinforcement was employed (Ferster and Skinner, 1957). Under this schedule, the food tray, containing meal, was presented for 4 seconds after every 20 chirps. An extremely high rate of responding was generated by this procedure; the average rate observed in a 1-hour sample after 10 hours of conditioning was 115 responses per minute. A typical sample of the performance obtained with the fixed-ratio 20 schedule is shown in Figure 2, in which cumulative chirp responses are plotted as a function of time. The diagonal marks on the curve indicate the presentation of food. The inter-reinforcement time under this schedule averaged about 16 seconds.

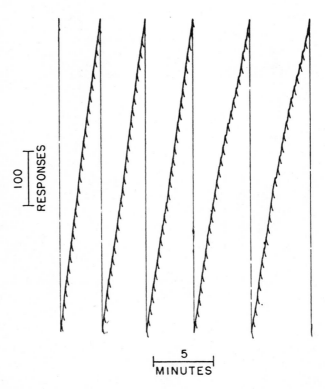

Figure 2. *Cumulative response curve for the chirp response of one chicken under a fixed-ratio 20 schedule of reinforcement.*

In the fourth experiment, a control, food was presented with the same frequency and duration as obtained under the fixed-ratio schedule: 4 seconds of access to the food tray every 16 seconds. However, this periodic feeding was provided independent of responding. Figure 1 shows that the rate under periodic feeding (bar *D*) was less than 10 percent of the rate observed under fixed-ratio (20) (bar *C*). Apparently, it is the response requirement rather than the food presentation alone that is reponsible for the high rate of responding under fixed-ratio schedule.

A fifth experiment demonstrated that the high rate of vocalizing obtained under fixed-ratio reinforcement was not simply the result of the stimulus change provided by response-dependent tray presentation. The procedure for this control condition was the same as that for the fixed-ratio condition, a 4-second tray presentation after every 20 responses, except that the food tray was now empty. The average rate of responding in the fifth hour under this condition is shown in Figure 1, bar E. When a formerly neutral stimulus is paired repeatedly with a primary reinforcer it acquires a temporary control over responding which dissipates if the stimulus continues to be presented without further pairing (Estes, 1949). In the vocalizing experiments reported here, the food tray and the food were presented concurrently on thousands of occasions. The effect on the rate of chirping of discontinuing this pairing was slight initially. By the second experimental hour, however, presentation of the empty tray had, for the most part, lost its control over the rate of chirping (see Figure 1). The terminal effect of the presentation of the empty tray may be compared to the effect of simple extinction—the sixth experimental condition—in which neither food nor tray is ever presented. Under the extinction procedure, the response rate fell to zero within a half hour.

In the final study, food was made contingent on responding during one stimulus and on not responding during a second stimulus. When a red light was on in the subject's compartment, food presentation was contingent on the first chirp, after 2 minutes had elapsed. Following one reinforcement on this fixed-interval schedule (Ferster and Skinner, 1957), a green light was turned on and food presentation was then contingent on a pause in responding of at least 2 minutes. These conditions alternated. Each of the birds learned the stimulus discrimination within an hour. High rates of responding were observed during the stimulus that was paired with fixed-interval reinforcement (S_1) and low rates of responding were observed during the stimulus that was paired with reinforcement for not responding (S_2). When cumulative chirps in S_1 are plotted as a function of time, a pattern of responding is obtained that is typical of operant performance under fixed-interval schedules of reinforcement: the interval begins with a pause and the rate increases as the time of reinforcement approaches. Figure 3 shows a sample of the cumulative response record obtained during a stable discrimination performance (average rates for this session appear in Figure 1, bars G and H). The average rate of responding during the fourth hour of training on the discrimination procedure was 22 responses per minute in S_1 and three responses per minute in S_2; the modal rate of responding in S_2 was zero.

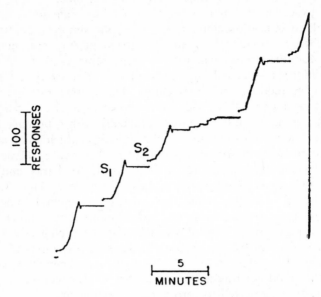

Figure 3. Cumulative response curve for the chirp response of one chicken under a discrimination procedure.

REFERENCES

ESTES, W. K. Generalization of secondary reinforcement from the primary drive. *J. comp. physiol. Psychol.,* 1949, *42,* 286–295.

FERSTER, C. B., and SKINNER, B. F. *Schedules of reinforcement.* New York: Appleton-Century-Crofts, 1957.

MOWRER, O. H. *Learning theory and personality dynamics.* New York: Ronald, 1950.

SKINNER, B. F. *Verbal behavior.* New York: Appleton-Century-Crofts, 1957.

8

Effect of Withdrawal of Positive Reinforcement on an Extinguishing Response in Young Children

Donald M. Baer

Punishment may be defined systematically in either of two ways: (*a*) as the presentation of a negative reinforcer for a response or (*b*) as the removal of a positive reinforcer for a response (Skinner, 1953). The first of these methods has seen extensive study in lower organisms (e.g., Estes, 1944; Skinner, 1938). The second has been subject to a certain amount of discussion in psychoanalytic terminology ("loss of love"), but has seen very little experimental investigation in any species. There are only three exceptions apparent to this statement. Ferster (1958) has used a withdrawal procedure ("time out") in studies with lower animals; Brackbill and O'Hare (1957) have used it as a punishment technique in facilitating discrimination in young children; and Lewis (1952) has used it to set up schedules of reinforcement in young children.

Yet the withdrawal of positive reinforcement as a punishing technique could prove a very significant process in the reinforcement history of the child. Punishment through the presentation of negative reinforcement is typically claimed to be ineffective in weakening responses. Estes concluded that ". . . a response cannot be eliminated from an organism's repertoire more rapidly with the aid of punishment than without it" (1944). Sears *et al.* claim that punitiveness in a parent ". . . is ineffectual over the long term as a technique for eliminating the kind of behavior toward which it is directed" (1957). But they also point out that half of the parents they interviewed use punishment at least moderately often and claim that spanking does some good. In the case of the child, it will often prove impossible

Adapted from *Child Development*, 1961, *32*, 67–74. With permission of the author and the Society for Research in Child Development.

to present a negative reinforcer without simultaneously withdrawing positive reinforcers. The parent who slaps or spanks almost inevitably will withdraw approval and the more obvious tokens of affection at the same time. Perhaps it is this withdrawal of reinforcement which is the significant technique here.

In any case, experimental studies of the punishing effect of the withdrawal of positive reinforcement in the child should prove of systematic and practical value. The present study was designed to yield data on the effectiveness of reinforcement withdrawal for the sole purpose of weakening a response in a situation where a competitive response is not deliberately strengthened through positive reinforcement.

METHOD

Subjects

Children from a day care center of the Seattle Day Nursery Association were used. All Ss were experimentally naive. At the outset of the experiment, 16 Ss were divided randomly into two groups, Punishment and Control. During the course of the experiment, which required that each child participate on five different sessions, six Ss were lost, usually to their family vacation, occasionally to illness, and in one case, to withdrawal of the child from the school. There remained 10 Ss, five in each group. The average age of the Punishment group was 6–10, and the Control group, 6–6. All Ss were within the normal range of intelligence and represented lower income groups.

Apparatus

The entire experiment was conducted in a mobile laboratory built into a 19-foot house trailer (Bijou, 1958), which was parked inside the play yard of the school. The interior of the laboratory included a one-way observation booth for the experimenter and a playroom for the child. The playroom contained a small chair, two tables holding toys or apparatus, a screen on which could be projected cartoons, and a partitioned corner in which an accompanying adult (A) could sit, out of the child's sight but still present.

The experiment centered about three pieces of apparatus. The first of these was a translucent screen, on which the experimenter could project cartoons. The screen was mounted in the wall separating child and experimenter; the movie projector, a Busch "Cinesalesman," operated from the experimenter's side. The projector contained three cartoons on an "endless" reel of film and could present these in an uninterrupted sequence for an indefinite number of cycles. The cartoons were of the Castle Films Woody Woodpecker series (Woody Plays Santa Claus, The Hollywood Matador, and The Dizzy Acrobats); each was black and white, with sound, and lasted 7 minutes.

A second piece of apparatus was a white box, approximately 1 foot on a side, mounted on one of the tables such that S could view cartoons and play with this "toy" at the same time. A bar projected from the front surface of the box. At the lower right side of the front surface was a slot from which peanuts could roll as a reinforcement for pressing the bar. Every bar press resulted in a mild buzz which lasted 1 second, but did not necessarily produce a peanut. A bar press could also result in a 2-second interruption of any cartoon being viewed at the time, if the experimenter chose.

The third piece of apparatus was a commercial toy (Playskool) which was mounted on the other table. It consisted of a cage of sticks, inside of which a small ball could be made to jump up and down a devious route by flipping a small lever at the base of the toy. This toy was not within reach of S as he sat viewing a cartoon.

Procedure

Ss were dealt with entirely by a young female adult, A. Before the experiment started, A had been a constant member of the play group and was thoroughly familiar with the Ss. Furthermore, she had told them that a trailer was coming and that all the Ss would be allowed to enter and play games. This generated a great deal of enthusiasm.

Each S was brought to the laboratory on five separate occasions by A. The first of these was to adapt the S to the laboratory and acquaint him with the cartoons. A would seat the S in the correct place and retire to her corner. Then the cartoons would start, and all three would play without interruption. At the end of the third cartoon (i.e., after 21 minutes), the projector was stopped, and A came out of her corner and took S back to the play yard.

The second visit was to establish a learned response in each S. Prior to this visit, A would ask S if he would like to do something different that day. When S entered the laboratory, A then showed him the toy which could dispense peanuts, saying, "This is a peanut machine." The S was seated by it (the same seat as visit 1), and A retired to her corner. In very short order, S would press the bar and receive a peanut. This started a series of bar presses, of which numbers 1, 2, 3, 5, 7, 10, 15, and 20 were reinforced with a peanut. Immediately after the twentieth response, as S was eating the peanut, A came out of her corner announcing, "That's all for today." They then left together before the child could respond further.

The third visit was to begin extinction of the learned response, punishing it as well in half of the Ss. Prior to this visit, A asked S simply if he would like to come again. Inside the laboratory, A seated S in the same seat and retired to her corner. The cartoons were started immediately. S was free to watch cartoons and to press the bar as he chose. For the five Ss of the Punishment group, any bar press during this session would turn off the on-going cartoons (picture and sound) for 2 seconds. For the five Control Ss, the bar press had no such action. In either case, the bar press produced the usual buzz, but no peanuts at any time. At the end of the third cartoon the projector was turned off, but A remained in her corner for at least 2 minutes, saying nothing. This gave S an interval during which the bar might be pressed, and there were clearly no cartoons to be turned off. Almost every S requested to leave by 2 minutes after the end of the cartoons. In the case of early requests, A was instructed to delay until the 2 minutes had passed to give each child equal opportunity with the bar. Thus, the visit lasted 23 minutes.

The fourth visit was to allow S to show any spontaneous recovery of the learned response, without punishment. Prior to this visit, A asked the child if he would like to see the cartoons again. Inside the laboratory, S was seated in the usual seat, A retired to her corner, and the cartoon was started. S could press the bar if he chose, but on this occasion the bar press did not turn off the cartoon, nor did it result in any peanuts. It did produce a buzz as before. Because it was expected that spontaneous recovery would be slight in either group only one cartoon was shown. Again, S was kept for 2 minutes after the end of the cartoon. Thus, this visit lasted 9 minutes.

The fifth visit was to examine the strength of the learned response in a situation where punishment was impossible. Prior to this visit, S was asked simply if he wanted to come again. Inside, he was told that there would be no cartoons today, but that he could play with anything he wanted. A then retired, leaving S with only two objects capable of play: the peanut apparatus and the Playskool toy. The peanut machine buzzed but did nothing else when the bar was pressed. This session lasted 5 minutes, which is rather long for children thoroughly adapted to the laboratory, with only two simple toys to play with.

In summary, then, Ss were successively adapted to the laboratory and the cartoons, taught a bar pressing response, allowed to extinguish this response with or without punishment, and allowed to show any spontaneous recovery of this response, in situations where the means of punishment was present and absent. This sequence is summarized in Table 1. The interval between the first and second visit was 7 days (plus or minus 2); between the second and third visit, 3 days (plus or minus 1); between the third and fourth visit, 5 days (plus or minus 1); and between the fourth and fifth visit, 3 days (plus or minus 1). All experimentation was conducted during late afternoon hours.

TABLE 1

Sequence of experimental conditions for punishment and control subjects.

Visit	Purpose	Number of Cartoons	Consequence of Bar Press	
			Punishment Group	Control Group
1	Adaptation	3	bar not present	bar not present
2	Strengthen bar press	none	peanuts	peanuts
3	Extinction —session 1	3	cartoon interruption	none
4	Extinction —session 2	1	none	none
5	Extinction —session 3	none	none	none

RESULTS

Recordings were made of the bar pressing response on a Gerbrands Harvard Cumulative recorder. Photographic facsimiles of these response curves are shown in Figure 1. Session 1 in this figure refers to S's third visit to the laboratory, during which the bar pressing response resulted in an interruption of the cartoon for Punishment Ss and otherwise represents an extinction period for all Ss. Session 2 refers to S's fourth visit, during which one cartoon was seen without punishment. Session 3 refers to S's last visit, during which he played freely with either the bar or the Playskool toy and no cartoons were shown.

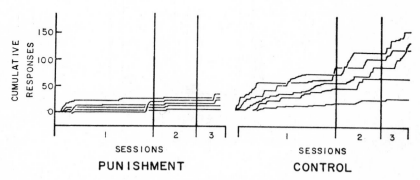

Figure 1.   Individual cumulative response curves of Punishment and Control Ss during repeated sessions.

It is apparent from Figure 1 that the interruption of the cartoon serves to reduce sharply the number of extinction responses Ss make to the bar. Furthermore, this reduction seems reasonably durable. During the last 2 minutes of Session 1, Punishment Ss show no particular tendency to increase responding, although there are no cartoons present, and hence they cannot be punished by their interruption. During Session 2, where Control Ss show considerable spontaneous recovery, Punishment Ss make either one or two responses (which are unpunished) and then cease responding, nor do they respond during the 2 minutes after the cartoon ends. During Session 3, Punishment Ss direct their play to the Playskool toy rather than to the bar far more than do Control Ss.

These individual response curves are summarized in Figure 2, which shows the mean number of bar presses made by each group during each session. Essentially the same picture emerges from a consideration of grouped data as from examination of individual curves.

CHILD DEVELOPMENT

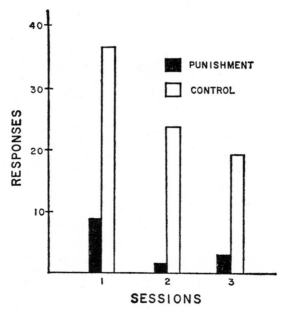

Figure 2. Mean responses of Punishment and Control Ss during repeated sessions.

The individual curves present a very clear case. However, there is one case of overlap between the two groups, and because of this an analysis of variance was performed on the data. The Punishment and Control Ss constitute two independent groups, and Sessions 1, 2, and 3 represent repeated observations of these groups. Use of number of bar presses per session as a raw score is not justifiable because of the heterogeneity of variance between the two groups evident in Figure 1. Consequently, a square root transformation was applied. The transformed data, subjected to Bartlett's test, yielded a χ^2 of 5.28 ($df = 5$, $.30 < p < .50$). A summary of the analysis of variance of the transformed data is given in Table 2. Punishment and Control Ss are clearly distinct at the .01 level. The Sessions' main effect is of no great consequence, since response is bound to decrease during repeated extinction sessions, especially when the sessions are of successively shorter duration. The absence of any interaction between the Punishment groups and Sessions makes for a gratifyingly simple conclusion.

TABLE 2

Summary of analysis of variance of responses during repeated sessions.

Source	df	Mean Square	F	P
Subjects	9			
Punishment	1	71.10	11.83	.01
Error	8	6.01		
Within subjects	20			
Sessions	2	11.00	10.78	.01
Sessions $\times$ punishment	2	1.24		
Error	16	1.02		
Total	29			

None of the Punishment Ss showed any obvious signs of emotionality during punishment. One S in this group, after making several (punished) responses during Session 1, was seen to very carefully take hold of the bar, slowly press it down, and, as the cartoon went off, whip his hand away from the bar, saying, "Wow!" Apart from this, all Ss took the experiment with great equanimity.

DISCUSSION

From the results obtained, it seems clear that the interruption of a cartoon which the child is viewing will serve very effectively as a punishing event; it will efficiently depress a recently strengthened response in the child's repertoire. The thesis that withdrawal of positive reinforcement is punishing is thereby strengthened, specifically for the case of the child. And it is tempting to wonder if the withdrawal of positive reinforcers may not possess punishing characteristics qualitatively different from the presentation of negative reinforcers.

An essential assumption here is that the cartoons are indeed positively reinforcing stimulation. Other research by the author with the same three cartoons indicated that they have a high and very uniform reinforcing value for children in this age range (Baer, 1960). Testimony to this assumption is that almost any child will learn quickly to press a bar to turn the cartoons back on when they are turned off by the experimenter every few seconds.

It may be important to stress certain aspects of this experiment which could prove critical to its conclusions. One of these is the fact that the response weakened in this procedure is a weak one of short standing. Eight peanuts cannot be taken as a significant amount of reinforcement to a healthy child (who has had juice and cookies in school the same afternoon). These reinforcements, with the increasing ratio schedule on which they are delivered, are sufficient to set up a response strong enough to be studied and manipulated, clearly, but may not give the response much resemblance to other behaviors of the child with more powerful and extensive histories of reinforcement.

Furthermore, in this study punishment has been effected in a very precise manner. Reinforcement was withdrawn immediately consequent to a response in a very consistent way. The fact that this procedure is effective may not guarantee that in a more typical situation, where punishment is offered to a child late, inconsistently, and perhaps incomprehensibly, the effect would be the same.

Finally, the effect of punishment in this study seems durable in terms of the duration of the study. But this is not a great deal of time. Possibly, given more time in the situation, Punishment Ss would emit responses equal in number to those of Control Ss. It seems more likely, though, that the Ss would satiate with the entire situation before this would happen.

Apart from these qualifications to any widespread generalizations, the data give a clear picture of stimulus control in depressing a response in young children. The mechanism is best stated as the withdrawal of positive reinforcement. The technique used here would seem to be a fruitful one for further study of this problem in the laboratory.

SUMMARY

Young children were taught to press a bar for peanuts. During later extinction of this response, five Punishment Ss were punished by turning off a cartoon they were watching at the time for 2 seconds as a consequence of every response. This served to depress the response considerably, relative to five Control Ss who were not punished for responding while watching the same cartoons. During later sessions, Control Ss showed considerable spontaneous recovery of the response, and Punishment Ss did not, even though no longer punished. It was concluded that the withdrawal of positive reinforcement is an effective technique of punishment, at least in situations like the experimental one.

REFERENCES

BAER, D. M. Escape and avoidance response of preschool children to two schedules of reinforcement withdrawal. *J. exp. Anal. Behav.*, 1960, *3*, 155–159.

BIJOU, S. W. A child study laboratory on wheels. *Child Develpm.*, 1958, *29*,
425–427.

BRACKBILL, Y., and O'HARE, J. Discrimination learning in children as a function of reward and punishment. Paper read at Western Psychol. Ass., Eugene,
Oregon, 1957.

ESTES, W. K. An experimental study of punishment. *Psychol. Monogr.*, 1944,
57, 1–40.

FERSTER, C. B. Control of behavior in chimpanzees and pigeons by time out
from positive reinforcement. *Psychol. Monogr.*, 1958, *72*, 1–38.

LEWIS, D. J. Partial reinforcement in a gambling situation. *J. exp. Psychol.*,
1952, *43*, 447–450.

SEARS, R. R., MACCOBY, E. E., and LEVIN, H. *Patterns of child rearing.* New
York: Harper & Row, 1957.

SKINNER, B. F. *The behavior of organisms.* New York: Appleton-Century-
Crofts, 1938.

SKINNER, B. F. *Science and human behavior.* New York: Macmillan, 1953.

9

Training Rats to Press a Bar
to Turn Off Shock

James A. Dinsmoor and Lawson H. Hughes

In recent years a number of writers have suggested that aversive stimuli
play a prominent role in human behavior in social and clinical settings.
Experimental studies of the functioning of this type of stimulation, however, have been largely restricted to relatively complex patterns of events
found in avoidance training and punishment. These procedures enable the
subject to keep himself from being stimulated on a given occasion by re-

Adapted from *J. comp. physiol. Psychol.*, 1956, *49*, 235–238. With permission of
the authors and the American Psychological Association.

sponding in an appropriate fashion before the stimulus is scheduled to appear. To provide an orderly account for the resulting behavior, we find it necessary to appeal to the action of conditioned or secondary aversive stimuli, often dependent on the subject's behavior rather than upon direct intervention by the experimenter (Dinsmoor, 1954, 1955).

The present writers wish to investigate the underlying problem of how, in the first place, behavior is affected by stimulus reduction or termination. We believe this can best be studied by using stimuli that can be manipulated directly and independently by the experimenter. Accordingly, we have turned to what is called simple escape training. Here there is no way for the subject to avoid the stimulus by responding in advance: only after the stimulus has appeared will his response be effective. We have been able to find only a handful of studies that deal in any systematic way with this type of procedure (Campbell, 1952; Campbell and Kraeling, 1953; Harrison and Tracy, 1955; Jones, 1953; Kaplan, 1952; Keller, 1942; Wolin, 1952; Zeaman and House, 1950). Accordingly, the first step in our experimental program has been to try to find a procedure that is appropriate for rapid and reliable training of our subjects to make the desired response. Specifically, this experiment is a study of the influence of two variables on the acquisition and maintenance by white rats of a response that terminates an aversive stimulus, namely electric shock. The first of these variables is the amount of current (0.2 or 0.4 ma.) to which the animal is subjected; the second is the length of time (5, 10, 20, or 40 sec.) for which the shock is turned off following each response. The response we require is that of depressing a bar or lever which projects through one wall of the experimental box.

METHOD

Subjects

As Ss we used 40 male white rats, about a year old at the beginning of the experiment. We also used one additional S to provide replacement data for tests of significance. Seven more records were rejected because we discovered substantial currents across the shock grid after the animals were removed.

Apparatus

The box in which we placed the S was constructed of Plexiglas, $\frac{1}{4}$ in. thick. Its internal dimensions were 5 in. wide, 10 in. long, and 12 in. deep. The top was hinged and latched to permit us to insert or remove the animal. The rat rested on a grid floor composed of 13 brass rods, $\frac{1}{8}$ in. in diameter, spaced at intervals of $\frac{3}{4}$ in. from center to center. This grid was 4 in. above the bottom of the box, leaving 8 in. of free space for the rat.

The bar we provided for the animal to press consisted of a section of stainless-steel tubing, ⅜ in. in outside diameter and 4 in. in length. We mounted this horizontally, about 3⅛ in. above the grid floor, just inside and parallel to the front wall. The supporting shafts passed through a ½ in. slot running horizontally across the front of the box. The depression of this bar by about 1 cm., which required a force in the neighborhood of 20 gm., actuated a pressure switch: this defined the response. The bar also served as an additional element of the grid.

The experimental box was in turn enclosed in a sound-resistant and lightproof chamber constructed of ½ in. of plywood on the outside and 1½ in. of Acousticelotex. This chamber was 12 in. wide, 24 in. long, and 14¾ in. deep, and could be opened from the top.

The current we used to shock the animal was induced by a transformer (output 600 v.) and was regulated by the grid potential of a 6SK7 tube. Since the grid potential depended in turn on the voltage drop across a resistor in series with the S, a relatively stable level of current was maintained for subject resistances up to several hundred thousand ohms. When set at a level of 0.2 or 0.4 ma. for a calibrating load of 300,000 ohms, the current dropped 15 to 20 percent by the time the load reached 800,000 ohms.

In order to prevent the animal from finding and remaining on a pair of electrodes of the same polarity, and so avoiding the stimulation (Skinner and Campbell, 1947), we passed the shock current through a switching system which varied the polarity of each element with respect to all other elements. The grid rods and the bar were linked in haphazard order to the common contacts of a series of pressure switches; the normally open and normally closed contacts were connected to opposite sides of the shock potential. The switches were mounted in a circle around a rotating disc bearing a cam which covered 1/16 of its circumference. The disc turned at a rate of 33⅓ rpm. If the animal remained on any two electrodes, it received 66⅔ pulses per min., or approximately 1 per sec. Current flowed during ⅛ of the period of contact. If it maintained contact with three electrodes, S received 100 pulses per min., and the current flowed during 3/16 of the period of contact. The entire switching system was housed in a sound-resistant enclosure.

The experimental program was conducted by an electronic and relay network, and the onset, duration, and termination of each shock and each depression of the bar were recorded on a constant-speed polygraph.

Procedure

We housed the rats with the rest of the departmental colony, three to a cage, until the start of the experimental session, and gave them continuous access to food and water. We then assigned them in random order to eight groups of five members each, in a factorial design. We subjected four groups to a stimulating current of 0.2 ma. and the other four to a current of 0.4 ma. The four groups at each level of current were relieved of the shock for 5, 10, 20, and 40 sec., respectively, following each response in its presence.

To start the experimental session, we placed three cage mates in their boxes and threw the master switch. In 5 to 8 sec. the shock came on. Thereafter, for the next 100 min., each depression of the bar in the presence of the shock was followed in about ⅓ sec. by the termination of the shock. The length of time the shock remained off was not affected by the length of time the rat held the bar down or by additional responses it might make while the shock was off. If it was holding the bar down when the shock came on, S was required to release it and press it again before the shock would be ended. We repeated the same procedure for a second session the next day.

RESULTS AND DISCUSSION

Two animals in the 5-sec., low-current group and one animal in the 40-sec., low-current group failed to make at least 100 responses in 200 min., that is, failed to condition. But in most cases S pressed the bar shortly after the first application of the shock (median latency 8 sec.), and continued to respond so promptly thereafter that it was impossible for us to draw a line between the original, preconditioned responding and the subsequent conditioned behavior. The median latencies for all animals for the first 40 trials are plotted in Figure 1. The plots for individual groups are similar, but less orderly. It is evident that the "learning curve," if any, is confined to the first few trials.

Turning to group differences in performance, we find the mean latency of the median animal in each group for the first hundred trials plotted

Figure 1. The median latency in seconds from the onset of the shock to the depression of the bar, as a function of successive trials.

in Figure 2. We see that this latency declines as a function of increases in the length of time the shock remains off up to 20 sec. for the high-current groups and up to 40 sec. for the low-current groups. With the exception of the 40-sec., high-current latency, these values provide a reasonable approximation to a rectilinear relationship between log latency and log no-shock period. The high-current groups all show shorter latencies than the corresponding low-current groups.

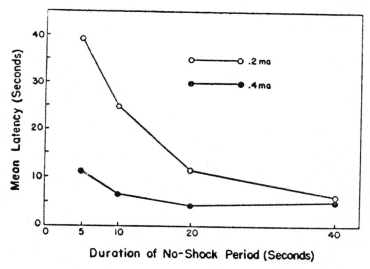

Figure 2. The mean latency for the first hundred trials of the median animal in each group.

Since three animals failed to condition, we omitted the 5-sec. groups from our analyses of variance and added the record of a replacement animal to the 40-sec., low-current group. This provides proportional cell frequencies but restricts our population to animals that do learn to make the required response. An analysis of the reciprocals of the mean latencies for individual animals shows that: (a) the difference between high- and low-current groups has a chance probability less than .01; (b) the differences among groups varying in the duration of the no-shock period have a chance probability less than .05; and (c) the interaction effect of the two variables has a chance probability less than .05. The orderliness of the relationships and the statistical significance of these differences indicate that our results should be replicable.

The functions we have obtained may be related, however, to another feature of the animal's behavior under the present procedure. Where food or water is used as a reinforcer, the reinforcement depends upon a consummatory sequence, which in turn depends upon the release of the bar. In our procedure, as in previous studies of this type (Jones, 1953; Kaplan, 1952; Keller, 1942; Zeaman and House, 1950), the reinforcement comes directly after the press. There is little reason for the animal to release the bar again until this becomes necessary to make the next press. The release of the bar is experimentally reinforced only as a member of the chain in which it is immediately followed by a press. As a result of these arrangements, and possibly of the $\frac{1}{3}$-sec. lag in shock termination imposed by our apparatus, the interval between the animal's press and its release of the bar becomes relatively long (see also Keller, 1942; Mowrer, 1940) and the interval between the release and the subsequent press relatively short. The animal comes to spend more of its time on the bar than off; often S is still holding the bar down when the shock returns. Our results may therefore be related to the punishing effects of the return of the shock while the animal is still holding. To check on this possibility, we plan in our next study to try a procedure in which not only the depression but the subsequent release of the bar is required for termination of the shock.

The continued holding of the bar through a part or all of the interval between shocks may also interfere to a substantial extent with the seemingly unmotivated "extra" (Keller, 1942) responding which occurs during this period. We have divided the number of responses recorded in the absence of the shock during the first hundred trials by the total time available, in minutes, to determine the mean rate of responding for each group (Table 1). An analysis of the variance in these data does show the rate of re-

TABLE 1

Mean presses per minute between shocks.

Current	Length of Time Shock Remains Off			
	5 sec.	10 sec.	20 sec.	40 sec.
0.2 ma.	4.00	1.67	1.40	1.79
0.4 ma.	3.89	2.46	3.62	1.99

sponding to be significantly higher ($p < .01$) at the higher current, but the variations in rate as a function of the length of time the shock remains off do not appear to be orderly and are not statistically significant ($F < 1$).

SUMMARY

We designed this experiment, first, to see how quickly and how consistently we could train rats to press a bar when we used the termination of electric shock as a reinforcement. Thirty-seven of our animals, out of 40, learned to make the response. In most cases, conditioning was immediate, with but slight improvement in the promptness of the response after the first few trials.

Secondly, we wanted to find out what conditions were most appropriate for this type of training. We used two variables, in a factorial design: (a) We subjected four groups of five rats to a stimulating current of 0.2 ma., the other four groups to a current of 0.4 ma. The high-current groups responded more promptly during their first hundred trials and made more "extra" responses between shocks. (b) Our second variable was the length of time for which we turned the shock off following each response in its presence. For the four groups at each level of current we turned the shock off for periods of 5, 10, 20, and 40 sec., respectively. The mean latencies declined as a function of the length of this interval up to 20 sec. for the 0.4 ma. groups and up to 40 sec. for the 0.2 ma. groups. The rate of "extra" responding, however, did not seem to be an orderly function of this variable.

The observation of prolonged depressions of the bar, often lasting until the return of the shock, suggested that somewhat different results might be obtained if not only the depression but the subsequent release of the bar were required before the shock was turned off.

REFERENCES

CAMPBELL, B. A., and KRAELING, D. Response strength as a function of drive level and amount of drive reduction. *J. exp. Psychol.*, 1953, *45*, 97–101.

CAMPBELL, S. L. Resistance to extinction as a function of number of shock termination reinforcements. Unpublished master's thesis, Indiana Univer., 1952.

DINSMOOR, J. A. Punishment: I. The avoidance hypothesis. *Psychol. Rev.*, 1954, *61*, 34–46.

DINSMOOR, J. A. Punishment: II. An interpretation of empirical findings. *Psychol. Rev.*, 1955, *62*, 96–105.

HARRISON, J. M., and TRACY, W. H. Use of auditory stimuli to maintain lever-pressing behavior. *Science*, 1955, *121*, 373–374.

JONES, M. B. An experimental study of extinction. *Psychol. Monogr.*, 1953, *67*, No. 19 (Whole No. 369).

KAPLAN, M. The effects of noxious stimulus intensity and duration during intermittent reinforcement of escape behavior. *J. comp. physiol. Psychol.*, 1952, *45*, 538–549.

KELLER, F. S. Light aversion in the white rat. *Psychol. Rec.*, 1942, *4*, 235–250.

MOWRER, O. H. An experimental analogue of "regression" with incidental observations on "reaction-formation." *J. abnorm. soc. Psychol.*, 1940, *35*, 56–87.

SKINNER, B. F., and CAMPBELL, S. L. An automatic shocking-grid apparatus for continuous use. *J. comp. physiol. Psychol.*, 1947, *40*, 305–307.

WOLIN, B. R. Generalization of response from an aversive motivation to a second aversive motivation and to an approach motivation. Unpublished doctor's dissertation, Indiana Univer., 1952.

ZEAMAN, D., and HOUSE, B. J. Response latency at zero drive after varying numbers of reinforcements. *J. exp. Psychol.*, 1950, *40*, 570–583.

10

Sequential Effects of Punishment

Nathan H. Azrin

The present report is concerned with the effects of punishment on behavior that is simultaneously being maintained by positive reinforcement. Previous studies (Estes, 1944) have indicated that responding is reduced so long as the punishment is in effect. The present findings reveal that the degree of suppression varies markedly during the course of the punishment process. White Carneaux pigeons, maintained at 80 percent of the weight they attained when allowed to feed ad libitum, were reinforced for 1 hour per day for responding (pecking) at an illuminated disc in accordance with a 1-minute variable-interval schedule of food reinforcement. Under this schedule, the response produces food reinforcement at varying time intervals, the average of which is 1 minute. This reinforcement procedure produces a fairly stable and uniform rate of responding which serves as a base line for evaluating the effects of punishment. This punishment was delivered immediately after every response and consisted of a brief electric shock delivered through implanted electrodes (Azrin, 1959).

Figure 1 shows the effect of the addition of punishment for 23 days to the food-reinforced responses of one subject. The punishment used here is a 30-v. 60-cy/sec shock of 30-msec duration delivered through 10,000-ohms resistance in series with the subject. It can be seen that responding is reduced immediately by the initial addition of the punishment. On succeeding days the number of responses gradually increases, and recovery is complete after several days. At that time, the number of responses during punishment is equal to or greater than the number before punishment was introduced. It can be seen that, when the punishment is removed, responding increases for the first 3 days and then returns to a level approximating the prepunishment performance. It may be noted that the variable-interval schedule employed permitted the animal to receive as many food reinforcements during the punishment period as during periods

Adapted from *Science,* 1960, *131,* 3400, 605–606. With permission of the author. Copyright 1960 by the American Association for the Advancement of Science.

without punishment as long as a low trickle of responses was made. The changes noted above of (1) a day-by-day recovery from the initial effects of punishment and (2) a temporary increase in responding upon the elimination of punishment have both been replicated with several other subjects.

Recovery from the effects of punishment occurs not only from day to day but also within each 1-hour session. Figure 2 shows the actual cumulative response record for a different subject under more severe punishment —a shock of 10-ma intensity. Before punishment (Figure 2, top) the rate of responding is fairly uniform throughout the hour, at about 110 responses per minute. Under punishment, however (Figure 2, bottom), the rate of responding shows a gradual recovery throughout the hour. In the first few minutes of the punishment period, the rate of response is essentially zero, but by the end of the hour, the rate of response stabilizes at about 15 responses per minute. The absence of complete recovery from punishment here is attributable to the greater intensity of the shock used. This response record was obtained after 20 days under punishment and represents a fairly stable state. The responses show an orderly increase throughout the hour, with no increase in variability such as is generally assumed to accompany punishment. The absence of such variability is in large part attributable to the corresponding lack of variability in the shock intensity, a nonvariability achieved through the use of implanted electrodes

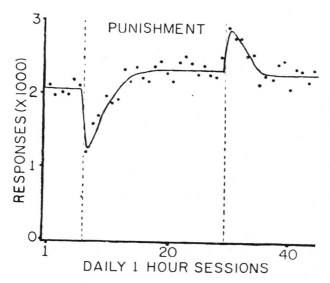

Figure 1. Effect of the addition and removal of punishment upon the food-reinforced responses of one subject. The punishment was a brief electric shock which followed every response on the days between those represented by the vertical dashed lines. Food reinforcement was produced according to a variable-interval schedule with a mean of 1 minute on all days.

rather than the usual electrified grid. This recovery from the initial effects
of punishment within each session has characterized the behavior of all of
the 14 other subjects studied, although the degree of recovery may be
somewhat more or less than that seen in Figure 2. It may be noted that
this recovery does not seem to be attributable to any local tissue changes,
since recovery continued when the locus of the electrodes was changed
during the recovery process. Rather, the phenomenon seems to be very

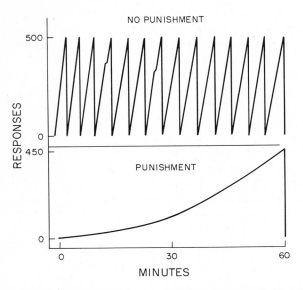

Figure 2. (Top) Cumulative record of the food-reinforced responses of one subject prior
to the addition of punishment. The food reinforcement (not indicated on the record) is
produced at variable intervals, the average of which is 1 minute. The vertical lines
represent the resetting of the recorder pen. (Bottom) A cumulative record of the responses
for the same subject during punishment. The same schedule of food reinforcement pre-
vails, but punishment in the form of a brief electric shock is produced by every response.

general. Similar recovery has been noted with several intensities of punishment, levels of food deprivation, and schedules of reinforcement, as well
as with electrified grids rather than implanted electrodes.

The temporary increase in responding after the removal of punishment
seems to involve some type of contrast effect. Previous studies have
revealed that the addition of punishment during extinction (Estes, 1944)
produced a reduction in responding and that the later removal of the
punishment produced a temporary increase in responding which appeared
to be a type of compensation for the behavioral reduction. The present
study reveals that this same temporary increase follows the removal of the
punishment, even though the punishment has ceased to be effective. It
appears, therefore, that this compensatory increase in responding does not

require that the behavior in question be suppressed at the time the punishment is removed.

REFERENCES

AZRIN, N. H. A technique for delivering shock to pigeons. *J. exp. Anal. Behav.*, 1959, *2*, 161–163.

ESTES, W. K. An experimental study of punishment. *Psychol. Monogr.*, 1944, *57*, 1–40.

SUGGESTED READINGS

FERSTER, C. B., and SKINNER, B. F. *Schedules of reinforcement.* New York: Appleton-Century-Crofts, 1957.

HULL, C. L. *Principles of behavior.* New York: Appleton-Century-Crofts, 1943, Chap. 6.

KIMBLE, G. A. *Hilgard and Marquis' conditioning and learning.* New York: Appleton-Century-Crofts, 1961, Chaps. 3, 4, 5, and 6.

SKINNER, B. F. *The behavior of organisms.* New York: Appleton-Century-Crofts, 1938, Chap. 3.

THORNDIKE, E. L. *Animal intelligence.* New York: Macmillan, 1911.

TOLMAN, E. C. *Purposive behavior in animals and men.* New York: Appleton-Century-Crofts, 1932, Chaps. 2 and 3. (Reprinted by University of California Press, Berkeley, 1949.)

Chapter V

DISCRIMINATION AND GENERALIZATION

The topic of discrimination is as old as the first systematic psychological treatise written in the western world: the *De Anima* of Aristotle. This work contains an extensive discussion of what J. H. Randall, Jr. (1960) has translated as "the power of selective response." The first systematic experimental investigations of how this "power of selective response" comes about were performed by Pavlov, who was also the first to demonstrate the phenomenon of stimulus generalization in the laboratory. The first selection of this chapter is again by Pavlov. It is followed by a description of the first of a series of ground-breaking experiments concerning stimulus generalization employing operant conditioning procedures. The authors, N. Guttman and H. I. Kalish, followed up and further developed a method first suggested by B. F. Skinner (1950). Their research, in turn, has led to a large number of recent investigations concerning generalization gradients (Mostofsky, 1965). Many of these experiments have employed schedules of positive reinforcement. Sidman's study of "stimulus generalization in an avoidance situation," made use of aversive control. The behavior of the subjects employed in Sidman's experiments was maintained by the avoidance conditioning procedure previously developed by the same author (Sidman, 1953a, b). The experiment by R. T. Kelleher first extended the use of operant conditioning methods to the study of concept formation in chimpanzees, a "complex behavioral process" previously almost exclusively investigated with human subjects (Bruner *et al.*, 1957).

The article by D. S. Blough provides a brief description of a technique successfully employed in the study of "animal psychophysics," the study of the discriminative capacities of animals. Blough's technique is ingenious but complex and intricate. The article here reproduced was published as a preliminary report. A more extensive description has been published elsewhere (Blough, 1958).

REFERENCES

BLOUGH, D. S. A method for obtaining psychophysical thresholds from the pigeon. *J. exp. Anal. Behav.*, 1958, *1*, 31–43.
BRUNER, J. S., GOODNOW, J. J., and AUSTIN, G. A. *A study of thinking.* New York: Wiley, 1957.

MOSTOFSKY, D. I. (Ed.) *Stimulus generalization*. Stanford: Stanford University Press, 1965.

RANDALL, J. H., JR. *Aristotle*. New York: Columbia University Press, 1960.

SIDMAN, M. Avoidance conditioning with brief shock and no exteroceptive warning signal. *Science*, 1953, *118*, 157–158. (a)

SIDMAN, M. Two temporal parameters of the maintenance of avoidance behavior by the white rat. *J. comp. physiol. Psychol.*, 1953, *46*, 253–261. (b)

SKINNER, B. F. Are theories of learning necessary? *Psychol. Rev.*, 1950, *57*, 193–216.

11

The Analysing and Synthesizing Activity of the Cerebral Hemispheres: (a) The Initial Generalization of Conditioned Stimuli. (b) Differential Inhibition.

I. P. Pavlov

Stimuli which evoke conditioned reflexes are perpetually acting as signals of those agencies in the environment which are in themselves immediately favourable or immediately destructive for the organism. Such signals are drawn sometimes from only one elementary property of the environing agencies, sometimes from a whole complex of these properties. This is possible only because the nervous system possesses on the one hand a definite analysing mechanism, by means of which it selects out of the whole complexity of the environment those units which are of significance, and, on the other hand, a synthesizing mechanism by means of which individual units can be integrated into an excitatory complex. Thus in studying the nervous activity of the cerebral cortex it is necessary to deal with two further and distinct phenomena, one involving a neuro-analysis and the other involving a neuro-synthesis. The analysing and synthesizing func-

Adapted from *Conditioned Reflexes*, 1927, Chapter VII, pp. 110–130. With permission of the Clarendon Press, Oxford.

tions of the nervous system constantly superimpose themselves upon and interact with one another.

Every type of nervous system presents a more or less complex analysing apparatus which readily admits of subdivision into what we may term the nervous analysers. For example, the visual analyser selects the vibrations of light, the acoustic analyser selects the vibrations of sound, and so on. Furthermore, each analyser differentiates its own selective medium of the environment into a very large number of elementary physiological stimuli. With regard to the structure of the analysers, each includes, on the one hand, the peripheral receptor with all its afferent nerves, and, on the other hand, the nerve cells which lie at the central termination of the nerve fibers. The peripheral receptors can be regarded as "transformers," which, in the case of any single analyser, are capable of accepting only one definite form of energy as an adequate stimulus for the initiation of a nerve impulse. It is obvious that both the peripheral receptors and the central nervous elements are involved in the analysing function of the nervous system. Inferior analysing qualities are of course manifested by lower parts of the nervous system, and even by the crudely differentiated nervous substance in those animals which lack a nervous system proper. An organism deprived of its cerebral hemispheres still responds in a great variety of ways to stimuli applied to its receptor surfaces, according to the site of application, the intensity and the quality of the stimuli. However, the highest and most subtle analysing activity of which an animal is capable can be obtained only with the help of the cerebral cortex. It is evident also that only with the progressive development of the analysing activity of the nervous system is the organism enabled to multiply the complexity of its contacts with the external world and to achieve a more and more varied and exact adaptation to external conditions. In contemporary research the study of the analysing function forms a very important section of the so-called physiology of the sense organs. This section has reached a very high state of development in the hands of some of the greatest physiologists, especially Helmholtz, and presents an abundant wealth of data concerning the activities of the peripheral structures of the different analysers and of their cerebral terminations. A good deal is known also about the limits of the analysing functions in man. But while the study of the physiology of the special sense organs suggests explanations of many complicated cases of the analysing function, and enunciates many fundamental laws to which this activity conforms, the greater part of the material which has been gathered is of a subjective character, being based on our psychical apperceptions which are the most elementary subjective indications of the objective correlations between organism and environment. This fact constitutes the greatest defect of this section of physiology, since it excludes the study of the analysing function in animals outside man, and therewith all the advantages of animal experimentation. The method of conditioned reflexes, however, gives over the study of the whole of this most important function of nervous analysis into the hands of the purely experimental physiologist. With the help of conditioned reflexes the scope and limits of the analysing functions in different animals can be exactly determined, and the laws regulating this function made clear. Although the study of the physiology of analysers has been as yet but little developed, research upon the new lines is making rapid progress and may be expected to add largely to our knowledge of the mechanism by which the exact correspondence between the organism and its environment is maintained.

The first step was to find a method by which the activities of the analysers could be objectively studied in animals by means of visible outward reactions. As was mentioned before, even insignificant changes in the external environment call forth if not a special inborn or acquired reflex activity, then a reaction of orientation (the "investigatory reflex"). It is obvious that the investigatory reflex can be used to determine the degree to which the nervous system of a given animal is capable of discriminating between various stimuli. If, for example, among the different environing agencies there is present a definite musical tone, any, even slight, alteration of its pitch will suffice to evoke an investigatory reflex in the form of a definite orientation of the ears and maybe of the whole body of the animal in relation to the tone. The same is true even of slight changes in various other elementary or compound stimuli. The investigatory reflex, of course, takes place only provided that the structure of the analysing apparatus is sufficiently delicate to register the change in the environment. This reflex can be used for the purpose of our investigation by itself, or, much better, through its inhibitory or dis-inhibitory effects upon conditioned reflexes, since these are the most delicate nervous reactions of which the animal is capable. However in spite of the high degree of sensitivity manifested by the investigatory reflex this reaction is in many respects unsuitable as a basis for the study of the analysing activity of the nervous system. One of its chief defects is that in the case of certain weak stimuli the reaction is only transient and cannot be repeated, and it is therefore useless for the purpose of exact experimentation. The detailed investigation of a conditioned reflex reaction, on the contrary, provides an eminently suitable method for an exact experimental research into the analysing function. A definite external agent is made, for example, to acquire by our usual technique the properties of a definite conditioned stimulus. By repeated reinforcement this particular stimulus is strengthened in its new properties, while the stimulus nearest to it in intensity, position, or quality is always contrasted by being left without reinforcement, with the result that it becomes readily and exactly differentiated from the established positive conditioned stimulus.

The successful development of analysis of external agencies by means of conditioned reflexes is always preceded by what we call a "period of generalization" (which may possibly be regarded as some form of synthesizing activity).

For instance, if a tone of 1000 cps is established as a conditioned stimulus, many other tones spontaneously acquire similar properties, such properties diminishing proportionally to the intervals of these tones from the one of 1000 cps. Similarly, if a tactile stimulation of a definite circumscribed area of skin is made into a conditioned stimulus, tactile stimulation of other skin areas will also elicit some conditioned reaction, the effect diminishing with increasing distance of these areas from the one for which the conditioned reflex was originally established. The same is observed with stimulation of other receptor organs. This spontaneous development of accessory reflexes, or, as we have termed it, generalization of stimuli, can be interpreted from a biological point of view by reference to the fact that natural stimuli are in most cases not rigidly constant but range around a particular strength and quality of stimulus in a common group. For example, the hostile sound of any beast of prey serves as a conditioned stimulus to a defence reflex in the animals which it hunts. The defence reflex is brought about independently of variations in pitch, strength, and timbre of the sound produced by the animal according to its distance, the tension of its vocal cords, and similar factors.

Besides this we have encountered in conditioned reflexes another form of generalization, the vital importance of which is not so immediately apparent. So far we have been dealing with a temporary form of generalization within a single analyser in the case of simultaneous and delayed reflexes. In the case of conditioned long-trace reflexes, with a pause of 1–3 minutes, the generalization becomes permanent and of a wider scope. Trace reflexes, like all delayed reflexes, present two phases—an initial, inactive phase based on internal inhibition, and a second, active phase based on nervous excitation. All that has been said about the effect of extra stimuli upon these two phases in the case of delayed reflexes is true also for the two phases in trace reflexes. The trace reflexes, however, have another characteristic of their own, namely, that they exhibit a permanent and universal generalization, involving all the analysers. For example, if we establish a long-trace conditioned reflex to a tactile cutaneous stimulus, it is found that stimuli which belong to other analysers and which have never been connected with the given reflex begin to act as conditioned stimuli to the same trace reflex. We shall deal with this phenomenon at some length, since the investigation presents some special points of interest.

The following experiments bearing upon this question are taken from a research by Dr. Grossman:

A tactile stimulation of the skin is used as the conditioned stimulus for a long-trace reflex to acid, the interval between the end of the conditioned stimulus and the beginning of the unconditioned being one minute. The experiments show the effect of a thermal stimulus at 0° C. and of a given musical tone, both applied for the very first time.

Time	Stimulus Applied During 1 Min.	Salivary Secretion in Drops During Successive Minutes from the Beginning of the Conditioned Stimulus	Remarks
Experiment of 6th February, 1909.			
11:39 A.M.	Tactile	0, 3	Reinforced by
11:55 A.M.	Tactile	0, 7	introduction of acid.
12:6 P.M.	Thermal at 0° C.	1, 4, 7, 7	Not reinforced by acid.
12:22 P.M.	Tactile	0, 4	Reinforced.
Experiment of 7th February, 1909.			
2:36 P.M.	Tactile	0, 9	Reinforced by
2:45 P.M.	Tactile	0, 15	introduction of acid.
2:54 P.M.	Tone	0, 3, 4, 6, 2, 0	Not reinforced.
3:2 P.M.	Tactile	0, 0	Reinforced by
3:10 P.M.	Tactile	0, 1	introduction
3:22 P.M.	Tactile	0, 6	of acid.

It is thus seen that stimuli which had previously never been connected with the reflex to acid have now acquired the property to excite this reflex. Furthermore, the stimuli, although applied for the very first time, act in the same manner as the stimulus used to establish the trace reflex, their effect being manifested not at the time of their application, but chiefly or exclusively after they have been discontinued. This similarity made us inclined to regard them as being due to a generalization of the original trace reflex. Of course, the evidence from a few isolated experiments of this type was not sufficiently strong to establish this conclusion beyond doubt, and in view of the intrinsic interest of this phenomenon it was subjected to rigid investigation.

On the experimental evidence available concerning conditioned reflexes only two further possible explanations of this phenomenon suggested themselves. In the first place a long-trace reflex is always formed slowly and with difficulty, and it was observed in our earlier experiments that before the formation of the trace reflex other conditioned reflexes were very easily established to any chance stimuli which happened to coincide with the actual administration of the unconditioned stimulus and of which the experimenter himself was often the cause. In the case we are speaking of at present the danger of interference by extraneous stimuli was therefore considerable, and these experiments had to be repeated in our new laboratory so as to make sure that any possible accidental influence of the experimenter upon the animal was excluded. Under these conditions the generalized character of the long-trace reflex was still found to persist.

The second explanation which suggested itself was as follows: When conditioned reflexes are being established in dogs for the first time, it is found that the whole experimental environment, beginning with the introduction of the animal into the experimental room, acquires at first conditioned properties. This initial reflex could be called, therefore, a conditioned reflex to the environment. But later on, when the special reflex to a single definite and constant stimulus has appeared, all the other elements of the environment gradually lose their special conditioned significance, most probably on account of a gradual development of internal inhibition. However, this inhibition is at first very easily dis-inhibited by any extra stimulus. The following is a striking example of such a case which was very common, when, as formerly, the experimenter remained in the room with the dog. The reflex to environment had in the given experiments just come to an end, the glands being now in a resting state except when the special positive conditioned stimulus was applied. As soon, however, as I myself entered the room, in order for the first time to watch the experiments, a copious secretion of saliva was produced by the dog, which persisted as long as I remained in the room. I myself presented in this case the extra stimulus dis-inhibiting the reflex to environment which had only just recently undergone extinction. Now it occurred to us that the phenomenon of the universal generalization of the long-trace reflexes might really be nothing but a dis-inhibition of the reflex to environment. However, after a thorough examination, this explanation had to be discarded. In the first place, a considerable generalization of long-trace reflexes could easily be observed even in dogs in which the reflex to environment had been deeply inhibited so long ago that it was now impossible to dis-inhibit it. In the second place, the supposition of dis-inhibition when followed up necessitated a further assumption which was easily disproved. It has been seen already that dis-inhibition of the inactive phase in delay was obtained immediately on application of the extra stimulus, i.e., without any such latent period as is observed for trace reflexes. If the generalized character of trace reflexes was in reality nothing but dis-inhibition, we should expect all the different stimuli also to act immediately, but as we have seen they act only after their termination and after about the same latent period as the initially established trace reflex. If it is still assumed that the effect is due to dis-inhibition of the reflex to environment, then in the case of trace reflexes all the different stimuli must act for some reason as very powerful extra stimuli which do not dis-inhibit the reflex to environment, but temporarily abolish all conditioned activity by producing a very powerful inhibition (as is also the case with very powerful extra stimuli in delay), and the ensuing dis-inhibition must be brought about by their traces which represent weaker stimuli. This assumption, however, is contradicted by the following facts. It is known that repeated application of the same powerful extra stimulus is followed by a gradual diminution of its inhibitory effect, which gives place, as was seen with delay, to dis-inhibition. But in the case of the generalized stimuli in long-trace reflexes the latent period does not diminish in spite of repeated applications. This shows that the reflex activity is due to a genuine generalization of the trace reflex and not to dis-inhibition. Finally, there is this striking fact, that in the case of trace reflexes following the application of various stimuli, which of course are never reinforced, the effect of the special conditioned stimulus to which the trace reflex was experimentally established also becomes temporarily diminished, and the secretion may fall to zero, a fact which cannot be reconciled with any supposition that we are dealing with a dis-inhibition of the reflex to environment. Indeed, there is no doubt that this weakening of the effect of the special conditioned stimulus represents a simple instance of extinction, as the result of non-reinforcement, of a reflex which has become generalized within the hemispheres.

Thus it is seen that in the course of the establishment of simultaneous and delayed reflexes a temporary generalization develops in the form of a number of accessory conditioned reflexes to associated stimuli. Generalizations of the reflexes can be effected also through the whole environment acting on the organism by the sum total of its individual units and leading to the formation of what we may call a synthetic environmental reflex. In other cases, namely, in long-trace reflexes, it is effected in virtue of the intrinsic properties of the nervous system itself, which give a more or less generalized character to the individual external stimuli in their capacity as conditioned stimuli. In many instances, some of which we have referred to above, it is obvious that this fact of generalization of stimuli has a definite importance in the natural correlation between the animal and its environment, but in other cases the generalization can have only a limited or temporary significance. In the latter cases the approximate, general, and under some conditions useful connection with the environment as a whole is replaced by a precise and definitely specialized connection with a definite stimulatory unit.

The question can now be discussed as to how the specialization of the conditioned reflex, or, in other words, the discrimination of external agencies, arises. Formerly we were inclined to think that this effect could be obtained by two different methods: the first method consisted in repeating the definite conditioned stimulus a great number of times always accompanied by reinforcement, and the second method consisted in contrasting the single definite conditioned stimulus, which was always accompanied by reinforcement, with different neighbouring stimuli which were never reinforced. At present, however, we are more inclined to regard this second method as more probably the only efficacious one, since it was observed that no absolute differentiation was ever obtained by the use of the first method, even though the stimulus was repeated with reinforcement over a thousand times. On the other hand, it was found that contrast by even a single unreinforced application of an allied stimulus, or by a number of single unreinforced applications of different members of a series of allied stimuli at infrequent intervals of days or weeks, led to a rapid development of differentiation. The method of contrast is now always employed in our experiments, as leading to a differentiation of external agencies in an incomparably quicker time.

We can now follow out the development of differentiation between external stimuli in the conditioned reflexes in greater detail. In the first place an interesting observation which remained for a long time without explanation may be considered: It was noticed that when, after a conditioned reflex to a definite stimulus (e.g., a definite musical tone) had been firmly established, the effect of another closely allied stimulus (a neighbouring musical tone) was tried for the first time, the conditioned reflex which resulted from the new stimulus was frequently much weaker than that obtained with the original conditioned stimulus. On repetition of the stimulus of the neighbouring tone, always, of course, without reinforcement, the secretory effect increased until it became equal to that given by the original established stimulus, but subsequently on further repetition began to diminish, falling finally to a permanent zero. Thus it appeared that at first the two closely allied stimuli were discriminated straight away, but that later this discrimination for some reason disappeared, only gradually to reestablish itself and finally to become absolute. To provide an explanation of this phenomenon we can revert to an interpretation which was advanced previously for similar events occurring in the process of development of conditioned inhibition. It will be remembered that when, in the formation of conditioned inhibition, a conditioned stimulus was accompanied for the first time by the new stimulus which later acquired the properties of a conditioned inhibitor, the combination produced either a very small positive effect or else remained totally ineffective. Later, although the inhibitory combination was never reinforced by the unconditioned stimulus, it produced again a reflex of full strength, which, however, after further repetitions gradually fell to a permanent zero. The explanation given in the case of conditioned inhibition, and fully borne out by experimental evidence, was that the additional stimulus elicited on its first application an investigatory reflex which immediately produced an external inhibition of the conditioned reflex; on repetition the strength of the investigatory reflex rapidly diminished and the positive effect of the conditioned stimulus was temporarily restored, being later gradually suppressed by the development of internal inhibition. Similarly, in the case of differentiation it is possible to regard stimuli neighbouring on the definite positive conditioned stimulus as bearing two aspects, one of similarity to, and the other of difference from, the positive conditioned stimulus. On account of the element which is in common, these neighbouring stimuli can act similarly to the positive conditioned one; it is the presence of the second factor, of difference, which determines a temporary investigatory reflex, bringing about external inhibition of the excitatory effect, but later serving as foundation for the development of a permanent and final differentiation of allied stimuli.

Time (P.M.)	Stimulus Applied During 30 Secs.	Salivary Secretion Recorded by Divisions of Scale (5 div. = 0.1 cc.) During 30 Secs.	Remarks
	Experiment of 15th February, 1917.		
3:13	Object rotating clockwise	27	Reinforced.
3:25	Object rotating anti-clockwise	7	Not reinforced.
	Experiment of 16th February, 1917.		
1:4	Object rotating clockwise	24	Reinforced.
1:14	" " "	26	"
1:25	" " "	27	"
1:34	Object rotating anti-clockwise	10	Not reinforced.
	Experiment of 17th February, 1917.		
2:45	Object rotating anti-clockwise	12	Not reinforced.
	Experiment of 18th February, 1917.		
2:48	Object rotating clockwise	19	Reinforced.
3:33	Object rotating anti-clockwise	34	Not reinforced.
	Experiment of 20th February, 1917.		
3:7	Object rotating anti-clockwise	26	Not reinforced.
3.28	Object rotating clockwise	26	Reinforced.
	Experiment of 21st February, 1917.		
3:00	Object rotating anti-clockwise	12	Not reinforced.

The strength of the reflex which is undergoing differential inhibition now diminishes progressively with small fluctuations until it reaches a permanent zero.

The correctness of this interpretation is borne out by the striking similarity in detail in the development of differentiation and of conditioned inhibition. The same variations occur in both cases. The initial diminution in the strength of the reflex during the first few applications of the new stimulus is sometimes succeeded by a transitory increase in strength as compared with the normal, and after this the reflex diminishes steadily below its normal value until it finally attains a permanent zero; in most cases, however, the initial diminution is succeeded by a phase of increase to the normal level, after which the reflex again falls steadily to zero with the development of the final differentiation; it rarely happens that a development of differentiation is established without such fluctuations, or that a gradual diminution of the reflex follows directly upon the sudden initial drop. While, in describing the formation of conditioned inhibition, the fluctuations received a considerable share of attention, no records of experiments were given. A presentation of the analogous experiments on the establishment of differential inhibition will make the matter clear.

In the first series of experiments (see p. 199), which were conducted by Dr. Gubergritz, an object rotating in a clockwise direction served as the positive conditioned stimulus, while the same object rotating in the opposite direction served as the stimulus undergoing differentiation.

Time (P.M.)	Stimulus Applied During 30 Secs.	Amount of Saliva Recorded by Divisions of Scale (5 div. = 0.1 cc.) During 30 Secs.	Remarks
	Experiment of 12th October, 1917.		
12:28	Tone	30	Reinforced.
1:0	Tone	35	Reinforced.
1:10	Semitone	9	Not reinforced.
	Experiment of 13th October, 1917.		
12:54	Tone	36	Reinforced.
1:5	Tone	36	Reinforced.
1:12	Semitone	32	Not reinforced.
2:1	Semitone	16	Not reinforced.
2:18	Tone	29	Reinforced.

The reflex to the semitone continues to fluctuate, gradually diminishing in strength until at the thirteenth repetition it has fallen to zero.

The above experiments were conducted on another dog, a musical tone serving as a conditioned alimentary stimulus and its semitone as the stimulus undergoing differentiation.

The dog employed in the next series of experiments is the same as was used in the first series. A luminous circle was used for a conditioned alimentary stimulus, and a luminous square of equal surface and equal brightness for the stimulus undergoing differentiation.

Time (P.M.)	Stimulus Applied During 30 Secs.	Amount of Saliva Recorded by Divisions of Scale (5 div. = 0.1 cc.) During 30 Secs.	Remarks
		Experiment of 28th December, 1917.	
1:20	Circle	14	Reinforced.
1:53	Square	3	Not reinforced.
		Experiment of 29th December, 1917.	
2:44	Circle	16	Reinforced.
3.0	Square	7	Not reinforced.
		Experiment of 30th December, 1917.	
1:24	Circle	15	Reinforced.
1:32	Square	10	Not reinforced.

Then with small fluctuations the reflex diminishes progressively, until after the eleventh repetition the square becomes permanently ineffective.

Some other interesting points besides those connected with the interference of the investigatory reflex have also come to light in recent experiments. In the first place it has been shown that the development of a differentiation of two very closely allied stimuli may be attempted directly, or, on the other hand, the same differentiation may be effected in stages, leading up through the differentiation of more remote stimuli. There is a considerable difference between the rates of development of a precise differentiation by these two methods. For example, if we begin with the first method we generally find the differentiation does not become established even after a considerable number of contrasts of the two very closely allied stimuli; but if we proceed to establish a differentiation of a remoter stimulus, working up gradually through finer differentiations until the very closely allied stimulus is again reached, it is found that this differentiation is now very rapidly established. The following experiments of Dr. Gubergritz serve to illustrate these relations:

A circle of white paper provided a conditioned alimentary stimulus from which it was required to differentiate a circle of grey paper of similar size made of No. 10 in Zimmermann's scale (50 shades from white to black). Seventy-five applications of the grey circle No. 10 without reinforcement, contrasted with frequent applications of the white circle which always remained reinforced, failed to produce the slightest sign of differentiation. A much darker circle No. 35 was now contrasted with the white, and a differentiation was quickly established. Differentiation was now carried out for grey circles Nos. 25 and 15, after which the attempt to differentiate circle No. 10 was made again, with the result that complete differentiation was established after a total of only 20 applications, in all, of the four different circles.

A similar experiment, also with a visual stimulus, but in a modified form, was carried out on another dog. In this case the conditioned alimentary stimulus was again a circle, while the stimulus to be differentiated from it was an ellipse cut from the same paper and of equal surface, with the semi-axes in the ratio of 8:9. Although at the beginning 70 applications of the ellipse were made with the method of contrast, no differentiation was obtained. Successive differentiations were now obtained in stages for ellipses with ratio of the semi-axes 4:5, 5:6, 7:8, and finally with the ellipse of the ratio 8:9. A precise differentiation of the latter was finally established after a total of only 18 applications, in all, of the four ellipses.

In building up a differentiation by stages, beginning with a remote stimulus, the development of the first crude differentiation takes place comparatively slowly, especially if it is desired to obtain an absolute differentiation giving a permanent zero. When, however, an absolute, or almost absolute, differentiation has been obtained, the succeeding stages of progress towards the finer differentiation are passed through with increasing rapidity, becoming, however, somewhat retarded as the limit of the analysing activity is approached. One example may be given in illustration:

A white circle of a given surface area was used for a conditioned stimulus, while ellipses of the same area and whiteness but with different rations of semi-axes provided the stimuli undergoing differentiation. In order to obtain a pronounced differentiation of the first ellipse, in which the ratio of the semi-axes was 4:5, 24 applications were required, with, of course, frequent contrastings by the circle. At this stage the circle elicited a secretion of 34 divisions of the scale in 30 seconds, whereas the effect of the ellipse was measured by only four divisions. The next ellipse, with a ratio of 5:6, required only 3 applications in contrast to the circle before it became fully differentiated. Three repetitions were required also for the next ellipse, in which the semi-axes were in the ratio 6:7.

It should be noted that irregularities in the curve of development of differentiation do not depend always on the disturbing influence of the investigatory reflex due to external stimuli; in all probability they are sometimes caused by variations in the intensity of the underlying nervous activity.

The stability of differentiation of a given stimulus can be measured by the length of time reckoned from the last application of the positive stimulus during which differentiation is fully maintained. When differentiation has only recently been established, the length of time during which the differentiated stimulus without intermediate practice will yet give a full zero on its next application is short; this length of time increases, however, as the differentiation becomes more firmly established. For practical purposes we take a differentiation as being fully established when it is maintained for not less than 24 hours, still giving a zero reflex when applied as the very first stimulus in an experiment.

Our repeated experiments have demonstrated that the same precision of differentiation of various stimuli can be obtained whether they are used in the form of negative or positive conditioned stimuli. This holds good in the case of conditioned trace reflexes also. The following experiment from a paper by Dr. Frolov gives an illustration of the differentiation of a trace stimulus:

A rate of 104 beats per minute of a metronome was established as a conditioned alimentary stimulus. The conditioned trace inhibitor undergoing differentiation was given by a definite tone of an organ pipe (No. 16) which was sounded for 15 seconds and followed after a pause of 1 minute by the stimulus of the metronome which remained in this case without reinforcement. A combination of the metronome with a trace of the tone of the next organ pipe (No. 15, an interval of one tone from the first) was contrasted with the first, being reinforced so that it became an excitatory stimulus. The differentiation of the trace inhibition is illustrated in the following experiment:

Experiment of 25th April, 1922.

Time (P.M.)	Stimulus	Duration of Stimulus (Secs.)	Salivary Secretion in Divisions of the Scale During Successive Periods of 15 Secs.
1:34	Tone of organ pipe No. 16	15	0.
	Interval	60	0, 0, 0, 0.
	Metronome	30	15, 40,[1] not reinforced.
1:40	Tone of organ pipe No. 16	15	0.
	Interval	60	0, 0, 0, 0.
	Metronome	30	0, 15, not reinforced.
1:48	Tone of organ pipe No. 15	15	0.
	Interval	60	0, 0, 0, 0.
	Metronome	30	25, 65, reinforced.

[1] Differentiations of trace-conditioned inhibitors are very easily subjected to disinhibition and are very unstable. It can be noticed in the above experiment that the first application of the organ pipe No. 16, the after-effect of which should have inhibited the secretory action of the metronome, failed to do so, when applied, as in this experiment, as the first stimulus after an interval of 24 hours from the pre-

It should be added that the above differentiation was obtained by passing through a long series of crude differentiations, beginning with traces measured by seconds, and with wider intervals of tones; but once developed the differentiation could be repeated from day to day.

With regard to the nature of the nervous process by which the initially generalized conditioned stimulus comes to assume an extremely specialized form, we have abundant experimental evidence that it is based upon internal inhibition; in other words, we may say that the excitatory process which is originally widely spread in the cerebral part of the analyser is gradually overcome by internal inhibition, excepting only the minutest part of it which corresponds to the given conditioned stimulus. This interpretation of differentiation as based upon internal inhibition rests upon evidence to be described now.

A differentiation is established between two closely allied stimuli, so that one of them which is reinforced gives a constant positive conditioned effect, while the other, which remains unreinforced, gives no secretory effect. If, however, the positive stimulus is applied a short time after the differentiated one, there is found to be a considerable diminution of its secretory effect. An illustration of such an experiment can be given from a research by Dr. Beliakov:

A definite tone of an organ pipe has been given properties of an alimentary conditioned stimulus, and an interval of one-eighth lower has been firmly differentiated from it by the usual method of contrast.

Experiment of 14th February, 1911.

Time (P.M.)	Stimulus Applied During 30 Secs.	Salivary Secretion in Drops During 30 Secs.	Remarks
12:10	Tone	5	Reinforced.
12:25	Tone one-eighth lower	0	Not reinforced.
12:26	Tone	0.5	Reinforced.
12:56	Tone	4	Reinforced.

It follows that after application of the differentiated tone there remains in the nervous system a state of inhibition which is for some time sufficiently powerful to weaken the excitatory process set up by the application of the positive stimulus.

---

ceding experiment. The second application of the organ pipe No. 16 exerted a powerful inhibitory after-effect, giving a secretion of only 15 divisions with a latent period of over 15 seconds as compared with a secretion of 90 divisions with a very short latent period with the use of organ pipe No. 15.

The inhibition which is exhibited in differentiation must be recognized as constituting the fourth type of internal inhibition, which may be called differential inhibition.

It would to our mind be quite appropriate to bring conditioned inhibition also under the heading of differential inhibition, since in both cases we deal with a removal by means of internal inhibition of an excitatory effect of simple or complex stimuli which acquired their excitatory properties spontaneously in virtue of their partial resemblance to the original positive conditioned stimulus.

The inhibitory after-effect in differential inhibition corresponds exactly with the inhibitory after-effect in conditioned inhibition, both becoming shortened by repetition. At the beginning they may persist upwards of an hour, but they become restricted finally to a matter of a few seconds.

It is necessary to emphasize in this place the fact that the finer the degree of differentiation the greater is the intensity of the inhibitory after-effect. The following experiments of Dr. Beliakov serve to illustrate this point:

A definite tone represents the conditioned stimulus in an alimentary reflex; the intervals of one-half and one-eighth were used for differentiation.

Time (P.M.)	Stimulus Applied During 30 Secs.	Salivary Secretion in Drops During 30 Secs.	Remarks
Experiment of 19th March, 1911.			
12:17	Semitone	0	Not reinforced.
12:37	Tone	4	Reinforced.
1:7	Tone	4	Reinforced.
Experiment of 29th March, 1911.			
3:55	One-eighth	0	Not reinforced.
4:15	Tone	1.5	Reinforced.
4:30	Tone	4	Reinforced.

Apart from the close connection already mentioned between conditioned inhibition and differential inhibition, the latter provides a close parallel in all other respects to the three types of internal inhibition which have been dealt with in previous lectures. Thus the inhibitory after-effect in differential inhibition, similarly to other forms of internal inhibition, undergoes summation on repetition of the stimulus. The following experiments are again taken from the researches by Dr. Beliakov:

Another dog is taken in which a conditioned alimentary reflex is established to a definite musical tone, while a semitone lower is firmly differentiated as an inhibitory stimulus.

Time (P.M.)	Stimulus Applied During 30 Secs.	Salivary Secretion in Drops During 30 Secs.	Remarks
	Experiment of 8th June, 1911.		
2:5	Tone	10	Reinforced.
2:35	Semitone	0	Not reinforced.
2:38	Semitone	0	Not reinforced.
2:39	Tone	7	Reinforced.
2.50	Tone	12	Reinforced.
	Experiment of 14th June, 1911.		
1.45	Tone	12	Reinforced.
2.0	Semitone	0	Not reinforced.
2.2	Semitone	0	Not reinforced.
2.4	Semitone	0	Not reinforced.
2.6	Semitone	0	Not reinforced.
2.7	Tone	1.5	Reinforced.
2.30	Tone	13	Reinforced.

In differentiation as in the other types of internal inhibition the intensity of inhibition stands in direct relation to the strength of the excitatory process on the basis of which it was established, and can therefore be disturbed by any increase in the intensity of the stimulus which developed the inhibitory properties, or by any change in the general or local excitability of the central nervous system. To illustrate this last condition we may take instances of differential inhibitions established on the basis of an alimentary reflex. If, for example, the dog has been kept entirely without food for a much longer period than usual before the experiment is conducted, the increase in excitability of the whole alimentary nervous mechanism renders the previously established differential inhibition wholly inadequate. Again, if the general excitability of the central nervous system has been increased, for example by an injection of caffeine, the previously established differentiation similarly becomes disturbed. This effect of an alteration of the general nervous excitability is fully illustrated by an experiment of Dr. Nikiforovsky:

A tactile stimulation of the fore-paw serves as a positive conditioned alimentary stimulus, while a tactile stimulation of the back is completely differentiated from it.

Time (P.M.)	Stimulus Applied During 1 Min.	Salivary Secretion in Drops During Successive Minutes from the Beginning of the Conditioned Stimulus	Remarks
12:52	Tactile stimulation of back	0, 0, 0	Not reinforced.
1:5	Tactile stimulation of fore-paw	5	Reinforced.
	Subcutaneous injection of 5 cc. of 1% solution of caffeine	—	—
1:18	Tactile stimulation of fore-paw	4	Reinforced.
1:33	Tactile stimulation of back	3, 3, 2	Not reinforced.
1:45	Tactile stimulation of fore-paw	7	Reinforced.

Lastly, in common with the other three groups of internal inhibition, differential inhibition is subject to dis-inhibition, becoming temporarily removed under the influence of mild extra stimuli belonging to the group of external inhibitors, so as to reveal the underlying excitatory process. Two experiments by Dr. Beliakov carried out on the same animal are given in illustration:

A tone of 800 cps served as a conditioned alimentary stimulus, and an interval of one-eighth (812 cps) was thoroughly differentiated from it. A sound of bubbling water and an odour of amyl acetate served as mild extra stimuli which by themselves did not evoke any secretory effect.

Time (P.M.)	Stimulus Applied During 30 Secs.	Salivary Secretion in Drops per 30 Secs.	Remarks
	Experiment of 18th June, 1911.		
12:30	800 D.V.	3.5, —	Reinforced.
1:0	812 D.V.	0, 0	Not reinforced.
1:20	800 D.V.	3, —	Reinforced.
1:35	812 D.V. + odour of amyl acetate	2, 2	Not reinforced.

Time	Stimulus Applied During 30 Secs.	Salivary Secretion in Drops per 30 Secs.	Remarks
		Experiment of 23rd June, 1911.	
11:55 A.M.	800 D.V.	4, —	Reinforced.
12:10 P.M.	812 D.V. + bubbling water	2, 1	Not reinforced.
12:30 P.M.	800 D.V.	3, —	Reinforced.
12:40 P.M.	800 D.V.	3, —	Reinforced.

It is interesting to note that dis-inhibition can also be obtained when mild extra stimuli influence the hemispheres while the after-effect of differential inhibition is still persisting. The following is an experiment carried out by Dr. Beliakov on the same animal. The extra stimulus is given by the sound of a metronome which by itself produced no secretion.

Time (A.M)	Stimulus During 30 Secs.	Secretion of Saliva in Drops	Remarks
		Experiment of 17th May, 1911.	
11:10	Tone	4.5 during 30 secs.	Reinforced.
11:30	Tone	4 " "	"
11:40	Tone ⅛ lower	0 " "	Not reinforced.
11:44	Tone ⅛ lower	0 " "	" "
11:44½	Metronome during 1 minute	1½ during 1 minute	" "

Among the extra stimuli which have been employed there were some which evoked, not an ordinary investigatory reaction, but specific reflexes of greater intensity and complexity; in these cases the dis-inhibitory after-effect was very much prolonged. An example of the use of such an extra stimulus can again be taken from an experiment by Dr. Beliakov performed on the same animal as before.

A strong extra stimulus was provided by the blare of a toy trumpet which produced voluminous and exceedingly discordant noises. The dog reacted by barking wildly, trembling, and trying to break away from the stand.

Time (A.M.)	Stimulus Applied During 30 Secs.	Salivary Secretion in Successive Periods of 30 Secs.	
10:58	Trumpet	0	
10:58½	Inhibitory tone (812 D.V.)	6, 3, 2	
11:3	" " "	3, 1, 1	Stimuli
11:7	" " "	1, 1, 1	not
11:11	" " "	1.5, 1.5, 0	reinforced.
11:15	" " "	Traces	

The experimental evidence advanced in this lecture leaves us in no doubt but that the establishment of differentiation is based upon the development of internal inhibition in respect to the differentiated agent.

On the evidence of our experiments we are also forced to the conclusion that there is an important difference between the cruder form of differentiation depending upon external inhibition, and the finer form of differentiation depending upon internal inhibition. The former and more generalized inhibition is brought about by the intervention of an excitatory process, in most cases in the form of an investigatory reflex, and this has only a secondary inhibiting or dis-inhibiting effect upon the conditioned reflexes; the latter is brought about by a primary development of an inhibitory process, resulting, so to speak, from a conflict between excitation and inhibition. This supremacy of the inhibitory process is sometimes gained only with considerable difficulty, and in some cases it is even beyond the power of the nervous system to resolve the conflict in favour of either process. In the latter case the antagonism between the excitatory and inhibitory processes may not always bring about a full utilization of the results of analysis of external stimuli for the general benefit of the organism. This being so, the study of the analysing activity of the nervous system by the method of conditioned reflexes will also have its limitations —a fact which in itself presents a problem of considerable interest.

12

Experiments in Discrimination

Norman Guttman and Harry I. Kalish

When you trade in your car for a new model, you do not need to take a refresher course in driving. The new car may have a different feel and call for somewhat different control motions, but as an experienced driver you easily adjust your training to the new situation and quickly come to operate the car with your usual skill. This is a simple case of "transfer of learning." But the nature of the transfer process is far from simple. Generations of psychologists have found it a thorny subject, full of disappointments and surprises. Often learning does not carry over where we might expect it to. Training received in the classroom may be of little avail in the factory or the office; the camp soldier may prove helpless in combat; the lessons learned on the playing fields of Eton have been known to fail in the Sudan. On the other hand, learning sometimes extends to unexpected areas in unexpected ways. This article will report some experiments that have cast interesting new light on the generalization of learning.

The particular transfer phenomenon that we have been studying is called "stimulus generalization." The term means that a learned response to a specific stimulus carries over to a whole class of similar or related stimuli. A child seeing a group of nuns approaching in the street exclaimed: "Mommy, see the penguins!" This is a graphic illustration of stimulus generalization. (The class of "penguins" also includes, of course, men in formal dinner dress.)

The great physiologist Ivan P. Pavlov (1927) was the first to recognize and study stimulus generalization as a measurable phenomenon. In the course of his famous experiments on conditioned reflexes in dogs, he discovered that a dog which had been conditioned to salivate when a vibrator was applied to a point on its thigh would also salivate, though less copiously, when the vibrator was touched to other points on its skin. The response declined in a regular gradient from the conditioned point on the thigh: the farther from this point the vibrator was applied, the fewer drops of saliva the dog emitted.

The late Clark L. Hull, with his co-worker Milton J. Bass (1934) verified Pavlov's finding and extended the experiments to human subjects. They worked with the galvanic skin reflex—a momentary decrease in the skin's electrical resistance in response to stress (it is used in lie-detection machines). Almost any intense stimulus will produce this response. Using Yale undergraduates as subjects, Hull and Bass conditioned them so that a vibrator applied to the shoulder or the calf of the leg evoked the skin reflex, and then they tested the effect of vibrations at other points on the body. As in the experiments on dogs, the response diminished in intensity with distance from the original point of stimulation.

Later Carl I. Hovland (1937a,b) and a number of other experimenters explored various stimuli and showed that there was a graded generalization of response to sounds and to visual stimuli—the response declining with changes in the pitch of the sound or in the brightness or size of the visual object.

Why the nervous system behaves in this way is still a mystery. Pavlov suggested the theory that when a stimulus excites its receptive center in the brain, the excitation spreads over the cerebrum, so that other portions of the brain respond to related stimuli in the same way as the stimulated point. But this idea fell to the ground when it was found that conditioning could be established successfully in animals whose cerebral cortex had been removed, and even in species of animals possessing no cerebrum at all. Nowadays psychologists are extremely cautious about speculating on the physiology of learning. They prefer the "black box" approach: put in a stimulus or put in training and see what comes out in behavior. They believe that studies of this kind will provide clues for finding out what happens inside the black box (i.e., the nervous system).

Our group at Duke University decided to pursue the investigation of stimulus generalization with the spectrum of light as the testing instrument. If you condition an animal to respond to a certain wavelength of light, how far will its generalization of the stimulus extend from that wavelength? Generalization should certainly work within a given color: conditioned to respond to a deep green, say, the animal can be expected to respond also to a yellower green. But will it jump the dividing line between one color and the next—say from green to yellow? This seemed not very likely. Here discrimination might be expected to take the upper hand over generalization: the difference would seem greater than the kinship. If it is true, as many psychologists believe, that discrimination is the enemy of generalization—the less you can discriminate, the more you generalize—then generalization should stop more or less abruptly at the borders of the colors.

For our subject we chose the pigeon. This animal's ability to distinguish colors resembles man's. It is easy to train, and it clings to its trained behavior. Instead of Pavlov's conditioning method, we use the sensitive and powerful training technique developed by B. F. Skinner (see Skinner, 1951; and Olds, 1956).

We first train the pigeon to peck at light of a certain wavelength, presented in the form of an illuminated disk. The food reward for pecking the disk is given not for each response but on an irregular schedule, controlled by an automatic device which gives food for one response in each minute on the average. The main reason for this system is that we do not want

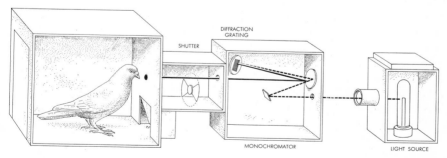

Experimental apparatus is shown in this schematic drawing. The color of the light seen by the pigeon is changed by tilting the diffraction grating with respect to the beam of light. The shutter enables the experimenter to black out the light while changing colors.

the bird to "expect" a reward for every response, because that would interfere with the later generalization tests. Paradoxically, the irregular reward method produces an extremely eager response by the pigeon. After a few hours of training the bird pecks steadily at the rate of 4,000 to 6,000 times per hour! What is especially important for our purposes, the response persists strongly when we stop giving the reward. The pigeon continues to peck for several hours, at a slowly declining rate. During this period we can carry out extensive generalization tests.

A test consists in presenting the pigeon with monochromatic light at 10 or 12 wavelengths other than the one to which it was trained to respond. The test stimuli are distributed over a considerable range of the color spectrum. If, for instance, the bird was trained to a green at the wavelength of 5,500 Angstrom units, it may be tested on wavelengths ranging from 4,800 Angstroms (blue) to 6,200 Angstroms (orange). These are presented in random order. The whole series of wavelengths is repeated a dozen times, each time in a different order. The bird's response to each disk is measured by its rate of pecking.

When we tabulated the performances of our pigeons on these tests, the results were not what we expected. In spite of the fact that the wavelengths had been shown in random order, the birds responded in a remarkably regular pattern according to the distance of each wavelength from the stimulus used in training. The curve of response was quite orderly: fast pecking at wavelengths close to the training stimulus, diminishing rates of pecking at more distant wavelengths (see upper chart in Figure 2). It was as if the pigeons were equipped with a frequency analyzer, accurately identifying each wavelength. In other words, they possess something like absolute pitch in the visual spectrum.

Even more remarkable, the curve of response crosses color boundaries without faltering. There is no abrupt drop in response as the curve passes from one color to another. And this is true no matter where in the spectrum the bird is tested: if it is trained in the green, the curve slopes down smoothly from green through yellow to orange; if it is trained to orange, it shows the same smoothly declining gradient back through yellow to green. Like a mechanical frequency analyzer, the bird appears to recognize wavelength entirely without reference to color. Its performance is especially puzzling because experiments have shown that the pigeon, like man, can distinguish hues more sensitively in some parts of the spectrum than in others. Yet this varying capacity for discrimination does not affect the animal's stimulus generalization: throughout all regions of the spectrum in which it has been tested, it is uniformly guided only by wavelength. These findings have led us to believe that generalization and discrimination may not be simple opposites, as commonly supposed.

Harley M. Hanson (1957) has made an extensive investigation of how training in discrimination affects generalization. He trained pigeons to

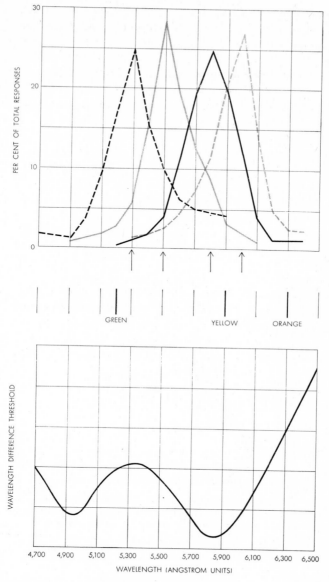

Responses of pigeons to wavelengths other than the one to which they have been
trained to respond are related to the difference in wavelength and not to variations in
the sensitivity of the pigeon's eye to various wavelengths. The curve at bottom shows this
variation in sensitivity. Above this curve are the colors related to the wavelengths below
it. Each of the four curves at top shows the responses of a pigeon trained to peck at the
flash of a light of the wavelength at the top of the curve (arrows). The pecking responses
of the pigeons to light of other wavelengths fall off regularly with the difference in
wavelength.

peck at one wavelength and to refrain from pecking at another. When this discrimination had been established, he tested their generalization of the positive stimulus and found that the curve of response was displaced away from the negative stimulus. The pigeon actually pecked at the highest rate at a wavelength different from the one to which it had been trained—that is, farther away from the negative stimulus. The size of this shift depended on the distance between the positive and negative stimuli. If the difference

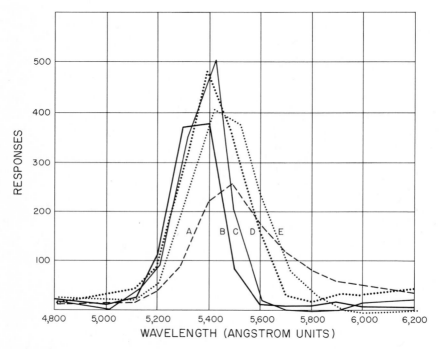

Displaced curves of generalization are shown for pigeons taught to discriminate negative stimuli from a positive stimulus (a light of 5,500 Angstrom units). The curve of pigeon A (a control) was not displaced. Pigeon B, whose negative stimulus was 5,550 Angstrom units, has a curve displaced far to the left; C, D and E, with negative stimuli farther to the right, did not displace so far to the left.

between them was 400 Angstroms, the peak shifted 50 Angstroms. If the two wavelengths between which the pigeon had been taught to discriminate were only 50 Angstroms apart (a very difficult discrimination which may take the pigeon as long as 10 hours to learn), the peak response shifted much farther away from the negative stimulus—about 150 or 200 Angstroms. In short, the pigeon's training in discrimination had not only extinguished a response but also enhanced its response to a new range of stimuli.

W. K. Honig (1962)[1] explored another question. What would happen if a trained pigeon was presented with a choice between two wavelengths shown at once (on separate disks)? Would it peck only one—the one closer to the wavelength at which it had been trained? Or would it peck both, giving more of its attention to the closer than to the farther one? Honig's pigeons took the latter course. They pecked both disks but pecked faster on the closer wavelength, in exactly the same ratio of preference as when the disks were presented at separate times.

One of our most important findings has to do with the intensification of the pigeons' responses with training. We found that as a pigeon's response to the conditioned stimulus increased, its response to the associated stimuli increased in the same ratio. For example, if its rate of pecking at the training wavelength rose from 20 to 40 times per minute, its rates for the other wavelengths also doubled. This simple multiplicative relation, first suggested by Hull (1943) in the general theory of behavior, indicates that we are dealing with a fundamental property of behavior. It may have an important bearing on human conduct.

Neal E. Miller (1944) has suggested that intensification of drives such as hunger, fear, or sexual excitement may heighten generalization and extend its range. Indeed, there is reason to believe that stresses of many kinds may have this effect in a multiplicative fashion. Under these circumstances a person would show exaggerated reactions to stimuli which ordinarily would evoke little or no response. In extreme cases the individual's responses would become so generalized that he would react indiscriminately to virtually all the stimuli in his environment, and go over to the bizarre reactions of the psychotic state. Thus stimulus generalization may be a useful concept in the study of psychopathology, as it is in investigations of normal learning processes.

REFERENCES

BASS, M. J., and HULL, C. L. The irradiation of a tactile conditioned reflex in man. *J. comp. Psychol.*, 1934, *17*, 47–65.

HANSON, H. M. Discrimination training effect on stimulus generalization gradient for spectrum stimuli. *Science*, 1957, *125*, 888–889.

HONIG, W. K. Prediction of preference, transposition, and transposition-reversal from the generalization gradient. *J. exp. Psychol.*, 1962, *64*, 239–248.

HOVLAND, C. I. The generalization of conditioned responses: I. The sensory generalization of conditioned responses with varying frequencies of tone. *J. gen. Psychol.*, 1937, *17*, 125–148. (a)

HOVLAND, C. I. The generalization of conditioned responses: II. The sensory generalization of conditioned responses with varying intensities of tone. *J. genet. Psychol.*, 1937, *51*, 279–291. (b)

HULL, C. L. *Principles of behavior*. New York: Appleton-Century-Crofts, 1943.

MILLER, N. E. Experimental studies of conflict. In J. McV. Hunt (Ed.), *Per-

[1] Based on a 1958 doctoral dissertation.

sonality and the behavior disorders. Vol. I. New York: Ronald, 1944.
OLDS, J. Pleasure centers in the brain. *Scientific American,* 1956, *195,* 105–116.
PAVLOV, I. P. *Conditioned reflexes.* (Translated by G. V. Anrep.) London: Oxford University Press, 1927.
SKINNER, B. F. How to teach animals. *Scientific American,* 1951, *185,* 26–29.

13

Stimulus Generalization in an Avoidance Situation

Murray Sidman

Investigators using the technique of Guttman and Kalish (1956) or related methods have reported a wide variety of generalization phenomena for behavior that is maintained by food reinforcement (e.g., Kalish and Guttman, 1957, 1959; Hanson, 1957, 1959; Pierrel, 1958; Thomas and King, 1959; Blough, 1959; Honig, Thomas, and Guttman, 1959; Jenkins and Harrison, 1960). The experiments to be reported here extend the series into the realm of avoidance behavior.

METHOD

Subjects and Apparatus

Two young male rhesus monkeys were used. They worked in a Foringer primate chamber, a 2-foot cubical space with the floor and one wall of stainless steel rods, and three walls and ceiling of aluminum sheeting. A telegraph-key lever was mounted on one wall, and an earphone was mounted outside at the level of the grid floor. The rods, walls, and lever comprised the shocking electrodes; and the shock, generated by a Foringer shock power supply, was delivered through a Foringer-type grid scrambler. Shock intensity was approximately 6 milliamperes for Monkey R-641 and

Adapted from *J. exp. Anal. Behav.,* 1961, *4,* 157–169. With permission of the author and publisher.

3 milliamperes for Monkey R-832. The values of shock duration are described below.

The click stimuli were generated by a Grass stimulator, with the frequency control replaced by a set of fixed resistors connected to an electrical stepping switch. The sequence of click frequencies was programmed automatically by the stepping switch and a system of relays and timers. Click rates were periodically monitored on a frequency meter.

Preliminary Training

The animal was shaped by receiving frequent brief shocks until it approximated a lever-pressing response. At that point, shocks were discontinued for 20–30 seconds. The response requirement was gradually restricted until the animal actually had to press the lever to terminate the shock sequence. From then on, the animal was shocked every 20 seconds unless it pressed the lever; each time it pressed the lever, it postponed the next shock for 20 seconds (Sidman, 1953a).

Auditory click stimuli were continuously presented to the animal, starting from the very beginning of the shaping procedure. The clicks sounded at either of two rates, or frequencies—2 clicks per second or 6 clicks per second. At first, the two click frequencies alternated every 15 minutes. When the clicks came at a rate of 2 per second (positive stimulus), the avoidance procedure was in effect; the animal was shocked if it did not press the lever rapidly enough. When the clicks came at a rate of 6 per second (negative stimulus), the animal could not receive any shocks, even if it failed to press the lever. The procedure, then, was a multiple schedule: shock avoidance in the presence of 2 clicks per second, and avoidance extinction in the presence of 6 clicks per second.

The procedure was continued until the animal was pressing the lever at a fairly steady rate, receiving few shocks when the positive stimulus was on, and rarely pressing the lever when the negative stimulus was on. (Approximately 5 percent of Monkey R-641's responses were in the negative stimulus, and 10 percent of Monkey R-832's responses.) Each session lasted 6 hours. The duration of the alternating stimuli was then gradually decreased from 15 minutes to 1 minute; positive and negative stimuli alternated every 60 seconds. The generalization phase of the experiment was then begun.

Generalization Testing

No shocks were delivered to the animal during generalization tests. In generalization sessions, the negative stimulus (6 clicks per second) was on during each alternate minute. In the 1-minute periods between each negative-stimulus presentation, test stimuli of 2.0, 2.5, 3.0, 4.0, or 5.0 clicks per second were presented to Monkey R-641 in mixed order; for Monkey R-832, the test stimuli were 2.0, 2.5, 3.0, 3.5, or 4.0 clicks per second. In a 6-hour session, the negative stimulus was presented 180 times, and each of the other stimuli were presented 36 times.

Interspersed between generalization sessions, on alternate days, were 6-hour reconditioning sessions in which the multiple avoidance-extinction procedure was in effect. One hour of this procedure also immediately preceded each generalization session.

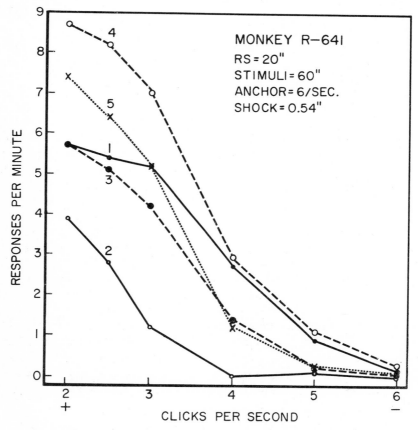

Figure 1. *Response rate during each click frequency in the first five generalization sessions.*

Absolute and relative response rates during each stimulus, plotted against click frequency, yield one wing of a generalization gradient for each

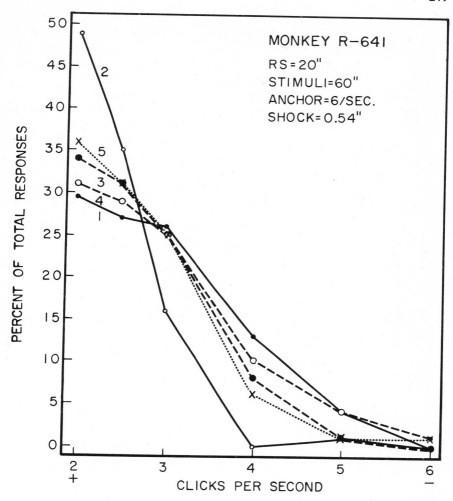

Figure 2. *Relative generalization gradients corresponding to the curves of Figure 1.*
Each point is the number of responses during each stimulus expressed as a percentage
of the total responses during all stimuli.

monkey during each generalization session. The shape of the gradient was
studied as a function of response-shock interval, shock duration, anchoring
stimuli, and length of the subject's involvement in the experiment.

RESULTS

The first five generalization gradients of Monkey R-641 are in Figure 1,
plotted in terms of absolute response rate as a function of click frequency.
All the gradients show the animal responding less frequently as the test

stimulus diverges from the positive frequency of 2 per second. Although the response rates vary considerably from one session to another, Session 2 is the only one in which the generalization gradient differs radically in shape from the others. This is brought out even more clearly in the gradients of Figure 2, in which the animal's responses during each stimulus are expressed as a percentage of the total responses to all stimuli (corrected for the larger number of presentations of the 6-per-second stimulus). Except for Session 2, the percentage gradients are similar to each other, in spite of the wide variations in absolute response rates.

Figures 3 and 4 show similar and even more consistent data for Monkey R-832.

It was considered possible that the 6-per-second "anchoring" stimulus, which was presented both before and after each of the other stimuli, could

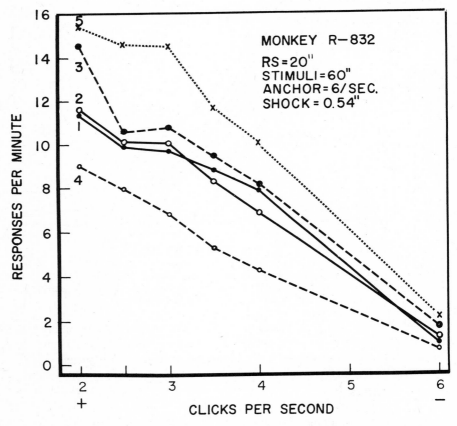

Figure 3. *Response rate during each click frequency in the first five generalization sessions.*

affect the shape of the generalization gradient. During generalization tests
6–10, therefore, the positive 2-per-second stimulus was used as the anchor
for Monkey R-641. In Sessions 11–15 the original procedure was repeated,
the 6-per-second stimulus alternating with each of the others.

The solid curve of Figure 5 is the median gradient of the first five sessions, of which the day-by-day data were shown in Figure 2. The curve
represents the median percentage for each stimulus for the five sessions.
When the anchoring stimulus was changed to 2 per second, the gradient
(open circles of Figure 5) became much steeper. However, the steeper

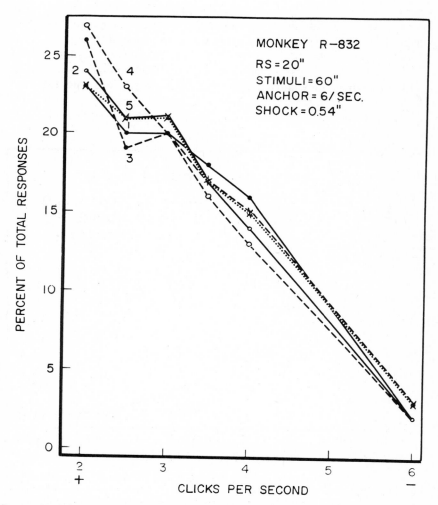

Figure 4.   Relative generalization gradients corresponding to the curves of Figure 3.

gradient possibly did not result entirely from the use of the positive stimulus as the anchor, because when the negative 6-per-second stimulus was again presented during alternate minutes, the gradient did not return completely to its original form. Whether the gradient would have become steeper simply as a function of continued generalization testing, or whether the 2-per-second anchor produced a partially irreversible change is not entirely clear from these data. The steep gradient of Session 2, along with subsequent developments to be noted below, suggests that the test procedure itself produces some sharpening of the generalization gradient. However, the partial recovery of the gradient in Figure 5 suggests that when the positive stimulus is used as anchor, the gradient becomes steeper than when the negative stimulus is so used, and steeper than would have been expected as a function of simple exposure to the procedure.

Monkey R-641 was then run for five sessions each on response-shock intervals of 10, 5, and 3 seconds, in that order. (The animal could receive shocks, of course, only during the reconditioning sessions and the hour

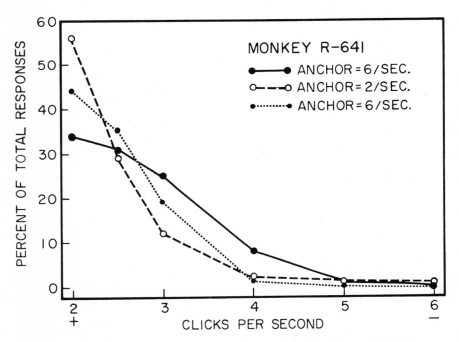

Figure 5. *Median relative generalization gradients when the anchor was first the negative stimulus, then the positive, and then the negative again. The percentage of responses per session in each stimulus was calculated, and each point represents the median percentage for five sessions.*

before generalization tests.) With the reduction in response-shock interval from 20 to 10 seconds, the duration of each stimulus presentation was also reduced from 60 to 30 seconds, where it remained for the rest of the experiment. Since the session duration remained at 6 hours, the 6-per-second stimulus was now presented 360 times during each generalization test, and each of the other stimuli was presented 72 times.

Figure 6 shows median generalization gradients for each response-shock interval, plotted in terms of absolute response rates during each stimulus. Except for the 3-second curve, the response rates increased (Sidman, 1953b) when the response-shock interval was lowered, as was to be expected. (Since the monkey was exposed to each response-shock interval for only five sessions, its behavior had probably not yet reached a stable state.)

The shorter response-shock intervals did indeed bring out more responses during click frequencies of 2.5, 3.0, and 4.0 per second; but, as Figure 7 indicates, the increase was a simple multiplicative one. The percentage gradients are almost identical for each response-shock interval.

After its first five generalization tests, Monkey R-832 was given five consecutive reconditioning sessions in which the response-shock interval had been reduced to 10 seconds, with stimulus durations of 30 seconds. There were no generalization tests. Then, the response-shock interval was reduced to 5 seconds and the stimulus durations to 15 seconds. At this point, the session duration was cut down to 3 hours, keeping the number of stimulus presentations the same as those for Monkey R-641.

A comparison of median response rates per stimulus at response-shock intervals of 20 and 5 seconds appears in the two lower curves of Figure 8. The percentage gradients may be seen in the corresponding curves of Figure 9. Again, the shorter response-shock interval brings out many more generalized responses; but, with the unexplained exception of the 6-per-second stimulus, there appears to be a simple multiplicative relation between the two gradients.

The response-shock interval was decreased rapidly for Monkey R-832 in order to avoid, if possible, a change such as had taken place in the gradient for Monkey R-641 after its extensive series of generalization tests. After the first four sessions of exposure to the 3-second response-shock interval, the gradient for Monkey R-641 suddenly became much steeper, as is indicated by the median curves of Figure 10. This change is not a simple multiplicative one, and is probably correlated with the formation of a new discrimination based on the greater variety of stimuli experienced by the animal during generalization tests. The monkey never received any shocks during periods when the series of click frequencies between 2 and 6 per second was presented; therefore, this series may itself have become a negative stimulus for avoidance behavior. Evidence in favor of this

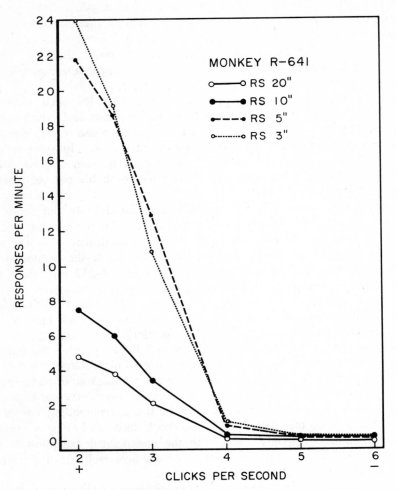

Figure 6. *Median response rate during each click frequency for different response-shock intervals. The response rate per session in each stimulus was calculated, and each point represents the median rate for five sessions.*

interpretation comes from a marked decline in total responses during generalization tests at this time, with the animal responding normally at the start of the session but gradually tapering off until it rarely pressed the lever during the latter part of the session.

Because of the changed gradient, the effects of any new operations could not be evaluated with respect to the previous data. The steeper gradient, however, was used as a base line for examining the effects of an increased shock duration. During previous experiments, the shock duration was

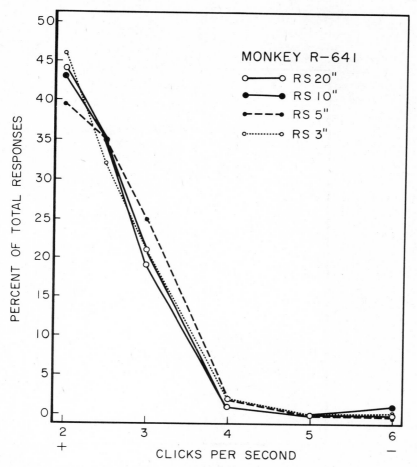

Figure 7. *Median relative generalization gradients corresponding to the curves of Figure 6.*

0.54 second, and it was now increased about threefold to 1.69 seconds, keeping the response-shock interval at 3 seconds. The longer shock duration produced only a slight increase in Monkey R-641's response rate and no great change in the amount of generalization, as may be seen in Figure 10.

The shape of the gradient for Monkey R-832 remained stable at a response-shock interval of 5 seconds; and when the shock duration was increased, the response rate increased considerably (Figure 8). Figure 9, however, indicates no consistent change in the percentage gradient for the longer shock duration.

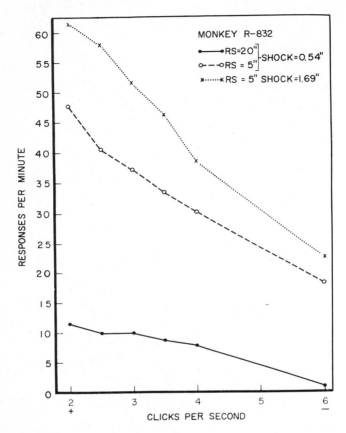

Figure 8. *Median response rate during each click frequency for two response-shock intervals and two shock durations.*

The data may be summarized by a generalization surface (Guttman and Kalish, 1956). For each test stimulus, the subject's response rate in the presence of that stimulus is plotted against the over-all rate for the session. In this analysis, no distinction is made among changes in over-all rate produced by variations in response-shock interval, shock duration, or uncontrolled factors.

The generalization surface for Monkey R-641 (Figure 11) includes all sessions from Session 11 (return to the negative anchoring stimulus) up to the point where the animal began to discriminate the generalization

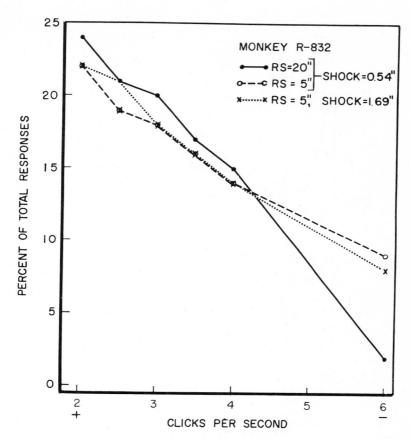

Figure 9. Median relative generalization gradients corresponding to the curves of Figure 8.

procedure. (See Figure 10.) The relation, fitted by the method of averages, is a positive linear one for all stimuli, with the slope decreasing as the test stimuli diverge from the positive stimulus. (Beyond a click rate of 4 per second, the response rates were so low as to yield essentially zero slopes.) If the slopes of these curves are plotted against click frequency, an idealized generalization gradient can be derived which is independent of over-all response rate.

Figure 12 shows similar results for the complete data of Monkey R-832. However, there is somewhat more variability around the fitted lines.

The generalization gradient is thus observed to be independent of changes in over-all response rate over the range of variables tested here.

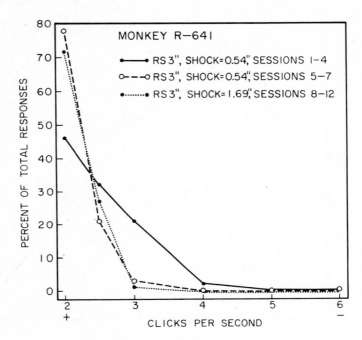

Figure 10. Median relative generalization gradients as a function of continued testing and shock duration.

These findings add great generality to the earlier work of Kalish and Guttman (1957), who used a different organism (pigeon), a different stimulus dimension (wavelength), food reinforcement rather than shock avoidance, and a different training procedure.

A comparison of the slopes of corresponding curves in Figures 11 and 12, however, suggests an exception to the rule that the shape of the generalization gradient is independent of the rate of avoidance responding. The slopes for Monkey R-832 are considerably steeper than those for Monkey R-641; the two sets of data could not legitimately be combined into a single generalization surface. Among the uncontrolled variables that account for these individual differences, there must be one or more that change the generalization gradient in a nonlinear fashion as a function of the over-all rate of avoidance responding.

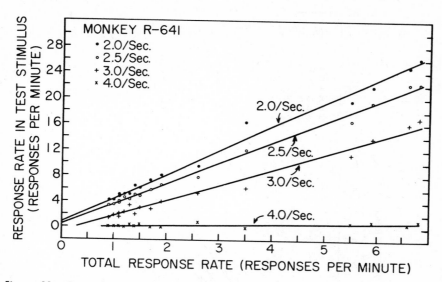

Figure 11. *Rate of responding during the test stimuli as a function of the over-all response rate for each session.*

SUMMARY AND FURTHER DISCUSSION

Generalization of avoidance behavior to auditory clicks differing in repetition rate was studied with two monkeys. After the subjects had received extended discrimination training (positive stimulus, 2 clicks per second; negative stimulus, 6 clicks per second), the shape of the generalization gradient was found to be independent of response-shock interval and of shock duration. However, there was some indication that extended exposure of the subject to generalization testing decreased the amount of generalization and sharpened the gradient. Except for unknown factors contributing to intersubject variability, the shape of the generalization gradient was independent of variables that altered the subjects' rate of avoidance responding.

At least one qualification must be appended to these findings: the subjects were tested for generalization after they had been given extended discrimination training. The simple fact that the animals had to be given specific training before they began to press the lever at different rates in the positive and negative stimuli indicates that the gradient was relatively flat both during and for some time after initial avoidance conditioning. Hearst (personal communication, 1960), has provided empirical confirmation of the flat generalization gradient for avoidance behavior before the animal has specific discrimination training.

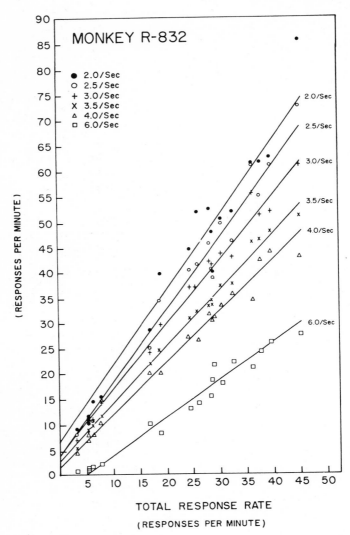

Figure 12. *Rate of responding during the test stimuli as a function of the over-all response rate for each session.*

REFERENCES

BLOUGH, D. S. Generalization and preference on a stimulus-intensity continuum. *J. exp. Anal. Behav.*, 1959, *2*, 307–317.

GUTTMAN, N., and KALISH, H. I. Discriminability and stimulus generalization. *J. exp. Psychol.*, 1956, *51*, 79–88.

HANSON, H. M. Discrimination training effect on stimulus generalization gradient for spectrum stimuli. *Science*, 1957, *125*, 888–889.

HANSON, H. M. Effects of discrimination training on stimulus generalization. *J. exp. Psychol.*, 1959, *58*, 321–334.

HONIG, W. K., THOMAS, D. R., and GUTTMAN, N. Differential effects of continuous extinction and discrimination training on the generalization gradient. *J. exp. Psychol.*, 1959, *58*, 145–152.

JENKINS, H. M., and HARRISON, R. H. Effect of discrimination training on auditory generalization. *J. exp. Psychol.*, 1960, *59*, 246–253.

KALISH, H. I., and GUTTMAN, N. Stimulus generalization after equal training on two stimuli. *J. exp. Psychol.*, 1957, *53*, 139–144.

KALISH, H. I., and GUTTMAN, N. Stimulus generalization after training on three stimuli: a test of the summation hypothesis. *J. exp. Psychol.*, 1959, *57*, 268–272.

PIERREL, R. A generalization gradient for auditory intensity in the rat. *J. exp. Anal. Behav.*, 1958, *1*, 303–313.

SIDMAN, M. Avoidance conditioning with brief shock and no extroceptive warning signal. *Science*, 1953, *118*, 157–158. (a)

SIDMAN, M. Two temporal parameters of the maintenance of avoidance behavior by the white rat. *J. comp. physiol. Psychol.*, 1953, *46*, 253–261. (b)

THOMAS, D. R., and KING, R. A. Stimulus generalization as a function of level of motivation. *J. exp. Psychol.*, 1959, *57*, 323–328.

14

Concept Formation in Chimpanzees

Roger T. Kelleher

Learning to respond to a class of stimuli on the basis of some common physical characteristic is referred to as "concept formation." Although concept formation has been demonstrated in animals (Fields, 1932; Hicks, 1956; Weinstein, 1945), the experimental analysis of this complex behavioral process has received little attention in recent years. This report presents some results obtained with a new technique for the study of concept formation. The technique is similar to one used for studying concept formation in human beings (Green, 1955).

The two subjects were food-deprived chimpanzees. These animals had

Adapted from *Science*, 1958, *128*, 3327, 777–778. With permission of the author and the American Association for the Advancement of Science.

been trained to press a telephone key for food reward (reinforcement). Above the telephone key there were nine small Plexiglas windows arrayed in a 3-by-3 square. Stimulus patterns were programmed by illuminating some Plexiglas windows while leaving others dark. A sequence of 26 successive stimulus patterns, 13 positive and 13 negative, could be programmed. One negative stimulus pattern in which all windows were dark appeared in all sequences. The positive stimulus patterns were characterized by a common element which was not present in any of the negative patterns.

During the presentation of positive stimulus patterns, a 100-response variable-ratio schedule of reinforcement was in effect—that is, the number of times that the subject had to press the key for food varied randomly from 1 to 200, with a mean of 100 (Ferster and Skinner, 1957). Positive stimulus patterns terminated at reinforcement. During the presentation of negative stimulus patterns, extinction was in effect—that is, responses were not reinforced. Negative stimulus patterns terminated when the animal had not pressed the telephone key for 1 minute. Experimental sessions were interrupted for a 30-second "time-out" period after the termination of each stimulus pattern and ended when 50 reinforcements had been delivered (Ferster and Skinner, 1957). The experimental procedures were automatically programmed, and the results were automatically recorded.

Two concept problems were investigated. Initially, on each of these problems, the animals were repeatedly exposed to one sequence of stimulus patterns. When the animals' behavior showed no consistent trend, the stimulus patterns were presented in a new sequence, but none of the specific stimulus patterns was changed. After several experimental sessions on the new sequence, six positive and six negative stimulus patterns were changed. However, the concept was not changed.

Representative positive and negative stimulus patterns from each of four sequences are shown in the upper sections of Figure 1. The dark squares correspond to illuminated windows. Cumulative response records from each of the four sequences are shown in the lower sections of Figure 1. Responses during positive and negative stimulus patterns were recorded separately, and they are presented in the upper and lower curves, respectively. The short diagonal strokes on these curves indicate the points at which stimulus presentations terminated. The records did not run during the 30-second intervals between stimulus presentations. Coordinates and representative slopes are presented in the lower right corner of the figure.

The stimulus patterns in the upper section of Figure 1*A* exemplify the first concept problem. The illumination of the bottom row of windows was the concept. The cumulative response records in the lower section of Figure 1*A* show the performance that had developed after about 100 experimental hours on the first sequence of stimulus patterns. The animals responded at high rates during positive stimulus patterns, but they seldom

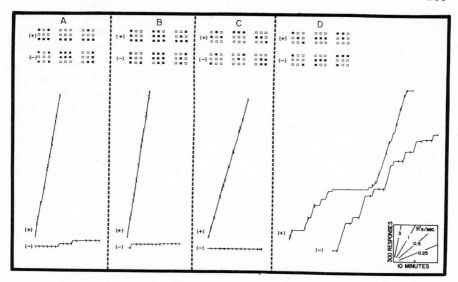

Figure 1. *Representative stimulus patterns and cumulative response curves, showing the effects of changing specific stimulus patterns without changing the concept. Sections A and B are from the first concept problem; sections C and D are from the second concept problem.*

responded during the negative stimulus patterns. When the stimulus patterns were presented in a new sequence, there was no disruption of this performance. When six positive and six negative stimulus patterns were changed without changing the concept, there was still no disruption of the performance. For example, the stimulus patterns shown in Figure 1*A* were changed to those shown in Figure 1*B*. Cumulative records from the first sequence following the change are shown in the lower section of Figure 1*B*.

The stimulus patterns in the upper section of Figure 1*C* exemplify the second concept problem. The illumination of three windows was the common element in positive stimulus patterns; two or four windows were illuminated in negative stimulus patterns. The cumulative response records in the lower section of Figure 1*C* show the performance that had developed after about 150 experimental hours on this sequence. As in the first concept problem, this performance was not disrupted when the stimulus patterns were presented in a new sequence. However, when six positive and six negative stimulus patterns were changed without changing the concept, performance was markedly disrupted. The changed stimulus patterns are exemplified in the upper section of Figure 1*D*; cumulative response records from the first sequence following this change are shown in the lower section of Figure 1*D*. There was excessive initial pausing in two of the positive patterns, and high rates of responding prevailed in the negative patterns that had been changed.

The animals developed clear discriminations on both concept problems. Neither discrimination was affected by changing the sequence in which the stimulus patterns were presented. However, the discriminations were differentially affected by changing specific stimulus patterns without changing the concept. Thus, the discriminations were qualitatively different. In the first concept problem, the discrimination was based upon response to the common element. In the second concept problem, the discrimination was based upon response to specific stimulus patterns—that is, the chimpanzees were responding appropriately to at least 12 specific stimulus patterns presented in successive fashion. In further studies, it would be possible to determine the maximum number of specific patterns to which these animals could respond effectively. Until such studies have been completed, investigations of complex discriminations with chimpanzees should be interpreted with caution, until the bases of the discriminations have been assessed.

With the procedure described above, concept formation was a function of the concept problem. The common element of the first concept problem (the bottom row of windows) had a specific spatial location; the common element of the second concept problem (any three windows) did not. This difference in the level of abstractness of the two problems may have been an important factor. With a different procedure, the chimpanzees could probably have been trained to respond to the common element of the second concept problem. If the stimulus patterns were changed after each sequence without changing the concept, for example, the animals would have been unable to maintain a discrimination by responding to specific patterns.

SUMMARY

Animals performed with a high degree of accuracy on two concept problems. The bases of these performances, however, differed qualitatively. In one problem, successful performance was based upon responding to specific stimulus patterns. In the other problem, successful performance was based upon responding to the common element or concept.

REFERENCES

FERSTER, C. B., and SKINNER, B. F. *Schedules of Reinforcement.* New York: Appleton-Century-Crofts, 1957.

FIELDS, P. E. Studies in concept formation: I—The development of the concept of triangularity by the white rat. *Comp. psychol. Monogr.,* 1932, *9,* 1–70.

GREEN, E. J. Concept formation: A problem in human operant conditioning. *J. exp. Psychol.,* 1955, *49,* 175–180.

HICKS, L. H. An analysis of number-concept formation in the rhesus monkey. *J. comp. physiol. Psychol.,* 1956, *49,* 212–218.

WEINSTEIN, B. The evolution of intelligent behavior in rhesus monkeys. *Genet. psychol. Monogr.,* 1945, *31,* 3–38.

15

Method for Tracing Dark Adaptation
in the Pigeon

Donald S. Blough

Animal subjects are not often used in psychophysical research, because they cannot follow complex instructions or report verbally what they see or hear. The method described in this paper represents an attempt to overcome these difficulties and to obtain with animals some of the efficiency and control that human subjects provide. The method owes much to the work of Skinner and his associates (1953) and to Békésy's method of human audiometry (1947). The procedure outlined here is designed for the study of dark adaptation in the pigeon, but, with modifications, it may be applied to a variety of animal discrimination problems.

Automatic apparatus is used. It includes the following items: (1) a light-tight adaptation box, containing a pigeon, response keys, food magazine, and stimulus patch; (2) a network of relays and timers that control the stimulus luminance and the presentation of food; (3) a light source and an optical system, with a device that continuously records the stimulus luminance.

A panel divides the adaptation box into two chambers. The bird is trained to stand in one chamber and place its head through a round hole in the panel (Figure 1). The bird faces a small window through which it views a stimulus patch, 1 cm. in diameter, 4 cm. beyond the frame of the window. The only light in the adaptation box comes from this stimulus patch. There are two small response keys, *A* and *B*, just below the window. Each peck on one of these keys momentarily opens a switch that is connected with the controlling relay network. When the bird is to be rewarded, a solenoid raises a magazine containing grain to an opening in the floor below the response keys.

Adapted from *Science*, 1955, *121*, 3150, 703–704. With permission of the author and the American Association for the Advancement of Science.

The stimulus patch is illuminated from behind by a beam of light. A motor-driven optical wedge in the path of the light beam regulates the luminance of the patch. A shutter may be closed to black out the stimulus patch completely. The movements of both the wedge and the shutter are controlled through the relay network.

The pigeon's basic task is to peck key *A* when the stimulus patch is visible and to peck key *B* when the patch is dark. Training on this discrimination proceeds in several stages. When the bird becomes proficient at one stage, the next stage is introduced; 50 training hours may be needed before experimental data can be collected.

First, the hungry bird (70 to 80 percent of free-feeding cage weight) is trained to peck the two keys at random by the "response differentiation" technique described by Ferster (1953). Next, the stimulus patch is illuminated, and the control circuit is so adjusted that a peck on key *A* closes the shutter, blacking out the patch. After a peck on key *A* has blacked out the patch, a peck on key *B* causes the food magazine to be raised within reach for about 5 seconds. Pecks on key *B* are useless when the patch is lighted, and pecks on key *A* are useless when the patch is dark. After most rewards, the shutter opens, and the lighted patch reappears. Continued darkness follows one reward in five; in this case, a peck on

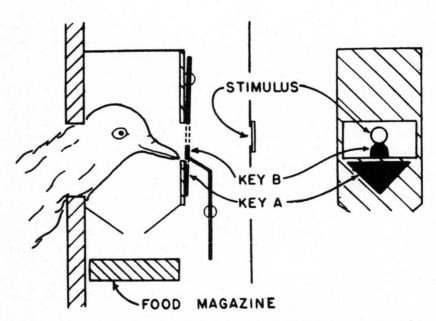

Figure 1. *Response chamber of the adaptation box. (Left) Side view, showing relative positions of pigeon, food magazine, response keys, and stimulus patch. (Right) Keys A and B and patch seen from the pigeon's position.*

key *B* brings food a second time. These double rewards train the bird to attend to the stimulus patch after eating; without them, the bird would always peck key *A* after eating, regardless of the condition of the stimulus patch.

In the next stage of training, several pecks in a row, rather than a single peck, are required on key *A* to close the shutter and on key *B* to obtain food. The number of pecks required is varied randomly between one and eight. This increases the time between rewards and prevents the bird from getting a reward simply by pecking the two keys alternately, without attending to the stimulus patch. The time between rewards is further increased by introducing an interval after each reward during which no amount of pecking can close the shutter. The duration of this interval varies randomly about a mean of 7 seconds.

When training is nearly complete, a final feature is added to the procedure: the luminance of the stimulus patch is put under the control of the bird's responses during the intervals between rewards. Each peck on key *A* reduces the luminance of the patch by a small amount, while each peck on key *B* increases the luminance of the patch. A pen continuously records these luminance changes. When the bird has learned to perform consistently under these conditions, the collection of threshold data can begin. Experimentation continues indefinitely without further alteration of procedure.

An account of a typical experimental session will serve to illustrate how the bird's threshold is traced. At first, the stimulus patch is brightly lighted, and the trained bird pecks only key *A*. The bird continues to peck key *A* until the patch becomes so dim that it falls below the bird's absolute threshold. Because the pigeon cannot distinguish this "dim-out" of the patch from the true "black-out" caused by the closing shutter, it begins to peck key *B*. But pecking key *B* increases the luminance of the patch, so in a short time the patch again becomes visible to the bird. When this happens, the bird switches its pecking back to key *A*, causing the stimulus to dim and to disappear as before. This process continues indefinitely; the bird alternately pecks keys *A* and *B*, and the stimulus fluctuates up and down across the bird's absolute threshold. The continuous record of the stimulus luminance traces the bird's absolute threshold through time. The randomly spaced rewards, when pecks on key *A* close the shutter and pecks on key *B* bring food, interrupt the continuity of this threshold record frequently but for only a few seconds.

During the first portion of an experimental session, the recording pen traces the pigeon's dark-adaptation curve. A reproduction of such a curve in a 1-hour session is shown on appropriate coordinates in Figure 2. Before this particular session, the bird had spent 1 hour in darkness, followed by 10 minutes in a box with white walls at a luminance of 22 millilamberts.

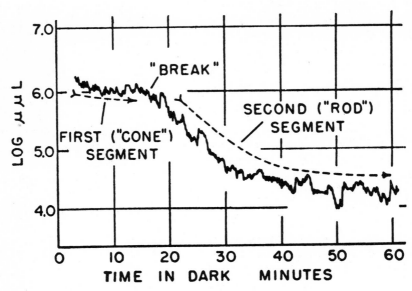

Figure 2.   Dark-adaptation curve secured from a bird in 1 hour. The luminance of the
stimulus patch, in log micromicrolamberts, is on the ordinate.

REFERENCES

Békésy, G. V. A new audiometer. *Acta Oto-Laryngol.*, 1947, *35*, 411–422.

Ferster, C. B. The use of the free operant in the analysis of behavior. *Psychol.
Bull.*, 1953, *50*, 263–274.

Skinner, B. F. Some contributions of an experimental analysis of behavior to
psychology as a whole. *Amer. Psychologist.*, 1953, *8*, 69–78.

A more extensive description of the procedure presented here is found in
D. S. Blough, "A method for obtaining psychophysical thresholds from the
pigeon," *J. exp. Anal. Behav.*, 1958, *1*, 31–43 (Ed.).

SUGGESTED READINGS

Keller, F. S., and Schoenfeld, W. N. *Principles of psychology.* New York:
Appleton-Century-Crofts, 1950, Chap. 5.

Kimble, G. A. *Hilgard and Marquis' conditioning and learning.* New York:
Appleton-Century-Crofts, 1961, Chaps. 11 and 12.

Mednick, S. A., and Freedman, J. L. Stimulus Generalization. *Psychol. Bull.*,
1960, *57*, 169–200.

Mostofsky, D. I. (Ed.) *Stimulus generalization.* Stanford: Stanford University
Press, 1965.

Skinner, B. F. *The behavior of organisms.* New York: Appleton-Century-
Crofts, 1938, Chap. 5.

Chapter VI

RESPONSE DIFFERENTIATION
AND INDUCTION

The process of response differentiation was first systematically investigated by Skinner (1938). The phenomenon of induction or response generalization had already been investigated by the middle of the nineteenth century. In 1844, E. H. Weber, who also pioneered the first psychophysical experiments, observed that "some children trained to write with the right hand were able without further training to produce very good mirror-writing with the left hand" (Woodworth, 1938, p. 181). However, the first to demonstrate a response generalization *gradient* was R. F. Hefferline in a paper reproduced in this chapter. The topics of response-differentiation, -generalization, -variability, and -stereotypy are all closely related. An extensive discussion can be found in Keller and Schoenfeld (1950). Together they constitute an area relatively neglected by experimenters, even though they involve theoretical questions of considerable importance. One such problem concerns the definition of such key terms as *response, movement,* and *behavior*. A discussion of the issues involved can be found in articles by MacCorquodale and Meehl (1954)[1] and Mueller and Schoenfeld (1954).[2]

One possible reason for the relative neglect of the topics of this chapter by experimenters may be the fact that research in these areas requires relatively complex and intricate equipment. In addition there is the large amount of numerical data that have to be dealt with. Recent progress in the development of solid state programming equipment and on-line computers especially designed for use in the psychological laboratory promise new data and techniques in these areas in the near future.

REFERENCES

KELLER, F. S., and SCHOENFELD, W. N. *Principles of psychology.* New York: Appleton-Century-Crofts, 1950.
MacCorquodale, K., and Meehl, P. E. Edward C. Tolman. In W. K. Estes, *et al. Modern learning theory.* New York: Appleton-Century-Crofts, 1954.

[1] Pp. 218–248.
[2] Pp. 353–358.

MUELLER, C. G., Jr., and SCHOENFELD, W. N. Edwin R. Guthrie. In W. K. Estes, *et al. Modern learning theory.* New York: Appleton-Century-Crofts, 1954.

SKINNER, B. F. *The behavior of organisms.* New York: Appleton-Century-Crofts, 1938.

WOODWORTH, R. S. *Experimental psychology.* New York: Holt, Rinehart and Winston, 1938.

16

Force Emission During Bar Pressing

J. M. Notterman

This experiment was concerned with a detailed description of the emission of forces by rats in a substantially conventional Skinner box as the animals proceeded through various stages of the learning process (specifically, operant level determinations, regular reinforcement, and extinction) without any experimenter-manipulated exteroceptive discriminative stimuli.

Rudimentary data of this type were obtained by Skinner (1938, p. 312), but they are—for present purposes— deficient in two respects: the measure of force used by Skinner was not linear with actual force, and the technique employed did not permit measuring the force of single responses. A subsequent major contribution to the systematic description of free force emission was made by Trotter (1956). Unfortunately, although he apparently had the instrumentation capability, Trotter failed to keep records during the acquisition phase of a knob-pressing operant, thereby precluding the kind of response-by-response analysis presented here. Nonetheless, his comments concerning "the physical properties of bar pressing behaviour" remain the clearest exposition of the physics of bar pressing to date.

METHOD

Apparatus. The general apparatus here described provides an analysis of three intensive aspects of bar pressing behavior: force, duration, and time integral

Adapted from *Journal of Experimental Psychology,* 1959, *58,* 341–347. With permission of the author and the American Psychological Association.

of force. The foregoing is achieved without sacrifice of the customary pulse recording techniques, simultaneous measures of digital and continuous response characteristics being possible with this system. In addition, and in anticipation of future research requirements, the same apparatus permits selective reinforcement in proportion to the magnitude of the particular response characteristic sensed.

A standard small animal cage is equipped with a modified bar, the innovation consisting in replacement of the microswitch with a pair of strain gauges. Pressure on the bar produces a minute change in the internal resistance of the strain gauges, thereby unbalancing a Wheatstone bridge to which the strain gauges are coupled. The pressure-proportional voltage thus made available is passed into a preamplifier, from which it enters an analog computer. The computer has several functions, some of which are mutually exclusive, these being exercised at E's discretion. Functions pertinent to the investigation here reported are as follows: (a) determination of the constant number of pellets by which each suprathreshold response is to be reinforced; (b) further amplification of the voltage originating from pressure on the bar, thereby producing a voltage-proportional force read-out on a strip-chart recorder; (c) generation of reference voltages used to determine the "response threshold," or the precise level of force required to activate the reinforcement circuit (accomplished jointly with a "Threshold Adjust" unit); and (d) determination of occurrence of suprathreshold responses on a "Yes-No" basis, for pulse counting and cumulative recording purposes.

As Functions c and d indicate, it is possible to obtain conventional operant behavior data, with the Threshold Adjust being set to some value corresponding to the force required to close the microswitch in the usual bar. It should be noted, however, that although the visual appearance of that portion of the bar which is within the experimental cage is identical with the conventional manipulandum, the tactual bar is quite different. In the present case, the bar remains more or less immobile during active responding (maximum movement being approximately 1–2 mm.), and was designed this way in order to lay the groundwork for potential experimental separation of movement from pressure cues (or "work" from "impulse").

Figure 1 is a linearity and calibration check between gram weights on the bar, and voltage output of the computer (Function b). As can be seen, the system is linear over a large range of forces. Similar checks with similar results have been obtained for time integral of force (gm.-sec.), and for the excursion of the recorder pens.

Figure 2 is a sample record. For this experiment, the critical threshold for reinforcement was set at 3 gm., this being well above the noise level of the system, but still low enough to provide S with essentially "free" lower and upper force limits. A response was defined as being in effect from the instant S emitted 3 gm. of force to the instant the force level went below 3 gm., as in "A." In the event that, during continuous contact with the bar, the force exceeded 3 gm., fell off to less than 3 gm., and then again increased past the critical threshold, two responses were counted ("B"). If the force failed to reach 3 gm., as in "C," it was not deemed a response.

The "Reinforcement Indicator" channel served the function of providing a

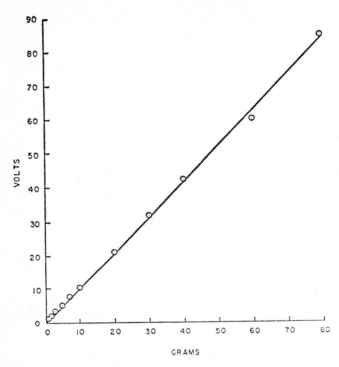

Figure 1.   Linearity check: voltage output as a function of grams weight of force on lever.

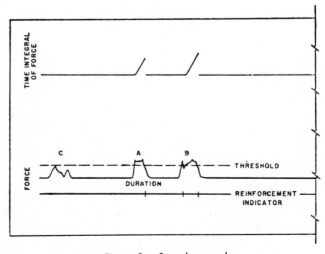

Figure 2.   Sample record.

convenient check on when the force level fell below the critical threshold. Each mark indicates delivery of one pellet, and corresponds to the instant that the force drops below critical threshold. (Duration and time integral of force data, although recorded, are not considered in the present paper.)

The foregoing convention concerning definition of a response was adopted in this experiment on the basis of its being most analogous to that of the usual bar pressing situation. (Other response criteria, e.g., calling each force emission a response, regardless of whether it reaches critical threshold are, of course, possible, and are currently being examined.) "B" is equivalent to the case in which S presses twice without releasing the bar, and "C" is similar to a bar contact not strong enough to close the microswitch. In general, then, the present bar is chiefly distinguished from the usual bar by its being much more "sensitive," and by its being an analog, rather than make-break, type of manipulandum.

Procedure. Six male Wistar rats, approximately 90 days old, were placed on 22-hr. hunger rhythm for 10 days prior to operant level determinations. The experiment proper was conducted over eight successive days (or sessions), as follows: *Operant Level*, two 35-min. sessions, followed by 20 min. of tray approach training; *Conditioning*, four sessions of regular reinforcement, one pellet per response, each session terminating upon procurement of approximately 50 pellets; *Extinction*, two 35-min. sessions. Pellets were standard Noyes Co., 45 mg. each. The Ss were fed Purina Chow for 1 hr. following each experimental session, and then again placed on deprivation.

RESULTS AND DISCUSSION

Figure 3 is a sequential plot of peak force attained by S_1 for each of the suprathreshold bar presses emitted during the entire course of the experiment. The data shown are characteristic of the remaining five Ss.

Noteworthy is the obvious drop in magnitude of response during the regular reinforcement sessions; this is accompanied by a decrease in response variability, or the development of "stereotypy." It is not surprising that the level of force characteristic of regular reinforcement is apparently related to the critical threshold. Skinner's data (1938, p. 312), for example, show that his S came to respond with a force of some 35–40 gm.; this for a bar which apparently required almost 20 gm. of force for activation. The Ss in this study come to press typically, during regular reinforcement, with approximately 5–6 gm.; but the critical force required was only 3 gm. Obviously, this is the result of the same sort of organism-mediated force differentiation which Skinner postulates on the basis of his data. The intriguing possibility exists that, over a significant range, Ss will stabilize during regular reinforcement at a force magnitude which is roughly twice that of the critical threshold, as determined by S's force discrimination difference limen.

Shortly after extinction is begun, both force magnitude and variability show a sharp increase. The trial-by-trial extinction data of Figure 3 may be in conflict with Skinner's (1938, p. 313) observation that: "Stronger re-

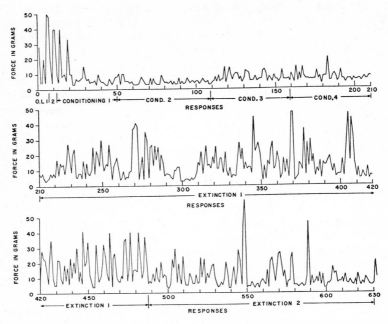

Figure 3. Sequential emission of peak forces during successive phases of the experiment. Data are for S_1.

sponses generally occur near the beginning of the extinction and give way to an unusually low force which is then steadily maintained." The present data, as represented by S_1, reveal a tendency for emission of fairly high magnitudes of forces well into extinction.

Figure 4 is a tracing of the usual cumulative response record obtained during bar pressing experiments, and is for the same animal as Figure 3. (Operant Level, Conditioning 1, and Extinction 2 data were omitted from

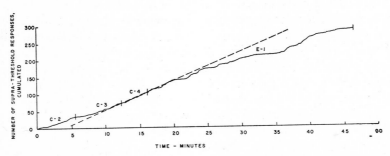

Figure 4. Cumulative response record for S_1, same responses, as in Figure 3.

this figure in order to permit as large a reproduction scale as possible.) The broken line represents the slope of Conditioning 4, and indicates that this phase produced the highest over-all rate. The early stages of Extinction 1 show the customary, momentary increases in rate, followed by an over-all decline. It should be noted that the cumulative recorder's mechanism was somewhat slower than that of the strip-chart recorder; hence, the latter occasionally indicated responses which were not sensed by the former. In all computations involving number of responses, the strip-chart data were considered definitive.

The four frequency distributions comprising Figure 5 show, in terms of

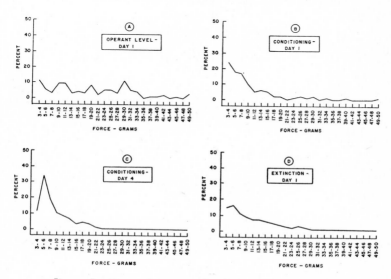

Figure 5. Group frequency distributions of peak forces.

percentage of total number of responses for each of the indicated experimental sessions, how the peak forces were distributed by the indicated scale intervals. These data are based on all six Ss; individual plots are quite similar. Most striking is the shift in distribution of forces as Ss proceed through the various phases of the experiment. The Operant Level data ("A") show quite clearly that prior to the response differentiation which takes place during conditioning, Ss exhibit a wide range of "freely" emitted forces. Conditioning 1 ("B") depicts the beginnings of a differentiation which is fairly sharp by the end of the fourth conditioning session ("C"). Noteworthy in connection with the latter is the decrease in frequency of occurrence of 3–4 gm. forces. The Ss apparently come to "play it safe," and typically emit forces at a level determined at the lower end by the critical threshold, and at the upper end perhaps by the negative aspects of unnecessary force expenditure. The latter speculation is, of course, intimately related to past notions of "least effort" or "work," and it is hoped that later analyses based upon the time integral of force measure (or "impulse") will permit careful sifting of that which may be of value in these earlier formulations.

The Extinction 1 data ("D") reveal the beginning of a return to the type of distribution characteristic of Operant Level. Whether the "random" nature of the latter is actually ever reached is presently uncertain. (The relation of force variability to Schoenfeld's [1950] and Antonitis' [1951] prior work in stereotyping has been investigated recently by Goldberg [1959].)

Figure 6 gives the group means and SDs of the peak forces emitted by all

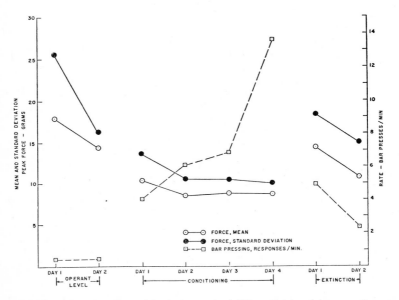

Figure 6.   Comparison of force (mean and SD) and rate of bar pressing.

six Ss over the course of the experiment. Mean bar pressing rates are presented for comparison purposes. The mean force data reflect the earlier observations based upon S_1's response-by-response performance (Figure 3). Similarly, the group bar pressing data show the same general trends revealed by S_1's cumulative record (Figure 4). The stereotyping evident in the earlier graphs is again shown here, this time by the approach to asymptotic values of force magnitude and standard deviation during the course of conditioning.

Of particular interest is the fact that bar pressing rate keeps rising sharply even as the force measures become stabilized. The rate measure, it will be recalled, is based upon approximately 50 responses produced by each *S* during each of the regular reinforcement sessions. Accordingly, the increase in rate is *not* the result of a greater number of responses having been emitted during successive, constant total time sessions, but rather the result of the same number of responses having been emitted during progressively shorter sessions. Such being the case, it is clear that it is the dropping out of intervening behavior (i.e., behavior between successive bar presses) which is responsible for the observed rate increases. Considered in this sense, bar pressing rate is a measure of bar pressing response strength *relative* to the strength of other ongoing behavior. As Skinner puts it: ". . . the main datum to be measured in the study of the dynamic laws of an operant is the length of time elapsing between a response and the response immediately preceding it or, in other words, the rate of responding" (Skinner, 1938, p. 58).

The point of the preceding comment is that bar pressing rate is inherently a composite measure of a given set of behavioral events separated in time by other (albeit chain-related) behavioral events. The intensive attributes of response, on the other hand, are by their very nature exclusively indices of the actual responses per se. This is not to imply that the one is a "better" or "worse" measure than the other. Obviously, frequency and intensity measures sample different properties of behavior. The former has been shown to bear such a predictable relation to reinforcement operations as to stand relatively unchallenged as a convenient index of these operations, and by definition has come to signify a property called "response strength." The latter, i.e., force, may as Skinner says bear "no simple relation" to response strength, but that may be begging the question. The real issue, as with bar pressing, is: Do lawful relations exist between *E*'s operations and the intensive characteristics of *S*'s response? Here the answer is affirmative as indicated by the foregoing graphs. That such lawfulness is predicated upon response differentiation, and not bar pressing rate, does not diminish its possible importance. It may be of considerable significance, for example, to know that differentiation of force takes place much sooner than stabilization of bar pressing rate (Figure 6), and that this differentiation is maintained at stable levels, even though bar pressing occurs at more frequent intervals, indicating the gradual disappearance of other ongoing behavior.

SUMMARY

A detailed description was made of the emission of forces by rats during acquisition (regular reinforcement) and extinction of the bar pressing response. It was found that the distribution of forces emitted during acquisition peaked at a value approximately twice that of the force required for reinforcement, and that both magnitude and variability of force decreased during acquisition and increased during extinction. The implications of an observed increase in bar pressing rate during acquisition, well after force stabilization had occurred, were examined.

REFERENCES

ANTONITIS, J. J. Response variability in the white rat during conditioning, extinction, and reconditioning. *J. exp. Psychol.*, 1951, *42*, 273–281.

GOLDBERG, I. Relations of response variability in conditioning and extinction. Unpublished doctoral dissertation, Columbia Univer., 1959.

SCHOENFELD, W. N. On the difference in resistance to extinction following regular and periodic reinforcement. Unpublished manuscript, Columbia Univer., 1950.

SKINNER, B. F. *The behavior of organisms.* New York: Appleton-Century-Crofts, 1938.

TROTTER, J. R. The physical properties of bar pressing behaviour and the problem of reactive inhibition. *Quart. J. exp. Psychol.*, 1956, *8*, 97–106.

17

Stereotypy and Intermittent Reinforcement

R. J. Herrnstein

Antonitis demonstrated that hungry rats will form strong preferences for particular locations when they are given equal opportunities to be fed at a number of different locations (1951). The experimental situation he used consisted of a box that had a long, narrow, horizontal slot in one wall, and the rat was given a single pellet of food after it put its snout into any part of the slot. Each rat developed a marked preference for some location along the slot. Later, Antonitis discontinued delivering pellets for this behavior and found that as the behavior disappeared it went through a phase of much-increased variability. Other experimenters (Frick and Miller, 1951; Guthrie and Horton, 1946; Skinner, 1938; Warden and Lubow, 1942) have also noted an increase in the variability of a learned response during the course of its extinction, and some have commented on the adaptiveness of this increase in bringing out new forms of behavior.

Adapted from *Science,* 1961, *133,* 3470, 2067–2069. With permission of the author. Copyright 1961 by the American Association for the Advancement of Science.

Antonitis reported that the stereotypy of responding returned when the behavior was again reinforced with pellets. The stereotypy after reconditioning was even greater than the stereotypy during the original training. These findings of Antonitis raise an interesting question about the relation between variability of responding and intermittency of reinforcement. The increase in variability during extinction suggests that a schedule of reinforcement that does not reinforce every occurrence of the selected response will generate more variability than a schedule that does. The heightened stereotypy in reconditioning seems to imply the opposite, namely that a schedule in which the animal is intermittently reinforced (that is, reconditioned) will generate less variability.

The experiment reported here was an attempt to establish merely whether variability increases or decreases as a result of intermittent reinforcement. Pigeons were used as subjects in an experimental chamber that contained a 10-in. by 1-in. rubber strip horizontally centered on one wall. A feeding device could be activated to give the pigeon access to grain for about 3 sec. The pigeons were trained to peck at the rubber strip, and the location of the peck was automatically recorded within one of ten 1-in. squares. Three pigeons were used.

In the first phase of the experiment, any peck on the rubber strip operated the feeding device. Approximately 2 weeks of daily experimental sessions were conducted; each session consisting of 60 reinforcements. In the second phase, the pigeons were reinforced according to a variable-interval schedule. Pecking the rubber strip operated the feeding device every 3 min., on the average. The range of time intervals between reinforcements in this schedule was from about 5 sec. to about 7 min. Reinforcements were still given without respect to the location of the peck on the rubber strip. Sessions were again conducted until the pigeon received 60 reinforcements.

Figure 1 summarizes the result of the experiments. Each horizontal row of graphs is for one pigeon; each vertical column for a particular measure of behavior. The points on the graphs are medians from five sessions. In each graph, frequency of responding, expressed as a proportion of the total frequency of responding, is shown as a function of the location on the rubber strip. The ten locations are numbered 1 to 10, going from left to right. The area under each graph approximates 1.0. The first column of graphs, labeled "CRF," (that is, continuous reinforcement) shows the distribution of responding obtained when each peck to the strip was reinforced. A horizontal line at 0.1 would indicate a random distribution of responding, and these graphs make it clear that some degree of stereotypy is present. Each pigeon manifests a tendency to peck at one or the other end of the rubber strip. The second column of graphs shows that the intermittent schedule of reinforcement ("VI 3'" or variable interval of 3 min.) produced increased stereotypy. With the first procedure the modal location got between 40 and 52 percent of the responding, with the second procedure the range was from 78

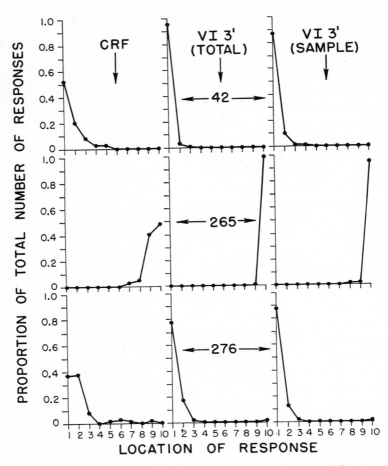

Figure 1. *Relative frequency of responding is shown as a function of location on the response-strip. Each horizontal row of graphs is for one pigeon. The first column of graphs is for a schedule of continuous reinforcement; the second and third columns are for intermittent reinforcement.*

to 99 percent. This increase in stereotypy was evident in the very first experimental session with intermittent reinforcement. The continuous records of location of responding showed that there was increased responding on the modal location after about 15 min. of the first session and that the final level was reached by the second or third session.

The third column of graphs is a check on possible artifacts in the results. Under the first procedure, the pigeon moved away from the rubber strip after every peck in order to go to the feeding device. Under the second procedure, only a small fraction of the pecks were followed by a movement to the feeding device. It seemed possible that the return to the rubber strip after eating caused a certain amount of variability in the location of responding. This factor would dominate the first procedure, but would be only negligible in the second. The third column of graphs is therefore based on only those pecks, under the variable-interval schedule, that immediately followed eating. Since there were 60 reinforcements in each session, this sample included 59 pecks per session. The distributions of responding in the third column show as much stereotypy as those in the second. It is therefore evident that the increase in stereotypy produced by intermittent reinforcement is due neither to the animal's being forced to move around in the situation nor to the large difference between the numbers of responses that entered into the computation of the first and second columns of graphs.

The duration of sessions under continuous reinforcement was about 10 min.; under variable-interval reinforcement it was about 3 hr. This difference in time may have been responsible for the difference in variability under the two procedures. The distributions of responding during the first 10 min. of sessions under variable-interval reinforcement make this explanation implausible. The amount of variability seen here was greater than that shown in the second and third columns of Figure 1, but was still well below the amount shown in the first column.

This experiment strongly suggests that stereotypy is enhanced by intermittency of reinforcement itself and not by some essentially trivial concomitant of the change in procedure from continuous to intermittent reinforcement. Stereotypy is to be expected when there is no benefit to the animal for moving around in the situation. The principle of reinforcement predicts that a location that is reinforced early in the animal's exposure to the procedure would gradually come to dominate the distribution of responding. Moreover, the spread of responding in extinction is empirically, although not theoretically, expected. Why responding becomes more stereotyped during intermittent reinforcement does not, however, follow easily from our present state of knowledge. The clarity of the present findings indicates that a significant but unexplored principle may be involved.

SUMMARY

Three pigeons were trained to peck at a horizontally oriented rubber strip 10 in. long. The spatial distribution of responding along this strip is found to be nonrandom when every peck is reinforced with food. The degree of nonrandomness increases markedly when the pecking is intermittently reinforced.

REFERENCES

ANTONITIS, J. J. Response variability in the white rat during conditioning, extinction, and reconditioning. *J. exp. Psychol.*, 1951, *42*, 273–281.

FRICK, F. C., and MILLER, G. A. A statistical description of operant conditioning. *Am. J. Psychol.*, 1951, *64*, 20–36.

GUTHRIE, E. R., and HORTON, G. P. *Cats in a puzzle box.* New York: Holt, Rinehart and Winston, 1946.

SKINNER, B. F. *The behavior of organisms.* New York: Appleton-Century-Crofts, 1938.

WARDEN, C. J., and LUBOW, L. Effect of performance without reward on the retention of the maze habit in the white rat. *J. genet. Psychol.,* 1942, *60,* 321–328.

18

Effects of Deprivation and Reinforcement-Magnitude on Response Variability

Peter L. Carlton

These experiments were designed to demonstrate the effects of changes in level of deprivation or in magnitude of reinforcement on directly measured variability of responding. The technique used to measure variability was similar to that used by Herrnstein (1961) and essentially the same as that used by Antonitis (1950, 1951) in that a two-membered response-chain was involved. The present technique differs from Antonitis' in that the terminal member of the chain was made more explicit. In particular, the programming equipment was set up so that under one stimulus condition, the animal could switch to a second condition by displacing any one of five plastic panels mounted in one wall of the response chamber. Under the second stimulus condition, and only under that condition, the animal could press a response lever in the opposite wall and thereby receive a small amount of milk. The first stimulus condition was reinstated coincident with the delivery of milk.

Level of deprivation was varied by changing the amount of food the animal was fed after each experimental session. In a subsidiary experiment, the effects of magnitude of reinforcement were briefly investigated by varying the concentration of the milk solution delivered to the animal.

Adapted from *Journal of the Experimental Analysis of Behavior,* 1962, 5, 481–486. With permission of Peter L. Carlton, Department of Psychology, Rutgers—The State University, New Brunswick, New Jersey.

METHOD

Subjects

Four adult, male, albino rats, initially maintained at about 75 percent of their free-feeding body weights, were used.

Apparatus

A standard sound-insulated and ventilated response chamber contained a small stimulus lamp, a larger lamp (the houselight), and a speaker through which auditory stimuli could be presented was used. The chamber was $10\frac{1}{2}$ in. long by $10\frac{1}{4}$ in. wide. A response lever was mounted in one wall of the chamber. Below the lever was an opening through which the cup of a motor-driven dipper could be presented. Behind the opposite wall, and $\frac{1}{2}$ in. above the floor, five plastic plates were mounted. The plates were accessible to the animal through a horizontal series of five evenly spaced, 1-in. holes in the wall; the spacing between holes was $1\frac{3}{4}$ in. center to center. The animal could displace any one of the plates (response keys) and thereby activate a switch behind the plate.

The responses to the keys and to the lever were automatically recorded on a set of counters. The various response contingencies to be described were programmed by a system of relays and stepping-switches.

Procedure

Experimental sessions were conducted daily except on weekends and holidays. The animals were first trained to go to and drink from the cup at the sound of the dipper-motor (one session). They were then trained to press the lever, each press operating the dipper (one session); and, subsequently, (a) to respond to the lever when the small stimulus lamp was on and a clicking sound was delivered through the speaker (S_2), and (b) not to respond when the houselight was on and the clicker and the stimulus lamp were off (S_1). Details of the discrimination procedure used have been described previously (Carlton, 1959).

After the discrimination had been established, the programming circuit was arranged so that pressing any one of the five keys in S_1 switched the stimulus to S_2; in S_2 the first lever-press activated the dipper and reinstated S_1. Lever-responses in S_1 were ineffective; key-responses in S_2 were recorded but had no effect on the stimulus condition.

The animals were initially "shaped" on the key-lever sequence. As needed, the center key of the five was "baited" with a drop of milk (at least once for each rat) to facilitate the acquisition of the key-pressing response.

Each animal rapidly learned to displace the keys with its nose. The terminal response sequence was; key pressing (in S_1), traversing the length of the response chamber and lever pressing (in S_2), and drinking from the cup and returning to the keys (in S_1). Each animal's session was usually continued until 200 reinforcements had been delivered.

Except as noted below, the animals were maintained at about 75 percent of their free-feeding weights, and the concentration of the milk (Borden's Star Brand condensed milk diluted with water) was 30 percent. For purposes of brevity, the details of the variations in deprivation and magnitude of reinforcement have been given below.

RESULTS

The distributions of key responding became reasonably stable after about 15 sessions. After 27 sessions at 75 percent body weight, the weights of all animals were shifted to 90 percent of their free-feeding values. Then, after 9 sessions at 90 percent, the animals were put on a free-feeding schedule; i.e., they had free access to food in their home cages. Finally, the animals were totally deprived. The only food they received was delivered during experimental sessions. A sample set of the distributions of key responses under each of these conditions is presented in Figure 1; the distributions were taken from Sessions 27, 32, 42, and 49. The shift from 75 percent to

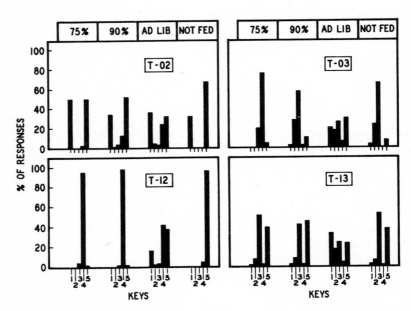

Figure 1.   Distributions of key responses for four animals under four conditions of deprivation.

90 percent body weight produced slight, if any, changes in the distribution of key responses, whereas the shift to free feeding was followed by an increase in the variability of the distributions. The increase was reversed by the introduction of total deprivation after 7–9 sessions on free feeding. Initial key-preferences were not constant throughout these variations.

One way of describing the changes in variability is in terms of the interquartile range (the range covered by the middle 50 percent of the responses) of the distributions obtained in each session. The interquartile ranges (IQR's) for three of the rats are plotted in Figure 2; the data for Rat T–02

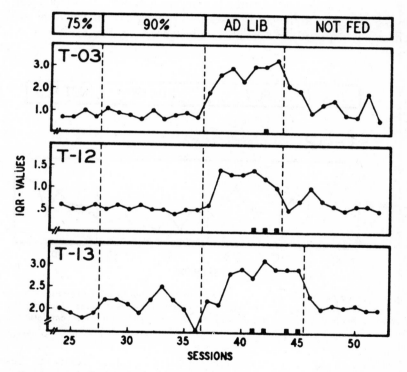

Figure 2. *Interquartile ranges for three animals under four conditions of deprivation. The squares on the abscissa indicate that the session was terminated before the usual 200 reinforcements had been delivered.*

are given separately in Figure 3. In all rats, variability was increased (increased IQR-values) with the decrease in deprivation level induced by free feeding and, conversely, decreased by the shift to total deprivation.

Unlike those for the other three animals, the IQR-values for Rat T–02 did not change appreciably following the changes in deprivation. This was due to the peculiar "U-shaped" distribution of the responses made by this animal. (See Figure 1.) So long as the animal made at least 25 percent of its responses to Key 1 and maintained a "preference" for Key 5, the IQR-values were necessarily about 3.5 regardless of any changes in the apparent variability of responding. Accordingly, the data for T–02 were treated in terms of the number of responses to the *one* key to which most responses were made, as a percentage of the total number of responses to all keys. As variability increases, the percentage made to any one key should decrease; decreased variability should be reflected as an increase in this percentage.

During the free-feeding phase, the total time required to complete the sessions increased. For example, the average number of key responses per min. was 2.19 in the last four free-feeding sessions, whereas the average rate was 8.62 per min. in the last four sessions of the phase in which the animals were totally deprived. In a number of instances (*cf.* Figures 2 and 3), the

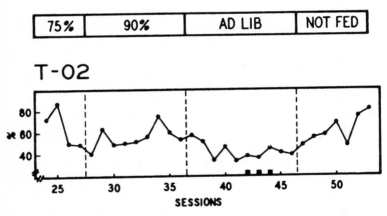

Figure 3. The number of responses to the one key to which most responses were made (as a percentage of the total number of responses to all keys) under four deprivation-conditions. As in Figure 2, the squares on the abscissa indicate incomplete sessions.

time limitations of the experimental routine necessitated removing the animals before the usual 200 reinforcements had been delivered.

During the free-feeding phase, there was also a tendency for the animals to emit more than the one key-response required to switch stimuli. The average numbers of such "extra" key-responses (expressed as a percentage of the total) were 3.5 percent, 2.9 percent, 21.2 percent, and 3.3 percent in the last four sessions of each successive phase of the experiment.

In the later portion of the phase in which the animals were totally deprived, the effects of decreased magnitude of reinforcement were briefly examined by reducing the concentration of milk from 30 percent to 1 percent or 3 percent for two of the animals. The effects of decreased magnitude of reinforcement are shown in Figure 4. In both cases the 1 percent solution produced an increase in variability; the 3 percent solution increased variability in only one of the animals.

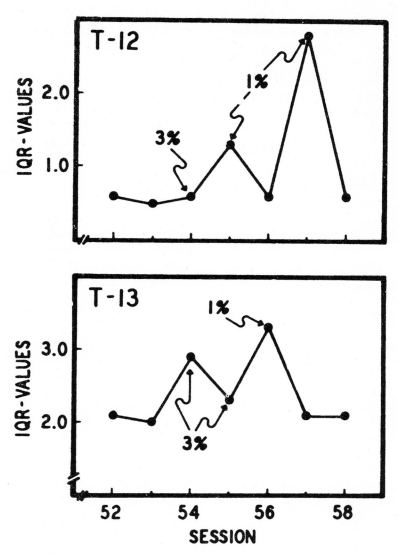

Figure 4. Interquartile ranges under conditions of reduced magnitude of reinforcement (expressed as percentage concentration of condensed milk, diluted with water) for two animals. The concentration was 30 percent except in those sessions in which concentration was reduced to 3 percent or 1 percent.

DISCUSSION

In general, the demonstration of changes in variability required rather drastic shifts in reinforcement-magnitude and deprivation. It should be borne in mind that the sweetened milk used as reinforcement is a highly "preferred" substance for the rat and would therefore be expected to be an effective reinforcement even when the animals are minimally deprived of laboratory chow. That is, the technique might have been a more sensitive one had reinforcements been dry food of the kind available in the home cages. The insensitivity of the procedure may also have been due to the use of such a gross technique for categorizing responses. (Studies involving 12 more closely spaced keys are currently in progress.) Further, note that the changes in variability were gradual ones. This finding suggests that these effects were related more to changes in body weight than to the acute effects of the feeding regimen.

The effects of deprivation on variability are similar to those reported by Elliott (1934). In contrast to the present study, however, Elliott found that the changes in variability were irreversible ones.

The fact that behavior is variable may reflect an innate and clearly adaptive tendency that is effectively counteracted by reinforcement. Variables that may control such variability have been discussed by a number of writers (e.g., Glanzer, 1953; Hull, 1943; Keller and Schoenfeld, 1950; Thompson, 1960). Whatever the mechanisms underlying variability may be, it is to be expected that experimental manipulations that tend to maximize reinforcement will decrease variability. Three such manipulations will be briefly discussed here.

The effectiveness of a reinforcement can be most directly manipulated by reducing its magnitude. Such reductions should, and do, increase variability. Reduction to zero (i.e., extinction) also results in markedly increased variability (Antonitis, 1950, 1951).

Second, shifts in level of deprivation may, as Stein has suggested (personal communication), produce correlated shifts in the effectiveness of a given magnitude of reinforcement. That is, as deprivation is decreased, the irrelevancy of the reinforcer to the animal's "need" is increased and the effectiveness of that reinforcer is accordingly decreased. This amounts to saying that food is not an effective reinforcer (i.e., equivalent to zero magnitude) to the nonhungry animal and that there are intermediate levels of decreased deprivation and correspondingly intermediate levels of effectively reduced reinforcement-magnitude.

It should also be noted that points of view (e.g., Hull, 1943; Spence, 1956) which assume that increased deprivation amplifies the differences between response tendencies would also predict increased variability with decreased deprivation, because of greater overlap of the probabilities of occurrence of the various classes of responses available.

Still a third manipulation involves the selective reinforcement of certain classes of responses. Under such circumstances, reinforcement is maximized and variability is reduced to the extent that the animal emits only those responses in the reinforced class.

Such differential contingencies could operate even though not explicitly controlled by the experimenter. In Antonitis' study (1950, 1951), for example, variability of responding increased during extinction following continuous reinforcement. When reconditioned, variability of responding was found to be less than that which had characterized the pre-extinction period and less than that of a control group that had not undergone extinction. It may have been that response tendencies that were greater during the initial continuous reinforcement session underwent relatively less weakening during the extinction sessions. This would be especially likely if, during extinction, initially nondominant responses were emitted about as often as the initially dominant ones. Examination of Antonitis' data (1950) indicates this was the case.

If such contingencies were in fact operative, it would be expected that the initial dominance of particular responses would be maintained and accentuated in the reconditioning phase. According to Antonitis (1960, p. 56): "The modal values of position distributions yielded by both experimental and control group animals in reconditioning sessions coincide closely with modal values of distributions on the fifth day of conditioning. . . ." Since the variability of responding of the experimental group was reduced, there would necessarily have been a relative increase in the frequency of initially preferred responses.

Such an "accentuation of preference" may also be seen in data reported by Herrnstein (1961). In this study, pigeons pecked at a rubber strip and, under continuous reinforcement for all responses, showed marked position preferences. The animals were subsequently switched to a variable-interval schedule. On this schedule the probability of nonpreferred responses occurring would be low and, therefore, the probability of their being reinforced extremely small. As expected, Herrnstein found that the relative frequency of occurrence of the initially preferred response increased, whereas that of nonpreferred responses decreased.[1]

The preceding point of view is essentially the same as that advanced by

---

[1] Intermittent reinforcement apparently has this effect on the extensive, but not the intensive, characteristics of responding. The variability of forces exerted by rats in pressing a lever has been found to increase when the reinforcement schedule is switched from continuous to fixed-interval (Goldberg, 1959). In contrast, changes in variability of forces during extinction and reconditioning were found (Goldberg, 1959; Notterman, 1959) to parallel those obtained by Antonitis. Related studies involving the duration of the lever response are in progress in this laboratory.

Weinstock (1958) in his discussion of the effects of partial reinforcement on subsequent extinction. The relevance of the present considerations to these effects will not be elaborated here.

As a final point, it is reasonable to suppose that the consequence of the three manipulations discussed should also affect the variability of responding in other components of the total behavior of the animal. Thus, in the present study, the times required to traverse the response chamber increased as variability of key responding increased, presumably because of the intrusion of time-consuming, irrelevant responses into the chain involved in moving between keys and lever. Similarly, the frequency of extraneous, "extra" key-responses increased under low deprivation. Other experimenters have reported related effects of reduced deprivation (Cotton, 1953) and of reduced magnitude (Pereboom and Crawford, 1958). Finally, the relatively greater weakening of nondominant responses has been advanced to account for the effects of repeated extinction and conditioning in a situation in which a jumping stand was used (Lauer and Estes, 1955).

SUMMARY

Animals were trained to displace any one of five response keys in order to put themselves in a stimulus condition in which reinforcement could be obtained by depressing a response lever. Decreased deprivation and magnitude of reinforcement were found to increase the variability of the distribution of key responses. The relevance of these findings to other experiments in which deprivation, reinforcement magnitude, and intermittent reinforcement were studied is discussed.

REFERENCES

ANTONITIS, J. J. Variability of response in the white rat during conditioning and succeeding extinction and reconditioning. Unpublished doctoral dissertation, Columbia Univer., 1950.

ANTONITIS, J. J. Response variability in the white rat during conditioning, extinction, and reconditioning. *J. exp. Psychol.*, 1951, *42*, 273–281.

CARLTON, P. L. Discrimination learning. *Science*, 1959, *130*, 1341–1343.

COTTON, J. W. Running time as a function of amount of food deprivation. *J. exp. Psychol.*, 1953, *46*, 188–198.

ELLIOTT, M. H. The effect of hunger on variability of performance. *Am. J. Psychol.*, 1934, *46*, 107–112.

GLANZER, M. Stimulus satiation: An explanation of spontaneous alternation and related phenomena. *Psychol. Rev.*, 1953, *60*, 257–268.

GOLDBERG, I. A. Relations of response variability in conditioning and extinction. Unpublished doctoral dissertation, Columbia Univer., 1959.

HERRNSTEIN, R. J. Stereotypy and intermittent reinforcement. *Science*, 1961, *133*, 2067–2069.

HULL, C. L. *Principles of behavior.* New York: Appleton-Century-Crofts, 1943.

KELLER, F. S., and SCHOENFELD, W. N. *Principles of psychology.* New York: Appleton-Century-Crofts, 1950.

LAUER, D. W., and ESTES, W. K. Successive acquisitions and extinctions of a jumping habit in relation to schedule of reinforcement. *J. comp. physiol. Psychol.,* 1955, *48,* 8–13.

NOTTERMAN, J. M. Force emission during bar pressing. *J. exp. Psychol.,* 1959, *58,* 341–347.

PEREBOOM, A. C., and CRAWFORD, B. M. Instrumental and competing behavior as a function of trials and reward magnitude. *J. exp. Psychol.,* 1958, *56,* 82–85.

SPENCE, K. W. *Behavior theory and conditioning.* New Haven: Yale University Press, 1956.

THOMPSON, M. E. A two-factor theory of inhibition. *Psychol. Rev.,* 1960, *67,* 200–206.

WEINSTOCK, S. Acquisition and extinction of a partially reinforced running response at a 24-hour intertrial interval. *J. exp. Psychol.,* 1958, *56,* 151–158.

19

Exteroceptive Cueing of Response Force

J. M. Notterman and D. E. Mintz

Following Skinner's (1938) original distinction, the term "discrimination" has come to refer to those behavioral situations in which an organism is reinforced for making a given response only when it is emitted following exposure to a specific exteroceptive signal. The term "differentiation" is used to describe those situations in which exteroceptive stimuli customarily remain constant, and the organism is reinforced only for responses having a specific form, intensity, duration, or other preselected property.

Skinner (1938, p. 338) suggests that many instances of behavior reflect a "double discrimination," combining the circumstances of discrimination and differentiation. This typically might involve a specific value of an exteroceptive stimulus indicating the particular intensity of response necessary for reinforcement.

The present report concerns itself with the "double discrimination" type of behavior Skinner was describing. This class of behavior has much to

Adapted from *Science,* 1962, *135,* 3508, 1070–1071. With permission of the authors.

teach us, for it deals with a rather commonplace behavioral situation: one in which an organism maintains successive responding, but adjusts each individual response value to that "required" by the value of a varying extero-ceptive cue. This type of behavior is implicit in common forms of closed-loop error detection and correction.

The performance curves shown in Figure 1 are frequency distributions of

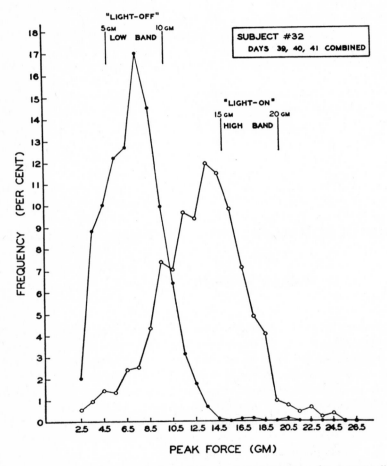

Figure 1. *Frequency distribution of peak force during "double discrimination" per-formance. Reinforcement occurred only for responses within the indicated bands.*

peak force emission for a single, male, Wistar rat, 90 days old at the start of the experiment. Under exteroceptive conditions of "darkness" or light-off, the animal was regularly reinforced with a 45-mg. pellet (after 23 hours' food deprivation) for pressing a lever with a peak force between 5 and 10 g. Notterman (1959) provides a description of the apparatus used in this study. However, when an overhead light was on (approximately 20 ft-ca. at the cage floor), the same animal was reinforced only for pressing between 15 and 20 g. The points shown are percentages for specific force levels obtained for the combined data gathered over the last three of 41 sessions. Each daily session was 20 minutes and 40 seconds in duration, and was divided into random presentations of "light-on" and "light-off" periods of 10, 20, 40, 80, or 160 seconds. The cumulative time-in-the-dark and time-in-the-light was evenly divided within each session. The two curves represent the relative distribution within each stimulus condition.

Although data are shown for a single subject only, a total of eight subjects were run. For four of these, conditions were as previously described. For the other four subjects, the relation between presence of light and force level required was reversed.

All subjects developed a tendency to respond with a force level appropriate to the particular exteroceptive signal presented. This was true regardless of the specific stimulus conditions (that is, light-on or light-off) correlated with either of the bands of force required for reinforcement.

In the performance shown in Figure 1, peaking in the low band is as might be expected; the peaking appropriate to the high band falls somewhat below the reinforcement range, with the distribution of forces being more variable than for the low band. This type of performance was characteristic of all eight subjects. Each animal's median peak force of response was within the reinforced range for the low band condition, but below the reinforcement band for the high band condition. Variability of the high band distribution was significantly greater than for the low band distribution for each subject (F ratio, two-tailed test, 5-percent level).

For the entire group of eight subjects, the force level of the first response following each change in the exteroceptive cue was significantly altered in the appropriate direction (that is, higher or lower) from that prevalent prior to the stimulus change (two-tailed sign test, 5-percent level). In other words, "double discrimination" behavior involving emission of force appropriate to the value of a specific exteroceptive cue, was effectively established.

SUMMARY

Food pellet reinforcement for rats was made contingent upon the peak force of a bar-pressing response falling within restricted limits. Two such "bands," 5 to 10 grams and 15 to 20 grams, were established, the momentarily correct "band" indicated by one of two exteroceptive stimulus values. Peak force of response tended to conform to the reinforcement requirements, the two stimulus values setting the occasion for differentiated distributions of response force.

REFERENCES

NOTTERMAN, J. M. Force emission during bar pressing. *J. exp. Psychol.,* 1959, *58,* 341–347.

SKINNER, B. F. *The behavior of organisms.* New York: Appleton-Century-Crofts, 1938.

20

Escape and Avoidance Conditioning in Human Subjects without Their Observation of the Response

Ralph F. Hefferline, Brian Keenan, and Richard A. Harford

When the human subject has "voluntary control" of the response to be conditioned, experimental results are in general less predictable and reproducible than those obtained from animals. This is commonly attributed to "self instruction"—that is, to variables experimentally uncontrolled. In the study reported here this problem was circumvented by working with a response so small as to preclude a history of strengthening through discriminable effect upon the environment—in fact, so small as to occur unnoticed by the subject.

The electromyographic setup employed was a modification of that previously reported (Hefferline, 1958). The subject sat in a shielded enclosure in a reclining chair. Recording electrodes were attached to the palmar base of the left thumb and to the medial edge of the left hand. Three additional sets of dummy electrodes were applied in some instances, to suggest that a comprehensive study of body tensions was being conducted. Muscle-action potentials across the left hand were amplified by a factor of 1 million and

Adapted from *Science,* 1959, *130,* 3385, 1338–1339. With permission of the authors and the American Association for the Advancement of Science.

rectified, and their average momentary values were displayed on a meter. They were also permanently recorded by an Esterline-Angus recording milliammeter.

Twenty-four adults served as subjects. Records from 12 were ruined by apparatus failure, excessive artifact, or failure of the subject to sit still. Results are reported from eight men and four women ranging in age from 18 to 50 and divided into four groups of three each.

Group 1, with four sets of electrodes attached, were told that the study concerned the effects on body tension of noise superimposed on music. Their task was to listen through earphones and, otherwise, do nothing. Group 2, also with all electrodes attached, were told that a specific response, so small as to be invisible, would temporarily turn off the noise or, when the noise was not present, postpone its onset. Their task was to discover and make use of the response. Group 3 (with recording electrodes only) were informed that the effective response was a tiny twitch of the left thumb. Group 4 were given the same information as Group 3 but had, in addition, a meter before them during the first half-hour of conditioning, which provided a potential basis for them to use the visual presentation of their response as a "crutch" for proprioceptive observation of the response.

Experimental procedure was identical for all groups. While the subject relaxed and listened to tape-recorded music through earphones, the experimenter watched the meter on his panel for 5 to 10 minutes to select for later reinforcement a response of a size occurring not more than once in 1 or 2 minutes. It was a ballistic swing of the pointer up and back over a few scale divisions. This represented, for a particular subject, a momentary voltage increment at the electrode of 1, 2, or 3 μv.

After the operant level for this response had been recorded for 10 minutes (*OL 1* in Figure 1), conditioning was begun by superimposing on the music an aversively loud, 60-cycle hum. Whenever the experimenter saw on the meter an instance of the selected response, he pressed a key. This turned off the noise for 15 seconds or, when it was already off, postponed noise resumption for 15 seconds. [This type of avoidance schedule, mentioned in 1950 (Hefferline), has been extensively employed by Sidman in animal work (1953).]

After an hour of conditioning, with a 5-minute intermission at the half-hour point, 10 minutes of extinction occurred during which the subject's response was ineffective in terminating continuously present noise. During final 10 minutes of music only, the extent of recovery of the original operant level was recorded.

Figure 1 presents cumulative response curves for each subject. Conditioning is clearly indicated by the positive acceleration in the rate of responding for all subjects except Subjects 2 and 3 in Group 3. These two kept so busy producing voluntary thumb-twitches that the small, reinforceable type of response had little opportunity to occur.

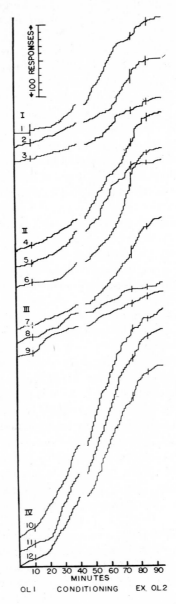

Figure 1. Cumulative response curves for adult human subjects in a situation where an invisibly small and unnoticed thumb-twitch either terminated or postponed noise stimulation. OL 1 and 2, initial and terminal operant level determinations, respectively; EX., extinction.

When interviewed later, all members of Group 1 still believed that they had been passive victims with respect to the onset and duration of noise, and all seemed astounded to learn that they themselves had been in control. Subjects 1 and 2 of Group 2 reported that they early gave up searching for an effective response and thus, in effect, transferred themselves to Group 1. Subject 3 of Group 2 professed to have discovered an effective response sequence, which consisted of subtle rowing movements with both hands, infinitesimal wriggles of both ankles, a slight displacement of the jaw to the left, breathing out—and then waiting. Subject 1 of Group 3 gave evidence of conditioning perhaps because he misconstrued the instructions. Instead of making the response a quick contraction, he spent his time very gradually increasing pressure on an imaginary switch button. This may have kept deliberate activity at a level low enough for the correct response to break through and be reinforced.

Group 4 subjects, provided with their own meter, obtained many more reinforcements than the others, an effect which continued through the second half-hour of conditioning, with the meter removed. While the meter did not enable them to achieve direct control of the discrete response, it seems to have provided a basis for rapid responding within a range which included the reinforced size. This showed on the meter as rapid oscillation.

The technique employed in this study offers possibilities for investigating human behavior, in a sense, at the animal level. Research now in progress is concerned with attempts to clarify the circumstances under which the human subject may come to discriminate verbally—that is, to become conscious of—his small responses.

SUMMARY

An invisibly small thumb-twitch increased in rate of occurrence when it served, via electromyographic amplification, to terminate or postpone aversive noise stimulation. Subjects remained ignorant of their behavior and its effect. Their cumulative response curves resembled those obtained in similar work with animals. Other subjects, informed of the effective response, could not produce it deliberately in a size small enough to qualify for reinforcement.

REFERENCES

HEFFERLINE, R. F. An experimental study of avoidance. *Genet. psychol. Monogr.*, 1950, *42*, 231–334.

HEFFERLINE, R. F. The role of proprioception in the control of behavior. *Trans. N.Y. Acad. Sci.*, 1958, *20*, 739–764.

SIDMAN, M. Avoidance conditioning with brief shock and no exteroceptive warning signal. *Science*, 1953, *118*, 157–158.

21

Amplitude-Induction Gradient
of a Small Human Operant in an
Escape-Avoidance Situation

Ralph F. Hefferline and Brian Keenan

"Shaping up" a response in short order has become a routine stratagem in conditioning demonstrations. The rat arrives quickly at bar pressing, or the pigeon at key pecking, when closer and closer approximations to the required behavior receive judicious reinforcement. In systematic studies of response differentiation, the progressive shift of the response along some chosen dimension (such as amplitude) is attributed to induction, which is the counterpart of stimulus generalization in discrimination work.

When a response is reinforced, further members of the response class of which the reinforced response is a member are made more likely to occur. Should the response class be divided into subclasses, it is assumed that the reinforcement strengthens most that subclass of which the reinforced response is a member and proportionately less the subclasses located to either side of it along the dimension. By selective reinforcement, one can move the modal subclass up or down a particular dimension more or less at will and, in doing so, perhaps observe extreme values which would have been quite improbable initially.

Investigations of amplitude differentiation have usually followed the pattern of getting the subject over higher and higher hurdles. Responses have been dichotomized into those which met or failed to meet the current reinforcement contingency, and little note has been taken of the *amount* by which the criterion level was exceeded or undershot. The response-induction gradient has consequently failed to achieve the kind of direct confirmation attained for the stimulus-generalization gradient.

Adapted from *Journal of the Experimental Analysis of Behavior*, 1961, *4*, 41–43. With permission of the authors and publisher.

The preliminary finding reported here stems from further processing of data from one of the subjects in a previous study (Hefferline, Keenan and Harford, 1959), which published only his cumulative record for the reinforced response. In Figure 1 we repeat the curve (heavy line) and add a family of curves for amplitude values of the same operant which were too large or too small to qualify for reinforcement. (The amplitude criterion had both a lower and an upper limit.)

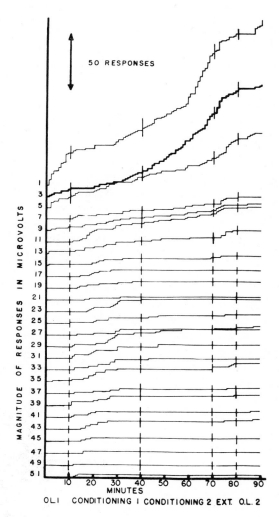

Figure 1. *Amplitude-induction gradient of a small operant (thumb contraction) for a single human subject in an escape-avoidance situation. OL 1 and OL 2 are initial and final operant-level determinations, and EXT is extinction. Values on the ordinate represent midpoints of steps 2 microvolts wide in size of electromyographic signal.*

The experimental arrangements for this subject will be reviewed briefly. He sat in a reclining chair in a shielded enclosure designed for electro-myographic recording (Hefferline, 1958). Four pairs of electrodes, three of them dummies, were attached, with the recording pair fastened to the left hand in such a fashion as to detect minute thumb contractions. The size of the contraction to be reinforced was determined on the basis of 10 minutes of operant-level observation (OL 1), while the subject listened to music through earphones.

The subject was told that after this period of clear music, noise would be added through the phones, and that his task was to make a specific response —so small as to be invisible and one which he must discover for himself— which would temporarily turn off the noise or, when noise was not present, postpone its recurrence. (The response eliminated or postponed noise for 15 seconds.)

As may be seen in Figure 1, during two 30-minute conditioning periods separated by a 5-minute intermission, the reinforced operant's rate accel-erated steadily. At the end of conditioning, noise was being avoided continuously for as much as a minute or more at a time. Ten minutes of extinction reduced the response to its initial rate, as indicated by a second operant-level determination (OL 2).

Before considering the inductive aspects of reinforcement, it may be noted that during OL 1 the response spectrum was narrow, with large amplitudes occurring only infrequently or not at all. (Values shown on the ordinate are midpoints of subclasses 2 microvolts wide.) A high rate is seen for the very smallest response, 1 microvolt, but this entire curve is suspect. The signal was so close to the bucked-out noise level of the system that minute changes of level probably produced "responses" artifactually. Eliminating this smallest category leaves us with a one-sided array of subclasses.

The first reinforcement was obtained at once after onset of noise, but it was more than 10 minutes before the next. The initial effect of the first re-inforcement appears most markedly in those subclasses just above that of the reinforced response. Larger amplitudes follow shortly in an irregular manner over the whole spectrum. Most of these had not occurred a single time during OL 1.

The larger values then diminish in frequency and disappear more or less in order of decreasing size, while those subclasses just slightly larger than the reinforced one do not disappear but seem to settle to a steady low rate. With the beginning of extinction, responses recur throughout most of the spectrum. The subclasses nearest the reinforced one display the form of typical extinction curves.

When the subject was asked later to state what he had done to obtain re-inforcement, his report suggested superstitious behavior based on knowledge of electrode placement: one on each hand and ankle and one on an earlobe. He professed to have discovered an effective response sequence, which consisted of subtle rowing movements with both hands, infinitesimal wriggles of both ankles, a slight displacement of the jaw to the left, breathing out —and then waiting.

A full-scale study of the induction gradient will be undertaken shortly, making use of a rather elaborate electronic impulse analyzer constructed for this and other work. This instrument, partially described elsewhere (Hefferline, Keenan, Harford, and Birch, 1960), provides and records automatic reinforcement, and, in addition, detects and records seven other amplitude values of the operant.

In the projected study, instead of termination or postponement of an aversive stimulus, reinforcement will consist of an increase in numerical score displayed to the subject by an illuminated readout system. Further, the response to be reinforced will be selected from the middle of the spectrum in order to make possible the recording of a two-sided gradient.

REFERENCES

HEFFERLINE, R. F. The role of proprioception in the control of behavior. *Trans. N.Y. Acad. Sci.*, 1958, *20*, 739–764.

HEFFERLINE, R. F., KEENAN, B., and HARFORD, R. A. Escape and avoidance conditioning in human subjects without their observation of the response. *Science*, 1959, *130*, 1338–1339.

HEFFERLINE, R. F., KEENAN, B., HARFORD, R. A., and BIRCH, J. Electronics in psychology. *Columbia Eng. Qu.*, 1960, *13*, 10–15.

SUGGESTED READINGS

KELLER, F. S., and SCHOENFELD, W. N. *Principles of psychology.* New York: Appleton-Century-Crofts, 1950, Chap. 6.

NOTTERMAN, J. M., and MINTZ, D. E. *Dynamics of response.* New York: Wiley, 1965.

SKINNER, B. F. *The behavior of organisms.* New York: Appleton-Century-Crofts, 1938, Chap. 8.

SKINNER, B. F. *Science and human behavior.* New York: Macmillan, 1953, Chap. 6.

Chapter VII

CHAINING AND CONDITIONED REINFORCEMENT

The research papers reproduced in this book so far have all dealt with the observation of a single class of responses. Although this may be quite justifiable at an early stage of analysis, it is clear that actually no response occurs in isolation. Normally each response is preceded and followed by other responses. It is this fact which is recognized by the term *chaining* (Skinner, 1938; Hull, 1952). Experiments in this area deal with sequences or chains of behavior and therefore involve the observation or recording of more than one single kind of response.

Within a chain of behavior, each response produces the stimulus for the next one. At any point in the sequence a stimulus serves simultaneously as the reinforcing stimulus for the response that produced it as well as the discriminative stimulus for the next response of the behavior chain. Since frequently many of the stimuli which are part of a behavior chain are conditioned reinforcers, the study of the effects of experimental manipulations within one link of a chain upon the strength of the behavior in other links of the sequence is an important way of learning more about conditioned reinforcement. Several articles reproduced in this chapter involve the explicit observation of more than a single link of a chain. In the case of the other articles, the concept of conditioned reinforcement remains the crux of the matter.

REFERENCES

HULL, C. S. *A behavior system.* New Haven: Yale University Press, 1952.
SKINNER, B. F. *The behavior of organisms.* New York: Appleton-Century-Crofts, 1938.
STAATS, A. W., and STAATS, C. K. *Complex human behavior.* New York: Holt, Rinehart and Winston, 1963.

22

Indirect Extinction of a Conditioned Response

Norman Guttman and William K. Estes

Can a conditioned instrumental response be extinguished without actual elicitation? We have attempted to answer this question by analyzing the sequence of movements comprising a bar-pressing habit into its component S-R correlations and then eliminating the final member of the sequence before beginning experimental extinction.

Two groups of four albino rats were first conditioned to press a bar for water reinforcement in a Skinner-type apparatus. After both groups had received 500 reinforcements, the experimental group was given six daily 30-minute periods of "indirect extinction." During these periods, the bars were removed from the apparatus. The animal was free to move about in the box during the entire period, and at intervals of about 90 seconds was stimulated by operation of the empty magazine. At first all animals approached the magazine whenever the motor sounded, but during the six periods this behavior extinguished. Finally, both groups were given experimental extinction of the bar-pressing response. During a 30-minute period, the animal was confined in the apparatus with the bar available but disconnected from the magazine. All bar-pressing responses were recorded.

Extinction curves for the bar-pressing response revealed marked differences in form. The experimental group started at a higher rate, but extinguished much more rapidly. The higher initial rate is presumably due to the previous separate extinction of the final component of the response, which reduces the minimum time required for extinction of a response. The more rapid extinction may be attributed to the elimination of secondary reinforcement.

Adapted from *Proceedings of the Indiana Academy of Science*, 1949, *59*, 287–288. With permission of the authors and publisher.

In summary, it appears that a conditioned instrumental response may be weakened, but not completely extinguished, by separate extinction of its final component.[1]

23

Sustained Behavior Under Delayed Reinforcement

Charles B. Ferster

In some preliminary research the rate of responding of pigeons pecking at a small illuminated disc was examined under delays of reinforcement of from 1 to 10 sec. It was found that the initial effect of a delay was a decrease in the rate of responding. When delay procedures were continued over longer periods, however, the frequency of pecking increased to a magnitude that might be obtained with no delay. The present experiments determine some of the conditions which influence the rate of a response whose reinforcement is delayed.

EXPERIMENT I

Problem

A study of the effect of long delays in reinforcement when Ss have had no special training.

Method. The Ss of the experiment were four adult pigeons. The experimental cage was a box which was lightproof and attenuated about 20 db. The front

Adapted from *Journal of Experimental Psychology*, 1953, *45*, 218–224. With permission of the author and the American Psychological Association.

[1] This paper is an early, relatively unknown, reference relevant to the literature on "latent extinction" which has grown to considerable proportions. The interested reader is referred to a review article by H. Moltz, "Latent Extinction and the Fractitional Anticipatory Response Mechanism," *Psychol. Review*, 1957, *64*, 229–241, for a different interpretation of the data as the one suggested by the present authors (Ed.).

panel of the box contained a grain magazine and an illuminated 1-in. circular hole behind which was a hinged Plexiglas assembly, the key. Pecking the key closed a contact and permitted recording and programming of the experiment. Operation of the magazine presented an illuminated hopper of grain to the bird for 4 sec.

A variable-interval schedule whose mean was 1 min. was used throughout the experiment. The intervals in the series ranged from 3 to 120 sec. in an arithmetic progression. These intervals, arranged in a random series, produced a steady rate of response by which the effect of delays in reinforcement could be measured. The top part of Figure 1 illustrates a variable-interval schedule of reinforcement. The arrows above the line define the intervals in variable-interval schedule, each arrow representing the "setting up" of a reinforcement. The first response after a reinforcement has been "set up" opens the magazine.

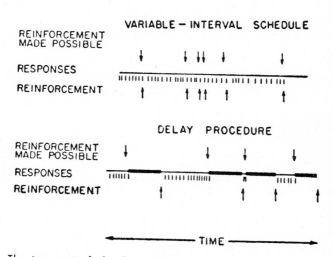

Figure 1. The top part of the figure illustrates a variable-interval schedule of reinforcement. The bottom part of the figure illustrates the delay procedure. The darkened portions represent the delay interval.

The box was darkened for the duration of the delay period in order to prevent S from responding. The bottom part of Figure 1 illustrates the delay procedure. Reinforcements are available on the 1-min. variable-interval schedule mentioned previously. The reinforced response turns out all the lights in the box. With the return to normal illumination after the delay interval, the magazine opens. Neither the recorder nor the reinforcement programmer operates during the delay interval. Four Ss were run on the variable-interval schedule until their rates of response were stable. On the same reinforcement schedule, reinforcements were delayed by 60 sec.

Results

Figure 2A is the cumulative record for one *S*. The segment of the curve before the arrow records the behavior without delay in reinforcement; it is typical of all prior behavior. Beginning at the arrow, where all rein-

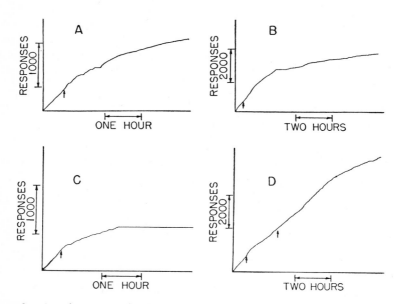

Figure 2. *Cumulative records of four pigeons showing the effect of a first encounter with a 60-sec. delay. The segment of the curve before the arrow records the stable state of a variable-interval schedule of reinforcement. At the arrow, reinforcements are delayed by 60 sec. At the second arrow, in D, the delay was increased to 120 sec.*

forcements were delayed by 60 sec., the rate of responding becomes progressively lower until the rate falls below one-sixth the original value. Figures 2B and 2C show a second and third *S* under the same procedure. In all three cases the rates of pecking decline substantially after the introduction of the delay in reinforcement. The record in Figure 2D is of a bird that was able to maintain a nearly normal rate of response under a 60-sec. delay in reinforcement. The 60-sec. delay (beginning at the first arrow) causes a small decline in rate. With a delay of 120 sec., however (beginning at the second arrow in Figure 2D), the rate falls off to about one-half the original value. The four *S*s were continued under the delay procedure for approximately 30 hr., during which the rate continued to decrease.

Since these birds were unable to maintain a rate of response appropriate to the schedule of reinforcement under 60-sec. delays, any subsequent

ability of the birds to maintain high rates of responding under 60-sec. delays must depend specifically on the training procedures employed.

EXPERIMENT II

Purpose

A study of the training by which pigeons were enabled to maintain high
rates of response under long delays in reinforcement.

Method. The four Ss that were unable to maintain normal rates of responding with long delays under the conditions of Experiment I were subjected to a
program which began with short delays which were gradually increased.

Results

Figure 3 is the complete record of one S showing the performance as
the delays were increased. The record covers approximately 90 hr. The
curves show that there are no major changes in rate during the 90 hr. of

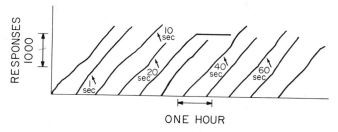

ONE HOUR

*Figure 3. The complete cumulative record for one S showing the result of a program
of gradually increasing delays. The size of the delay was changed at the arrows to
the values that are given on the record.*

training in which the delay was increased from 1 to 60 sec. The rate during the last segment of the curve where the delay was 60 sec. does not
differ from the first segment where the delay was 1 sec.

One bird afforded a dramatic example of learning to bridge the delay.
Figure 4 shows the effect of introducing a 60-sec. delay in reinforcement
after training on a 40-sec. delay. The initial decline in rate is followed
by an exceedingly smooth acceleration to a rate of 3 pecks per sec.

Since some amount of "art" was involved in judging when it was possible to increase the delay without "extinguishing" the response, the procedure was not the same for all Ss. The delays were increased too rapidly
for the fourth S. Under 60-sec. delayed reinforcement it did not maintain
a rate of response appropriate to the schedule of reinforcement. The three

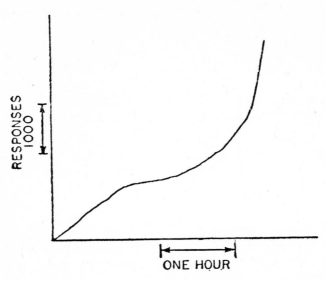

Figure 4. A dramatic example of learning to bridge the delay: the effect of a
60-sec. delay in reinforcement after training on a 40-sec. delay.

Ss that did maintain normal rates of response under 60-sec. delays were
continued under the same procedure for several hundred experimental
hours each. They exhibited no tendency to slow down.

EXPERIMENT III

Purpose

A control experiment on the effect of the blackout without reference to
delay in reinforcement.

Method. The choice of a method by which the reinforcements were delayed
was arbitrary. It would have been possible to slide a gate over the key during
the delay period, for example. The blackout was chosen, however, and the
question arose as to whether any of the extinction effects observed when Ss
were first exposed to long delays were due to the blackout without reference
to its delaying function. Accordingly, a control experiment was carried out to
find the effect of the blackout when it was not related to the reinforcement.

Three birds were conditioned on a 1-min. arithmetic variable-interval schedule of reinforcement until the rates of pecking were stable. Three different
procedures were applied: (*a*) a variable-interval schedule with no blackout;
(*b*) a variable-interval schedule with 60-sec. blackouts occurring independently of both responses and reinforcement; (*c*) a variable-interval schedule
with blackouts occurring as a consequence of a response but independent of

reinforcements. The occurrence of the blackouts was determined on a variable-interval schedule identical with the reinforcement schedule but out of phase with it. Each S underwent some 100 hr. of experimentation during which the three procedures were rotated. Six hours were spent on a procedure before the next was introduced.

Results

The resulting records did not differ from each other and it was concluded that the effect of the blackout (not correlated with the occurrence of reinforcements) is simply to introduce a period of "dead time" into the experiment.

EXPERIMENT IV

Purpose

A study was made in order to obtain direct observation of the behavior which occurs during the delay period. This was designed to determine what factor in Experiment II accounts for the persistence of normal rates of pecking under 60-sec. delayed reinforcements. A reasonable suggestion is that some form of "superstitious" behavior becomes conditioned during the delay period, which bridges the gap introduced by the delay (Keller and Schoenfeld, 1950; Skinner, 1948).

Method. To make it possible to check on the presence of a "superstitious" delay response the procedure of Experiment III was changed so that the box was illuminated continuously. When a reinforcement was available (on the same variable-interval schedule that was used in the preceding experiments), a peck turned out the key light for 60 sec. (but not the general box light). At the end of the 60-sec. period, the magazine opened and the light behind the key came on again. If S pecked during the delay period, the opening of the magazine was postponed an additional 60 sec. In this manner it was impossible for any peck to precede the opening of the magazine by a period greater or less than 60 sec. As is usual in the formation of a discrimination the frequency of pecking the darkened key soon dropped to zero.

Results

Observation of Ss through a one-way screen revealed that each S had acquired a characteristic delay response which it executed consistently and at a moderate rate during the delay period. In two Ss the delay response was "turning in a circle with the head stretched high." From 35 to 45 turns were made during an 80-sec. delay period. The third S's "superstition" was "pacing back and forth in front of the key panel with the head stretched high." The recording of such behavior offers a serious problem of instrumentation since the response which will be acquired during the delay period cannot be predicted. In this experiment it was sufficient to observe the birds visually. The "superstitious" delay responses occurred consistently over an experimental period of approximately 100 hr., during which the pecking response was maintained at a rate appropriate to the schedule of reinforcement.

EXPERIMENT V

Purpose

The purpose of this study was the demonstration of a chain analogous to the delayed-reinforcement chain. Another method of checking the preceding analysis of delayed reinforcement is to demonstrate that a chain which is deliberately conditioned by E can function in the same way as the "superstitious" chain conditioned as a consequence of the delay procedure. This was done by setting up a chain in which two members could be recorded.

Method. The apparatus was similar to the above except that either a red or a blue lamp could be illuminated behind the key. A discrimination was established between the red and the blue light. The first response that occurred 1 min. after the blue light came on was reinforced (S^D) and the key color changed to red. No responses were reinforced in the red (S^Δ). After a variable interval in red, without reference to S's behavior, the color changed to blue and the cycle repeated. After 4 hr. the rate of pecking the red key fell to zero, while the performance on the blue key was characteristic of a fixed-interval schedule of reinforcement.

The procedure was now changed so that the key color did not change from S^Δ to S^D unless the bird responded during S^Δ. After 1 hr. of continuous reinforcement of the S^Δ responses by a change to S^D, the schedule of reinforcement in S^Δ was changed to a variable-interval schedule. A chain of responses was now required as follows: Pecking the red key was reinforced on a variable-interval schedule by a change to blue. On a 1-min. fixed-interval schedule responses to the blue key were effective in opening the magazine. This situation differs from the discrimination procedure only in that the occurrence of S^D is contingent on a response in S^Δ. The two members of the chain were recorded separately with tandem recorders. When one recorder operated, the other did not. The difference between the S^Δ rate under the discrimination procedure and the S^Δ rate under the chain procedure must be ascribed to the reinforcing effect of the discriminative stimulus.

Results

Figures 5A and 5B show the records for the S^Δ and S^D behavior, respectively, for one pigeon. The behavior in the presence of each key color

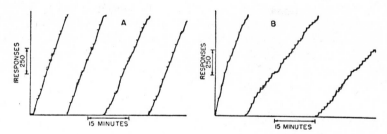

Figure 5. Cumulative records for one S for the two members of the chain. The two recorders operated alternately; the small horizontal lines mark reinforcements. (A) Red key: Responses are reinforced on a 1-min. variable-interval schedule by a change to blue. (B) Blue key: Responses are reinforced on a 1-min. fixed interval by the operation of the magazine.

is appropriate to the schedule of its reinforcement. The second member of the chain which is on a fixed-interval schedule of reinforcement shows the typical pause after reinforcement and the acceleration to the final rate. The first member of the chain which is on a variable-interval schedule of reinforcement shows a constant rate. Thus each part of the chain derives its character from the schedule of reinforcement appropriate to that member via the discriminative control of the key color. To make the chaining procedure analogous to the delayed-reinforcement procedure, it was necessary only to break the contingency between the opening of the magazine and the response to the blue key. Pecking the red key still changed the key color to blue on a 1-min. variable-interval schedule as before. The magazine opened 1 min. after the key turned blue whether the bird pecked or not. The red key responses which produced the S^D (blue) correspond to the pecking responses in the delayed-reinforcement experiment. The blue key responses—the magazine opens independently of the response— correspond to the "superstitious" behavior that took place during the delay period in the delayed-reinforcement procedure. Figures 6A and 6B

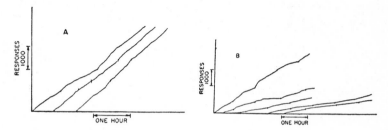

Figure 6. Cumulative records for the two members of the chain for one S where the magazine opened whether or not S pecked the blue key. (A) Red key: Responses are reinforced on a 1-min. variable-interval schedule by a change to blue. (B) Blue key: The magazine opens 1 min. following the change to blue whether or not S pecks.

show the S^Δ and S^D record, respectively, for the chaining procedure in which the magazine opens without reference to whether S pecked the blue key. The S^Δ records are typical of the performance on the regular chaining procedure and remain stable. The S^D rates, however, show a smooth decline to a lower but stable value even though the response reinforcement contingency is superstitious.

SYSTEMATIC ANALYSIS

The preceding experiments have shown that a delay in reinforcement is not a static parameter of the effect of reinforcement on behavior. The effect of a delay on the frequency of a response depends critically on the way in which the bird is introduced to the particular delay. By introducing S to short delays which were gradually increased to 60 sec., it was possible to maintain normal rates of response under long delayed reinforcement. If the first delay had been of this magnitude, the response would have extinguished.

Reasons for the maintenance of normal response rates in spite of the long intervening period between the response and the appropriate reinforcing stimulus may be found first, in an examination of the behavior taking place during the delay period, and second, in the chaining of the delay responses (Keller and Schoenfeld, 1950).

Any behavior that occurs at the end of the delay period will be reinforced by the opening of the magazine, under the discriminative control of the darkness. The relation between this behavior and the opening of the magazine is spurious, since the magazine will open whether or not the response is made. This kind of behavior has therefore been called "superstitious." The "superstitious" behavior is not likely to be weakened by its occurring when the light is on because the pecking response is prepotent by virtue of its longer history of reinforcement. Any extinction of the "superstitious" response will, therefore, occur in the dark. Where the first delay in reinforcement was of the order of 60 sec., there was ample time during the delay period for the extinction of the response which had been conditioned in the previous delay period.

Because of the extinction taking place during the 60-sec. delay the opening of the magazine is preceded by a wide variety of behaviors and no single response is likely to be reinforced frequently enough to acquire any strength. If the delays are of the order of 1 to 5 sec., however, the likelihood of the same response occurring prior to the opening of the magazine is high, and members of a single response class will be reinforced frequently enough to be conditioned. When the delay interval is lengthened after a number of reinforcements of the same response, the delay defines a fixed-interval schedule of reinforcement of the superstitious response. The schedule is different from those ordinarily employed only in that the magazine will open whether or not the response is made. To maintain the "superstitious" behavior in the dark, it is necessary to adjust the interval of the delay so that the magazine will open when the frequency of the "superstitious" response is highest.

The properties of a fixed-interval schedule of reinforcement will have a crucial bearing on whether a rate of occurrence of the "superstitious" response will be high at the time that the magazine opens. A fixed-interval schedule produces different effects after long training, when a stable performance is reached, than it does early in training. In the early stages of fixed-interval reinforcement the frequency of the behavior is high at the beginning of the interval and declines regularly until the next reinforcement occurs. These conditions are adverse for the maintenance of the "superstitious" behavior unless the delay is adjusted so that the magazine opens at a time when the rate of response due to the preceding reinforcement is still high. After sufficient training, however, the rate picture is reversed. The rate is low at the beginning of the interval and gradually increases until a stable rate (characteristic of the fixed interval) is reached. Under these conditions the delay interval can be lengthened more rapidly without producing many instances of the opening of the magazine being preceded by a response other than the one previously conditioned.

If some response becomes conditioned under the discriminative control of the delay, stimulus pecking will be immediately reinforced by the beginning of the delay period. The strength of the pecking response will not be maintained directly by the presentation of food, but depends on the food-reinforced mediating behavior. A chain of responses will have been established as follows: Pecking the lighted key is reinforced on a variable-interval schedule by darkness, which is the occasion upon which some superstitious response is effective in opening the magazine. The schedule of reinforcement of the second ("superstitious") member is necessarily a fixed interval whose length is equal to the delay of reinforcement. It makes no difference that the dark response does not open the magazine in a strict sense. So long as the behavior is followed by the opening of the magazine sufficiently often, the resulting contingency will be sufficient to maintain the behavior in the same way that the usual fixed-interval schedule does.

SUMMARY

The effect of delayed reinforcements was shown by using a variable-interval schedule of reinforcement as a base-line. It was found that in three out of four pigeons the effect of a 60-sec. delay in reinforcement was a decline in the rate of pecking to a value near zero. The fourth S maintained near normal rates of responding under 60-sec. delayed reinforcement, but slowed down under 120-sec. delays.

The same Ss that extinguished under 60- and 120-sec. delays were reconditioned on the original variable-interval schedule without delay. Short delays were then introduced and the value of the delays was gradually increased as S's behavior became stable under any particular delay. It was possible in three out of four of the cases to sustain normal rates of response under delays of 60 sec.

A control experiment showed that the effect of a delay in reinforcement is not due to the aversive properties of the blackout by which the reinforcements were delayed.

Visual observation of Ss under the delay procedure showed the presence of "superstitious" behavior during the delay interval.

The function of the "superstitious" behavior in the delayed reinforcement was investigated further by setting up a chain in which two members could be recorded which could function in the same way as a "superstitious" chain conditioned as a consequence of the delayed procedure.

The factors governing the effect of a particular delay and the effect of the change from one delay to another are the same as those determining the formation of a chain of responses.

REFERENCES

KELLER, F. S., and SCHOENFELD, W. N. *Principles of psychology.* New York: Appleton-Century-Crofts, 1950.

SKINNER, B. F. Superstition in the pigeon. *J. exp. Psychol.,* 1948, *38,* 168–172.

24

Studies on Detour Behaviour

W. Wyrwicka

INTRODUCTION

If an animal, e.g., a dog, running to his usual feeding place finds an obstacle in his way, he will go around it sooner or later—according to the shape and size of the obstacle—and continue his way to the food. This ability, well known as "detour" or "round-about behaviour" is considered as one of the simplest forms of so called "problem solving behaviour." This detour behaviour problem is dealt with in the first chapter of Köhler's well known monograph (1925) in which he describes such experiments on a child, dogs, monkeys, and hens. Köhler considers this form of behaviour a result of insight. The similar view is also maintained by other investigators who found the ability of round-about behaviour in other animals: rats (Higginson, 1926; Hsiao, 1929; Tolman and Honzik, 1930), birds (Lorenz, 1932, 1939; Teyrovsky, 1930), reptiles (Fischel, 1933),

Adapted from *Behaviour,* 1959, XIV, 240–264. With permission of the author and E. J. Brill, Ltd.

and fishes (von Schiller, 1942). On the other hand Thorpe (1956) discussing these results held the view that before one can be sure whether an insightful solution takes place or not, one must know the first response of the untrained animal and its previous experience; these conditions have not always been fulfilled.

The problem of round-about behaviour was also considered by some physiologists. Beritoff and his collaborators (Beritoff, 1941; Beritoff and Akhmeteli, 1941) performed some detour behaviour experiments on dogs, rabbits, hens, and pigeons. According to Beritoff, the animal looks for a round-about way because of a psycho-nervous process which reproduces in his mind a picture of the external world, thus guiding his movements towards the food. Pavlov however maintained that detour behaviour had an acquired conditioned-reflex character (Pavlovskie Sredy, 1949).

To test this view of Pavlov some experiments were carried out on pups. The preliminary results of these experiments showed clearly the conditioned-reflex characteristics of the detour behaviour (Wyrwicka, 1954).

In the meantime, the view of Pavlov was also confirmed by Roginsky and Tikh (1956). They described in chickens, young rats, and monkeys the course of elaboration of the reaction of going round a glass obstacle. They showed that the rate of establishment of this reaction depends on the level of phylogenetic development of the species to which the experimental animal belongs; monkeys learnt quickest, chickens—slowest.

The present paper contains the experimental results on detour reaction obtained as well as an attempt to analyse these data from the point of view of physiology of the higher nervous activity.

METHODS

Experiments were performed on 28 pups, both male and female, from 8 different litters (5 bitches and 8 male dogs). Pups were controlled from birth; each litter housed in a large box (2–3.5 m.²). Pups used in experiments were 32–131 days old; younger pups were not used because, according to Troshikhin (1953) and others, the motor as well as other analysers are not yet developed in the first weeks of life.

Experiments were performed in a room or in the garden. The general arrangement of the experimental situation was as follows. A partition of wire-netting was placed in an empty room or in a corner of the garden so that the experimental place was partially divided into two parts with a convenient passage at least 30 cm. wide between them (Figure 1). Schematic sketches of experimental situations used in successive series of experiments can be found in the next part of this paper. The wire-net partition is also referred to as "the obstacle," "the wire netting," or "the netting."

The course of preliminary training was as follows. For some successive days pups were brought singly or in pairs to the experimental compartment

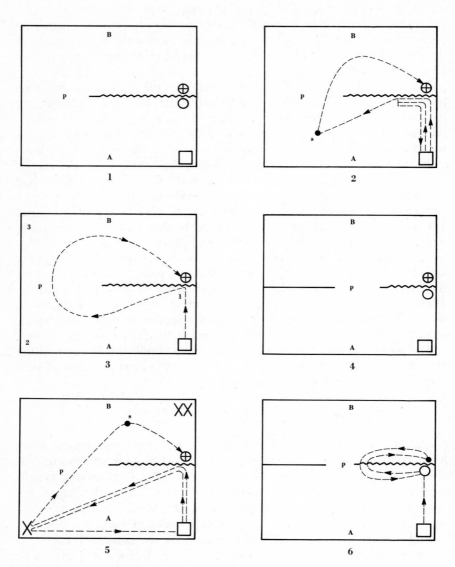

Figures 1-12. Sketches of experimental compartments.

〜〜〜 — wire-net partition
————— — wood partition
A, B   — parts of compartment situated before (A) and behind (B) the partition
p   — passage
○   — place of the bowl during a usual experiment
⊕   — place of the bowl during a key experiment

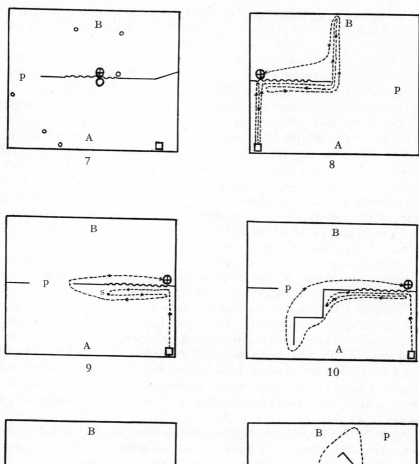

☐ — starting place
OO — trees
X — experimenter I
XX — experimenter II

────▶── — trace of the pup's way
S — stopping place
1,2,3 — feeding places in Figure 3

and subjected to a preparatory procedure; they came hungry not having received food for some hours. The preparatory procedure was usually the same for all pups of the same litter. Depending on the plan of further experiments, the pup was allowed to remain for 10–15 min. either in both parts of the compartment (A and B, Figure 1) or in part A only. Animals usually received food (milk or grits with milk) at the beginning of the experiment. The bowl with food was always placed in the same spot just in front of the wire-net partition (circle in Figure 1); only one pup received food in a different place each day (see further). The bowl was put in place before the beginning of the experiment so that the animal began its daily training by running to the food from its starting point (square in Figure 1). When the dog finished eating the bowl was immediately taken away and the pup was still allowed to run freely for some minutes. In some series of preliminary experiments such a trial was repeated several times (4–5) each day, i.e., after eating the animal was taken out of the experimental compartment for a while and then put back to the starting place so that it might again run to a new portion of food. Pups which were allowed to remain only in part A were never punished if they wanted to go to part B; they were however stopped by touching, calling, etc.

Preliminary training was carried out daily for 3 to 20 days and even more in various series. Then the key experiment followed, or experiments were transferred to another situation where training was continued for some more days and then the key experiment took place. This experiment consisted in placing the bowl of food behind the wire-netting (circle with cross in Figure 1), just opposite the usual feeding place. Results of each series of these experiments are described in detail in a later section of this paper.

After the key experiment further training was usually carried on for some days during which the bowl was placed behind the obstacle several times. Some modifications in the size and shape of the obstacle were also applied, as well as moving the passage between parts A and B to a different position. Afterwards the key experiment was performed also in a new situation, one in which the animal found itself for the first time. Finally, chronic extinction of the detour reaction was performed and its effect on the same reaction in another situation was tested.

RESULTS

Series I

Experiments with pups which were allowed to remain in both parts of the compartment (i.e., in front as well as behind the partition) during the preliminary training.

Experiments of this series were carried out on 12 pups from 3 litters (3 bitches).

In the first group there were 4 animals (No. 17–20), 104 days old. The preliminary training was performed in a room (Figure 1); after eating from the bowl placed in front of the wire-net partition, puppies were allowed to run singly in both parts of the room. After 15 days the bowl was put behind the obstacle. To reach food the pup had to turn to the left, go a distance of 1 m. to the edge of the obstacle, then turn right at an angle of 180° and go along the opposite side of the wire-netting for a further 1 m. to the bowl, i.e., to "circle" the obstacle. It was found that at first a direct reaction to the food appeared lasting some seconds, then each pup began to run here and there, found the passage rather easily and reached food. The length of time which elapsed from the beginning of the trial to reaching the bowl was for pups No. 17–20: 16 sec., 29 sec., 14 sec., and 48 sec. respectively. The behaviour of pups No. 18 and 20 was characteristic, as may be seen in an extract of the protocol.

Protocol No. 1 (Pup. No. 18). "After a short direct reaction, the pup moves here and there in Part A, then sits down at the side (point in Figure 2). After 29 sec. the pup suddenly starts and widely circles the obstacle to reach the bowl." (The way traced in Figure 2.)

Pup No. 20 behaved very similarly.

The second group consisted of 3 pups (No. 9, 10, and 11), 44 days old. Experiments were performed in a room (Figure 1). The obstacle was 70 cm. long and the passage—40 cm. wide. Pups No. 9 and 10 received food always at the same place in front of the partition; then the bowl was taken away and each pup ran singly for some minutes in the whole room. After 20 days the key experiment was performed. It was found that finding the bowl proved very difficult for both pups (Protocol No. 2).

Protocol No. 2 (Pup No. 9). "The animal sniffs milk through the wire-netting, returns to the start and back again to the wire-netting; after 20 sec. it passes to part B, going back immediately, however, to the start. It runs again to the obstacle, whines and barks, then returns. After a further 2 min. it runs once more to the wire-netting and sniffs milk. Yet 3 more times (after 3 min. 25 sec., 4 min., 5 min.) the animal goes to part B but each time returns back without reaching the bowl. It barks aloud. Finally, after 7 min. 30 sec. the pup goes to part B, sees the bowl, approaches it, and drinks milk."

The behaviour of pup No. 10 was very similar, it, however, found the bowl after 6 min. 10 sec. The immediate detour reaction appeared in both pups after 4 training experiments.

Preliminary training with pup No. 11 was somewhat different. The bowl with milk was set every day in another place, i.e., just before the obstacle or in a corner of the room (see corresponding numbers 1, 2, and 3 in Figure 3). After eating the pup ran for some minutes in both parts of the compartment, just as pups No. 9 and 10. When after 27 days of such training the bowl was placed behind the wire-netting the pup circled the obstacle immediately, going, however, in a big arc (traced in Figure 3).

The third group consisted of 5 animals (No. 12–16), 48 days old. Preliminary training was carried out in a room (Figure 1); the obstacle was 1 m. in length. One of the puppies (No. 12) remained alone in the compartment while others ran there in pairs; they played joyfully; sometimes when one was on the opposite side of the wire-netting, the other came to him there.

The key experiment was performed separately for each animal. Pup No. 12 which was trained alone, showed at first a direct reaction to the bowl, then it went to the edge of the obstacle but almost immediately turned back to the starting place, going once again to the wire-netting and back, repeating these movements several times. Only after 40 sec. did the pup, being at the edge of the wire-netting, notice the bowl and go to it.

Four other animals (which previously ran in pairs), after a short direct reaction, circled the obstacle easily. The latent period for this reaction was 6 sec., 3.5 sec., 10 sec., and 4 sec. for pups No. 13–16 respectively. Moreover, their way to the bowl was without interruption.

Experiments of the first series show that most pups which were allowed to run in both parts of the compartment during the preliminary training, knew how to find the way to food when it was placed behind a wire-net-obstacle. This act was, however, easier for pups that had previously remained in the room in pairs as well as for a pup which had formerly received food in various places.

Series II

Experiments with pups which previously made a detour around some objects in another situation.

Experiments were performed on 5 pups from 2 bitches.

Pups of the first group (No. 7 and 8) were 32 days old. For 4 successive days the animals were allowed for about 10 min. daily to run together in the garden where various obstacles of wood and wire-netting were placed. None of these objects were longer than 1 m. It was observed that pups ran cheerfully here and there, rather willingly going through narrow passages between obstacles. Food was not given.

Afterwards experiments were transferred to a room (Figure 4) and here the animals were allowed to remain only in part A, where they received food at the beginning of each experiment. The wire-net partition was 25 cm. long. After 8 days the bowl with milk was placed behind the obstacle. Here is an extract of the protocol of this experiment.

Protocol No. 3 (Pup No. 8). "The pup runs to the obstacle, sniffs milk and whines. After 5 sec. it goes back to the starting place and again runs to the wire-netting, turns towards the passage and finds the bowl 9 sec. after the experiment started."

The reaction of the pup No. 7 was similar, it, however, only found the bowl after 15 sec.

Pups of the second group, No. 21, 22, and 23, were 49 days old. For 7 days they were allowed to run singly in the garden for 10 min. around a wire-net fence, 3 m. in length. Food was not given. Afterwards the training was transferred to a room where the pup received food in front of the wire-netting in part A (Figure 5). After eating the animal was called by the experimenter standing at the place marked x in Figure 5, so that the way from the starting place to the bowl and from there to the place marked x, formed a triangle. After 3 experiments of 4–5 trials each, the key experiment was performed. Here is the protocol of this experiment with the pup No. 21.

Protocol No. 4 (Pup. No. 21).

"*Trial I.* The bowl before the wire-netting. The pup behaves in the usual way.

Trial II. The bowl behind the wire-netting. A direct reaction is observed; the animal scrapes the wire-netting, whines, then runs to the place of exit (marked x) and from there to the starting place, then again to the obstacle and to the exit place, repeating this movement several times. The animal does not pass to part B. The trial is interrupted after 5 min.

Trial III. The bowl before the wire-netting. Pup shows normal behaviour.

Trial IV. The bowl behind the obstacle. The pup shows a direct reaction, sniffs milk, scrapes the wire-netting, then runs to the exit and returns again repeating this set of movements several times, as in the second trial. After 3 min. the pup having reached the place x, it is called by a second experimenter standing in part B of the compartment (at the place marked xx in Figure 5). Thus the pup enters part B and after a while notices the bowl, goes to it and begins to eat." [1]

The behaviour of the pup No. 22 was similar. The pup No. 23, however, being very quick by nature, ran here and there along the wire-netting noticed the bowl and found it himself 20 sec. after the beginning of the trial. A further trial was even more successful, the animal found the bowl after 12 sec. When, however, the bowl was for the third time placed behind the obstacle (on the 6th successive trial) the pup for 5 min. showed only a direct reaction to the bowl and it did not go to part B. In the end, it was helped by the experimenter to find the bowl.

The immediate detour reaction appeared in all pups only after 4–5 experiments.

Summarizing the results obtained in the second series of experiments we may say that 2 pups which were previously allowed to remain together in the garden and to circle some objects there, knew how to find in a room the round-about way to food. The same successful behaviour was observed in a third pup which had previously remained several times alone in the

[1] This course is traced in Figure 5.

garden and there circled a fence. However, 2 other pups trained in the same way as the third pup, did not know how to find food when the bowl was placed behind an obstacle in the room.

Series III

Experiments on pups which remained only in front of the obstacle during the preliminary training.

Experiments were performed on 11 pups from 4 bitches.

In the first group were 4 pups from 2 bitches. Pups No. 1 and 2 were 32 days old and pups No. 3 and 4—33 days old. Experiments were conducted in a room (sketched in Figure 4). Animals were trained singly. They were allowed to remain only in part A of the room, where they received milk at the beginning of each experiment. The length of the wire-net partition was 110 cm.

After 23 days the key experiment was performed on 2 pups (No. 1 and 3). It was found that neither of them knew how to reach the bowl placed behind the wire-netting. Here is the protocol of this experiment.

Protocol No. 5 (Pup No. 1). "The animal, put at the starting place, runs as usual to the wire-netting, looks at the milk and sniffs it for 5 sec., then returns to the start and immediately goes again to the obstacle, repeating such oscillatory movements several times. After 15 sec. the pup does not go any more to the wire-netting."

The behaviour of pup No. 3 was almost identical; the animal, however, after 3 sec. returned to the starting place; the number of times it went to the obstacle and back was somewhat greater.

This experiment was repeated after some days with the same result. Thinking the obstacle too long and this perhaps to be the cause of the pups reacting in such a way, we shortened the obstacle to 25 cm. and performed the key experiment once more. Here is the protocol of this experiment.

Protocol No. 6 (Pup No. 1). "On coming to the wire-netting the animal looks at milk for a while, then returns to the start and goes back again to the wire-netting, repeating the movement there and back for 15 sec., then it finally goes away. After some minutes it is brought to the passage and turned towards the bowl so that it can see the milk; whereupon it runs to the bowl and drinks."

Pup No. 3 behaved similarly; when it was brought to the passage it showed some resistance against turning towards the bowl; this defense reaction disappeared, however, when the animal noticed the bowl.

Pups No. 2 and 4 were trained before an obstacle 110 cm. in length, as were No. 1 and 3, for 23 days and then after shortening the obstacle to 25 cm. for a further 29 days. At the time of the key experiment they were 103 and 99 days old.

It was found that the reaction of both pups to the bowl set behind the wire-netting was identical to that of pups No. 1 and 3. Oscillatory movements of pup No. 4 lasted, however, 50 sec. The same experiment was repeated next day; it was decided to wait as long as was necessary for the animal himself to find the way to the bowl (see Protocol No. 7).

Protocol No. 7 (Pup. No. 2. An extract from the protocol). "After several oscillatory movements lasting 20 sec., the pup remains some seconds at the starting place; then from time to time goes to the netting and back. After 1 min. 43 sec. the animal strays by chance to the passage, notices the bowl, and runs to it."

Pup No. 4, however, did not find the way to the bowl and after 2 min. 45 sec. was helped to go to the passage and directed towards food.

On the following days experiments with all 4 pups were conducted in this way: every 2–3 days the bowl was placed behind the obstacle, while on the other days it was placed before the wire-netting. It was found that a single going around of the obstacle was not always sufficient to teach the pup how to go to the bowl when it was set behind the wire-netting. Pups No. 1 and 3 had to be directed passively towards the bowl for a further 2 experiments. Pup No. 2 already on the second experiment found the way to food without any help after 10 sec., and pup No. 4—after 14 sec. During this latent period animals showed not only the mentioned oscillatory movements but also a direct reaction to food, sniffing it, scraping the wire-netting and even beating it. The latency became shorter and shorter in the next experiments, this process was, however, irregular ("wavy"), as is shown on Diagram 1.

The following fact was observed in all pups during the training: after drinking milk from the bowl placed on the day in question before the obstacle, the animal circled the wire-netting and ran to the spot on the other side of the obstacle, where the bowl was sometimes set, sniffed that place for some seconds and only then returned to the start (this course is traced in Figure 6). Moreover, pup No. 4 sometimes interrupted eating, ran to the other side of the obstacle, sniffed the feeding place, and then returned to finish its meal.

An immediate reaction of detour was obtained after 6 experiments (on an average), during which the bowl was set behind the obstacle.

Pups of the second group, No. 5 and 6 belonging to the same litter as pups No. 3 and 4, were 131 days old at the beginning of the experiments. These pups were originally trained singly in the garden; a sketch of the situation is given in Figure 7. Training consisted in running from the start to the bowl placed in front of the wire-net obstacle; puppies were allowed to remain in part A some minutes after eating. A daily experiment consisted of 1 or 2 such trials. After 8 days the key experiment was performed. The distance from the bowl to the edge of the obstacle was 1.2 m.

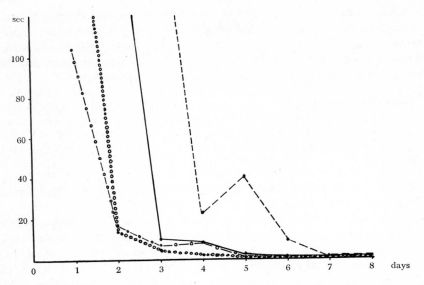

Diagram 1. *Elaboration of the detour reacton. Abscissa: successive experiments. Ordinate: latency of the reaction in sec.*

—————— pup No. 1; —— · —— pup No. 2; - - - - - pup No. 3; . . . . . pup No. 4

It was found that none of the pups knew how to circle the wire-netting. Here is an extract from the protocol of this experiment.

Protocol No. 8 (Pup No. 5). "The animal sniffs milk through the wire-netting, goes a little to the side, and after 7 sec. returns to the starting place. After 5 sec. it runs again to the obstacle and almost immediately comes back, repeating this movement two more times. After about 1 min. the pup gives up running to the obstacle."

Pup No. 6 behaved in a similar manner.

When, on the next day, the experiment was repeated, the reaction of pup No. 5 was the same as previously. Pup No. 6, however, stopped 1.5 m. from the obstacle and returned to the start. The pup did not want to go any more to the wire-netting, even when the bowl was placed before the obstacle. In the end the animal would go to the bowl only with the experimenter who showed food to it; once there, however, the puppy ate its food with appetite.

Experiments with pups No. 5 and 6 were afterwards transferred to a room (Figure 4). Here after 8 experiments with the bowl before the wire-netting, training with the bowl behind it was performed, similar to the one described previously in relation to pups No. 1–4. In consequence the reaction of detour became immediate.

The third group consisted of 5 pups (No. 24–28) belonging to 2 different litters (2 bitches). All these pups were born and kept in the usual compartments for adult dogs; there were no objects save a bowl in these compartments, so that the animals had no occasion to circle anything. In the front of the compartment was a door to the corridor made from bars; therefore pups frequently saw other animals and people going through the corridor; however they never left the compartment.

When experiments began, pups No. 24 and 25 were 116 days old and pups No. 26, 27, and 28—120 days old. Experiments were performed in a room (sketched in Figure 8). As the preliminary training had to be performed in a short time (due to conditions outside the experimenter's control) it was limited to 4 experiments carried out over 2 days. Each experiment consisted in 4 trials. During each trial the pup remained several minutes in part A of the room where it received food. In order to keep alimentary excitability high the animals were not given food outside the experiments. Already on the second day of training all the pups easily found the bowl in front of the wire-net partition, 1 m. long, and behaved cheerfully; only pup No. 28 showed an aggressive-defensive reaction against the experimenter.

The key experiment was performed on the second day of training, some hours after the fourth preliminary experiment. The bowl was placed behind the wire-netting on the successive second trial. Two extracts from protocols of this experiment characterize the reaction of pups.

Protocol No. 9 (Pup No. 25). "After a short direct reaction (scraping of wire-netting) the pup runs to part B of the room, it goes, however, straight (at an angle 90° to the obstacle). After 8 sec. it returns to the starting place and from there again to the wire-netting, scraping and even beating it. After 12 sec. it goes to part B and stops far from the obstacle. Returning, it notices the bowl and reaches it, 50 sec. after the beginning of the trial" (Figure 8).

Behaviour of pup No. 24 was similar.

Protocol No. 10 (Pup No. 10). "After a direct reaction to food lasting 10 sec., the animal returns to the starting place and after a while goes again to the obstacle, repeating this movement many times. Finally, after 3 min. the pup goes to part B, stops far from the obstacle, then returns to part A, without noticing the bowl. After 6 min. 30 sec. the experimenter gives the food to the animal in the passage between parts A and B of the room."

Puppy No. 27 showed a similar reaction.

Only the behaviour of pup No. 28 which previously showed an aggressive-defensive reaction, was somewhat different. This pup showed very strong direct reaction to the bowl, then lay in front of the wire-netting and gazed at the bowl for several minutes; it showed no tendency to go to part B. This trial was repeated 3 times with a similar result.

Results of the third series of experiments may be summarized as follows. Pups that had previously no occasion to circle any obstacle did not know how to find a way to food when the bowl was placed behind a short wire-net fence instead of in its usual place for this situation before the fence. Only 4 pups found the bowl when they noticed it by chance. Seven other pups had to be led passively to the bowl. The behaviour of 5 pups kept in compartments with bars (through which they acquainted themselves with the environment) was not different from that of other pups. In order to get an immediate detour reaction it was necessary to perform about 6 training experiments with food placed behind the obstacle.

EXPERIMENTS ON GENERALIZATION OF THE DETOUR REACTION

(a) Modification on the Obstacle

Experiments were carried out on 8 pups (No. 1–8) in which the detour reaction was firmly established during the previous training. In these experiments we observed the behaviour of pups when confronted with a change in the size and shape of the obstacle as well as with a change of direction in circling it. Experiments were performed in the room sketched in Figure 4, where the pups were previously trained.

The first modification, consisting in the lengthening of the obstacle to 45 cm. (from 25 cm.) was introduced for 2 pups (No. 1 and 3). No preliminary training was performed, the bowl was placed behind the wire-netting on the same day as changing the obstacle. Here is an extract from the protocol of this experiment.

Protocol No. 11 (Pup No. 1). "The pup runs immediately to the left but stops at the spot where the obstacle ended on the previous day (x in Figure 9), then it returns, goes again alongside the obstacle to the place x and back, repeating these movements 3 times, then it goes somewhat further to the edge of the wire-netting and after 7 sec. it is in the passage; from there it runs straight to the bowl."

The course is traced in Figure 9.

Pup No. 3 behaved similarly, it was already in the passage, however, after 5 sec.

With 6 other pups the obstacle was lengthened at once to 85 cm. It was found that the detour reaction was delayed in all cases; there was a delay of even 22 sec. with pup No. 2. It was observed that 3 animals (No. 2, 4, and 6) stopped in the spot of the previous passage, i.e., behaved as pups No. 1 and 3.

An obstacle 85 cm. in length was still applied on the following days so that the pups were trained to circle it immediately.

The obstacle was lengthened and its shape changed several times in the next period. Each change caused a transitory increase of the latency and, sometimes, stopping in the spot of the previous passage. Finally, the shape of the obstacle was so changed that the animal had at first to turn back, move several steps away from the wire-netting, and only then reached the passage; the whole length of this obstacle was 145 cm. (Figure 10). This last test trial was performed on 6 pups (No. 1–6). It was found that 3 of them (No. 1, 2, and 3) circled the obstacle almost immediately; the other 3 animals, however, showed an increase of latency to 7 sec., 8 sec., and 10 sec. respectively (the way traced in Figure 10); this period became again short (1–2 sec.) when the trial was repeated on the following day.

Next, we transferred the passage between the two parts of the room to another place, so that the pup had to turn to the right in order to reach the passage, and not to the left as it did up to then (Figure 11). At first the bowl with food was placed before the wire-netting in part A and only on the next day was it put behind the obstacle. Pup No. 1 found the way to the bowl easily; when, however, the trial was repeated on the next day the animal showed a tendency to go at first to the left (as in previous training) and, being confronted with a wall, then only turned to the right. Pups No. 2, 4, and 5 went at first to the spot where the bowl was formerly placed in front of the partition and then to the passage (and to food); these pups also frequently turned at first to the left.

The reaction of pups No. 3, 6, 7, and 8 was somewhat different. Here is an extract of the experiment with pup No. 3, which characterizes the behaviour of all these pups.

Protocol No. 12 (Pup No. 3). "The pup runs at first to the left, then to the right up to the spot where the bowl was formerly placed before the wire-netting, repeating this several times; then after 22 sec., the pup passes to part B and turns right to the previous feeding place, sniffs this spot for some seconds, turns back, then notices the bowl and reaches it."

This course is traced in Figure 11.

Experiments on circling the obstacle with a change of direction were also carried out in another way. The bowl was placed before the wire-netting just when the pup was in part B, i.e., behind the obstacle. The animal had then to turn in the opposite direction from the one it took up to now. Such a trial was performed on 3 pups (No. 1, 2, and 14). It was found that all showed at first a direct reaction and then, after some seconds (even 22 sec. in pup No. 14), they went to the passage and so to the bowl.

Another fact occasionally obtained should also be mentioned here. The detour reaction, established in the room, was tested in the garden in pup No. 4. After finding the bowl behind the obstacle and having eaten food, the animal did not know how to find its way back to the experimenter. The pup showed a direct reaction, scraping the wire-netting, then went to the back of part B; on returning, however, the animal noticed the passage and so came to part A. It must be added, however, that this fact happened in the initial period of the training of the detour reaction.

(b) The Detour Reaction in Other Situations

Experiments were carried out either in another room or in the garden on most pups, when their detour reaction became immediate in the usual situation. The room designed for this purpose was different from the usual one and was located in another building. The obstacle was set obliquely in relation to the walls (Figure 12). Only a single experiment was performed in this situation.

At first the bowl was placed in front of the obstacle, then, in the second trial it was set behind the wire-netting. It was found that after a direct reaction lasting some seconds, all pups found the passage to part B but their way to the bowl was not always straight.

A trial of circling the obstacle in the garden (Figure 7) was performed on 10 pups (No. 7, 8, 12–16, and 21–23) in which the detour reaction was previously established in a room. Most of them (first seven animals) received food before the wire-netting at first. When on the next day the bowl was set behind the obstacle, all the pups easily passed to part B but to go all the way to the bowl seemed to be difficult for them and they wandered here and there in part B before reaching food. The time required to reach the bowl was for pups No. 12, 13, 14, and 16 sec., 17 sec., 25 sec., and 167 sec. respectively. Pup No. 15 did not pass at all to part B going repeatedly only between the starting place and the wire-netting. This animal was further trained in the room for some days and then the trial in the garden was repeated; this time the pup circled the obstacle in 2 min. 17 sec.

As to pups No. 7 and 8 which previously circled various objects in another part of the garden (see second series of experiments), the latency of their reaction was not shorter than that of other animals, being 18 sec. (No. 7) and 1 min. 10 sec. (No. 8).

Pups No. 21, 22, and 23, as already described (series II) were allowed to run around a fence in the garden in this same situation (without food reinforcement) at the very beginning of experiments, i.e., some weeks before the present trial, while in the mean time the animals were obtained in a room. The course of the experiment was similar to that of other pups. Pup No. 21 circled the obstacle almost immediately (after 2 sec. of latency), pup No. 22 looked at first into part B several times then reached the bowl after 40 sec. Pup No. 23 showed a prolonged (40 sec.) direct reaction, then it went away and sniffed pebbles in part A for the next few minutes. It was then taken away for a while, the experimenter went behind the wire-netting and stood near the bowl and the pup was again put back to the start. This time it circled the obstacle after only 3 sec., easily finding food.

Results of above described experiments show that pups which circled a definite obstacle many times, knew how to do it also when the size and shape of the obstacle as well as the direction of circling was changed. Each modification, however, caused an increase in the time required to circle the obstacle. Pups in which the detour reaction was established in a definite situation in a room knew how to go around another obstacle in a different room as well as in the garden. Generalization of the detour reaction was also found in experiments on chronic extinction and renewal of this reaction; these experiments are described in detail in the next part of this paper.

EXPERIMENTS ON THE CHRONIC EXTINCTION OF THE DETOUR REACTION

These experiments were performed on 3 pups (No. 21, 22, and 23). Preceding experiments with these animals were described in the last section and only a short summary of them will be given here. At first the detour reaction was established in a room during 7 days of training, then the experiments were transferred to the garden. Here, after the test experiment described previously, the training was further continued for some days. During a training experiment the bowl was placed 3 times in front of the obstacle and twice behind it. Already on the second day of training all pups immediately circled the obstacle. After 3 days this reaction seemed to be strongly established.

Then the extinction experiments began in the garden (Figure 7). During a daily experiment consisting of 7 trials, the bowl with food was 5 times placed before the obstacle; in two trials the bowl was set behind the wire-netting, no food, however, was in it; the detour reaction remained thus unreinforced. Extinction trials were applied every day in a different order, e.g., one day the order of positive and inhibitory trials went as follows: 1 +, 2 +, 3 −, 4 +, 5 +, 6 −, 7 +, and on the next day: 1 +, 2 −, 3 +, 4 −, 5 +, 6 +, 7 +, etc. (figure with + corresponds to a successive positive trial, figure with − corresponds to an inhibitory one). Sometimes there were 3 extinction trials during one experimental session.

During the first experiments with extinction all pups immediately circled the obstacle; they sniffed the empty bowl, returned to part A and back again to the bowl. The first signs of inhibition, however, appeared on the second day of extinction; on one trial pups No. 21 and 23 came only to the passage and turned back without reaching the bowl. On the third day pup No. 21 showed a partial inhibition of the reaction in both extinction trials, i.e., it passed to part B, but stopped some distance before the bowl and returned to the start. During the same experiment the other pups reached the bowl each time, sniffed it, and then returned to the starting place. On the fourth day pup No. 23 turned back not having come to the bowl in either trial. On the fifth day all pups went only a part of the way, stopping 2–3 m. before the wire-netting and turned back. However, on the following days the full detour reaction sometimes appeared: the pup ran to the empty bowl and licked it.

After 10 days, the experiments were increased to 2 daily, one in the morning and one in the afternoon, so that there were 4 extinction trials every day. At the same time the pups received less food outside the experiments.

After 33 extinction trials the reaction of all pups to the bowl placed behind the wire-netting was to stop some meters before the obstacle and then return to the starting place. The behaviour of pup No. 23 was very characteristic; this animal stopped far from the wire-netting and seemed to look for something on the ground; it did it only when the bowl was set behind the obstacle and never during intervals between trials. The same pup, however, showed at times the full detour reaction and it was only after 55 extinction trials that the inhibition of this reaction became perfect, while in other pups full inhibition was established after 38 extinction trials. In all, during 22 days, 49 extinction trials were performed on pups No. 21 and 22, and 57 extinction trials on pup No. 23. Diagram 2 shows the course of extinction in all three animals.

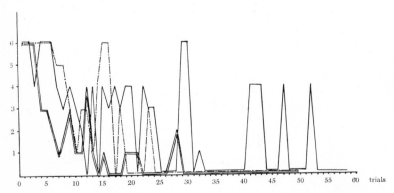

Diagram 2. The course of chronic extinction of the detour reaction. Abscissa: successive trials (for about 20 days). Ordinate: type of reaction: 0—no reaction; 1—stopping for several seconds in front of the obstacle or performing some steps towards the passage; 2—coming to the passage and looking into part B; 3—coming to part B, however, stopping some distance before the bowl; 4—slow full reaction (reaching the bowl) after more than 5 seconds; 5—full reaction with latency of 3-5 sec.; 6—immediate full reaction.

===== pup No. 21; —·— pup No. 22; ——— pup No. 23

Afterwards the experiments were again transferred back to the former situation, i.e., to a room (Figure 5). Here an experiment was performed consisting of 5 positive trials during which the bowl was placed before the obstacle. On the next day food was at first given 3 times before the wire-netting but on the fourth trial an empty bowl was placed behind the obstacle. It was found that pup No. 21 at once ran around the obstacle to the bowl; when, however, on the sixth successive trial the bowl was again set behind the wire-netting, the pup went there slowly, after some seconds of latency. Pup No. 22 looked at the bowl through the wire-netting and went away; it behaved in the same manner when the trial was repeated. Pup No. 23 went to the passage, stopped sniffing the floor, then slowly went to the bowl, licked it and went away; the same happened on a further trial with the bowl behind the wire-netting.

On the next day the experiment was repeated. It was found that this time not one of the pups came to the bowl; they turned back at once. Only pup No. 21 went alongside the obstacle up to the edge and looked into part B, then turned back.

As we see, the detour reaction extinguished in the garden was also inhibited in the room. Complete inhibition of this reaction was observed only in pup No. 22; in the other 2 animals a single training experiment was sufficient to renew inhibition.

Once again the experiments were transferred to the garden and it was decided to restore the detour reaction there. The procedure used till now was applied, only now the bowl always contained food when it was set behind the obstacle. It was found that each pup stopped before the wire-netting and returned to the start, without trying to go to part B, as it did previously. Then the bowl was placed in the passage and the experimenter stood nearby, encouraging the pup to come and eat. The animals came to the bowl, however, with some hesitation. On the following trials the bowl was placed farther and farther behind the wire-netting; in all 5 such trials were performed that day. On the next day, however, the detour reaction was still inhibited; the pups did not want to circle the obstacle and the procedure of the preceding day had to be repeated. It seemed that the presence of the experimenter in the passage encouraged the animals to go there and eat food. It was found that only after 4 such successive experiments during which 17 "restoring" trials were applied, did the pups again begin to go immediately around the netting when the bowl was placed behind it. It was observed, however, that all pups frequently interrupted eating or ate only a part of their portion.

Then the experiments were once more transferred to the room and the bowl with food was several times placed behind the obstacle. It was found that all pups immediately ran to the bowl. Puppy No. 22, however, did not finish its portion in the first 2 trials; on the following trials the whole portion was eaten. Then the detour reaction renewed in the garden became also restored in the room.

Results of this part of the experiments showed that (1) the reaction of detour could be chronically extinguished if it was many times not rein-

forced by food, (2) after the extinction of this reaction in one situation
—in the garden, it was inhibited also in another situation—in the room,
(3) after the restoration of this reaction in the garden, it became also renewed in the room.

DISCUSSION

The results obtained may be summarized as follows.

1. The pups easily went around the obstacle on their way to food, if they
had been allowed previously to remain in the whole area of the experimental compartment, i.e., in front of the obstacle as well as behind it, or
if they had previously been around some similar objects in another situation.

2. The pups did not know how to go around the obstacle, if they had
remained previously only in the area before the obstacle and if they had
never circled any obstacles of this kind in another situation.

3. Such pups learned to make a detour around an obstacle by the
trial-and-error method; the course of their learning was irregular and 5–6
experiments were required to make the reaction immediate.

4. The acquired detour reaction was generalized, i.e., it appeared also
to obstacles of other size and shape; moreover, it was not limited to the
usual situation but it was observed also in other situations.

5. The detour reaction might be subjected to chronic extinction, if
stopped being reinforced, i.e., when, beginning from a given day, the bowl
placed behind the obstacle was always empty; after the extinction this
reaction was also inhibited in another situation.

Comparison of the first 2 points of the above summary may suggest that
the orientation-defense reflex to the new part (B) of the compartment, a
part unknown for some pups, accounted for the fact that they did not know
how to get there around the obstacle. The behaviour of pups No. 3, 5, and 6
seems to confirm this supposition. On the other hand, there are other facts
which contradict such interpretation. Pups No. 9 and 10, for instance,
which were allowed to run for 20 successive experiments in the whole experimental compartment so that the last trace of the orientation reflex
disappeared, had much difficulty in finding the detour way to the bowl.
Also pups No. 21 and 22, while not showing any orientation-defense reflex in the room because of their previous training in the garden, did not
know how to make a detour around the obstacle. Moreover, a single passing of the obstacle did not abolish the difficulty and 5–6 training experiments had to be performed before the reaction became smooth and immediate. It seems then that the orientation-defense reflex raises difficulty
in going around the obstacle but is in itself not the main cause of the absence of the detour reaction.

It may also be argued that the pups did not know how to go around the obstacle because their central nervous system was not sufficiently developed. In order to test this, experiments on adult dogs would have to be performed; such dogs should from birth live under the control of the experimenter and they should never be allowed to circle any obstacle till the key experiment. As such experiments could not be realised for technical reasons (independent of the author), the investigation was carried out on 4 adult rabbits, 3 years old. These rabbits were born in the laboratory, never left their boxes and they had no opportunity to go around any obstacle during their life. It was found that none of the rabbits knew how to pass around a wire-netting obstacle, 1 m. in length, to get to a bowl of food placed behind it. These rabbits were, nevertheless, capable of learning this reaction; this learning, however, required more training experiments than was found necessary for pups. (These data will be published later.)

Now, let us consider our results as a whole. At first, points 2–5 of the above summary will be discussed. As can be easily seen, the course of establishment of the detour reaction, its generalization, the capacity of extinction and restoration is in complete agreement with the laws found for conditioned reflexes. Namely, when after many wrong movements the animal reached the bowl for the first time, it was only by chance or with the help of the experimenter. Such a trial had to be repeated several times so that the reaction became smooth and immediate; the latency of the reaction diminished rather irregularly (Diagram I). Moreover, this reaction, established to one definite obstacle, appeared also to other obstacles set in other situations. So the detour reaction obeys the laws of establishment and generalization of conditioned reflexes.

Further, this reaction may be extinguished if food is not given any more, after passing the obstacle. The course of extinction of the detour reaction is also the same as for conditioned reflexes. Namely, the chronic inhibition of the reaction requires many trials repeated for several successive days; the course of this process is irregular and after extinction a complete detour reaction sometimes appears again; in the conditioned-reflex terminology this phenomenon is called "disinhibition." In order to restore the detour reaction food reinforcement must be given several times; renewal of the reaction occurs considerably quicker than extinction, according to the laws found for conditioned reflexes by Konorski and Szwejkowska (1952).

All this confirms the view that the detour reaction is a conditioned reflex of locomotor character presenting one of the forms of the conditioned reflex type II of Konorski (1948, Ch. XII). This conclusion is supported by some facts which were frequently obtained during the course of our experiments. These facts, seemingly strange, become understandable when considered in light of conditioned reflexes.

Let us take first the oscillatory movements between obstacle and starting place which appear in the initial period of elaboration of the detour reaction. At this time, there are not yet established the cerebral connections between stimuli originating from the bowl standing behind the obstacle, the movements of going around the obstacle and the food reinforcement. At the same time the previously established connections between the movements of running to the wire-netting and the food persist. When the latter reaction was not reinforced as usual by reaching food, a series of runs from the starting place to the obstacle appeared (likewise a learned movement is repeated many times by a dog in the course of the acute extinction of a motor conditioned reflex in an experimental chamber). Only after some runs which remain without reinforcement does this reaction cease to appear (i.e., it is extinguished), and the pup begins to perform some other locomotor movements resulting in the occasional finding of the passage to part B.

The other fact, namely passing to the other side of the obstacle after eating from the bowl placed in front of the netting, or the interruption of eating in order to go behind the partition (Figure 6), which was frequently observed at the beginning of the training of the detour reaction, may be understood, if we remember the scheme of the motor conditioned reaction (Wyrwicka, 1952). According to this scheme the motor conditioned reaction is evoked by stimuli derived simultaneously from two sources, namely from the alimentary centre and the centre corresponding to the external stimuli (the usual situation). In the case under discussion both centres are excited, therefore the locomotor reaction may appear. Similar facts consisting in the performance by the animal of the learned movement in the conditioned-reflex chamber immediately after or even during eating are frequently observed; they are explained in the same way. Such a behaviour is, of course, mainly observed at the beginning of training; later on the process of differentiation occurs and then the animal reacts only to a definite complex of stimuli, e.g., the dog in the conditioned-reflex chamber performs the learned movement only to a conditioned signal and our pup goes around the obstacle only when the bowl is placed behind the wire-netting.

Later, in the case of the lengthening of the obstacle, the fact of stopping in the place of the previous passage (Figure 9) must be considered. The performance of every movement is signalized to the cerebral cortex and when the movement is repeated the nervous signals from it are connected with signals from the experimental situation in which the movement is performed. If a change is made in the place where the animal usually turns at an angle of 180°, an orientation reflex is evoked and there is a disturbance in the pattern of the sensory-motor excitation in the cortex, resulting in inhibition of the animal's movements.

Finally, the fact of going to the old site of the bowl, when it is put in another place behind the obstacle (Figure 11) may be explained in the following way. The stimuli derived from the bowl which is behind the wire-netting, evoke the same reaction which was connected with it in previous training, i.e., the old locomotor reaction; so the animal passes around the obstacle in the "old" direction, opposite to the one in which it should go to reach food. This type of reaction did not appear, however, in all pups; if the animal going through the passage sees the bowl in another place, it goes to it and in this case the old locomotor reaction is not performed.

Now, let us consider the behaviour of animals that remained in both parts of the compartment or went around some objects in another place during the preliminary training. Most of these pups found the detour way to the bowl on the first trial. Passing the obstacle was easiest for pups trained in pairs. In these experiments the pups frequently found themselves on opposite sides of the wire-netting and one pup came to the other, going around the obstacle. So the conditioned detour reflex could have been established on the basis of an unconditioned social reflex. It is quite possible that some unconditioned reinforcements replace each other; this seems to be true especially in the case of the conditioned detour reaction, because an animal meets and goes around obstacles not only to reach food but also for many other purposes.

The ability of pups which ran singly in both parts of the compartment during the preliminary training, to pass the obstacle, may to some extent be explained in the same way. It seems, in this case, that the conditioned detour reaction might have been established on the basis of an exploratory unconditioned reflex (which also played a part in the former case). These pups had, however, more difficulty in finding the bowl behind the wire-netting than the ones trained in pairs; therefore we may conclude that the conditioned detour reflex established on the basis of an exploratory reflex was not as strongly formed as that elaborated on the basis of a social reflex.

The behaviour of pup No. 11 should also be explained. This animal was trained singly but in spite of this, easily passed the obstacle, whereas other pups of the same litter (No. 9 and 10) had some difficulty with this task. Such different results may be due to preliminary training during which pup No. 11 was fed in various places in the room (Figure 3), while other pups always received food in the same place. In consequence, pup No. 11 was trained to look for the bowl in various places and this probably helped it to find the bowl behind the obstacle.

Finally, the behaviour of some other pups should be considered, those which after some minutes of "reflection" suddenly started to pass the partition and reach food (pups No. 18 and 20); similar behaviour was described by Köhler (1925) and others in relation to experiments on detour behaviour. Similar facts were also observed in conditioned-reflex practice. The period of "reflection" may be considered—in keeping with our previous conclusions—as the period in which a definitive complex of external stimuli acting on the animal increasingly stimulates a corresponding conditioned-reflex pattern; when this excitation reaches its supraliminal value, the conditioned reaction immediately appears. This period of growing excitation in the reflex pattern is probably dependent upon: (1) the degree of fixation of the conditioned reflex, (2) the excitability of the unconditioned reflex (i.e., alimentary one in our case), and (3) the similarity of the present external stimuli with the stimuli to which the conditioned reflex was previously established. The stronger these three factors are the shorter the period of evoking the suitable reflex pattern, or in other words, the shorter the "reflection." Perhaps the idea of "insight" may be replaced, in the case of the detour reaction, by the idea of the evoking of the corresponding conditioned-reflex pattern.

Summarizing, we may conclude that the detour reaction is a conditioned reflex type II established to a complex of stimuli derived from a definite "aim" (food, company, etc.) and an obstacle in the way to this aim; the reaction consists in going to the edge of the obstacle and passing around it at an angle of 180°; reaching the goal is the reinforcement of this reaction. Once acquired—usually early in the animal's life—this conditioned reflex appears, because of wide generalization, in all conditions similar to those to which it was primarily established.

SUMMARY

Experiments were performed on 28 pups, 32–131 days old, both male and female, from 8 litters (5 bitches and 8 male dogs). The pups were controlled from birth and housed in large boxes where they had no occasion to go around any objects. Experiments were carried out in an empty room and in the garden; the experimental place was partially divided into 2 parts by a partition of wire-netting (Figure 1). At first preliminary training was performed. Eleven pups were allowed to remain singly for 10–15 min. daily in the part in front of the partition only, and 12 pups (8 of them trained singly and 4 in pairs)— in both parts of the compartment. The other 5 pups (3 of them trained singly and 2 as a pair) were at first allowed to run around a wire-net fence in the garden and then for several daily experiments, they remained singly in a room, in front of the partition only. At the beginning of every experiment, the animals usually received food in a bowl which was always put before the wire-net partition (circle in Figure 1); when the dog finished eating, the bowl was immediately taken away. After some days a key experiment was performed. This consisted in placing the bowl behind the wire-net partition (circle with cross in Figure 1), so that the pup had to make a detour around the partition to reach food. The key experiment was performed separately for each animal.

It was found that most pups which were previously allowed to remain in the whole experimental place or which previously went around a fence in another situation, knew how to find the way around the partition to reach food. This task was easiest for pups originally trained in pairs. The animals, however, which had previously remained only before the partition and never made a detour around any object did not know how to go to the bowl, and they found the way to food only by chance, according to the "trial-and-error" principle. These pups, however, were capable of learning how to make a detour around the obstacle; nevertheless, about 6 experiments were required to make the reaction immediate (Diagram 1).

Pups which had learned to make a detour round a definite obstacle knew also how to do it when the size and shape of the obstacle as well as the direction of going round it were changed; the pups knew in addition how to make a detour in other situations (in another room or in the garden). Each change caused a temporary increase in the time required to go round the obstacle.

In 3 pups chronic extinction of the detour reaction was performed in the garden by setting an empty bowl behind the wire-net obstacle, i.e., the detour way discontinued to be reinforced. After about 50 repetitions of such a procedure over 20 days, the detour reaction was completely extinguished. After transferring the experiments to the room the pups showed a complete (1 animal) or almost complete (2 animals) inhibition of this reaction. After the restoration of the detour reaction in the garden, it became also renewed in the room.

The conclusion drawn is that the detour reaction is a locomotor conditioned reflex which is acquired by an animal usually early in its life; this reflex is then widely generalized, i.e., it may appear in all conditions similar to those to which it was primarily established. Such a view makes understandable some facts obtained during the course of experiments, as the interruption of eating by a pup in order to go behind the wire-net partition or going there immediately after eating in spite of the absence of the bowl behind the obstacle (Figure 6); stopping in the place of the previous passage after a lengthening of the obstacle (Figure 9); going to the old feeding place when the bowl was put in another spot (Figure 11).

It is very probable that pups which were allowed to remain in the whole experimental compartment or to go round a fence in another situation during the preliminary training, acquired this reaction on the basis of an exploratory unconditioned reflex (in the case of singly trained pups) or a social unconditioned reflex (in the case of pups trained in pairs; it was frequently observed that both animals found themselves on opposite sides of the obstacle and one pup came to the other).

REFERENCES

BERITOFF, J. The comparative study of individual behaviour in dogs, rabbits, and hens. *Trans. J. Beritashvili physiol. Inst.*, 1941, *4*, 229.

BERITOFF, J., and AKHMETELI, M. On the behaviour of pigeons in overcoming an obstacle (Summary). *Trans. J. Beritashvili physiol. Inst.*, 1941, *4*, 248.

FISCHEL, W. Über bewahrende und wirkende Gedächtnisleistung. *Biol. Zbl.*, 1933, *53*, 449–451.

HIGGINSON, G. D. Visual perception in the white rat. *J. exp. Psychol.*, 1926, *9*, 337–347.

HSIAO, H. H. An experimental study of the rat's 'insight' within a spacial complex. *Univ. Calif. Publ. Psychol.*, 1929, *4*, 57–70.

KOHLER, W. *The mentality of apes.* (Rev. ed.) London: Routledge, 1927.

KONORSKI, J. *Conditioned reflexes and neuron organization.* London: Cambridge University Press, 1948.

KONORSKI, J., and SZWEJKOWSKA, G. The dependence of the course of extinction and restoration of conditioned reflexes on the 'history' of the conditioned stimulus. *Acta Biol. Exp.*, 1952, *16*, 95.

LORENZ, K. Betrachtungen über das Erkennen der arteigenen Triebhandlungen der Vögel. *J. Ornithol.*, 1932, *80*, 50–98.

LORENZ, K. Vergleichende Verhaltungsforschung. *Zool. Anz. Supp.*, 1939, *12*, 69–102.

PAVLOVSKIE SREDY. Moskwa (Russian text), 1949, 574.

ROGINSKY, G. Z., and TIKH, N. A. Roundabout ways in animals (Summary). Problems of the modern physiology of the nervous and muscle systems. *Tbilisi*, 1956, 384.

SCHILLER, P. Umwegversuchen an Elritzen. *Z. Tierpsychol.*, 1942, *5*, 101–130.

TEYROVSKY, V. A study of ideational behaviour in the Garden Warbler. *Pub. Fac. Sci. Univ. Masaryk*, No. 122, 1930.

THORPE, W. H. *Learning and instinct in animals.* Cambridge, Mass.: Harvard University Press, 1956.

TOLMAN, E. C., and HONZIK, C. H. Insight in rats. *Univ. Calif. Publ. Psychol.*, 1930, *4*, 215–232.

TROSHIKHIN, W. A. Razwitie orientirovočnoi reakcii i stanovlenie dvigatelnych uslovnooboronitelnych refleksov u šceniat (Russian text). *Fizjol. Zurn.* USSR, 1953, *39*, 265.

WYRWICKA, W. On the mechanism of the motor conditioned reaction. *Acta Biol. Exp.*, 1952, *16*, 131–137.

WYRWICKA, W. Fizjologicny mechanism reakcii obhodzenia preskody (Physiological mechanism of the 'roundabout way' reaction—Short English summary). *Acta Physiol. Pol.*, 1954, *5*, 500.

25

Some Factors Involved in the Stimulus Control of Operant Behavior

W. H. Morse and B. F. Skinner

The stimuli which are present when an operant is reinforced modify the subsequent frequency of emission of the response. For example, if a hungry pigeon is reinforced with food when it pecks a translucent key upon which a monochromatic light is projected, it will subsequently peck most rapidly when the light is of the same wavelength. Guttman (1956) has reported that a difference of 2 millimicrons can produce a lower rate. As the difference increases the rate falls in a "generalization gradient." If responses are reinforced at one wavelength and extinguished at all others, the gradient is sharpened. These facts are now well known, but the significance of the relevant conditions has not been fully analyzed.

When a response is reinforced in the presence of a stimulus, the stimulus (S^D), the response (R), and the reinforcement (rft) occur in close temporal proximity, as the result of certain arbitrary arrangements. At first, S^D usually has no demonstrable control over the response; it does not elicit the response as in a reflex and is chosen from many possible stimuli. The relation between R and rft is arranged by the reinforcing circuit. Once these two connections have been established, there is a fairly close temporal contiguity between S^D and rft. But which of these relations is responsible for the stimulus-generalization gradient (with or without differential reinforcement)? In particular, is the role of the response in bringing S^D and rft close together essential to the development of stimulus control, or is the temporal association between S^D and rft enough to make any R which produces rft more frequent in the presence of S^D.

This point has been the subject of several experiments. K. Walker (1942) has shown that a discriminative stimulus developed in connection

Adapted from *Journal of the Experimental Analysis of Behavior*, 1958, *1*, 103–107. With permission of the authors and publisher.

with one operant has an appropriate effect upon another. The introduction of a tone which had been the discriminative stimulus for a running response facilitated lever-pressing. Estes (1943) reinforced pressing a lever on a fixed-interval schedule, then removed the lever and repeatedly presented a stimulus for 60 seconds before the "free" presentation of food. When the levers were replaced and the response extinguished, a higher rate was observed in the presence of the stimulus which had preceded the presentation of food. In that experiment the response was conditioned before the contingency between the stimulus and food was set up. In a later experiment (Estes, 1948), a stimulus preceded food before the lever was introduced. The rat was then reinforced for 10 responses to the lever and, subsequently, on a fixed-interval schedule for 1 hour. When the stimulus was then introduced during extinction, it increased the rate of responding as in the previous experiment.

A similar experiment differing in several significant features has been performed with pigeons. In a first stage a food magazine is operated on an intermittent schedule in the presence of one stimulus but never in the presence of another. In a second stage the pigeon is conditioned to peck a key for food, with neither stimulus present, and a substantial rate is built up with intermittent reinforcement. In the final stage the response is extinguished while the two stimuli are alternately presented. Under these conditions the stimuli were found to exert a differential control over the rate.

APPARATUS AND PROCEDURE

All inside surfaces of a standard experimental box with inside dimensions of 11 by 10 by 13 inches high were painted a uniform flat white. The space was illuminated by a ceiling light which could be white, red, or green. The magazine presented food for 5 seconds at each operation; a supply of water was present.

Stage 1

Four naive male pigeons were reduced to 80 percent of their free-feeding body weight. Each bird was then placed in the box for daily sessions of 144 minutes each. The light in the box was alternately red and green for periods which varied between 6 and 300 seconds, with a mean of 120 seconds. In the presence of one color (red with two pigeons, green with two) the food magazine was operated (without respect to the bird's behavior) on a 1-minute, variable-interval schedule. In the presence of the other color the magazine was never operated. There was no explicit period of "magazine training," but by the second daily session all the birds ate from the magazine whenever it appeared. There were 20 such experimental sessions for each bird.

Stage 2

A key consisting of a hinged plastic plate behind a 1-inch circular open-ing at head height in one wall of the box was illuminated only by the ceiling light. In white light all birds were conditioned to peck the key and reinforced 72 times a day for 2 days. They were then reinforced on a 1-minute, variable-interval schedule for 6 days, receiving 72 reinforce-ments per session. All birds developed stable rates typical of the VI per-formance in the first session.

Stage 3

The key was present but responses were never reinforced. (No food was received for any reason.) The illumination in the box was alternately red and green following the schedule of Stage 1. Responses to the key were recorded in the two extinction curves, one showing responses in the red light, the other those in green. Thus, a small segment of one curve was recorded, then a small segment of the other, and so on. The recorder not in use was stopped. A single process of extinction was thus recorded in two curves showing alternating performances in red and green lights.

RESULTS

Figure 1 shows the extinction curves obtained in red and green lights for the two pigeons which received food in red light, and Figure 2 for the two pigeons which received food in green light at Stage 1. In all cases the extinction session began with the red light present.

Bird 1 (Figure 1) begins to respond almost immediately (at *a*) in spite of the fact that heretofore the operant has been reinforced only in white light. At *b* the light was changed to green, and the small segment ending at *c* was then recorded. The performance then continues, beginning at *b*, and so on, throughout the session. The initial rates of responding in the presence of the two colors are of the same order, but are less than half of the rate on the VI 1 in white light. Beginning at *d*, responding almost ceases in green light, although it continues at a substantial though irreg-ular rate in red light for at least 2 hours. The experiment was stopped at the end of the records. The total numbers of responses emitted in the red and green lights are in the ratio of 3.3 to 1.

Bird 2 in Figure 1 shows a more marked effect of changing from the white light prevailing under VI 1. Both rates begin low but subsequently rise. Here again, responding in the green light drops essentially to zero while there is still considerable activity in red light. The ratio of responses is here about 2 to 1 in favor of red light.

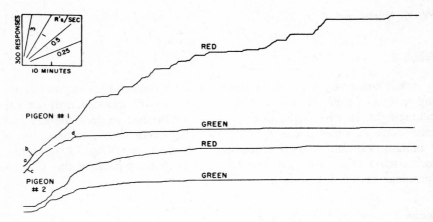

Figure 1. *Performance during extinction recorded separately according to the presence of red and green lights, which alternated randomly. Previously, the pigeons had received food (without respect to behavior) in red light on a 1-minute, variable-interval schedule, but never in the presence of green light.*

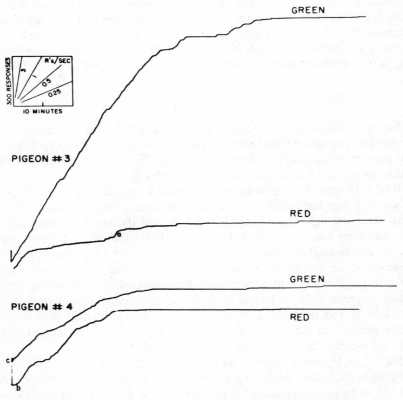

Figure 2. *Performance during extinction recorded separately according to the presence of red and green lights, which alternated randomly. Previously, the pigeons had received food (without respect to behavior) in green light on a 1-minute, variable-interval schedule, but never in the presence of red light.*

The curves for the two birds receiving food in green light at Stage 1 are shown in Figure 2. Both birds extinguished fairly rapidly. Bird 3 continues to respond in green light at a high rate for approximately 30 minutes, although responding in red light drops to a low value after about 3 minutes, except for a slight burst at a. The ratio of responses in favor of green (the color present during the reception of food at Stage 1) is 4.5 to 1.

Bird 4 showed no effect of Stage 1 during the first session of extinction. The session begins at b (Figure 2) with a slight acceleration in the rate, which decreases slightly when the light is changed to green (beginning at c). There are at least two periods of responding in the red light when the rates are considerably more rapid than in the green light, although responding continues for a slightly longer time in the presence of the green light. The numbers of responses in red and green lights are about the same for the session. When this bird was put in the apparatus on a second day, however, it emitted 110 responses in green light (the color previously correlated with food) and 5 in red. (All the other birds also responded more to the food-correlated color during a second extinction session.)

CONCLUSION

In evaluating these four pairs of extinction curves, it should be noted that the design of the experiment favors a contrary result. The repeated presentation of food to a hungry pigeon usually sets up "superstitious" behavior (Skinner, 1948); and during the 20 sessions of Stage 1, incidental responses were probably reinforced under the discriminative control of the light correlated with food. In extinction at Stage 3 such behavior would compete with the response to the key. The bird would have more time to respond in the presence of the light not correlated with food. The pairs of curves may, therefore, inadequately indicate the extent to which a given light has acquired control over an operant subsequently conditioned.

The experiment confirms Estes' finding that the contingency [1] between S^D and rft is sufficient to give S^D some control over a response subsequently conditioned with rft. In a standard experiment on discrimination, the same temporal correlation may be partly responsible for the ultimate stimulus control. It should be noted, however, that the pairs of extinction curves in the figures show much less control than would have been obtained if Stages 1 and 2 had been combined—if the response had previously been reinforced in one light and extinguished in the other.

[1] The term "pairing" is more appropriate here (Ed.).

REFERENCES

ESTES, W. K. Discriminative conditioning. I. A discriminative property of conditioned anticipation. *J. exp. Psychol.*, 1943, *32*, 150–155.

ESTES, W. K. Discriminative conditioning. II. Effects of a Pavlovian conditioned stimulus upon a subsequently established operant response. *J. exp. Psychol.*, 1948, *38*, 173–177.

GUTTMAN, N. The pigeon and the spectrum and other perplexities. *Psychol. Rep.*, 1956, *2*, 449–460.

SKINNER, B. F. 'Superstition' in the pigeon. *J. exp. Psychol.*, 1948, *38*, 168–172.

WALKER, K. C. The effect of a discriminative stimulus transferred to a previously unassociated response. *J. exp. Psychol.*, 1942, *31*, 312–321.

26

Schedules of Conditioned Reinforcement During Experimental Extinction

Roger T. Kelleher

If a stimulus is repeatedly presented in conjunction with a reinforcer, the stimulus becomes a conditioned reinforcer. One way to demonstrate this conditioned reinforcing effect is to allow the stimulus to alter the course of experimental extinction. This technique was used in an early experiment by Skinner (1938).

Whenever the sound of a food magazine occurred, food was delivered into a tray. The hungry rats in this experiment learned to approach the tray only at the sound of the food magazine. The rats were then trained to press a lever that operated the food magazine. After this chain of responses was thoroughly established, the food magazine was disconnected. Under this procedure, an extinction curve occurred in which response rates decreased to low values. Next, the food magazine was again connected, although food was still not delivered; that is, each response produced

Adapted from *Journal of the Experimental Analysis of Behavior*, 1961, *4*, 1–6. With permission of the author and publisher.

only the sound of the magazine. Response rates increased markedly, and a second extinction curve occurred (Skinner, 1938, p. 103). Skinner attributed the increased response rates to the conditioned reinforcing effect of the magazine sound.

Recent criticisms of this technique for demonstrating conditioned reinforcement have emphasized the importance of distinguishing between the effects of a stimulus as a conditioned reinforcer and the effects of a stimulus as a conditioned stimulus. Bugelski (1956) suggested that the sound of the food magazine is not a conditioned reinforcer but is instead a conditioned stimulus that *evokes* responding. Wyckoff, Sidowski, and Chambliss (1958) also suggested that the sound of the food magazine is not a conditioned reinforcer; however, they believe that the magazine sound is a discriminative stimulus controlling increased activity and consequently increasing the probability of responding.

The purpose of the present experiment was to elucidate the effects of the magazine sound during extinction by scheduling the presentation of the magazine sound just as the presentation of food is usually scheduled (Ferster and Skinner, 1957). The results demonstrate that the magazine sound can be used as a conditioned reinforcer.

SUBJECTS AND APPARATUS

The two subjects were male, White Carneaux pigeons maintained at 75 percent of their free-feeding weights. These birds had been trained to peck a Plexiglas key to obtain reinforcements. A reinforcement consisted of a 4-second access to a hopper of grain. The sound of a solenoid pulling the hopper into place produced a distinct magazine sound which preceded each reinforcement. The pigeons had about 50 hours of experience on a 5-minute, fixed-interval schedule (FI 5) just before the present experiment. The apparatus and recording equipment has been described generally (Ferster and Skinner, 1957).

PROCEDURE

During the experimental sessions described in this report, the hopper of grain was disconnected and the birds did not receive food; however, the magazine sound was produced according to a schedule. On one schedule, the magazine sound occurred whenever the bird paused for a specified period of time. I shall refer to this schedule as the differential reinforcement of pausing (DRP). On a second schedule, the magazine sound was produced by the first response occurring after 5 minutes had elapsed (FI 5). On a third schedule, the magazine sound was produced whenever the bird emitted a specified number of responses; that is, the magazine sound was produced on a fixed-ratio (FR) schedule. In the first two experimental extinction sessions, the DRP schedule and the FR schedule alternated. Food was not presented during these two sessions. Following the second session, the birds were returned to an FI 5 schedule of food reinforcement for 15 experimental sessions. Then, the food magazine was again disconnected, and both birds had a third experimental extinction session in which the magazine sound was produced on FI 5, FR, and DRP schedules.

RESULTS

Figure 1 presents the results with one bird during the first two experimental extinction sessions. In the first session (Frame A), the magazine sound initially occurred on a DRP of 10 seconds. Periods during which low response rates resulted in the frequent occurrence of the magazine sound are shown at *a* and *b*. During the 75 minutes in which the DRP schedule was in effect, the average response rate was 14.2 responses per minute.

Immediately after the pause at *b,* the next response produced the magazine sound (CRF). For the remainder of this first extinction session, responses produced the magazine sound on an FR schedule. The response requirement was increased from FR 5 to FR 25. The results are presented in the third and fourth cumulative-record segments in Figure 1A. During the 28 minutes in which the FR schedule was in effect, the average response rate was 27.9 responses per minute.

On the following day (Frame B), the DRP schedule was again in effect at the start of the session. The results are presented in the first cumulative record in Figure 1B. Again, low response rates at *c* resulted in frequent presentations of the magazine sound. During this exposure to the DRP schedule, the average response rate was 18.3 responses per minute. Immediately after *c,* the magazine sound was again presented on FR schedules of the values indicated. As shown in the second cumulative record of Figure 1B, average response rates increased to 36.6 responses per minute. In the third cumulative record of Figure 1B, the DRP was again introduced, and the average response rate decreased to 18.5 responses per minute. Low response rates at *d* resulted in frequent presentations of the magazine sound. In the fourth record of Figure 1B, the FR procedure was again introduced, and the average response rates increased to 35 responses per minute.

The results for these first two sessions of experimental extinction demonstrate that the schedule of presentation of the magazine sound can be used to manipulate response rates even when food is not presented. The results with the DRP schedule indicate that the magazine sound may be followed by a low or zero response rate. However, even after a demonstration of this very low response rate following the magazine sound, high

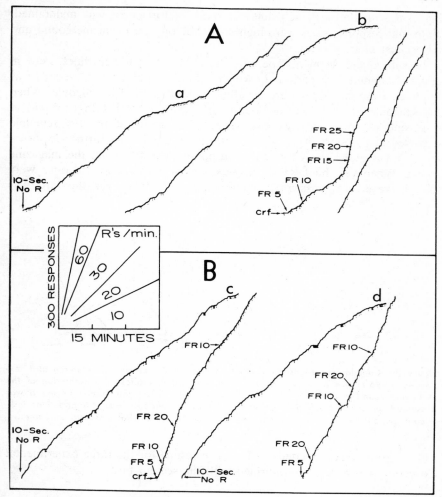

Figure 1. Cumulative-response records showing first (Frame A) and second (Frame B) sessions of experimental extinction. Performances on DRP 10 seconds and various FR values are presented. Pips indicate presentations of the magazine sound.

response rates can still be produced if the magazine sound is on an FR schedule.

After an additional 15 hours on the FI 5 schedule of food reinforcement, another session of experimental extinction was conducted. Cumulative-response records for one bird are presented in Figure 2. In this session, all three schedules of presentation of the magazine sound were used. Changes from one schedule to another are designated.

As shown in the first two segments of Figure 2, the magazine sound was produced on an FI 5 schedule, and the positively accelerated responding characteristic of FI schedules of food reinforcement was maintained. Note that response rates were highest just before the magazine sound and lowest just after.

In subsequent segments, periods during which FR schedules were in effect alternated with periods in which either FI 5 or DRP 5 seconds was in effect. Response rates were usually high during the FR schedule. When the schedule of the magazine sound was shifted from FR to FI 5 (as at *a, c,* and *e*), the high response rates characteristic of the FR schedule occurred at the start of the FI 5 segment. In each case, further exposure to FI 5 (as at *b*) decreased these response rates following the magazine sound. Whenever the DRP 5 seconds was in effect, response rates were low; however, response rates increased rapidly whenever the bird was

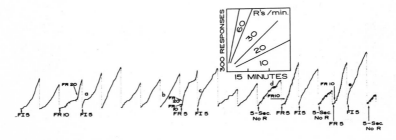

Figure 2. Cumulative-response records showing third session of experimental extinction. Performance on FI 5, FR, and DRP 5-second schedules of presentation of the magazine sound are shown. The recording pen reset when the magazine sound was presented on the FI 5 schedule or when the type of schedule was changed. Pips indicate presentations of the magazine sound on the FR or DRP 5-second schedules.

shifted from DRP 5 seconds to FR. The results for the three experimental extinction sessions were confirmed with the second bird.

DISCUSSION

When the sound of the food magazine was used as a conditioned reinforcer, response rates and patterns of responding could be manipulated during experimental extinction. When the magazine sound was scheduled to occur only when the bird paused for a brief period of time (DRP), low response rates developed. Performance on this schedule demonstrated that the magazine sound, as a discriminative stimulus, could control a zero response rate in extinction. When the magazine sound could be produced on an FI 5 schedule, characteristic FI performances were developed; that is, the response rate was lowest following the magazine sound, and then increased as the interval elapsed. When the magazine sound could be produced on an FR schedule, high response rates prevailed.

The FR schedule produced high response rates even after low response rates had been produced on the DRP schedule. Abrupt shifts from the FR to the FI schedule caused transient disruption in the FI response pattern. That is, the birds responded at a very high rate following the magazine sound. The patterns of responding that occurred when the birds were shifted from the FR to the FI schedule are similar to those occurring on mixed FI FR schedules of food reinforcement (Ferster and Skinner, 1957).

Other investigations have suggested that the presentation of the magazine sound enhances resistance to experimental extinction only because the magazine sound is either a conditioned stimulus which elicits responding (Bugelski, 1956) or a discriminative stimulus which controls a high rate of responding (Wyckoff, Sidowski, and Chambliss, 1958). The present experiment demonstrates that the magazine sound can control either a high or a low rate during experimental extinction. In either case, the magazine sound is a conditioned reinforcer that can be used to maintain or develop characteristic patterns of responding in individual organisms during experimental extinction.

SUMMARY

Pigeons that had been trained on a 5-minute, fixed-interval schedule of food reinforcement received three sessions of experimental extinction. During the extinction sessions, the birds could produce the sound of the food magazine according to different schedules. Schedules of presentation of the magazine sound were effective in controlling response patterns and response rates during extinction. The magazine sound can be used as a conditioned reinforcer.

REFERENCES

BUGELSKI, B. R. *The psychology of learning.* New York: Holt, Rinehart and Winston, 1956.

FERSTER, C. B., and SKINNER, B. F. *Schedules of reinforcement.* New York: Appleton-Century-Crofts, 1957.

SKINNER, B. F. *The behavior of organisms.* New York: Appleton-Century-Crofts, 1938.

WYCKOFF, L. B., SIDOWSKI, J., and CHAMBLISS, D. J. An experimental study of the relationship between secondary reinforcing and cue effects of a stimulus. *J. comp. physiol. Psychol.*, 1958, *51*, 103–109.

27

Stimulus-Producing Responses

in Chimpanzees

Roger T. Kelleher

Recent analyses of discrimination learning have emphasized a distinction between responses which are instrumental in obtaining food and responses which result in exposure to the discriminative stimuli (Ehrenfreund, 1948; Spence, 1940; Wyckoff, 1952). These responses will be classified in terms of their contingencies; that is, a response of the former type will be referred to as a food-producing response (Rf), and a response of the latter type will be referred to as a stimulus-producing response (Rs).

Most analyses have dealt with Rs as a theoretical construct to be inferred from Rf performance (Ehrenfreund, 1948; Spence, 1940). On the other hand, Wyckoff (1952) developed a technique for dealing with Rs directly. He used pigeons as Ss in a free-operant situation. The Rf was pecking a translucent key; the Rs was pressing a pedal on the floor of the experimental enclosure. Periods in which Rf was reinforced on a ½-minute, fixed-interval schedule (positive periods) alternated randomly with the periods in which there was no possibility of reinforcement (negative periods). The key remained white throughout both positive and negative periods unless Rf occurred; in this case, the key changed from white to red or green. One of these colors was correlated with positive periods and the other with negative periods. Although Rs did not alter the probability of reinforcement, it did enable the bird to discriminate between the two conditions. As long as the pedal was held down, the discriminative stimuli remained on, but the bird had to leave the pedal to eat. The durations of the pedal-pressing responses increased as the

Adapted from *Journal of the Experimental Analysis of Behavior*, 1958, *1*, 87–102. With permission of the author and publisher.

discrimination developed, but decreased when the positive and negative stimuli were reversed or made nondifferential.

The Wyckoff technique had the disadvantage that the pedal-pressing response had a very high operant level, and frequently the Rs rates were high despite poor discriminations. Wyckoff inferred the strength of Rs from the duration of the response. A temporal response measure makes it difficult to assess the frequency of a response or to schedule the appearance of the stimuli which are contingent upon the response.

The purpose of the present experiments was to investigate variables determining the frequency of stimulus-producing responses and their relationships to discrimination performance.

METHOD

Subjects. Chimpanzee No. 125, 6-year-old male; experimental history: visual deprivation (Riesen, 1947), spatial discrimination (Robinson, 1955), play (Welker, 1956). Chimpanzee No. 160, 5-year-old female; experimental history: visual deprivation (Riesen, 1947), play (Welker, 1956). Food deprivation: 80 to 85 percent of body weight at start of experiments. Reinforcements: 8-gram pieces Purina Lab Chow. Diet supplement: vitamins, oranges, skim milk.

Apparatus. Experimental chamber: 24- by 36- by 38-inch concrete cubicle, plywood door, expanded metal floor; 24- by 38-inch panel of 1/4-inch aluminum mounted in one wall. Manipulanda: two telephone keys, 3 inches apart on 5- by 8-inch Plexiglas window in panel. Stimuli: 60-watt overhead lamp, audible click as "feedback" for depression of either key, doorbell chime accompanying operation of food magazine, red and blue lamps behind telephone keys. Sound mask: continuous white noise. The procedures were automatically programmed and results automatically recorded (Ferster, 1953).

Procedure. Session length: 7 hours (2 hours in Experiment I) or 60 food reinforcements. All stimuli off for 1-minute time out (Ferster, 1954) following each food reinforcement, and off indefinitely to terminate each session. After key-pressing was "shaped-up" (Skinner, 1953), 30 successive responses were reinforced. Then, a 1/2-minute fixed interval (FI 1/2) of food reinforcement was instituted on one key and the other was disconnected. This schedule was shifted from one key to the other at random (changing only at reinforcement). Each S received three sessions under this procedure, and low and equal rates of responding (about 0.75 per minute) developed on each key. The red and blue lamps were not illuminated during this preliminary training.

EXPERIMENT I

The purpose of this experiment was to develop a stimulus-producing-response technique for use with chimpanzees, and to determine suitable parameters for further experiments.

Method

Pressing the left key was Rf, and pressing the right key was Rs. As in the Wyckoff procedure, positive and negative periods alternated randomly. During the negative periods, extinction was in effect on the left key (Rf ext); there was no possibility of food reinforcement. The lamps behind the keys remained dark throughout both positive and negative periods unless Rs occurred, in which case the window was illuminated by the red or blue lamps. These colors were correlated with FI ½ and ext, respectively. Following every Rs, the current stimulus was displayed for a specified interval of time (St). If the positive and negative periods alternated during this interval, the stimulus color changed accordingly. Over Sessions 1–22, St was 3 minutes; over Sessions 23–26, St was 1 minute; over Sessions 27–35, St was ½ minute. The mean duration of positive and negative periods was 3 minutes, with a range of ½ minute to 5½ minutes. After Session 16, the procedure was modified so that Rf could not result in reinforcement if it occurred within 3 seconds of a preceding Rs. For example, if Rs occurred just as a food reinforcement was "set up" by the FI schedule, the availability of this reinforcement was postponed for 3 seconds. The occurrence of Rs did not alter programming of the positive and negative periods or the possibility of food reinforcements. S could "choose" between mixed (no exteroceptive stimuli) and multiple (exteroceptive stimulus for each component) schedules of reinforcement (Ferster and Skinner, 1957).

The dependent variables were the Rs rate, the Rf rate, and the discrimination ratio (DR). The latter value is obtained by computing the ratio of the rate of responding in Rf ext to the rate of responding in FI ½, and then taking the complement of this ratio (Dews, 1955). If the rates in positive and negative periods are equal, DR will be 0.00; if responding occurs only in positive periods (FI ½), DR will be 1.00. The DR provides an index of the level of discrimination, which is relatively independent of absolute rates of responding.

Results

By the 11th session, both Ss had developed clear discriminations (DRs were more than 0.90). Throughout the experiment, Rf rates in the positive periods were highly variable, and ranged from 1.46–11.46 per minute for No. 125 and from 1.61–11.10 per minute for No. 160. By Session 15, both Ss had developed very high Rs rates (more than 2 responses per minute), although an Rs rate of 0.33 response per minute would keep the discriminative stimuli continuously visible. When the procedure was changed in Session 16, the Rs rates dropped precipitously. Over Sessions

16–22, mean Rs rates for No. 125 and No. 160 were 0.45 and 0.68 per minute, respectively. The median DRs over the same sessions were 0.98 and 0.93 for No. 125 and 160, respectively. Comparable DRs were maintained at each value of St. Rs rates were also quite variable both within and between sessions at each value of St; however, the most stable Rs rates were obtained when St was ½ minute.

EXPERIMENT II

In this experiment, Rf was reinforced by food on a 100-response, variable-ratio schedule (VR 100), and Rs was reinforced by the onset of the discriminative stimuli on fixed-ratio (FR) schedules. The intermittent reinforcement of Rs should make possible a more sensitive analysis of the reinforcing effect of the discriminative stimuli.

Method

The Ss had been on free feeding for 6 weeks following Experiment I, but were reduced to the body weight of Experiment I before this experiment. During the positive periods, VR 100 (range: 1 to 200) was in effect on the left key. During the negative periods, ext was in effect; St was ½ minute. The durations of the alternating VR 100 and ext periods varied randomly from ½ minute to 10 minutes (mean, 4 minutes). These values were held constant throughout this experiment. During the preliminary training period of 3 days, the discriminative stimuli were on continuously. The discriminative stimulus was displayed after each Rs for Sessions 1 to 7; that is, Rs was continuously reinforced (Rs crf). For the remainder of the experiment, Rs had to occur a specified number of times to produce the discriminative stimulus; that is, Rs was reinforced on a fixed-ratio schedule (Rs FR). For example, in Session 8, every tenth Rs resulted in the appearance of the current discriminative stimulus for ½ minute (Rs FR 10). Both Ss received 11 sessions at Rs FR 10 and 8 sessions at each of the following: Rs FR 20, Rs FR 30, and Rs FR 60, in that order, followed by one session of Rs ext (the discriminative stimuli could not appear). Beginning with the last session on Rs FR 30, the frequency with which both keys were pressed simultaneously was recorded. This record indicated the frequency with which S used both hands simultaneously.

Results

During the preliminary training, high stable Rf rates developed in VR 100. Table 1 presents the median Rf rates in VR 100 and median DRs for each value of the Rs schedule.

TABLE 1.

Median responses per minute in positive periods (Rf VR 100) and DRs.

Rs Schedule	No. 125		No. 160	
	Rf VR 100	DR	Rf VR 100	DR
crf	80.86	0.97	76.25	0.99
FR 10	90.53	0.99	92.07	0.99
FR 20	104.37	0.99	84.87	0.99
FR 30	107.95	0.99	63.03	0.98
FR 60	97.64	0.99	82.10	0.98

Representative Rf performances are shown in the upper records of Figures 1 and 2. The segments labelled 1 and 2 in each figure correspond to VR 100 and ext periods, respectively. During Rf VR 100, both Ss have over-all rates of about 1.50 responses per second; during Rf ext, the rates are close to zero. With few exceptions, the positive and negative periods can be easily distinguished on the basis of the Ss' behavior. Long pauses in the record of No. 160 did occur often, and almost invariably began in Rf ext periods. Rs performances, shown in the lower records, were recorded concurrently with the Rf curves. Some segments are labelled with the same numbers and letters to facilitate comparison. It should be noted that the cumulative recorders continued to run while the discriminative stimuli were visible (during St), but not during time outs.

During the segment labelled 1 in Figure 1, a very high Rf rate was maintained; however, the Rs rate was just high enough to keep the red light on throughout the period. In the segment labelled 2, the Rf rate was zero, and the Rs rate was higher than in Segment 1; however, the responses occurred in bursts and the blue light was off for some of the period. In another negative segment labelled 3, the darkened portions of the Rf curve approximate the times that the blue light was on, and the small arrows on the Rs curve indicate the response or responses which brought it on. Throughout the experiment, both Ss tended to pause (on both keys) following the appearance of the blue light. The short pauses which occasionally occurred on the Rf curve during positive periods correspond to momentarily high Rs rates (as at a and c) or to a pause on the Rs curve during which the red light disappeared (as at b). At this stage of training, both Ss showed a zero Rf rate when neither discriminative stimulus was displayed.

In Figure 2, the lower record shows the performance of No. 160 on Rs FR 20. Under this schedule, both Ss developed local Rs rates of approximately 3 responses per second. The segments labelled 1 and 2 show representative performances during positive and negative periods, respectively. The small arrows indicate bursts of responding on the Rs curves and the corresponding brief pauses on the Rf curve. In Segment 2, the Rf rate dropped to zero, but the bursts on the Rs curve continued. During

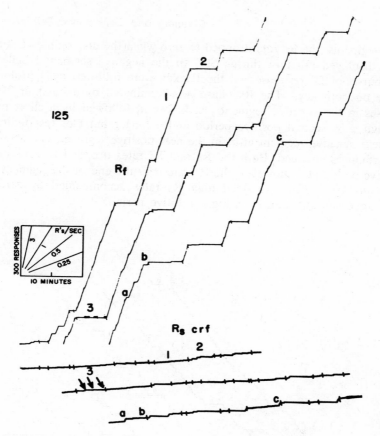

Figure 1. Representative cumulative-response records for No. 125 at Rs crf. Each alternation of positive and negative periods is marked by a pip. Food reinforcements are not shown.

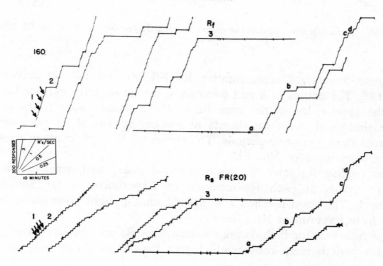

Figure 2. Representative cumulative-response records for No. 160 at Rs FR 20.

both segments, the Rs rate dropped to zero when the discriminative stimuli were displayed (that is, during St). In the negative segment labelled 3, two bursts of 20 responses on the Rs key were followed by a prolonged pause on both keys. The Rs pause was terminated by a burst of 20 responses in the negative segment just before *a*, followed by a short pause through a 30-second positive period and a longer burst of responding in the next negative segment at *a*. In the next positive segment, characteristic performances emerged. Both the Rs and Rf rates dropped to zero in the positive period at *b;* however, the Rs rate near the end of the segment was unusually prolonged. Sustained high Rs rates accompanied by zero Rs rates appeared at *c* and *d* during a positive period.

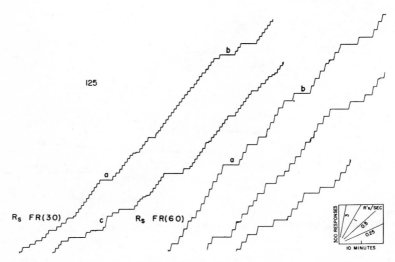

Figure 3.   Representative cumulative-response records for No. 125 at Rs FR 30 and Rs FR 60.

Figure 3 contains representative Rs FR 30 and FR 60 curves for No. 125. The pauses at *a* and *b* occurred during negative periods following the appearance of the blue light. These pauses were frequent but never prolonged. Sustained bursts of responding (as at *c*) occasionally occurred during positive periods. The curves of No. 160 contained longer pauses than those of No. 125.

The median Rs rates for positive (solid lines) and negative (dotted lines) periods at each Rs schedule of Experiment II are shown in Figure 4. The cross-hatched and dashed lines present comparable functions from Experiment III. (See below.)

The functions for both Ss are similar. After Rs crf, the rates during the positive periods were consistently higher than those during the negative

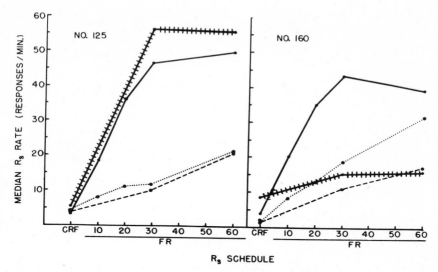

Figure 4. Median Rs rates at each Rs schedule in Experiments II and III. The first
session at each value was omitted in computing these medians. Solid lines represent
positive periods and dotted lines represent negative periods of Experiment II. Cross-
hatched lines represent positive periods and dashed lines represent negative periods
of Experiment III.

periods. The rates during the positive periods increased to Rs FR 30, but
then remained the same or fell off at Rs FR 60.

Analysis of the cumulative-response records indicated that the lower
Rs rates during negative periods resulted from the tendency of both Ss to
initiate pauses on both keys. Although DRs remained high, it is important
to note that Rf rates were usually zero in the absence of the red or blue
stimuli. At Rs FR 30 and FR 60, No. 160 began to show intermediate Rf
rates in the absence of the discriminative stimuli; therefore, the DR values
were lowered for this S. Observation of No. 160 indicated that S was using
both hands simultaneously on the two keys; No. 160 showed 30 such
responses in the last session at Rs FR 30 and hundreds of simultaneous
responses at Rs FR 60. However, no simultaneous responses were recorded
for No. 125.

The positive and negative periods can no longer be distinguished on the
basis of the response patterns of either S on Rs ext (Figure 5). Discriminations of both Ss were abolished in this extinction session (DRs were zero).
The lettered Rf curves show pauses intermingled with intermediate and
high Rf rates. The Rf rates of No. 160 were erratic, but high, and S received
60 reinforcements. No. 125 showed low over-all Rf rates and responded
only sporadically in the hours of the session remaining after the arrow
which terminates the curve. The negatively accelerated Rs ext curves
were sizable (No. 160: 1341 responses; No. 125: 3112 responses). The

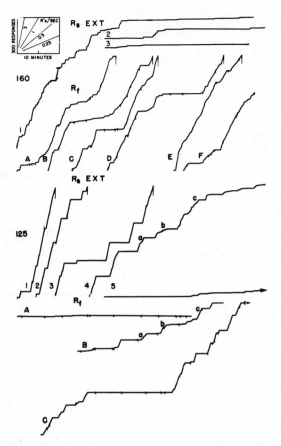

Figure 5. The cumulative Rs (numbered) and Rf (lettered) records of both Ss in Rs ext. Pips on Rf curves indicate alternation of positive and negative periods.

earlier portions of these curves tended to be bi-valued, but some inter-mediate rates did occur as the asymptote was approached. During Rs ext, 4 and 27 simultaneous responses were recorded for No. 160 and 125, respectively. The segments at *a, b,* and *c* in the Rf and Rs records of No. 125 are corresponding, and these probably were the segments in which *S* used both hands.

EXPERIMENT III

The purpose of this experiment was to re-determine the functions ob-tained at some of the Rs schedules used in Experiment II. Both *S*s received four sessions at each of the following Rs schedules: crf, FR 30, and FR 60. These were followed by one session of Rs ext.

The median Rs rates in positive (cross-hatchbed lines) and negative (dashed lines) periods at each Rs schedule of Experiment III are shown in Figure 4. Again, the first session at each value was omitted in computing the median. The median Rs rates and DRs for No. 125 were little changed. However, the rates of No. 160 at Rs FR 30 and FR 60 were considerably lower than in the determinations of Experiment I, and the function is flatter. The median DRs of No. 160 dropped to 0.90 and 0.95 at Rs FR 30 and FR 60, respectively. This drop resulted from frequent responding in the absence of the discriminative stimuli.

Many simultaneous responses (ranging from 6 to 67) were recorded for No. 160 over these sessions. This S's frequent use of both hands was not related in any consistent way to an Rs schedule. No simultaneous responses were recorded for No. 125 in these sessions.

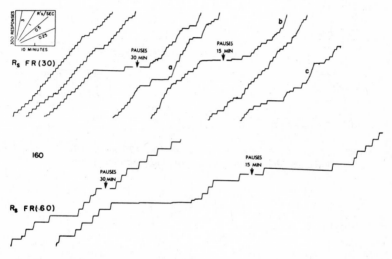

Figure 6.   Representative cumulative-response records for No. 160 at Rs FR 30 and Rs FR 60.

The local rates of responding at Rs FR 30 and FR 60 (Figure 6) remained stable at about 3 responses per second. Thus, the changes in the over-all Rs rates of this S were primarily due to the frequency and duration of pauses. The broken segments indicate sections of the curve in which S was pausing and have been omitted for convenience in presentation. Corresponding pauses occurred in the Rf records (as in Figure 2). The pauses were still initiated in negative periods. Prolonged bursts of responding (as at a, b, and c) occurred frequently in both positive and negative periods. Both Ss continued to show high Rf rates. In the absence of the discriminative stimuli, No. 125 sometimes had low Rf rates, and No. 160 had some high Rf rates. The sessions of Rs ext which directly followed Rs FR 60 are shown in Figures 7 and 8. Again, the DRs were

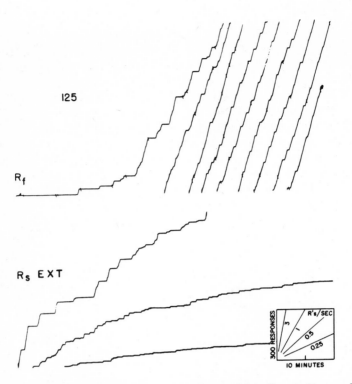

Figure 7.   The cumulative Rf and Rs records of No. 125 in Rs ext. Pips on Rf curves
indicate alternation of positive and negative periods.

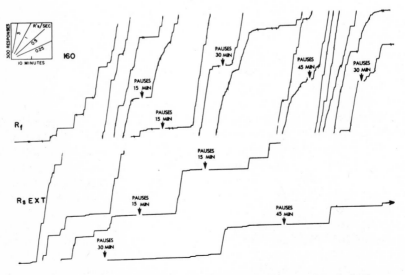

Figure 8.   The cumulative Rf and Rs records of No. 160 in Rs ext.

close to zero for both animals. The Rf curve of No. 125 (Figure 7) was low for about the first 30 minutes of the session, but then became high and sustained. The Rs ext curve contained 1715 responses. Although this extinction curve was smaller than the preceding one, it showed the same general characteristics; that is, bi-value rates of responding gave way to some intermediate rates and over-all negative acceleration. In this Rs ext session, 34 simultaneous responses were recorded for No. 125.

The Rf curve of No. 160 (Figure 8) was characterized by an initial portion which was highly similar to that of No. 125. For the remainder of the session, however, prolonged bursts of responding alternated with pauses ranging from a few minutes to more than 45 minutes. The Rs ext curve of No. 160 contained 3576 responses. The over-all curve again showed negative acceleration; however, the initial portion was steeper and more prolonged than the previous Rs ext curve. Large bursts of responding still occurred late in the session, and intermediate rates were infrequent. For No. 160, 15 simultaneous responses were recorded on Rs ext.

EXPERIMENT IV

The purpose of this experiment was to determine the effects of eliminating the discriminative function of the stimuli by making them nondifferential with respect to positive and negative periods.

Method

The system of alternation of positive and negative periods was the same as in Experiments II and III, and St was again ½ minute. Periods in which either the red or blue lights would appear following Rs also continued to alternate randomly; however, this schedule of alternation was independent of the alternation of positive and negative periods; that is, the red and blue lights were no longer correlated with either type of period exclusively. The Rs schedule was FR 60 for Sessions 1–19. Over Sessions 20–24, the stimuli remained on continuously even when the Rs rate was zero. Over Sessions 25–31, the stimuli were again discriminative and remained on continuously. The DRs were still computed on the basis of rates of responding in positive and negative periods rather than the presence of the red or blue stimulus.

Results

The DRs remained close to zero throughout the sessions in which the stimuli were nondiscriminative; therefore, the Rf rates for both positive and negative periods will be combined. The Rs rates will also be combined since they no longer differed with respect to positive and negative periods.

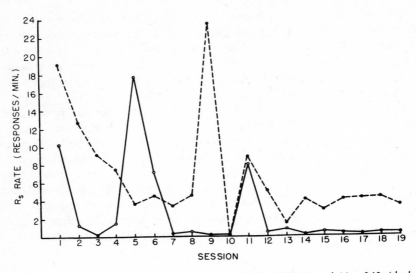

Figure 9.   The daily over-all Rs rates for No. 125 (solid line) and No. 160 (dashed line) in Experiment IV.

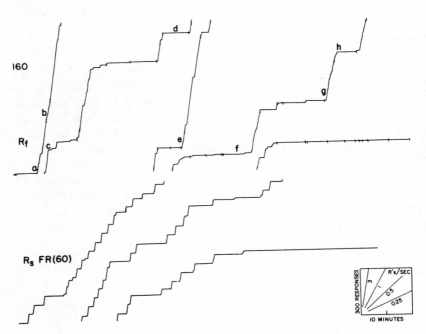

Figure 10.   Cumulative Rf and Rs records of No. 160 from Session 2 in Experiment IV. Pips on Rf curves indicate alternation of positive and negative periods.

By the third session, the Rf rates had fallen to low values (1.14 and 10.52 responses per minute for No. 125 and 160, respectively). These rates subsequently recovered, and median Rf rates over Sessions 13–19 were 73.27 and 34.23 responses per minute for No. 125 and 160, respectively.

The daily Rs rates for both Ss are shown in Figure 9. The curves fall slowly and there are several reversals. The rates of No. 125 (solid line) remained close to zero over Sessions 13–19, while those of No. 160 (dashed line) stabilize at about 3.5 responses per minute. Figure 10 shows a portion of the cumulative record of No. 160 from Session 2. The Rf records are characterized by bursts of responding alternating with pauses. At this stage of the experiment, the Rs records of No. 160 differed little from those of the previous experiment (Figure 6). The Rs rates of No. 125 were lower during this session than in the previous experiment. For most of this session, the Ss' rates were still under the control of the red and blue lights even though these were no longer discriminative stimuli. The first segment in the Rf record of Figure 10 was a negative period. When the red light appeared at *a,* a high rate developed immediately; however, this rate was sustained through a positive period (at *b*) although the blue light was on during the segment. Shifts from high rates during the red light to low rates at the appearance of the blue light are shown at *c* and *h.* Both of these periods were negative. Positive periods in which zero rates accompanied the blue light followed by negative periods in which high rates accompanied the red light are shown at *d* and *e.* Positive periods in which the red light was on are shown at *f* and *g.* There was only slight attenuation of stimulus control in this session.

No. 160 emitted 20 simultaneous responses in Session 2, 15 in Session 3, 19 in Session 11, and 11 in Session 12. No. 125 showed only 1 simultaneous response over the first 3 sessions. In Session 4, 131 simultaneous responses were recorded; and, in Session 5, 12 simultaneous responses were recorded. After Session 5, however, such responses were very infrequent for No. 125.

Figure 11 is the cumulative-response record of No. 125 from Session 19. The over-all Rf rate remained high throughout both positive and negative periods. The over-all Rs rate was close to zero, and the stimuli did not appear since 60 responses were not emitted in the session. The Rs rate of No. 160 was still high enough at this stage of the experiment to produce the discriminative stimulus occasionally.

Figure 12 contains a portion of the cumulative-response record of No. 125 from Session 20 in which the stimuli remained on continuously. In general, high rates of responding still prevailed in the red light (as at *e*); however, pauses did occur occasionally (as at *a*). When the color changed to blue, there was still a tendency to pause, but short bursts of responding were frequent in the blue light (as at *b, c, d,* and *f*). The

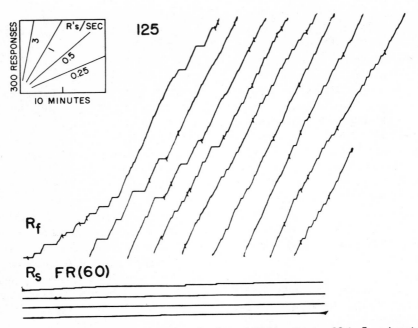

Figure 11. Cumulative Rf and Rs records of No. 125 from Session 19 in Experiment IV. Pips on Rf curves indicate alternation of positive and negative periods.

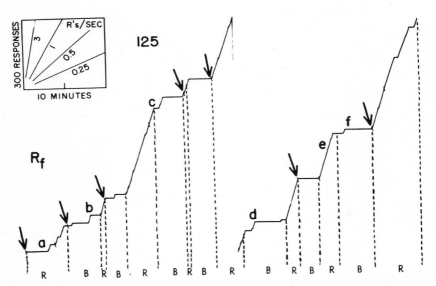

Figure 12. Cumulative Rf record of No. 125 from Session 20 in Experiment IV. Pips indicate alternation of positive and negative periods. Periods of red (R) and blue (B) lights are marked by dashed lines.

figure shows that stimulus control remained strong in this session. By Session 22, the response rates had become equal in both colors. Rs rates remained close to zero throughout these sessions.

For Sessions 25 to 31, the stimuli were again correlated with the respective schedules of reinforcement and were on continuously. The DRs of No. 160 rose rapidly, and the median DR over Sessions 29–31 was 0.97. No. 160 recovered the discrimination more slowly; the median DR over the last three sessions was 0.75.

DISCUSSION

The results of Experiment I confirm Wyckoff's finding that discriminations can be developed under conditions where the appearance of the discriminative stimulus is dependent upon Ss' behavior (1952). The results also show that Rs rates can be sustained at the three values of St used. Unfortunately, there was much variability in both Rf and Rs rates. Under an FI schedule, the passage of time during Rs responding increases the probability that Rf will be reinforced. Thus, an Rf following a series of Rs's is likely to be reinforced and a chain of responding develops. Observation of Ss suggested that this factor was responsible for the high Rs rates which developed under the first procedure when St was 3 minutes. When the procedure was changed to militate against the development of such a chain (Method, Experiment I), the Rs rates dropped precipitously. The new procedure did change the characteristics of the FI schedule, however, and may have increased the variability in Rf rates. This finding suggested the desirability of using a schedule of food reinforcement which is not programmed by time. It should be noted that Wyckoff's procedure involved an FI schedule, which may have influenced his results.

Experiments II and III demonstrate that substantial Rs rates can be sustained at FR schedules ranging up to 60. The Rs FR performances of both Ss had the same characteristics as FR schedules of food reinforcement (Ferster and Skinner, 1957). The over-all Rs rates apparently reached an asymptote at about Rs FR 30 at the Rs schedules used here.

The over-all Rs rates of No. 160 were quite low in Experiment III. The differences in Ss' performances in Experiment II may have resulted from No. 160's starting to respond with both hands simultaneously before the Rs ext session. The Rf rate of No. 125 remained very low in Rs ext, and few food reinforcements were received in the absence of the discriminative stimuli. On the other hand, No. 160 maintained high Rf rates in Rs ext and received many food reinforcements in the absence of the discriminative stimuli. Probably because of this experience in Experiment II, No. 160 showed some high Rf rates in the absence of the discriminative stimuli in Experiment III. The cumulative records of No. 160 from Experiment III show that the discrimination was not at all attenuated in the presence of the discriminative stimuli; thus, the lowered DRs resulted from responding in the absence of these stimuli.

The pauses following the appearance of the blue stimulus which resulted in the lower Rs rates during negative periods suggest that the conditioned-reinforcing effect of the negative stimulus was lower than that of the positive stimulus.

The Rs ext sessions provide one control for artifacts; that is, the only change in the programming equipment was the disconnection of the red and blue lamps. The fact that the DRs fell to zero indicates that these colored lights provided the only discriminative stimuli. The Rs ext curves are similar to those obtained in the extinction of FR schedules of food reinforcement. Clearly, the appearance of the discriminative stimuli maintained the Rs performance. The possibility remained, however, that their appearance rather than their function as discriminative stimuli provided the reinforcing effect.

The results of Experiment IV demonstrate that the discriminative function of the stimuli is necessary if they are to function as conditioned reinforcers. However, the Rs rates extinguished far more rapidly when the stimuli did not appear at all. In the early portions of Experiment IV, the Rf rate remained high in the formerly positive (red) stimulus and remained close to zero in the formerly negative (blue) stimulus. Thus, almost all food reinforcements still occurred in the formerly positive stimulus; however, the reinforcements occurred only half as frequently, and Ss often emitted hundreds of responses when the formerly positive stimulus was displayed (Figure 10) without receiving a reinforcement. With extensive exposure to this condition, the stimuli lost their effectiveness as conditioned reinforcers and the Rs rates fell to very low values. At the same time, a high Rf rate developed and was maintained throughout each session (Figure 11).

Simultaneous responses on both keys were recorded for both Ss in the Rs ext sessions and in the earlier sessions of Experiment IV. In both cases the experimental operations eventually resulted in extinction of Rs rates. Further study would be necessary to specify the factors involved in such simultaneous responding.

When the stimuli were on continuously in Session 20 of Experiment IV, there was a "spontaneous recovery" of the stimulus control (Figure 12). This occurred despite the fact that the Rs rates had been maintained at very low values for about seven sessions. This finding suggests that the number of responses necessary to produce the discriminative stimulus (the Rs schedule) may be critical.

The technique used in these experiments could prove to be invaluable in assessing the effects of many variables upon discrimination performance (for example, aversive stimuli, brain lesions, drugs). If S will respond to produce the discriminative stimuli, we can assume that it is "attending" to these stimuli; the Rs rates could serve as an operational index of "attention." Investigators sometimes indicate that they are not subjectively sure whether a discrimination was *really* lost or whether S just stopped "attending" to the stimuli. The present objective technique might enable us to make a useful distinction between these possibilities.

REFERENCES

DEWS, P. B. Studies on behavior. II. The effects of pentobarbitol, methamphetamine and scopolamine on performances in pigeons involving discriminations. *J. pharmacol. exp. Ther.*, 1955, *115*, 380–389.

EHRENFREUND, D. An experimental test of the continuity theory of discrimination learning with pattern vision. *J. comp. physiol. Psychol.*, 1948, *41*, 408–422.

FERSTER, C. B. The use of the free operant in the analysis of behavior. *Psychol. Bull.*, 1953, *50*, 263–274.

FERSTER, C. B. Use of the blackout in the investigation of temporal discrimination in fixed-interval reinforcement. *J. exp. Psychol.*, 1954, *47*, 69–74.

FERSTER, C. B., and SKINNER, B. F. *Schedules of reinforcement.* New York: Appleton-Century-Crofts, 1957.

RIESEN, A. H. The development of visual perception in man and chimpanzee. *Science*, 1947, *106*, 107–108.

ROBINSON, J. S. The sameness-difference discrimination problem in chimpanzees. *J. comp. physiol. Psychol.*, 1955, *48*, 195–197.

SKINNER, B. F. *Science and human behavior.* New York: Macmillan, 1953.

SPENCE, K. W. Continuous versus non-continuous interpretations of discrimination learning. *Psychol. Rev.*, 1940, *47*, 271–288.

WELKER, W. Variability of play and exploratory behavior in chimpanzees. *J. comp. physiol. Psychol.*, 1956, *49*, 181–185.

WYCKOFF, L. B., Jr. The role of observing responses in discrimination learning. *Psychol. Rev.*, 1952, *59*, 431–442.

28

The Functional Properties of a Time Out from an Avoidance Schedule

Thom Verhave

I. INTRODUCTION

There are four possible ways for an experimenter to arrange a contingency between the behavior of an organism and reinforcement. When a specific act occurs, he can (1) present a positive reinforcer, (2) present a negative reinforcer, (3) remove a negative reinforcer, or, (4) remove a positive reinforcer (Skinner, 1938, 1953).

The actual *presentation* of certain reinforcers, e.g., food, is an occurrence of only brief duration. Studying the consequences of the *removal* of such reinforcement always involves the removal of stimuli that have been correlated with the reinforcing event. In other words, these studies involve the manipulation of secondary or conditioned reinforcers.

Ferster's (1958) monograph is the most extensive investigation of stimuli associated with the discontinuation of positive reinforcement. Ferster studied the effects of withdrawing a stimulus correlated with positive reinforcement by using a stimulus in whose presence the animals could no longer obtain reinforcement. He called this stimulus the time-out stimulus (TO) (Ferster, 1957), and demonstrated that the removal of such a conditioned positive reinforcer had many properties in common with the effects of conventional aversive events, such as electric shock.

In terms of the fourfold classification of reinforcement contingencies, Ferster's experiments raise the question of whether a stimulus correlated with a time out from shock avoidance (TO_{av}) will be a conditioned, positive reinforcer.

In the first series of experiments to be reported here, a discrimination

Adapted from *Journal of the Experimental Analysis of Behavior,* 1962, *5,* 391–421. With permission of the author and publisher.

procedure was used in which free-operant avoidance behavior was maintained in the presence of one set of stimuli; in the presence of other stimuli, the animals (rats) were never shocked (TO_{av}). These initial experiments failed to produce any evidence that TO_{av} acquired positive reinforcing functions.

In subsequent experiments, the animals had a second lever that they could press and so produce TO_{av} (Verhave, 1959). This procedure yielded positive results and opened the way for a continuing series of experiments with TO_{av}. The purpose of this report is to present initial data concerning several characteristics of behavior controlled by such a stimulus. Sidman (1960, 1962) has independently investigated a similar situation with monkeys, confirming the basic findings of the present research. More recently, Granda and Hammack (1961) have used a similar procedure with sleeping human subjects.

II. ESTABLISHMENT OF A *MULT AVOID TO* PERFORMANCE WITHOUT PREVIOUS CONDITIONING OF THE AVOIDANCE BEHAVIOR

Method

Subjects. The subjects were male rats, 4 to 6 months old at the start of experimentation. They were maintained on free food and water in individual living cages.

Apparatus. The experimental cages were 10½ in. long, 5¼ in. wide, and 8½ in. high. Each cage was enclosed in a lightproof and sound-resistant box (attenuation, 10 db), and several such boxes were placed in a sound-resistant cubicle (attenuation, 10 db). A sound mask of white noise (75 db) was fed continuously into the cubicle. The automatic programming and recording equipment was outside the cubicle. The sides and top of the experimental cages were ⅛-in. Plexiglas; the front and rear walls, ¼-in. aluminum alloy; and the grid flooring, transverse stainless steel rods, ⅛ in. in diameter, spaced 1 in. apart. Stainless steel plates ¹⁄₁₆ in. thick covered the entire inside of the plastic side-walls. The plates were insulated from the aluminum end-walls and the grid flooring. Each wall and floor rod was successively opposed in polarity by a "grid scrambler," consisting of a series of microswitches operated by cams rotating at a high speed. A constant-current stimulator passing half-wave, 60-cycle DC at 350 v and 1.5 ma. provided electric shock. Dinsmoor and Hughes (1956) have described the current-stabilizing circuit. The lever (Verhave, 1958) was center-mounted 2¼ in. above the grid floor in one end-wall of the experimental cage. A small pilot light was also center-mounted in the same end-wall 6 in. above the grid floor. This light was recessed into the aluminum alloy end-wall and covered with a flush-mounted piece of transparent plastic, 1 in. in diameter. Another light was mounted on the outside of the cage behind the end wall opposite to the lever.

Procedure. Sidman (1953) has described the free-operant avoidance procedure. Briefly, a 0.2-sec. shock occurred every 2 sec., unless the animal pressed the lever; in Sidman's terminology, the SS (shock-shock) interval was 2 sec. Every time the animal pressed the lever, it postponed the shock an additional 20 sec.; that is the RS (response-shock) interval was 20 sec. The animal received a shock each time 20 sec. elapsed without a response, and from then on every 2 sec. until it pressed again. Holding the lever down following a press did not prevent the shock.

The avoidance contingencies were in effect during 15-min. intervals alternating with 10-min. periods during which no shock was administered, even if the animal did not press the lever. During the 15-min. avoidance-conditioning periods, only the light above the lever was on. During the 10-min. time-out periods, only the light mounted outside the cage was on. The TO$_{av}$ started immediately after the 15-min. avoidance period had ended; the animal did not have to respond to produce the time-out.

Each session consisted of nine avoidance and nine TO$_{av}$ periods, and started with an avoidance period. At least 1 day intervened between sessions.

Results and Discussion

Figure 1 presents the cumulative records of one animal and illustrates the results obtained with 14 other rats. The data of all the animals in

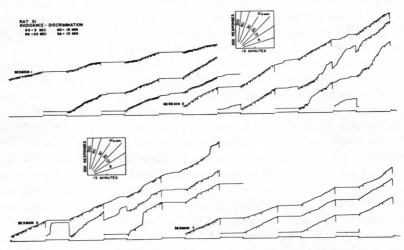

Figure 1. Development of avoidance behavior under external stimulus control without previous establishment of the avoidance behavior.

which the discrimination was established in the present manner show a characteristic course of events. Initially, a very low rate of responding in TO_{av} is correlated with a pattern of responding during the avoidance periods that still results in a high shock frequency. Subsequently, as the avoidance performance improves, as shown by a reduction in the shock frequency, the response rate in TO_{av} increases simultaneously. This response rate then decreases again, while the avoidance responding improves still further.

The initial difference in the rates during the avoidance and the TO_{av} periods can be obtained without the presence of the exteroceptive avoidance and TO_{av} stimuli. The discrimination, if it may be called this, is at first based on the nonoccurrence of shock during TO_{av}. In many animals, the initially frequent shocks during the avoidance periods may generate enough responding to account for the initial difference in the response rates. Observations on animals run under the present conditions, but with the TO_{av} stimulus omitted, bear out this interpretation.

As the shock frequency decreases, the first discrimination breaks down, and a "true" discrimination is formed based on the presence and absence of the exteroceptive cues. The temporary increase in the TO_{av} responding can be interpreted as due to a generalization effect.

RAT 53 Session 16

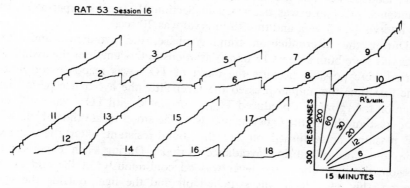

Figure 2. Performance of an atypical animal on a mult avoid TO procedure.

Figure 2 shows the record of Rat 53 after 15 sessions. This animal differed from the other 14 rats in that its rate in TO_{av} still had not dropped to zero after 15 sessions, and it persisted for another 50 sessions. Another feature is that the highest rate of responding in TO_{av} usually occurred just before the onset of the avoidance period. The reasons for this particular aspect of the performance are not yet clarified (Herrnstein and Brady, 1959).

The last two phases in the development of the mult avoid TO performance are not unique to procedures in which one component of the multiple schedule is controlled by aversive contingencies. Skinner has previously described similar data in which an operant was maintained by continuous positive reinforcement during S^D (Skinner, 1938). The present illustrations of "induction" differ from Skinner's only in the magnitude of the effect.

The behavior of Rat 51 (Figure 1) leaves no doubt that proper stimulus control does develop under the present conditions. Session 7 shows that (1) responding in the avoidance stimulus may start promptly without being primed by a shock; and (2) it ceases immediately after the onset of TO_{av}. All 15 animals formed the tone-controlled discrimination within 10 sessions. There was considerable variability among animals with respect to the length of the stages in the development of the final performance.

III. ESTABLISHMENT OF A *MULT AVOID TO* PERFORMANCE WITH PREVIOUS CONDITIONING OF THE AVOIDANCE BEHAVIOR AND RESPONSE-CONTINGENT TO_{av}

Method

The subjects and apparatus were as described previously except that a 4-in. loudspeaker was mounted inside the sound-resistant shell. The basic avoidance procedure was described in Section II. In this experiment, the SS interval was 5 sec., and the RS interval was 20 sec.

During the discrimination training phase, the avoidance and TO_{av} intervals were both at least 15 min. Variations in the length of the avoidance period were possible because the onset of TO_{av} was response-correlated. The first time the animal pressed the lever after the avoidance period had been on for 15 min., it produced TO_{av}. Correlated with TO_{av} was a 433-cps tone, just audible to the experimenter when he stood inside the cubicle with the masking noise turned off but the sound-resistant outer shell closed. The tone was off during avoidance periods. During each experimental session, the light above the lever was on continuously; at the end of the session, this lever light was switched off and the light outside the cage turned on. Between 12 and 15 avoid TO_{av} cycles were programmed during a session. A session always started with an avoidance period. At least 1 day intervened between successive sessions.

Results

Figures 3, 4, 5, and 6 present the data of two animals, Rats 100 and 101. The top frame of Figure 3 shows the performance of Rat 100 during the last regular avoidance-conditioning session (Session 8). During Session 9 (same frame), the tone was introduced at regular 15-min. intervals. The down position of the baseline pen indicates the tone-on periods. During

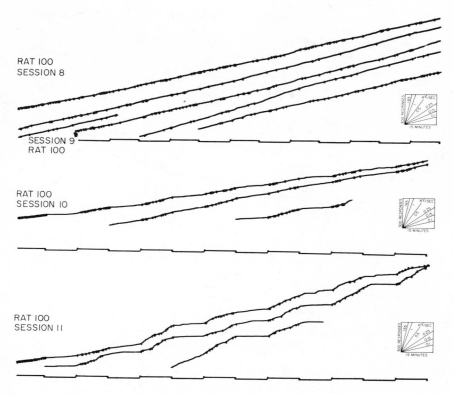

Figure 3. Development of avoidance behavior under external stimulus control with prior establishment of the avoidance behavior.

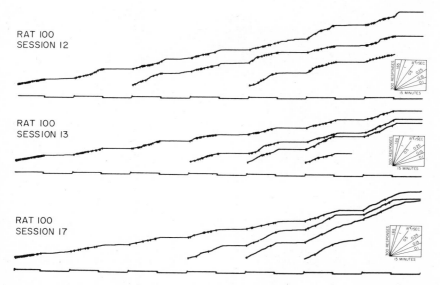

Figure 4. Development of avoidance behavior under external stimulus control with prior establishment of the avoidance behavior.

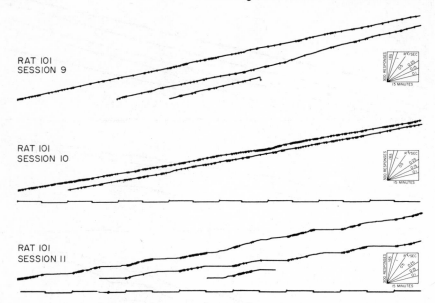

Figure 5. Development of avoidance behavior under external stimulus control with prior establishment of the avoidance behavior.

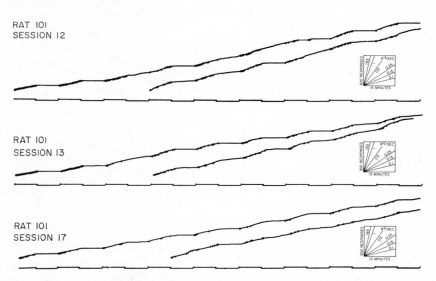

Figure 6. Development of avoidance behavior under external stimulus control with prior establishment of the avoidance behavior.

this entire session, however, the avoidance contingency was still in effect when the tone was on. Starting with Session 10, the avoidance contingency was cancelled during the tone-on periods (TO_{av}). Rat 101 was treated similarly. In this case, Session 9 (Figure 5, top frame) was the last regular avoidance-conditioning session. During Session 10, the tone was introduced without an actual TO_{av} condition being in effect. Session 11 was the first session on the mult avoid TO procedure.

Introduction of the tone-on periods produced a change in performance of only Rat 101 (Figure 5, Session 10). During Session 10, this animal's rate of responding was lower, and the shock rate had increased greatly. The effect was temporary and already disappearing toward the end of Session 10.

Four of the six animals rapidly developed a discriminative performance. As early as its second session on the discrimination procedure, Rat 100 (Figure 3) responded much more rapidly in the avoidance than in the TO periods. Rat 101 showed the smallest difference in its avoidance and TO_{av} rates. As late as Session 17, however, both rats still occasionally "ran through" the TO_{av} periods (Figures 4 and 6).

Discussion

These data are relevant to a point discussed in the previous section: is the discrimination in the early sessions based on tone or shock? Figures 3 and 5 seem to indicate that even for animals pretrained on avoidance, this is so. This is not necessarily the case, however. Both Rats 100 and 101 were still relatively poor avoiders at the time that discrimination training was started. When the avoidance performance is well established (as indicated by a low-shock density, e.g., less than 10 shocks per hr. for SS-3 sec., RS-30 sec.) before discrimination training is started, the problem of a discrimination based on shock during the initial phase of discrimination training does not arise.

The present data are similar to Appel's findings (1960) that if a mult avoid TO procedure is introduced after pretraining the animals on avoidance, the discrimination usually develops during the first few sessions.

Appel also noted that the animals decreased their response rate in the avoidance component of the mult avoid TO procedure during 30 successive 4-hr. sessions (Appel, 1960, p. 46). Rat 51 (Figure 1), like many other animals trained on the mult avoid TO procedure in my laboratory, also decreased its rate of responding during the avoidance periods within seven 3¼-hr. sessions.

This decrease is not unique to the mult avoid TO procedure, but is probably common to free-operant avoidance schedules which generate

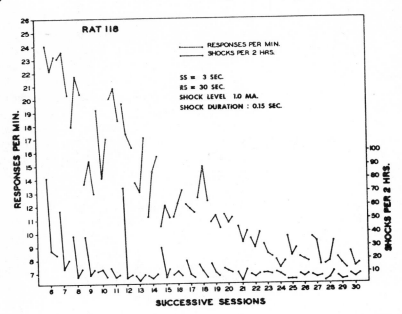

Figure 7. *Progressive decrease in rate of avoidance responding during 30 successive 6-hr. sessions in a free-operant avoidance situation. The three data points per session indicate the average rates obtained during three successive 2-hr. periods.*

temporal discriminations. In Figure 7, for example, Rat 18 shows a progressive decrease in its rate of avoidance responding during a period of 30 sessions (180 hr.). (The data of the first five sessions are omitted from the figure.) No TO was involved in this procedure. The phenomenon represents the gradual development of a temporal discrimination (Sidman, 1954), which may proceed long after the shock rate has become stable.

On the assumption that removal of a stimulus associated with an aversive schedule might be positively reinforcing, one might expect the development of positively accelerated rate changes (scallops) superimposed on the constant rate generated by the avoidance schedule. Procedurally, the responding during the avoidance periods is reinforced by the TO on a fixed-interval schedule. However, no scallops appeared during Session 17 for either Rat 100 or Rat 101; and none was observed after an additional 180 hr. of experimental time under the same conditions, even though there was an explicit FI contingency. Figure 1 shows a similar absence of positively accelerated rate changes during avoidance periods.

The first attempt to obtain the effect was to increase the duration of the TO_{av} period. Then TO durations of 30 and 60 min. were tried unsuccessfully for 12 sessions each. The experimenter was not reinforced, and the data will not be presented.

IV. A PRELIMINARY DEMONSTRATION OF THE POSITIVE REINFORCING FUNCTION OF TO$_{av}$

The above-described failures to observe any evidence of a positively reinforcing effect of the TO$_{av}$ prompted a more direct investigation of its possible reinforcing properties (Verhave, 1959a, 1959b). Instead of having the animal both postpone shock and produce the TO$_{av}$ with the same response, a second lever was made accessible to the animal for obtaining the TO$_{av}$. The question to be answered was whether the animal's behavior could be generated and maintained when its only reinforcement was a time-out period from an avoidance schedule. (See also Sidman, 1960, 1962.)

Method

Subjects. The subjects were four male rats, 6 months old at the start of experimentation. They were maintained on free food and water in individual living cages.

Apparatus. The apparatus consisted of an experimental cage, 10½ in. long, 10 in. wide, 8½ in. high. Two levers (Verhave, 1958) were mounted 2¼ in. above the grid floor in one end-wall of the cage. A distance of 6 in. separated the centers of the 1½-in.-long T bars of the levers. A pilot light was mounted 3 in. above each lever. An aluminum plate could be inserted between the two levers across the entire length of the cage. This divided the cage into two 5-in.-wide compartments, each with its own lever. All other features of the apparatus were identical to those described in Section II.

Procedure. The animals were given preliminary training on the avoidance procedure as described previously. Throughout the entire experiment, the SS interval was 3 sec., and the RS interval was 30 sec. The shock level was 1.5 ma. and the shock duration 0.15 sec. During this initial training, the aluminum insert was in place, and only one lever was available to the rat. Once avoidance responding was well established, a 433-cps tone came on at irregular intervals during only one session. The avoidance schedule stayed in effect throughout this session. During the next session the second lever was made available to the animal. This lever will be referred to as the TO lever and the other as the Av lever. By pressing the TO lever, the animal could produce a 10-min. TO from the avoidance schedule. The 433-cps tone was correlated with the TO$_{av}$ periods.

During the initial avoidance-training phase, only the light above the Av lever was on during an experimental session. Once the TO lever was added, the lights above both levers were turned on during a session. Termination of each session was signaled by switching off the lever light(s) and turn-

ing on a light mounted on the outside of the cage behind the end wall opposite to the lever. An experimental session lasted from 6 to 10 hr. Each
animal was used every other day, excluding weekends.

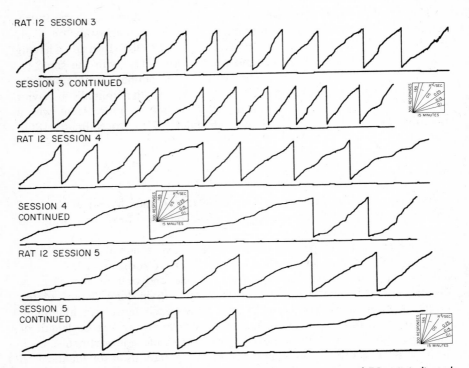

*Figure 8.   The early development of TO$_{av}$ behavior. The presence of TO$_{av}$ is indicated
by a depression of the base line. During Session 4, the shocks seem to come after the
start of the TO, because the pens were slightly out of line.*

Results

Because the general features of the data are similar for all four rats,
only the performance of Rat 12 will be presented. The two top panels of
Figure 8 show the avoidance performance of Rat 12 during the third session on the initial avoidance-training phase. During this session, the tone
came on at irregular intervals, with the avoidance schedule in effect at all
times. No consistent effect of the tone is observable. The next two panels
(Session 4) show the animal's responses on the avoidance lever during
the first session in which the TO$_{av}$ lever was also available. By pressing
the TO lever almost immediately after the start of the experiment, the
animal produced the first TO$_{av}$ at the beginning of the session. The depression of the base line indicates TO$_{av}$ periods, and the oblique marks on

the cumulative record itself represent shocks. The 4th and 5th time-out periods produced by the animal followed each other very closely and showed the beginning of extinction of the avoidance responding during TO. During much of the remainder of Session 4, avoidance responding during TO progressively decreased, while the frequency of TO periods increased.

The cumulative record of responding on the avoidance lever during the next session (Session 5) appears in the lower two panels of Figure 8. The avoidance behavior recovered in rate during the first half of this session, but by the end of Session 5 the animal was pressing the avoidance lever even less frequently than at the end of Session 4, and the TO_{av} frequency had almost reached its maximum possible value.

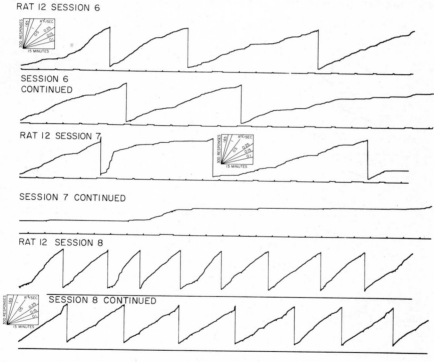

Figure 9. Continued development (Sessions 6 and 7) and extinction (Session 8) of TO_{av} behavior. The presence of TO_{av} is indicated by a depression of the base line.

Sessions 6 and 7 (four top panels of Figure 9) demonstrate the continued decline in the rat's avoidance responding. During the last half of Session 7, the animal spent almost all of the experimental time in TO_{av}.

As an initial check on the reality of the TO_{av} period as the reinforcing event that maintained responding on the TO lever, an extinction session on only the TO lever was programmed during Session 8. In the first 8 min. of this session, the animal took a few shocks, after which the avoidance rate abruptly changed to a higher value (two bottom panels of Figure 9). During these first 8 min., the animal pressed the TO lever approximately 100 times;[1] but simultaneously with the abrupt change in its rate of avoidance behavior, it stopped pressing the TO lever. For the remainder of the session, the animal only occasionally emitted a few bursts of responding on the TO lever. These bursts were usually correlated with the occurrence of shock and a temporary drop in the rate of responding on the avoidance lever.

During the next three sessions (9, 10, and 11), Rat 12's behavior on the TO lever was reconditioned (Figure 10). The cumulative records of responding on the avoidance lever show the declining response rate and

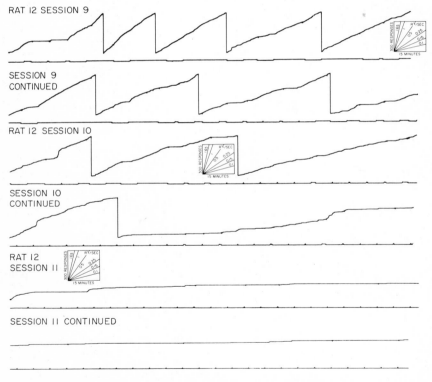

Figure 10. *Reconditioning and continued development of* TO_{av} *behavior. The presence of* TO_{av} *is indicated by a depression of the base line.*

[1] Cumulative recorder data of the TO lever responding of this animal are not available.

increasing TO frequency described earlier. The first TO period of Session 11 was the last one during which any initial spontaneous recovery of the avoidance behavior was clearly observable. The animal's performance from Session 12 through Session 25 was identical to the one shown in the last half of Session 11.

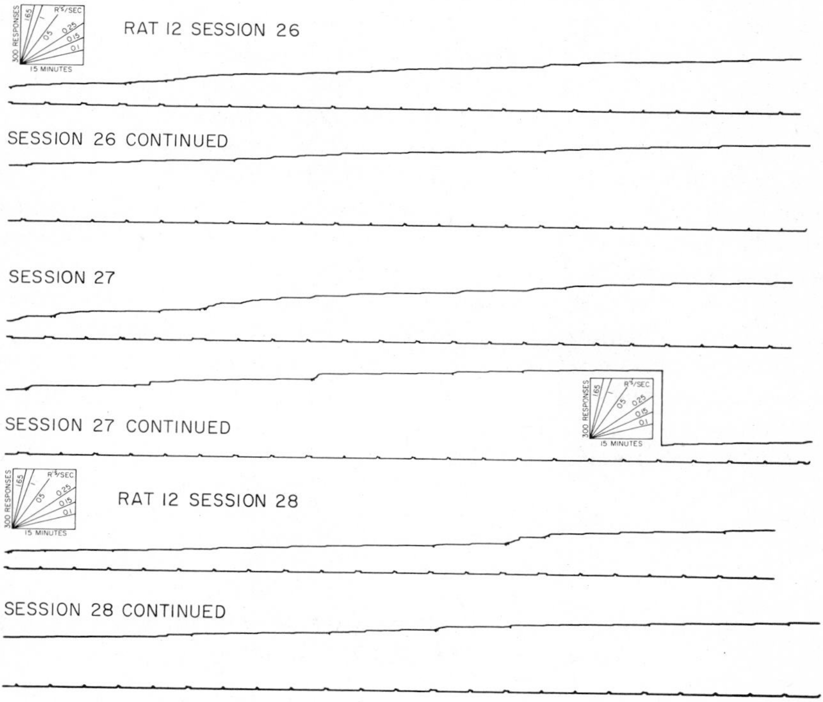

Figure 11. Maintenance of TO_{av} behavior on FR schedules. Session 26: FR 5; Session 27: FR 10; Session 28: FR 15. The presence of TO_{av} is indicated by a depression of the base line.

During Sessions 26, 27, and 28, the behavior on the TO lever was maintained on fixed-ratio schedules (Figure 11). During the first part of Session 26, the FR schedule on the TO lever was increased one step at a time with each successive time out. The animal was required to press the TO lever only once to obtain the first TO_{av}, twice to get the second and so on. Once it reached FR 5, the TO_{av} behavior was maintained at this value for the remainder of the session. During Session 27, FR 10 was programmed on the TO lever except for the first TO_{av}, which the rat obtained by pressing the TO lever five times. During Session 28, the first TO_{av} was obtained on FR 10; but for the remainder of the session, FR 15 was programmed. The high frequency of TO periods during these sessions (Figure 11) shows clearly that small, fixed-ratio schedules can maintain the behavior on the TO lever. Just how large a fixed-ratio schedule can be programmed before the animal stops responding and returns to the avoidance lever is a question that will be discussed elsewhere. A more detailed account of the characteristics of the FR behavior on the TO lever will be given in a later section of this paper.

The data on the other rats were similar to those of Rat 12. The main difference among animals appeared when FR schedules were being programmed on the TO levers. At FR values above 10, two of the other three rats (Rats 9 and 10) stopped responding and returned to the avoidance lever. Their behavior on the TO lever could be re-established by lowering the FR requirement. Usually, the animal first had to be put back on CRF.

Although Rats 10 and 11 developed the behavior on the TO lever at much the same rate as Rat 12, Rat 9 ran for many sessions without pressing the TO lever. The animal began to show TO-producing behavior like the other rats only after it was given a special discrimination-training period during which the TO_{av} periods occurred at irregular intervals.

All four animals rarely pressed the TO lever during TO periods. Three of them did so fewer than 20 times per session during Sessions 9 through 29, and one (Rat 10) did not respond even once during this time. Since the animals obtained most of the time outs on CRF, with only one response approximately every 10 min, cumulative records of responses on the TO lever are not presented. Confirmatory data will be shown later in this report.

V. THE DESCRIPTIVE PROPERTIES OF BEHAVIOR REINFORCED BY TO_{av} WHEN PROGRAMMED ON A FIXED-RATION SCHEDULE

Figure 12 shows sample cumulative records of responses on both levers during Session 40, when FR 35 was programmed on the TO lever. The TO_{av} periods are indicated by the numbered depressions in the cumulative curves. Shocks are recorded as oblique marks on the base line and are also numbered.

These sample records bring out the following features: (1) Discriminations on the Av lever and TO lever are very good. The animal responds almost continuously on both levers only during TO Period 2. (2) Although the animal has two levers to press, one to postpone shock and one to produce the TO, the performance is so well integrated that even on FR 35, the animal can obtain TO_{av} without getting a single shock. (See the avoidance period between TO_{av} Numbers 5 and 6.)

Figure 13 shows the same performance on the TO lever as Figure 14, but in more detail. This record was obtained with a third recorder whose motor stopped during TO_{av}. The TO's are indicated by the oblique marks

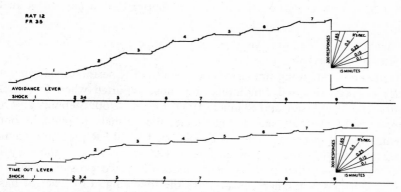

Figure 12. Performance on avoidance and TO_{av} levers. The TO_{av} is scheduled on FR 35. The TO_{av} periods are indicated by depressions in the cumulative records and numbered consecutively.

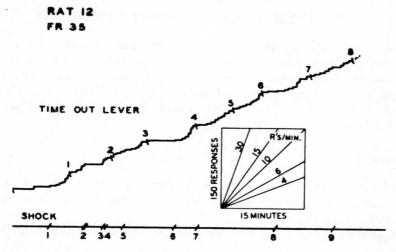

Figure 13. Enlarged record of TO_{av} behavior of Figure 14. The TO_{av} periods are left out.

and numbered as in Figure 12. This record reveals the following features of the FR performance (*cf.* Sidman, 1962):

1. The animal responds in rapid bursts which are separated by distinct pauses.

2. The number of responses in the bursts tends to increase toward the end of the avoidance period.

3. Almost each avoidance period starts with a long pause before the animal presses the TO lever.

4. Pauses between bursts tend to become shorter toward the end of an FR run.

Phenomena 2 and 4 give a scalloped appearance to the cumulative records of responding on the TO lever.

There are outstanding similarities between the FR performance generated under our experimental conditions and those reported when food is the reinforcement (Ferster and Skinner, 1957; Owen, 1960; Stebbins and Sidman, 1954). The rate has a dual value; the animals respond in bursts alternating with pauses. A long pause like the typical FR postreinforcement pause occurs after the end of each TO. However, there is the very important difference that pauses occur frequently. Two possible causes for this, which may act synergistically, are the following: (1) The rat has to stop responding on the TO lever at least every 30 sec. in order to press the avoidance lever if it is to prevent occurrence of the shock. (2) If the TO_{av} period is a relatively weak reinforcer, such a performance is not unusual, even with food reinforcement (e.g., Owen, 1960).

VI. TO_{av} PROGRAMMED ON A "HEFFERLINE" SCHEDULE

Since TO_{av} was an effective, although apparently weak, positive reinforcer, the performance characteristics of the TO_{av} behavior were examined by using various other schedules of reinforcement. The first schedule to be used was a modification of the Hefferline schedule, in which reinforcement is secured by holding the lever down (Hefferline, 1950).

Method

Subjects. The subjects were two male rats, 6 months old at the start of experimentation. They were maintained on free food and water in individual living cages.

Apparatus. The apparatus was identical with that described for Section 4.

Procedure. The animals had preliminary training on the free-operant avoidance procedure. Throughout the entire experiment, the SS interval was 3 sec. and the RS interval was 30 sec. The shock level was maintained at 1.0 ma. and the shock duration at 0.3 sec. During the initial avoidance-training period, two levers were always available to the rats; and both levers were equally effective in postponing shock. During the next phase, the animals were trained to produce a 10-min. TO_{av}. A 433-cps tone was used as the TO_{av} cue.

During the Hefferline schedule phase, the animal produced the TO_{av} condition (tone) only when it held the TO lever down. As soon as it released the lever, the tone went off and the free-operant avoidance schedule (the 30-sec. RS timer) took effect. Other experimental conditions were similar to those described in Section V.

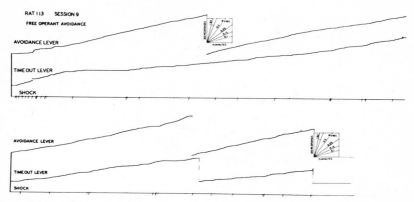

Figure 14. *Performance of a rat in a free-operant avoidance situation with two levers. Each lever is equally effective in resetting the RS timer. The levers are already labelled with respect to their future functions. During the first 12 min. of the session, the reinforcement marker was depressed because of circuit trouble, which also partially accounts for the high initial shock frequency.*

Results

Figure 14 depicts the avoidance responses on the two levers during the last session of the initial avoidance-training phase. The records show some of the "spontaneous" switching from one lever to the other which has been described in detail elsewhere (Verhave, 1961d). The TO_{av} contingency on the TO lever went into effect at the start of Session 10. Figure 15 shows the finished development of the discriminations concerning the

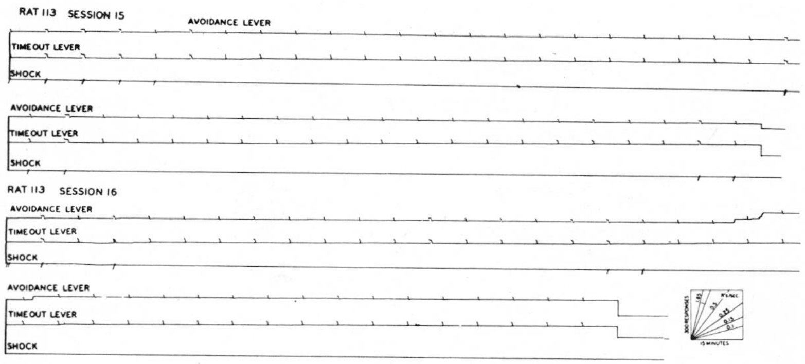

Figure 15. *Final stage of development of TO_{av} behavior.*

functions of the tone, the avoidance lever, and the time-out lever. These data confirm information reported in Section IV.

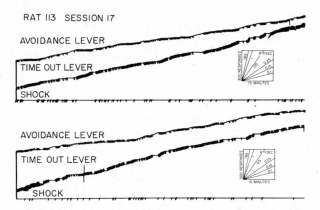

Figure 16.   *Development of holding behavior when TO_{av} is put on a Hefferline schedule. Depressions of the TO lever are indicated by downward deflections of the reinforcement markers of both cumulative recorders.*

The Hefferline schedule was initiated at the start of Session 17 (Figure 16). The first long "holds" appear during the second half of the session. (See arrows.) Whenever the time-out lever was held in the downward position, the reinforcement-marker pen of both cumulative recorders was also held in the down position. The first arrow on the left side of the bottom panel of Figure 16 indicates the occurrence of the first hold of any sig-

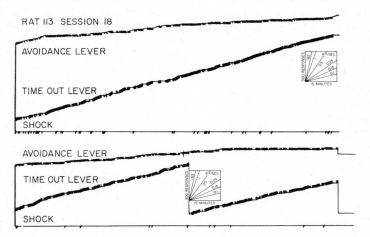

Figure 17.   *Continued development of holding behavior when TO_{av} is put on a Hefferline schedule.*

nificant duration. Notice that when the reinforcement-marker pen of the time-out lever recorder is in the up position for any significant length of time, the animal usually shows a sufficiently high rate of responding on the avoidance lever to keep the shock away. Figures 16, 17, 18, and 19 give a record of the development of the performance on the schedule.

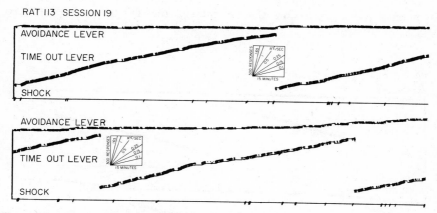

Figure 18.   Continued development of holding behavior when TO_{av} is put on a Hefferline schedule.

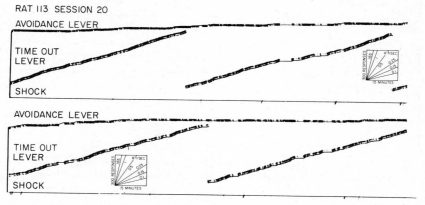

Figure 19.   Continued development of holding behavior when TO_{av} is put on a Hefferline schedule.

The following features can be noted: (1) a gradual decrease in the avoidance rate, and (2) a gradual increase in the frequency and duration of "holds." [2] At no time within the period of seven sessions (42 hr.),

[2] There were nine clearly visible "holds" of any significant duration during Session 17.

however, did the animal depress the lever for more than a few minutes. The greater part of a session was characterized by frequent lever release-press sequences. (3) An immediate increase in the rate of responding on the time-out lever. This effect can be explained by the fact that from the start of Session 17, each down-press produced the onset of the tone as a conditioned reinforcer.

Furthermore, the TO lever now served the same function as the avoidance lever. Each time the rat pressed the TO lever, it postponed shock for 30 sec.

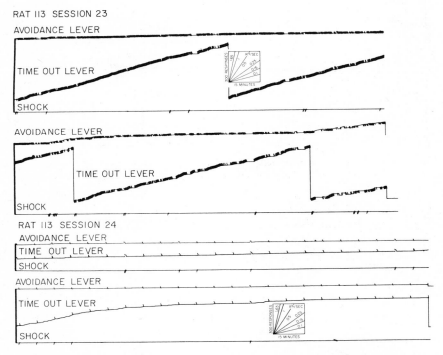

Figure 20. Continued development of holding behavior when TO_{av} *is put on a Hefferline schedule and there is a return to normal CRF* TO_{av} *conditions.*

The data for the second animal were practically identical. This rat was maintained on the Hefferline schedule for 24 sessions (144 hr.) without showing holds of any greater length than those by Rat 113 during Session 23 (Figure 20). Holds of 10 min. and longer, as reported by Hefferline, were never obtained.

One reason for this difference might be that the conditioned aversive stimulus in the present experiment may be less effective than Hefferline's bright light. Unlike Hefferline's animals, the subjects here could release the lever for as long as 30 sec. without producing the aversive stimulus.

There is one other feature of the course of the performance during a single session that is worth noting. Harrison and Abelson (1959) reported that the rate of escape responding (bar presses) tended to remain fairly constant throughout a session, whereas the rate of bar releases showed a progressive decrease during the first 15 to 20 min. of a session. Similar phenomena appear in the TO lever record obtained during Session 23, except that the warm-up takes considerably longer than 20 min. The frequency of holds does not increase noticeably until after the first 90 min.

In Session 24 (Figure 20), Rat 113 could again produce a 10-min. TO by pressing the TO lever. The animal almost immediately regained its performance of Session 16, although it pressed the TO_{av} lever considerably more often than was necessary during the latter half of the session.

VII. TO_{av} PROGRAMMED ON A FIXED-INTERVAL SCHEDULE

Because the properties of the FI performance are well known, it is of interest to compare results obtained with TO_{av} with the data obtained by means of other reinforcers. The results might also clarify the initial failure to show the reinforcing effect of TO_{av} with the single-lever mult avoid TO procedure.

Method

One subject, Rat 113, had been returned to a TO_{av} procedure (Session 24, Figure 20) with continuous reinforcement (CRF) for pressing the TO lever. The conditions were then maintained unchanged for three sessions (25, 26, 27). During the next phase of this experiment, the TO_{av} was programmed on an FI schedule, which was gradually lengthened during several successive sessions. In Sessions 28 and 29, the animal could produce the 10-min. TO whenever the avoidance procedure had been in effect for a fixed interval of 20 sec.; in Session 30, the FI was 30 sec.; from Session 31 through 34, the FI was 2 min.; thereafter, FI 5, 10, and 15 min. were programmed in succession with each value maintained for six sessions. The schedule was then returned to CRF for another six sessions (53 through 58).

A second animal was trained on the free-operant avoidance procedure as described in Section VI. The TO_{av} was then programmed on an FI schedule, and the rat moved through the series of FI schedules in the same manner as Rat 113.

Results

Figure 21 shows the cumulative records obtained during the last session that Rat 113 spent on FI 5 (Session 40), FI 10 (Session 46), FI 15 (Ses-

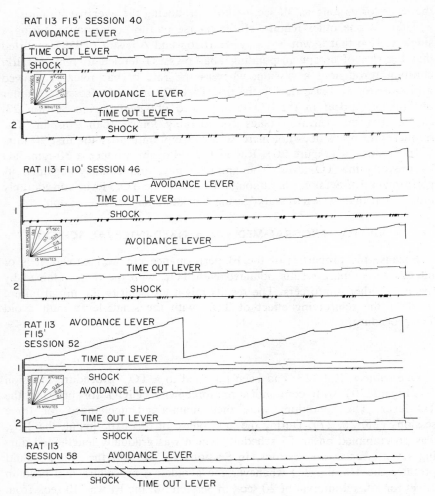

Figure 21. *Performance when various FI schedules are scheduled with respect to* TO_{av}.

sion 52), and CRF (Session 58). Each of these FI schedules clearly maintained the TO-producing behavior. Even with FI 15, the animal only occasionally spent unnecessary time on avoidance. But there was no evidence of the positively accelerated responding commonly associated with FI schedules of food reinforcement. The animal pressed the TO lever at an extremely low rate.

Again, the weakness of TO_{av} as a reinforcer, as well as the fact that the TO-producing behavior had to be emitted concurrently with the regular avoidance behavior, may account for the absence of a typical FI response pattern. Because of these findings, it is not surprising that no scallops were superimposed on the avoidance rates in the single-lever mult TO_{av} experiments of Sections II and III.

The second animal's data were identical with those of Rat 113, and will not be presented here.

VIII. SOME EXPERIMENTS CONCERNING THE SIGNALLING FUNCTION OF THE TO_{av} STIMULUS

A question arises about the function of the stimulus (tone) correlated with the TO from the avoidance periods. Without the tone as a "start and stop" signal, animals might not have been able to develop the complex performances that have been described. The next experiments were designed to study the discriminative function of the tone in contrast to its reinforcing function.

Method

Subjects. The subjects were eight male rats, 6 months old at the start of experimentation. They were maintained on free food and water in individual living cages.

Apparatus. The apparatus consisted of three experimental cages similar to the one described for the preceding series of experiments. All other features of the apparatus were identical to those described for the experiments of Section IV.

Procedure 1. Four animals (Rats 1, 2, 3, and 4) had preliminary training on the free-operant avoidance procedure (Sidman, 1953). Throughout the experiment, the SS interval was 3 sec. and the RS interval was 30 sec. The shock level was maintained at 1.5 ma., with a duration of 0.15 sec. From the very first session on, two levers were available to the subject in the experimental cage. Throughout the avoidance-pretraining phase, each lever was equally effective in postponing shock. The animal started a new 30-sec. RS interval each time it pressed either lever. The four animals received different periods of pretraining on the avoidance schedule, ranging from 9 to 12 sessions.

During the next phase of the experiment, the rat could produce TO_{av} by pressing the TO lever once (CRF). This procedure is analogous to the situations described in Sections V, VII, and VIII. The only difference is that in the present experiment, no tone was correlated with TO_{av}.

During a third phase, the tone was introduced as an exteroceptive stimulus correlated with TO_{av}. It was subsequently taken out and replaced several times more.

Procedure 2. Four animals (Rats 51, 52, 53, and 55)[3] had different periods of preliminary training on the free-operant avoidance schedule.

---

[3] These animals are not the same rats as those of Section II.

As with Rats 1, 2, 3, and 4, two levers were available from the start. Both levers were functional.

Subsequent to the avoidance-pretraining phase, all four animals were trained to produce TO_{av} by pressing one of the two levers. A 433-cps tone was the TO_{av} signal.

After the TO_{av}-producing behavior was well established and responding on the two levers during the TO_{av} periods had been extinguished, the tone signal was taken out for the first time. It was subsequently reintroduced and removed several times more for each of the animals.

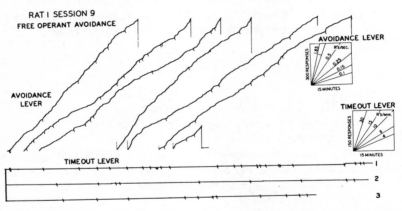

Figure 22. Performance of a rat in a free-operant avoidance situation with two levers. The levers are already labelled with respect to their future functions.

Results with Procedure 1

Figure 22 illustrates the performance of Rat 1 during Session 9, the last session of the free-operant avoidance procedure before introduction of the TO_{av} periods without a cue. The animal rarely pressed the TO lever. Figures 23, 24, and 25 present the progressive changes in performance on both levers during Sessions 10, 11, and 12, when the animal could produce unsignalled 5-min. TO periods. The animal obtained its first three TO periods near the end of Session 10. (See arrows.) A brief but complete change in prepotency from the avoidance lever to the TO lever occurred during the second TO period. A more lasting shift in prepotency from the avoidance lever to the TO lever occurred at the start of Session 11, with a second reversal at Arrows A and B (Figure 24). During Session 12, responding on the avoidance lever remained prepotent, with one exception. (See arrows, Figure 25.) During Sessions 13, 14, and 15, the performance of Session 12 was maintained, with no increase in the number of TO periods.

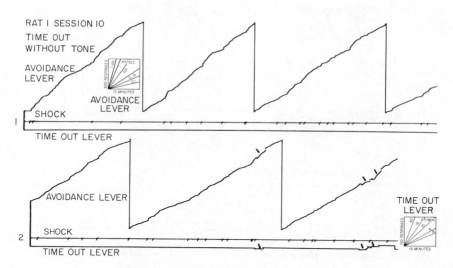

Figure 23.   Progressive changes in performance after introduction of TO_{av} without an external cue.

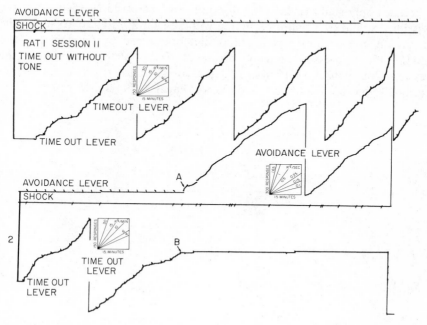

Figure 24.   Progressive changes in performance after introduction of TO_{av} without an external cue.

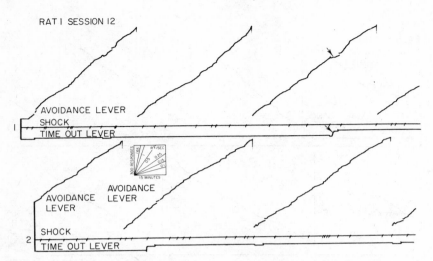

Figure 25. *Progressive changes in performance after introduction of TO_{av} without an external cue.*

From Session 16 on, the tone was introduced. During Sessions 16, 17, and 18, the TO_{av} duration was 5 min. Because the number of TO_{av}'s increased only slightly, the TO_{av} duration was increased to 15 min. during Session 18, and to 30 min. beginning with Session 20. Figure 26 shows the degree to which the discriminations had progressed by Session 25. The animal seldom pressed the avoidance lever. Except at the beginning of the session, "outbreaks" of prolonged bursts of responding still occurred occasionally on the TO lever. (See arrows, Panel 3, Figure 26.)

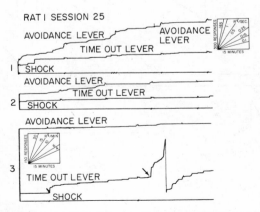

Figure 26. *Development of cued TO_{av} performance after a period during which TO_{av} was available without being correlated with an external cue.*

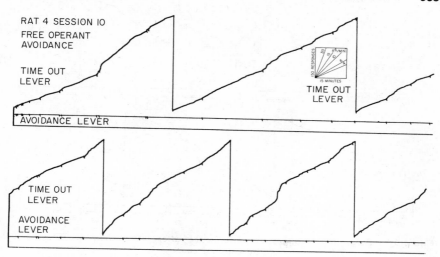

Figure 27. Performance of a rat in a free-operant avoidance situation with two levers. The levers are already labelled with respect to their future functions.

The data of Rat 4 tell a different story. Like Rat 1, this animal confined most of its responses to one lever; but this time, it was the TO lever. Figure 27 shows the output on both levers during the last session of the free-operant-avoidance procedure before the animal could produce the unsignalled TO_{av}. During the next eight sessions, Rat 4 continued to press the TO lever almost exclusively.

Because of Rat 4's pattern of behavior, the schedule in effect was similar to the percentage-shock schedule described by Boren and Sidman (1957); when the animal failed to respond within 30 sec. of a previous response, the pause was only occasionally followed by shock. Shocks could occur only when the animal was not in TO_{av}.

Because the animal was rarely shocked after it paused longer than 30 sec., its response rate on the TO lever eventually declined. Figures 28 and 29 show the performance during the first and last sessions on the unsignalled TO_{av} procedure. There is evidence that at the same time, the animal formed a discrimination with respect to "getting a shock and making one or several presses on the lever." This can be seen during Session 17 (Figure 29). On several occasions (Arrows A, B, C, and D), the rat was shocked, emitted a burst of responses on the TO lever, and then paused for several minutes. Occasionally, the animal pressed the avoidance lever in a similar pattern. (See Figure 29, Arrows E and F.)

The tone was introduced at the start of Session 18. By Session 30 (Figure 30), the performance came close to the pattern typical of the final stage under regular TO_{av} conditions.

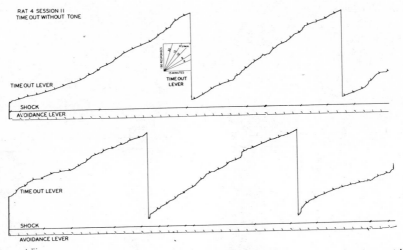

Figure 28. Progressive changes in performance after introduction of TO_{av} without an external cue.

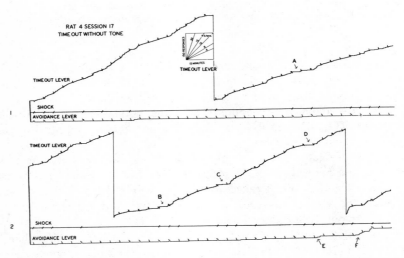

Figure 29. Progressive changes in performance after introduction of TO_{av} without an external cue.

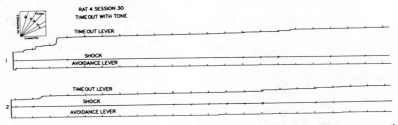

Figure 30. Cued TO_{av} performance after a period during which TO_{av} was available without being correlated with an external cue.

Results with Procedure 2

Figures 31 to 34 show the effects of removing the tone on the performance of animals pretrained on the TO_{av} schedule with the tone as a cue.

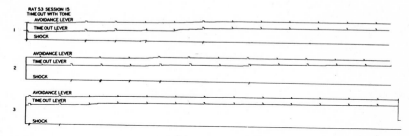

Figure 31. Final stage of TO_{av} behavior before removal of external cue correlated with TO_{av}.

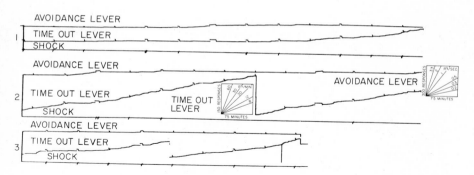

Figure 32. Effect of removing external cue correlated with TO_{av}.

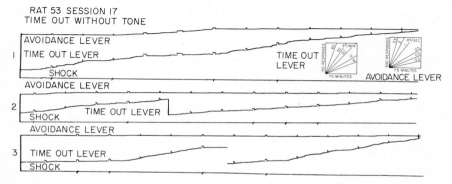

Figure 33. Continued effect of removing external cue correlated with TO_{av}.

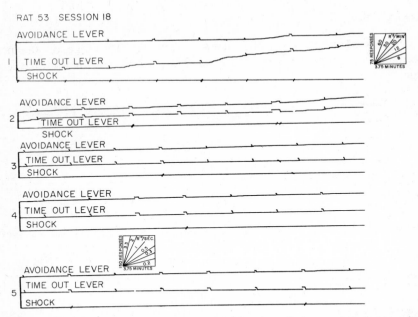

Figure 34. *Return to normal cued TO$_{av}$ performance after a period during which the external cue correlated with TO$_{av}$ had been removed.*

Session 15 (Figure 31) was Rat 53's last regular session on the two-lever time-out avoidance procedure before the removal of the tone as the discriminative TO$_{av}$ cue. The next two figures, 32 and 33, show the results of removing the tone during Sessions 16 and 17. The outstanding effect was a gradual, but eventually quite large, increase in the response output on the TO lever. Figure 34 (Session 18) shows the rapid return to the previous performance after the tone was re-introduced as a cue. The experiment was repeated several times with the same results. Identical results were also obtained with the three other animals used in this series, and will not be presented.

These experiments clearly show that the tone has an important signalling function, controlling the amount of responding during TO$_{av}$. The results of removing the tone, however, depend on the animal's training history. The reasons for the various aspects of performance of animals on Procedure 1 have already been outlined and need not be repeated. The increase in rate after removal of the cue in animals of Procedure 2 may be partially explained by an increase in shock frequency. With sufficient experience, the rats on Procedure 2 might eventually behave like the rats on Procedure 1 without tone.

IX. SOME OBSERVATIONS ON THE EXTINCTION
OF THE TO$_{av}$ BEHAVIOR

The TO$_{av}$ behavior can be extinguished in two ways. First, TO$_{av}$ can be withheld as the reinforcement for pressing the TO lever. This leads to extinction of only the TO-producing response. Second, extinction can be produced by eliminating the shock that the animal would otherwise receive for not pressing the avoidance lever. Removal of the shock should result in extinction of both responses.

If an animal successfully and consistently produced TO$_{av}$ and consequently received a shock only rarely, extinction of its behavior by eliminating the shock may take a long time. The behavior of the poor avoider, that is, of the animal that received many shocks, therefore extinguishes more rapidly.

Both extinction techniques were tried out on almost every animal used in the TO$_{av}$ experiments. Representative data on an animal whose shock frequency was intermediate between "very good" and "very poor" will suffice.

Method

Subject. The subject was a male hooded rat (Rat 31), 60 days old at the start of experimentation. It was maintained on free food and water in its own living cage.

Apparatus. The apparatus was identical with that described for Section V.

Procedure. The animal was first trained on the free-operant avoidance procedure for 24 sessions. The SS interval was maintained at 3 sec., the RS at 30 sec., the shock level at 1.5 ma., and the shock duration at 0.15 sec. During this phase, only one lever was available to the animal. In Session 24, the TO lever was introduced; by pressing it, the rat produced a 10-min. TO$_{av}$ (correlated with a 433-cps tone as cue) on CRF.

Results

The TO$_{av}$ behavior was first extinguished during Session 34 by not presenting TO$_{av}$ when the animal pressed the TO lever. Figure 35 presents the cumulative records. Extinction began at Arrow 1. The nature of the pre-extinction performance can be judged by the portion of the records before this arrow.

The immediate effect of withholding TO$_{av}$ was a burst of activity on the TO lever during which the animal received several shocks (SS was 2 sec.).

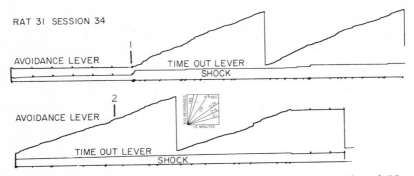

RAT 31 SESSION 34

AVOIDANCE LEVER   TIME OUT LEVER
                              SHOCK

2

AVOIDANCE LEVER

TIME OUT LEVER
                    SHOCK

Figure 35.   Extinction of TO_{av} behavior by removal of the availability of TO_{av}.

After this initial burst, the rat switched back at once to the avoidance
lever, only occasionally pressing the TO lever, usually in small bursts. The
TO_{av} was again made available at Arrow 2, but the animal did not obtain
the first TO_{av} until the end of the record. The performance on both levers
then returned to its pre-extinction pattern. This phenomenon clearly demonstrated the functional independence of the responses on the two levers.

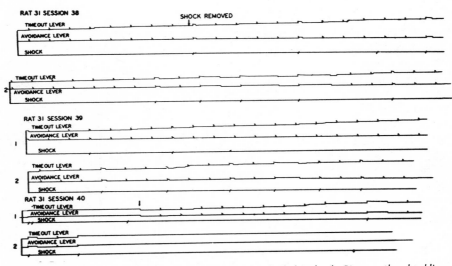

RAT 31 SESSION 38
TIME OUT LEVER   SHOCK REMOVED
AVOIDANCE LEVER
SHOCK

TIME OUT LEVER
2 AVOIDANCE LEVER
   SHOCK

RAT 31 SESSION 39
   TIME OUT LEVER
   AVOIDANCE LEVER
1
   SHOCK

   TIME OUT LEVER
2 AVOIDANCE LEVER
   SHOCK

RAT 31 SESSION 40
   TIME OUT LEVER
1 AVOIDANCE LEVER
   SHOCK

   TIME OUT LEVER
2 AVOIDANCE LEVER
   SHOCK

Figure 36.   Extinction of TO_{av} behavior by removal of the shock. Pips on the shockline
indicate where the animal would have been shocked if the avoidance contingencies
had still been in effect.

Figure 36 demonstrates extinction by removal of the shock (indicated
by the labeled arrow). The first extended periods in which the animal did
not press either lever appeared near the end of Session 38. In the last

half of Session 39, the periods of no responding had lengthened considerably. By the beginning of Session 40, the avoidance behavior had extinguished, and spontaneous recovery did not occur. The TO-producing behavior also appeared to be extinguished at first, but the animal then (at the arrow) produced a long series of TO periods before it eventually ceased pressing the TO lever.

A fairly advanced stage of extinction was reached during Session 41 (Figure 37). The behavior was then reconditioned by re-institution of the shock. (See labeled arrow.)

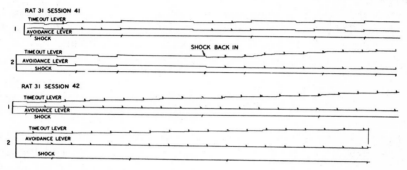

Figure 37.   *Advanced stage of extinction of both Av and* TO_{av} *behavior after removal of the shock and reconditioning of the behaviors on both the* TO_{av} *and Av levers.*

X. REVERSAL OF THE FUNCTION OF THE LEVERS

If an animal presses the avoidance lever, and almost instantly thereafter presses the TO lever, a superstitious chain may develop. In an experimental situation similar to the one used here, Sidman (1962) has demonstrated superstitious chaining of the two responses in monkeys. Sidman's monkeys apparently were more susceptible to such spurious contingencies than the rats of my experiments, and he found it necessary to introduce additional contingencies to prevent the occurrence of superstitious chains. In the many rats I have used, I have not discovered a single instance of such superstitions. However there is always the possibility that they occur unnoticed. The preceding section illustrated one method (extinction) of showing the functional independence of the two concurrent operants. Another method is to reverse the functions of the two levers. If the animal switches its output to the preferred time-out lever whenever a reversal of function occurs, independence of the behavior on the two levers is again demonstrated. This experiment is not so definitive a test of independence as is extinction, since the superstitions may reverse, too.

Method

Subjects. The subjects were two male rats, 6 months old at the start of training. They were maintained on free food and water in individual living cages.

Apparatus. The apparatus was identical with that described for Sections VII and VIII.

Procedure. The preliminary training was identical with that described for the animals of Section VII. The values of the temporal and shock parameters were also the same as in Section VII.

After the TO$_{av}$ producing behavior had been established and the behavior in TO$_{av}$ was almost entirely extinguished, the functions of the levers were switched. After several sessions, the initial functions of the levers were re-established. The same procedure was repeated several more times.

Results

Figure 38 shows the data obtained when the functions of the levers were switched for the third time. Session 31 shows the usual performance

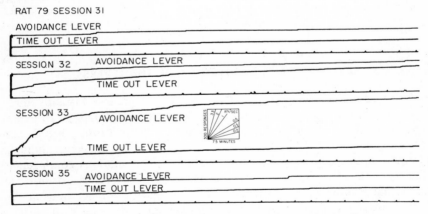

Figure 38. Switching of the functions of the Av and TO$_{av}$ levers.

under normal conditions. The functions of the levers were reversed during Session 32 and re-established during Session 33. Session 35 illustrates the complete return to the initial performance of Session 31. Because the changes were significant only during the first part of the sessions, only the records obtained during this period are reproduced.

The major effect of the reversal of the function of the levers was to increase the rate of responses on the TO lever (previously the avoidance lever). Immediately after the reversal during Session 33, the response output on the regular avoidance lever was increased. Both increases were temporary. The animal quickly adapted to the new arrangements. Similar findings were obtained with the other rat used for this experiment.

XI. THE DEVELOPMENT OF STIMULUS CONTROL OVER THE TO$_{av}$ PRODUCING BEHAVIOR

As part of a projected series of experiments (Verhave, 1959a, b; 1961, a, b, c), it was considered useful to bring the responses on the TO lever under the explicit control of a discriminative stimulus. In this manner, avoidance behavior could be evoked without the simultaneous occurrence of the TO$_{av}$ response. In addition, the animal could be forced to spend a definite minimum amount of time on the regular avoidance procedure.

Method

Subjects. The subjects were eight male rats, 6 months old at the start of training. They were maintained on free food and water in individual living cages.

Apparatus. The apparatus was identical to that described for Section IV.

Procedure. The preliminary training of the animals proceeded as described for Section VI. After an animal consistently produced TO$_{av}$ and the inappropriate responding during the time-out periods had been almost extinguished on both levers, the next phase of the procedure was initiated. After each TO$_{av}$ period, the animal could not produce the next TO$_{av}$ period for 5 min. During these 5 min., which is, in effect, a TO period for the TO lever, a light above the TO lever was extinguished. Both lever lights were on during TO$_{av}$, however. Responding on the TO lever was thus only reinforced when the light above this lever was on, outside TO$_{av}$ periods. In Figures 39 and 40, the periods in which the TO lever was ineffective are indicated by a depression in the top line above the cumulative records. The line is labeled T.O.D. (time-out discrimination) procedure. The length of the TO periods was 10 min. All other conditions were as described for Sections V and VII.

Results and Discussion

Session 13 (Figure 39) shows the final performance on both the time-out and avoidance levers during the last session before introduction of the T.O.D. procedure. The initial result of the 5-min. TO lever extinction

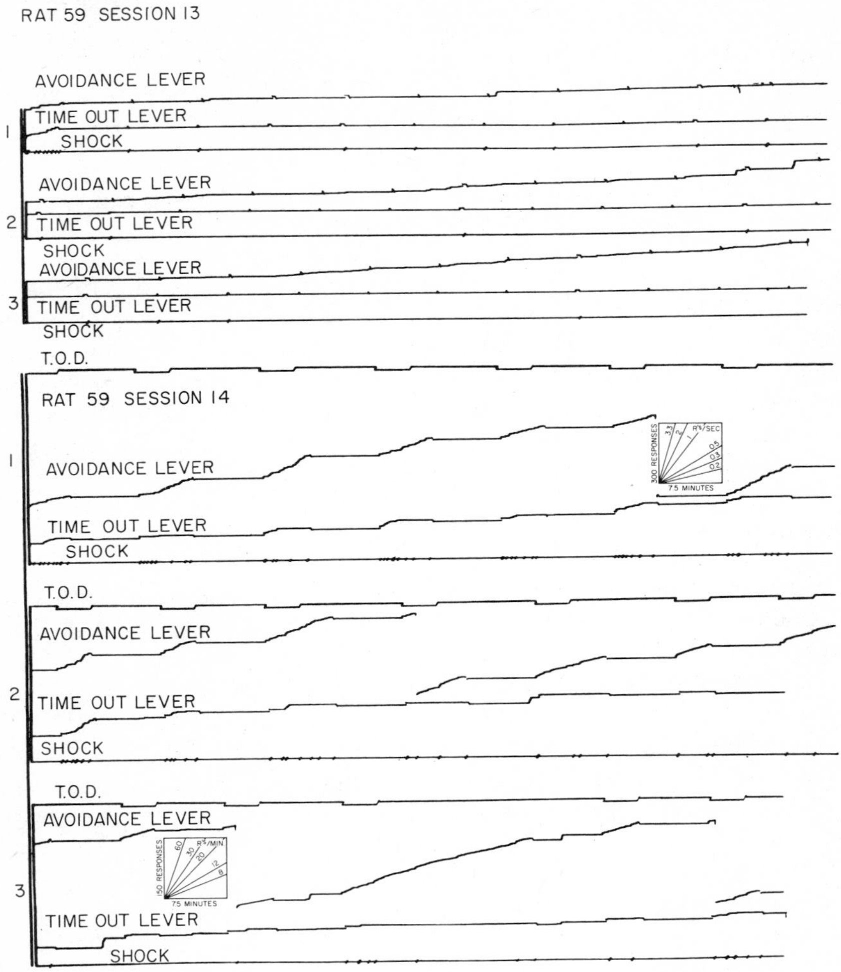

Figure 39. Development of discriminative control over the TO_{av} behavior by a separate external cue.

periods (Session 14) was a series of extinction curves of the TO lever behavior during the T.O.D. periods. The shock frequently also increased. Both effects were temporary and disappeared gradually during Sessions 14, 15, 16, and several other successive sessions. During the latter part of Session 16 (Figure 40), the number of TO lever responses emitted during the T.O.D. periods has greatly diminished. Similar results were obtained with the other seven animals. The present data illustrate once again the functional independence of the two operants.

Figure 40. Continued development of discriminative control over the TO_{av} behavior by a separate external cue.

XII. GENERAL DISCUSSION

The series of experiments in Sections V through XI has demonstrated that "a stimulus associated with a period of time-out from a stimulus associated with an avoidance schedule" (TO_{av}) can function effectively as a positive reinforcer.

Various reinforcement schedules generated performances on the TO lever which had many features of the performance patterns produced by the same schedules with conventional positive reinforcers. The main differences can be explained by two factors.

(1) Behavior by which the subject produces TO_{av} is always in competition with the behavior on the avoidance lever. The animal must stop pressing the TO lever frequently, and, instead, press the avoidance lever if it is to keep the shock from occurring.

(2) The TO_{av} period is a relatively weak reinforcer. The performance it maintains shows many similarities to performances maintained by food under low deprivation. For example, behavior reinforced by TO_{av} can be maintained only at low-valued ratio schedules (100); the FR straining is relatively excessive for the low FR values involved. With FI schedules, there are no scallops, and the response output is just about minimal. Extinction proceeds rapidly, and the "holding-the-lever-down" behavior with the Hefferline schedule is of relatively short duration.

XIII. THE SIGNIFICANCE OF THE DEMONSTRATION OF TO_{av} AS A REINFORCING EVENT FOR THE THEORETICAL INTERPRETATION OF AVOIDANCE CONDITIONING

A rather simple interpretation of avoidance behavior has become widely accepted in one form or another (Schoenfeld, 1950; Solomon and Wynne, 1953; Mowrer, 1960). The reinforcing events responsible for the acquisition and maintenance of avoidance behavior are held to come from two sources: the termination of the warning signal and its proprioceptive concomitants (Schoenfeld, 1950), or the fear or anxiety induced by these events (Mowrer, 1960). In another presumably competing formulation, it has been suggested that the very absence of the shock strengthens the operant avoidance behavior (Hilgard and Marquis, 1940; Kamin, 1957, 1959). The perennial question is: how can the absence of a stimulus (such as shock) be a reinforcing stimulus?

The present experiments, which are a continuation and further development of the avoidance schedules initiated by Sidman (1953), may help to answer this question. "The absence of shock" is in fact always a *stimulus condition* associated with nonoccurrence of shock, in other words, TO_{av}. Earlier formulations overlooked the fact that the termination of one stimulus (condition) *ipso facto* produces another one. The intertrial interval of the traditional avoidance experiment may be considered as another TO_{av}.

SUMMARY

Investigations are reported of some of the discriminative (cue) and reinforcing properties of stimuli (TO_{av}) correlated with the discontinuation of a free-operant avoidance schedule. After several unsuccessful initial attempts to demonstrate the positively reinforcing effect of TO_{av}, a special technique was developed. The subjects were trained by means of a free-operant avoidance procedure to press a lever and postpone electric shock; by pressing a second lever, they could produce a cue correlated with the TO_{av} period. The importance of a distinct cue correlated with TO_{av} was demonstrated in experiments in which this signal was eliminated from the procedure. The reinforcing function of the TO_{av} period was explored by showing its effectiveness under various schedules of reinforcement.

Other observations were made concerning the course of extinction of both TO_{av} producing responses and avoidance behavior.

In further experiments in which TO_{av} was used as a reinforcer, the TO_{av} behavior was also brought under separate stimulus control. The development of the various discriminations involved in the resulting performance were described.

REFERENCES

APPEL, J. B. The aversive control of an operant discrimination. *J. exp. Anal. Behav.*, 1960, *3*, 35–48.

BOREN, J. J., and SIDMAN, M. Maintenance of avoidance behavior with intermittent shocks. *Canad. J. Psychol.*, 1957, *11*, 185–192.

DINSMOOR, J. A., and HUGHES, L. H. Training rats to press a bar to turn off shock. *J. comp. physiol. Psychol.*, 1956, *49*, 235–238.

FERSTER, C. B. Withdrawal of positive reinforcement as punishment. *Science*, 1957, *126*, 509.

FERSTER, C. B. Control of behavior in chimpanzees and pigeons by time out from positive reinforcement. *Psychol. Monogr.*, 1958, *72*, No. 8, 1–38.

FERSTER, C. B., and SKINNER, B. F. *Schedules of reinforcement*. New York: Appleton-Century-Crofts, 1957.

GRANDA, A. M., and HAMMACK, J. T. Operant behavior during sleep. *Science*, 1961, *133*, 1485–1486.

HARRISON, J. M., and ABELSON, R. M. The maintenance of behavior by the termination and onset of intense noise. *J. exp. Anal. Behav.*, 1959, *2*, 23–42.

HEFFERLINE, R. F. An experimental study of avoidance. *Genet. Psychol. Monogr.*, 1950, *42*, 213–334.

HERRNSTEIN, R. J., and BRADY, J. V. Interaction among components of a multiple schedule. *J. exp. Anal. Behav.*, 1958, *1*, 293–300.

HILGARD, E. R., and MARQUIS, D. G. *Conditioning and learning*. New York: Appleton-Century-Crofts, 1940.

KAMIN, L. J. The effects of termination of the CS and avoidance of the US on avoidance learning: an extension. *Canad. J. Psychol.*, 1957, *11*, 48–56.

KAMIN, L. J. CS-termination as a factor in the emergence of anticipatory avoidance. *Psychol. Rep.*, 1959, *5*, 455–456.

MOWRER, O. M. *Learning theory and behavior*. New York: Wiley, 1960.

OWEN, J. E. The influence of *dl-*, *d-* and *l-* amphetamine and *d*-methamphetamine on a fixed-ratio schedule. *J. exp. Anal. Behav.*, 1960, *3*, 293–310.

SCHOENFELD, W. N. An experimental approach to anxiety, escape and avoidance behavior. In P. H. Hoch and J. Zubin (Eds.), *Anxiety*. New York: Grune and Stratton, 1950.

SIDMAN, M. Avoidance conditioning with brief shock and no exteroceptive warning signal. *Science*, 1953, *118*, 157–158.

SIDMAN, M. The temporal distribution of avoidance response. *J. comp. physiol. Psychol.*, 1954, *47*, 399–402.

SIDMAN, M. Time-out from avoidance as a conditioned positive reinforcer. Paper read at the 1st annual meeting of the Psychonomic Society, Chicago, September, 1960.

SIDMAN, M. Time out from avoidance as a reinforcer: A study of response interaction. *J. exp. Anal. Behav.*, 1962, *5*, 423–434.

SIDMAN, M., and STEBBINS, W. C. Satiation effects under fixed-ratio schedules of reinforcement. *J. comp. physiol. Psychol.*, 1954, *47*, 114–116.

SKINNER, B. F. *The behavior of organisms.* New York: Appleton-Century-Crofts, 1938.

SKINNER, B. F. *Science and human behavior.* New York: Macmillan, 1953.

SOLOMON, R. L., and WYNNE, L. C. Traumatic avoidance learning: acquisition in normal dogs. *Psychol. Monogr.*, 1953, *67*, No. 4, 1–19.

VERHAVE, T. A sensitive lever for operant-conditioning experiments. *J. exp. Anal. Behav.*, 1958, *1*, 220.

VERHAVE, T. Recent developments in the experimental analysis of behavior. Proc. 11th Res. Conf., Am. Meat Inst. Found., 1959, 113–136. (a)

VERHAVE, T. An adjusting fixed-ratio schedule for a time-out from an avoidance schedule as reinforcement. *J. exp. Anal. Behav.*, 1959, *2*, 253. (b)

VERHAVE, T. A demonstration of an avoidance schedule preference. Paper presented at Eastern Psychol. Ass., New York, 1961. (a)

VERHAVE, T. Strength of time-out from avoidance behavior as a function of time-out duration. Paper presented at meeting of Psychonomic Society, 1961. (b)

VERHAVE, T. Toward a calculus of reinforcement value. Paper presented at a symposium concerning "The Regulation of Behavior by Self-Adjusting Procedures," Am. Psychol. Ass., New York, 1961. (c)

VERHAVE, T. Some observations concerning prepotency and probability of postponing shock with a two-lever avoidance procedure. *J. exp. Anal. Behav.*, 1961, *4*, 187–192. (d)

29

Water-Deprivation-Produced Sign Reversal

of a Conditioned Reinforcer Based

Upon Dry Food

Stanley Pliskoff and Gerald Tolliver

Much of the research in the area of conditioned reinforcers has focused on such problems as strength of the reinforcer as related to the parameters of the conditioning situation, their functional significance in behavior chains, and their relationship to deprivation operations. The experiment to be reported in this paper properly falls into the class of experiments dealing with deprivation operations: it demonstrates that a positive conditioned reinforcer established and maintained by means of appropriate correlation with dry-food reinforcement can function as a negative reinforcer when the organism is water-deprived.

The experiment is divided into two parts: the first describes the effect of water deprivation on the frequency of subject-produced time outs (TO's) from dry-food-reinforced ratio behavior; the second part identifies the behavioral mechanism (S^r sign reversal) responsible for the observed effect.

SUBJECTS AND APPARATUS

The subjects (Ss were four experimentally naive, male, hooded rats from the colony maintained by the Walter Reed Army Institute of Research. At 5 months of age their weights were slowly reduced to about 60 percent of the stabilized values determined by a 60-day, free-feeding schedule.

The experimental chamber was a standard, commercially available

Adapted from *Journal of the Experimental Analysis of Behavior*, 1960, *3*, 323–329. With permission of the authors and publisher.

(Foringer & Co., Inc.) rat box with two modified telegraph key levers on the front wall. Above either lever was a small stimulus light. A pellet hopper was mounted at the same level as, and equidistant between, the levers. A force of about 15 grams was required to actuate the levers after an excursion of 4 millimeters. Actuation of either lever produced a sharp feedback click from a relay mounted in the box. The box was isolated in a white noise-filled, soundproofed room. The programming of the experiment and the recording of data were accomplished through the use of the usual automatic equipment.

PROCEDURE

Part I

Preliminary Training. Following magazine training and CRF in which the Ss were required to alternate levers for successive dry-food reinforcements (0.045-gram pellets, J. P. Noyes Company), each rat was trained to stable performance in the two-lever situation. Throughout the procedure to be described, both levers were always available to S. One lever, the food lever, was always immediately beneath the stimulus light that was not illuminated, while the other lever, the TO lever, was always beneath the stimulus light that was illuminated.

The food lever was on a fixed-ratio (FR) schedule of reinforcement. The values of the ratio for the several rats were: Rat 1, FR 25; Rat 2, FR 20; Rat 3, FR 10; Rat 4, FR 25. For all Ss, a single response made at any time (except during TO) on the TO lever produced a 5-minute TO. During a TO, (a) the houselight was illuminated and a 1000-cycle-per-second tone was present in the box; and (b) responses on either lever produced only the feedback click.

At the end of the 5-minute TO, the "food-available" condition (time in or TI) was automatically reinstated and remained in effect until S produced another TO. During TI, there was no tone in the box, and the houselight was extinguished; the only source of illumination was the stimulus light over the TO lever.

Daily sessions with the two-lever procedure were terminated at 50 reinforcements or 2 hours, whichever came first. The left-right positions of the TO and food levers were varied nonsystematically from session to session, and water was never available in the box.

The Experimental Variable. After about 1000 reinforcements on the above procedure, the water-deprivation variable was introduced. Each rat was subjected to total water deprivation on seven separate occasions, but no more frequently than once per week. Each subjection was for a 3-day period, during which daily sessions were run exactly as described above.

Part II

Rats 1 and 4 were utilized in the extension of the experiment. Rat 2 was used for other purposes, and Rat 3 died soon after the second part of the experiment was begun.

Except for the fact that the food lever was always on the right, the two rats were treated in sufficiently different fashion as to make separate presentation advisable.

Rat 1. Rat 1 was continued on the original procedure, including periodic subjection to water deprivation. However, the response requirement on the TO lever to produce a TO was changed to FR 10. After five 3-day water-deprivation periods, the contingency on the TO lever was changed to extinction, i.e., TO's could no longer be produced.

Rat 4. Although the original daily running procedure continued in effect, subjection to water deprivation was discontinued. Instead, (a) an attempt was made to simulate the effects of water deprivation by feeding Rat 4 large quantities of dry food; and (b) the requirement on the TO lever to produce a TO was changed to FR 10.

Since no significant results were realized in the attempt to simulate water deprivation, the procedure was abandoned. Rat 4 was then subjected to two 3-day water-deprivation periods, and its TO behavior with the FR 10 requirement on the TO lever was examined.

RESULTS AND DISCUSSION

Part I

The major behavioral effects of water deprivation are shown in Figures 1 and 2. Figure 1 presents the median number of TO's taken by the four Ss during the several days of water deprivation (1, 2, 3 on abscissa), including the session before (SB) and the first session after its termination (SA). The points at O are for all other nonwater-deprived days. Figure 2 shows the relative median FR running rate on the food lever for the SB through SA sessions. Running time was computed by subtracting TO, eating, and pause-after-reinforcement times from session length. The medians are expressed relative to (i.e., divided by) the median running rates for the 0 sessions of Figure 1.

Note the following:
   1. In Figure 1, Rats 1 and 3 show the greatest TO frequency on the third thirst (equals water deprivation) day. In Figure 2, the same animals show the greatest single rate drop from the second to the third thirst session. Both effects occur irrespective of food-lever position.
   2. In Figure 1, Rat 2 shows a peak in TO frequency on the second

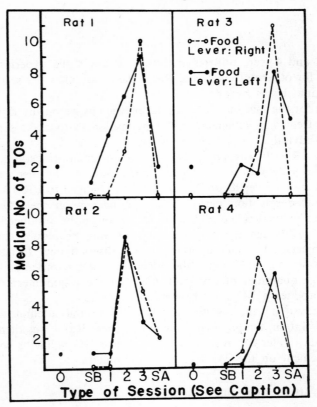

Figure 1. *Median TO frequency plotted against the type of experimental session. On the abscissa: 1,2,3 refer to the three days of water deprivation; SB is the session before a 3-day thirst period; SA is the first session after its termination, and O represents all other (nonwater-deprived) sessions.*

thirst day. In Figure 2, it shows the greatest single rate drop from the first to the second thirst session. Both effects occur irrespective of food-lever position.

3. The data of Rat 4 are more complicated in that the shapes of its TO and rate functions depend on food-lever position. With the food lever on the left, its functions are similar to those of Rats 1 and 3; with the food lever on the right, its functions are similar to those of Rat 2.

The above observations imply a relationship between the two sets of functions shown in Figures 1 and 2. Whereas it may *not* be concluded that where running rate is lowest, TO frequency is greatest (Rat 2 and "food lever: right" for Rat 4), it may be concluded that TO frequency is greatest in that session showing the greatest drop in running rate relative to the session before.

The experimental procedure described above is fundamentally that of

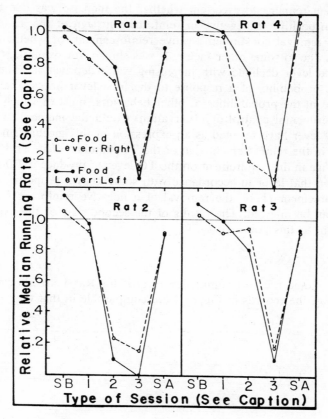

Figure 2. *Relative median running rate on the food lever plotted against the type of experimental session. Median running rates are relative to (i.e., divided by) median running rates for O-type sessions of Figure 1. The abscissa is the same as that of Figure 1.*

a discrimination experiment in which a behavior is "favorably" (in terms of reinforcement return for time and effort) reinforced in the presence of one stimulus complex (TI) and not reinforced in the presence of another (TO). General knowledge about this experimental paradigm and the one referred to as "chaining" indicates that the positive stimulus (TI complex) becomes not only a discriminative stimulus for the reinforced behavior but also takes on positive-reinforcement properties. A behavior which eliminates such a stimulus and replaces it with a TO is weakened, since the removal of a positive reinforcer constitutes negative reinforcement.

It was found that water deprivation increased the frequency of TO's.[1]

[1] Kendler (1951, 1952, 1954) studied the effect of water deprivation after dry-food reinforcement in a series of three maze studies. The design of those experiments permits no inferences with regard to the problem studied in this paper. Kendler's general conclusions, however, are supported by the results of the present research.

The problem remains to ascertain whether the increase was due to a reversal from positive to negative in reinforcement sign of the TI stimulus,
so that its removal constituted positive reinforcement, or whether the increase was due to some other factor. It was shown, for example, that rate
on the food lever declined with increasing water deprivation. The reduction in the probability of a response to the food lever implies necessarily
an increase in the probabilities of other behaviors, most of which are not
under experimental control or observation. Could the increase in activity
on the TO lever have resulted as an expression of this mechanism without
a reversal in the reinforcement sign of the TI stimulus? If it can be shown
that a change in the requirement on the TO lever to produce a TO modifies
behavior on that lever in accordance with some known properties of positive reinforcement (here, the removal of a negative reinforcer), then the
reversal can be inferred. The results of the second part of the experiment
are relevant to this point.

Part II

Rat 1. Some relevant cumulative records for Rat 1 are shown in Figure 3. All of the records in Figure 3 are comparable in that they (*a*) were

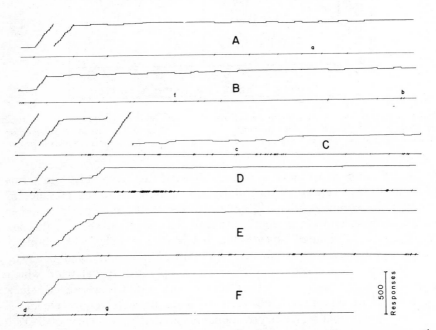

Figure 3.   Sample cumulative records. The cumulating pen marks responses on the
food lever, and the event pen marks responses on the TO lever. The records have been
artificially reset to the base line in order to conserve space. Records A, B, C, D, and E
are for Rat 1 under several TO lever requirements. (See text.) Record F is for Rat 4
with FR 10 on the TO lever.

taken on the third day of 3-day thirst periods, and (b) represent 2-hour sessions. The cumulating pen marks responses on the food lever; "pips" indicate reinforcements, and the extensive offsets mark TO's. Responses on the TO lever are recorded by the event pen. Records A and B are from the last two 3-day thirst periods in the earlier part of the experiment. There is an occasional tendency to produce TO's with short bursts on the TO lever, such as at b in Record B. The tendency to burst might be comparable with the one observed by Sidman (1954) in a shock-avoidance situation. Note, however, the TO's produced by single responses at a in A and the occurrences of spaced responses as a f in B. The total response frequencies on the TO lever are 31 and 41 for A and B, respectively. (A burst at the beginning of Record A is omitted from the figure.) Record C depicts the effect of changing the requirement on the TO lever to FR 10. That record is from the fourth 3-day thirst period with the FR 10 requirement, and the increased output and marked tendency to burst such as at c are apparent. In Record C, the next to the last third-thirst-day session with the FR 10 requirement on the TO lever, 118 responses occurred on the TO lever. The final session produced 144 responses on the TO lever, but that record was smudged beyond presentation. Record D shows the initial effect of changing the TO lever contingency to extinction. A total of 242 TO lever responses occurred in the session of Record D. The increased output is not unlike the effect often obtained with the introduction of extinction after positive reinforcement. Record E is from the tenth 3-day thirst period with the extinction contingency on the TO lever. Total response output by this time has dropped to a steady value of about 65, approximately half the output under the TO lever requirement of FR 10, but, notably, about twice the previous output under FR 1. The effect seems due primarily to the continued occurrence of long bursts. Record F shows the second of the two 3-day thirst periods that terminated the experiment for Rat 4. Two TO's occurred at the beginning of the session, both produced by sharp bursts of responding (d and g, Record F). The tendency to burst is in marked contrast with the earlier TO-producing behavior of Rat 4, which differed from that shown for Rat 1 (Records A and B) in that Rat 4's third-thirst-day TO lever output per 2-hour session was about half that for Rat 1 (medians: Rat 1, 41 responses; Rat 4, 22 responses), with almost no tendency to burst.

The results obtained in the second part of the experiment with Rats 1 and 4 conform to expectations if one assumed that the TI stimulus complex functioned as a negative reinforcer when the rats were water-deprived.

SUMMARY

Fixed-ratio behavior on one lever of a two-lever box was maintained by dry-food reinforcement. A single response on the second lever produced a 5-minute TO. The four rats were periodically subjected to three consecutive days of water deprivation, and it was found that this variable reduced running rate on the food lever and increased the frequency of TO's in such a fashion as to indicate that TO frequency due to water deprivation is greatest in that session showing the largest drop in running rate relative to the session before.

The question was raised as to whether the increased frequency of TO's was due to a reversal in sign of the reinforcing properties of the TI stimulus complex. In the second part of the experiment, the requirement on the TO lever to produce a TO was changed. It was found that when the requirement was raised, response frequency on that lever increased; when that lever was put on extinction, response output dropped after an initial, sudden increase such as is often noted with the onset of extinction after positive reinforcement. An attempt was made with one rat to stimulate the effect of water deprivation with heavy feedings of dry food, but this attempt was unsuccessful.

REFERENCES

KENDLER, H. H., KARASIK, A. D., and SCHRIER, A. M. Studies of the effect of change of drive: III. Amounts of switching produced by shifting drive from thirst to hunger and from hunger to thirst. *J. exp. Psychol.*, 1954, *47*, 179–182.

KENDLER, H. H., and LEVINE, S. Studies of the effect of change of drive: I. From hunger to thirst in a T-maze. *J. exp. Psychol.*, 1951, *41*, 429–436.

KENDLER, H. H., LEVINE, S., ALTCHEK, E., and PETERS, H. Studies of the effect of change of drive: II. From hunger to different intensities of a thirst drive in a T-maze. *J. exp. Psychol.*, 1952, *44*, 1–3.

SIDMAN, M. The temporal distribution of avoidance responses. *J. comp. physiol. Psychol.*, 1954, *47*, 399–402.

SUGGESTED READINGS

Chaining

HULL, C. L. The mechanism of the assembly of behavior segments in novel combinations suitable for problem solution. *Psychol. Rev.*, 1935, *42*, 219–245.

KELLER, F. S., and SCHOENFELD, W. N. *Principles of psychology.* New York: Appleton-Century-Crofts, 1950, Chap. 7.

SKINNER, B. F. *Science and human behavior.* New York: Macmillan, 1953, Chaps. 14 and 15.

STAATS, A. W., and STAATS, C. K. *Complex human behavior.* New York: Holt, Rinehart and Winston, 1963, Chaps. 3 and 5.

Conditioned Reinforcement

KELLEHER, R. T., and GOLLUB, L. R. A review of positive conditioned reinforcement. *J. exp. Anal. Behav.*, 1962, 5, 543–697.

KELLER, F. S., and SCHOENFELD, W. N. *Principles of psychology.* New York: Appleton-Century-Crofts, 1950, Chap. 8.

MOWRER, O. H. *Learning theory and behavior.* New York: Wiley, 1960, Chaps. 4, 5, and 6.

MYERS, J. L. Secondary reinforcement: A review of some recent experimentation. *Psychol. Bull.*, 1958, 55, 284–301.

Chapter VIII

MOTIVATION

It was stated in the introductory chapter that the meaning of the term motivation is far from being agreed upon. Atkinson in a recent text (1964) tentatively defines the study of motivation as having "to do with [the] analysis of the various factors which incite and direct an individual's action" (p. 1). In a similar vein P. T. Young (1961) defined the study of motivation as "a search for the determinants (all determinants) of human and animal activity" (p. 24). Such a viewpoint makes the study of motivation coextensive with psychology itself. It is for this reason that many writers of texts about motivation "have narrowed the definition of motivation and therefore have reduced the span of their coverage" (Cofer and Appley, 1964, p. 17). Among the various topics a study of motivation might concern itself with, most of the recent textbook authors include the investigation of the effects of deprivation; the process of satiation in the case of food, water, and sex as reinforcers; the problem of the nature of reinforcement in general; and the "relative attractiveness of specific goals." The papers reproduced in the present chapter are in one way or another relevant to these issues.

REFERENCES

ATKINSON, J. W. *An introduction to motivation.* Princeton: Van Nostrand, 1964.

COFER, C. N., and APPLEY, M. H. *Motivation: theory and research.* New York: Wiley, 1964.

YOUNG, P. T. *Motivation and emotion.* New York: Wiley, 1961.

30

The Effect of Hunger on Discriminated Responding

James A. Dinsmoor

While the process by which the human observer acquires discriminative reactions to a variety of verbal stimuli remains somewhat obscure, it is clear that the existence of such reactions has provided a very convenient basis for determining the effects of immediate environmental events in the psychophysical laboratory. Merely by employing verbal instructions at the beginning of the session, an experimenter can establish a ready-made correlation between the subject's response and whatever stimulus dimension he may be employing; extraneous variables, for the most part, are minimized; by "focussing" the subject's reaction, so to speak, on the relevant aspects of the situation, the experimenter is able to obtain lawful and dependable data (Graham, 1934, 1950; Keller and Schoenfeld, 1950). Despite the apparent naiveté of this technique, its practical convenience has been a major factor in the development of sensory and perceptual research.

At the same time, it has influenced its direction. Because it is so difficult for the experimenter to control the previous experience and the current motivation of the human subject, these factors have rarely been treated as experimental variables in laboratory investigations. Social and clinical psychologists, who are forced in their practice to deal with just such factors, often at the intuitive level, have understandably been sensitive to this limitation, and have frequently expressed their dissatisfaction with the "narrowness" of traditional psychophysical work, its "artificiality," and its "sterility." Since neither the clinic nor field surveys have provided an adequate proving ground for choosing among the welter of conflicting theories, a need has been felt for the extension of the more rigorous techniques of experimental determination to such problems (e.g., Bruner and Good-

Adapted from *Journal of Abnormal and Social Psychology,* 1952, 47, 67–72. With permission of the author and the American Psychological Association.

man, 1947; Carter and Schooler, 1949; Miller, 1950). Unfortunately, however, many of the experimenters who have taken up this task have themselves derived not only their inspiration but their terminology and their conceptual patterns from social and clinical description. Their definitions tend to be vague, in many instances; the referents or S^D's for their terms have been obscure; lists of examples have been substituted for operational specification. They speak, for instance, of a distinction between "objective," "realistic," or "autochthonous" factors, on the one hand, and those which are "subjective," "dynamic," "behavioral," or "autistic" on the other. The first set of terms apparently refers to the effects of the immediate situation; this is the traditional subject-matter of the psychophysicist. The second set refers to such prior determinants as drive and reinforcement, which are customarily ignored in sensory and perceptual studies. Under this heading, frequent reference is made to "needs," "values," "gratifications," "frustrations," "defenses," "stresses," "tensions," etc., which are extremely difficult to specify. Often, such words refer to inferred variables for which there is little or no evidence. When properly constructed (Spence, 1944), such variables may perhaps have a degree of utility (but cf. Skinner, 1950); when introduced ad hoc, on the other hand, they serve primarily to confuse the reader and to retard scientific description.

Again, owing to the difficulty of controlling or manipulating such factors as drive, emotion, reinforcement, and prior training in the human subject, the employment of groups differing in some such social index as age, attitude, education, or income is frequently substituted for the use of a genuine experimental variable. This is not a trivial distinction. Such group differences tend to be complex; a number of factors are covarying, and it is difficult or impossible to determine which of the many factors are responsible for the observed differences in behavior. In a recent and rather intriguing experiment by Bruner and Goodman (1947), for example, and its replication (with less striking results) by Carter and Schooler (1949), children from rich and poor families were employed. The greater overestimation of the size of coins by the children from the homes of lower income was attributed to differences in the subjective "value" of the coins to either group; it might as readily, and perhaps as plausibly, have been attributed to differences in familiarity, or to a host of other factors. To winnow out the effects of a single factor, independent manipulation of an isolated variable is necessary. This cannot be accomplished by employing human subjects of unknown histories.

Among the experiments on "dynamic" factors in perception which have been distinguished by a relatively explicit specification of the independent variable are four which deal with the effects of the degree of hunger on perceptual or discriminative reactions. In an experiment by Sanford (1936), ten school children were asked to produce verbal associations to lists of words "which . . . might possibly elicit responses logically related to food or to the eating situation" (p. 131) and to interpret twenty ambiguous pictures that could be considered as "having to do with food" (p. 132). The children gave more food-related words when hungry, immediately before a regular meal, than when satiated, shortly after the meal. In a later and more thorough experiment by the same author (Sanford, 1937), college students were substituted for the children as subjects, and, in particular, one group was tested after twenty-four hours of fasting. Again, the number of appropriate responses increased regularly with each increment in hunger. These findings were interpreted as demonstrating the effects of drive on "the imaginal process."

In a similar experiment by Levine, Chein, and Murphy (1942), several undergraduates were asked to "identify" meaningless figures and ambiguous drawings of miscellaneous food and household articles, which were presented behind a ground-glass screen. The experimental group (5 Os) were tested at one, three, six, and nine hours of hunger, and were promised, and given, food at the close of the session, "to keep a food-set operating" (p. 287). The data themselves were somewhat ambiguous, since the number of food responses rose, at first, with increases in deprivation, and then declined. The authors offered a double *ad hoc* explanation, involving the following pair of hypotheses: "(*a*) an autistic process operating in the direction of gratification; (*b*) a process of mobilization of perceptual energies in the direction of accurately perceiving the means-objects in the sense of greater alertness. The first of these hypotheses is substantiated by the rise in the curve, the second by the subsequent fall" (pp. 291–292).

The most thorough of this series of investigations was performed by McClelland and Atkinson (1948), employing 130 candidates for submarine training school. In this study, large groups were tested at 1–2 hours after eating, 4–5 hours, and 16–18 hours; they were asked to guess what (nonexistent) pictures were being projected on a screen at extremely low intensities of illumination. The necessity of making some response to each "picture" was emphasized in the instructions. "Write down something for every picture. . . . When you are certain you don't see anything then your guess is the impression we want. . . . Don't expect to see much at all. . . . Write down the impression that comes to your mind" (pp. 208–209). On nine of the twelve stimulus presentations, a choice among three possible responses was required; in the other three cases, no "hints" were given. In general, the frequency of food-related responses increased reliably with the number of hours since the last regular meal. This was interpreted as a "projection" of the subjects' "needs," a change in their "perceptions."

In studies of this type, where human subjects and verbal responses are employed, it is very difficult to formulate a systematic interpretation of the data. The acquisition-history of these variegated verbal responses, and hence their relation to the experimental stimuli, has not been determined.

It is not clear, for example, why in the McClelland and Atkinson study (1949) there should be discrepancies between the effects of hunger on "instrumental" food-related responses (e.g., eating utensils) and on "goal" responses (e.g., foods). By analogy with more systematic data obtained in infra-human studies, one may presume that the emission of a broad class of words known as "food-responses" has in the past been reinforced with social approval and with food itself; this reinforcement has most often occurred in the presence of edible objects and the food conversations of others. Such visual and verbal stimuli, plus whatever stimulation may have been induced by the food-deprivation itself, would then be positive discriminative stimuli, or S^D's, for the use of these words, and the frequency of responses in this situation would be high (Keller and Schoenfeld, 1950; Skinner, 1947a, 1947b). A generalization of these responses to stimuli which resemble the original S^D's is then to be expected, particularly if these stimuli are not themselves effective S^D's for strong competing responses; i.e., if they are "ambiguous." Any "structuring" of the stimuli tends to evoke competing responses which interfere with the appearance of those related to food. By the use of instructional stimuli, the over-all frequency of verbal responses of some kind is raised, and certain available categories may sometimes be specified. In general, although elements of the original stimulus pattern may be present, the experimental situation is one which merely resembles the S^D; since food words have not previously been reinforced in this situation, it may legitimately be termed an S^Δ. Hence, the findings of Sanford (1936, 1937) and of McClelland and Atkinson (1948) may be summarized by saying that verbal responses in S^Δ tend to increase in frequency with an increase in the relevant drive; the atypical results obtained by Levine, Chein, and Murphy (1942) may be related to special techniques employed (e.g., feeding the subjects at the end of the session) or may merely be the result of chance fluctuation.[1]

Such an increase in the frequency of S^Δ responses might be an expression of either of two principles. First, it is possible that the "perception" is "distorted," that the discrimination is "breaking down," to use the vernacular, that the gradient of generalization is spread or broadened by the increase in drive. This would be indicated by a *disproportionate* increase in S^Δ responding as compared to that in S^D—i.e., a distortion of the relative response probability. Alternatively, it is possible that both S^D and S^Δ responding are proportionately increased, and that the greater frequency in S^Δ is merely a special instance of the more general increment. Some evidence for such an interpretation may be noted in an observation by McClelland and Atkinson that "the gradient of increase as hunger in-

---

[1] The present writer has consulted the published frequencies for the individual subjects (Levine, Chein, and Murphy, 1942, Table 1), but has not been able to establish the statistical significance of this decline.

creased was the same for the items yielding frequent food responses as for the items yielding infrequent food responses" (1948, p. 217).

An explicit test of these alternative behavioral tendencies, however, requires the employment of infra-human subjects, so that the training process and the consequent relationship of the response to the stimuli employed may be specified in experimental terms. It requires the selection of a response which is known to vary in a simple and orderly fashion as a function of typical experimental operations. Finally, an appropriate measure must be selected such that a pair of independent reflexes would maintain their proportionality despite the changes induced by the manipulation of drive; such that their transformation would be linear. It has been demonstrated in previous studies that varied rates of occurrence of such a freely-emitted response as bar-pressing in the rat will all be multiplied by the same constant when the degree of hunger is raised or lowered. A complementary pair of studies by Williams (1938) and Perin (1942), for example, indicate that a formula relating the number of responses in extinction to the number of prior reinforcements (food pellets) requires only a multiplicative constant to express the effect of differing drives. Similarly, Skinner (1940, 1950) has shown that two rates of responding under periodic reinforcement and throughout various stages of extinction retain their proportionality when the difference is one of drive. One extinction curve may be superimposed upon the other by simple multiplication with a factor derived from the ratio of the rates under periodic reinforcement. This suggests that the effect on a pair of discriminated reflexes, $S^D.R$ and $S^\Delta.R$, would be to change their rates by the same factor, if the drive has no effect on the gradient of generalization, per se. A disproportionate increase in the rate of S^Δ responding, on the other hand, would indicate a direct effect of heightened drive on the discrimination itself. The present experiment is designed to test these alternatives.

APPARATUS AND PROCEDURE

Six male white rats, about 200 days in age, were starved down to 85 percent of their normal body weight and were conditioned to depress a bar or lever which procured 1/15 gm. pellets of food. When this response was well established, discrimination training was begun. Five-minute periods of light were alternated with five-minute periods of darkness. Responses occurring in the presence of the light—the positive stimulus, or S^D—were reinforced aperiodically, at a mean interval of two minutes, with further pellets. Reinforcement was withheld, however, in the darkness—S^Δ.[2]

By the end of 16 daily sessions of 100 min. apiece, the rates in S^D and in S^Δ appeared to have approached their respective limits. The degree of hunger

[2] This procedure is similar to one currently employed with pigeons by Prof. B. F. Skinner, at Harvard University.

was then manipulated in the following manner: For three rats, a body weight 75 percent of that under continuous feeding was determined. Following further starvation to reduce their weight below this norm, they were fed on each of five successive days an amount of powdered food equal to the difference in grams between their actual weight and the calculated value. A 100-minute test run was then conducted, following the usual discrimination procedure, immediately prior to the next scheduled feeding. By the same technique, these animals were successively tested at 80, 85, 90, 95, and 100 percent of their original weight; finally, they were tested under continuous feeding (satiation). The other three rats followed the same schedule in descending order. Since some disruption of the discrimination was observed in the first few minutes of each test session, only the final 90 minutes of responding was tabulated.

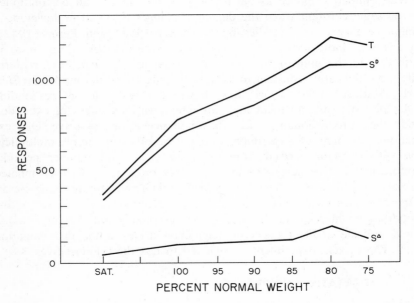

Figure 1.   The mean number of bar-pressings by six rats as a function of degree of hunger. The top curve represents the total (T) number of responses in ninety minutes of alternating stimulation, the other two the number made in the presence of the positive stimulus (S^D) and the negative stimulus (S^Δ) respectively. The first point on each curve represents a test following continuous feeding (satiation); for the operations specified by the percentage values, consult the text.

Standard living-experimental cages, bars, and recording apparatus (Dinsmoor, 1951) were used throughout. The light which served as the S^D was a diffuse illumination of 3.8 foot-candles, furnished from a hood mounted in a white wooden ceiling, which had been placed on the top of the cage as a substitute for the usual metal lid. The animals were effectively insulated from the sound produced by the control and recording apparatus but not from the sounds produced by other animals or their food magazines, within the same group of three.

RESULTS AND DISCUSSION

The mean number of responses at each level of hunger is represented in Figure 1. From this figure it may be seen that the over-all rate of responding is relatively low following continuous feeding (satiation), and that it rises consistently as the weight of the animal declines to 80 percent of normal. The relatively high rate at 80 percent and the succeeding drop under the 75 percent condition may represent experimental errors, due to chance fluctuation, or the drop may be a result of the physical weakness of the animals, due to malnutrition (Heron and Skinner, 1937). It may also be seen that the separate totals under S^D and S^Δ follow a similar pattern.

TABLE 1

Percentage of total responses occurring in S^Δ on each test.

		Percent of Normal Body Weight (Drive)					
Animal	Sat.	100	95	90	85	80	75
12	7.9	7.2	5.3	6.6	3.5	5.2	6.3
13	9.4	8.7	11.2	11.7	9.3	17.1	10.0
14	13.0	11.9	14.9	16.8	15.4	15.4	9.4
15	13.2	9.8	6.4	13.1	8.2	15.1	18.3
16	10.6	15.1	9.0	7.9	15.4	15.6	10.8
17	5.5	11.5	8.1	7.0	5.1	13.0	12.9
Mean	9.9	10.7	9.2	10.5	9.5	13.6	11.3

A more precise measure of this relationship is presented in numerical form in Table 1. Here the number of responses in S^Δ is expressed as a percentage of the total number of responses made by each animal, and these percentages are averaged for each level of body weight. Although the values fluctuate to quite an extent, no systematic trend is observable in the mean percentages. Analysis of variance reveals no significant differences between these means.

Finally, the corresponding mean totals under S^D and S^Δ are plotted on perpendicular coordinates in Figure 2, and a rectilinear function is calculated by the method of averages, assuming a zero intercept. In this calculation, one point, which appears somewhat deviant, has been ignored; the remaining six points cluster closely about the theoretical fit. It is apparent that the two rates remain roughly proportional: if the discrimination is measured by the *relative rates of responding under S^D and S^Δ* (Dinsmoor, 1951), it may be said to remain unaffected by changes in the degree of hunger. The increase in S^Δ responding represents merely an instance

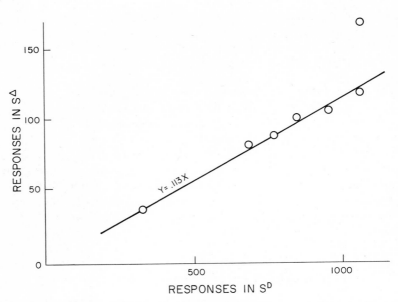

Figure 2. The mean number of bar-pressing responses in S^Δ as a function of the mean number in S^D for a group of six rats tested at seven levels of hunger. A straight line has been fitted to six of the seven points by the method of averages, on the assumption of a zero intercept.

of the more general increase under either stimulus condition. There is no evidence for what might be called a breakdown of the discrimination or a distortion of the perception.

This finding does not conflict with the data obtained by the use of verbal responses in human subjects, with the exception of the unreliable and uncorroborated decline in frequency reported by Levine, Chein, and Murphy (1942) at their higher levels of drive. It does, however, illustrate the fact that the employment of infra-human subjects and the establishment of a discrimination *de novo* make possible a more complete analysis of the immediate observations on changes in the frequency of the response. With such a procedure, moreover, there is less of a temptation to indulge in explanatory fictions, which, for all their imaginative appeal, are entirely gratuitous in a scientific discussion.

SUMMARY AND CONCLUSIONS

The present experiment was conducted in order to analyze in a more systematic fashion, without speculative embellishments, previously reported observations on the increased frequency of generalized verbal responses at high levels of drive. The corresponding bar-pressing rates of six white rats under positive (reinforced) and negative (nonreinforced) stimulation have been compared at seven levels of hunger. With the exception of a single deviant value, the two rates remain closely proportional; one is a linear function of the other. It is concluded that the increase in rate is general, and that a stimulus discrimination, as measured by the relative rates of response, is not affected by changes in drive.

REFERENCES

BRUNER, J. S., and GOODMAN, C. C. Value and need as organizing factors in perception. *J. abnorm. soc. Psychol.*, 1947, *42*, 33–44.

CARTER, L. F., and SCHOOLER, K. Value, need, and other factors in perception. *Psychol. Rev.*, 1949, *56*, 200–207.

DINSMOOR, J. A. The effect of periodic reinforcement of bar-pressing in the presence of a discriminative stimulus. *J. comp. physiol. Psychol.*, 1951, *44*, 354–361.

GRAHAM, C. H. Psychophysics and behavior. *J. gen. Psychol.*, 1934, *10*, 299–310.

GRAHAM, C. H. Behavior, perception and the psychophysical methods. *Psychol. Rev.*, 1950, *57*, 108–120.

HERON, W. T., and SKINNER, B. F. Changes in hunger during starvation. *Psychol. Rec.*, 1937, *1*, 51–60.

KELLER, F. S., and SCHOENFELD, W. N. *Principles of psychology.* New York: Appleton-Century-Crofts, 1950.

LEVINE, R., CHEIN, I., and MURPHY, G. The relation of intensity of a need to the amount of perceptual distortion: A preliminary report. *J. Psychol.*, 1942, *13*, 283–293.

McCLELLAND, D. C., and ATKINSON, J. W. The projective expression of needs: I. The effect of different intensities of hunger drive on perception. *J. Psychol.*, 1948, *25*, 205–222.

MILLER, J. G. (Ed.) *Experiments in social process.* New York: McGraw-Hill, 1950.

PERIN, C. T. Behavior potentiality as a joint function of the amount of training and the degree of hunger at the time of extinction. *J. exp. Psychol.*, 1942, *30*, 93–113.

SANFORD, R. N. The effects of abstinence from food upon imaginal processes: A preliminary experiment. *J. Psychol.*, 1936, *2*, 129–136.

SANFORD, R. N. The effects of abstinence from food upon imaginal processes: A further experiment. *J. Psychol.*, 1937, *3*, 145–159.

SKINNER, B. F. The nature of the operant reserve. *Psychol. Bull.*, 1940, *37*, 423. (Abstract.)

SKINNER, B. F. Lectures on verbal behavior. Columbia University Summer Session, 1947. (Mimeo.) (a)

SKINNER, B. F. William James Lectures, Harvard University, 1947. (Mimeo.) (b)

SKINNER, B. F. Are theories of learning necessary? *Psychol. Rev.*, 1950, *57*, 193–216.

SPENCE, K. W. The nature of theory construction in contemporary psychology. *Psychol. Rev.*, 1944, *51*, 47–68.

WILLIAMS, S. B. Resistance to extinction as a function of the number of reinforcements. *J. exp. Psychol.*, 1938, *23*, 506–522.

31

Satiation Effects Under Fixed-Ratio
Schedules of Reinforcement

Murray Sidman and William C. Stebbins

In a fixed-ratio schedule the reinforcing stimulus appears only after a fixed number of responses has been emitted. Skinner (1953a, p. 385) has pointed out three consequences of such a schedule:

a. The probability that a reinforcement will appear during a rapid burst of responses is high. As a result, rapid responding is selectively strengthened.

b. Rapid responding produces more frequent reinforcements. This in turn increases the rate of responding still more. A cyclic process is set up which culminates in a maximal rate.

c. The fixed number of responses becomes a discriminative occasion for reinforcement. Each successive response, as this number is approached, sets up a stronger occasion for reinforcement. This has the effect of making the behavior "self-generating." As successive responses are emitted, there is an increasing probability that the run will be completed.

Skinner has presented data illustrating these phenomena in rats (1938) and pigeons (1953b), and has indicated the importance of ratio size and amount of reinforcement (1953a, pp. 103, 386). The present experiments were designed to investigate the effects of partial satiation upon food-reinforced fixed-ratio responding, and to determine whether the phenomena observed could be extended to cats and monkeys.

Adapted from *Journal of Comparative and Physiological Psychology*, 1954, *47*, 114–116. With permission of the authors and the American Psychological Association.

METHOD

Subjects

Four male Wistar rats, two male stock cats, and one female rhesus monkey served as Ss. All animals had extensive previous experience with lever pressing on regular and fixed-ratio schedules of reinforcement.

Apparatus

Skinner boxes of sizes appropriate to the different species were used. A system of relays and timers automatically controlled the scheduling, recording, and reinforcement delivery. Responses were recorded on a Harvard Cumulative Recorder.

The cats, monkey, and two rats received liquid reinforcement. This consisted of water for the rats, a 50 percent mixture of evaporated milk and water for the cats, and water sweetened with table sugar for the monkey. Two rats were reinforced with food pellets, .045 gm. in weight and manufactured from Purina Laboratory Chow.

Procedure

Partial satiation was accomplished first by running the animals for long sessions, during which a large number of reinforcements was secured, and second, by feeding the animals before running. The experiment was conducted in two phases. In the first phase, the liquid-reinforced rats were deprived of water for 48 hr. before running; the cats were kept at 70 percent of their ad libitum body weight; and the monkey was deprived of food and water for 40 hr. The two food-reinforced rats received all their food in the experimental situation and were run every day. The Ss ran for 60 to 150 hr. at various fixed ratios in phase 1.

Only the monkey and the two liquid-reinforced rats were used in the second phase. Prior to phase 2, these animals were placed on a ratio of 25 responses per reinforcement for three sessions. They were kept on this ratio for three sessions in the second phase. Immediately prior to running, the rats had access to water for ½ hr., and the monkey was fed approximately 500 cc. of the sugar solution.

RESULTS

Sample records from the first phase are presented in Figure 1 for one rat, one cat, and the monkey. The rate for a given individual is essentially two-valued, with a zero rate occasionally appearing just after a reinforcement and a high, constant rate prevailing at other times. In the case of the cat, short pauses follow each reinforcement, even at the beginning of the

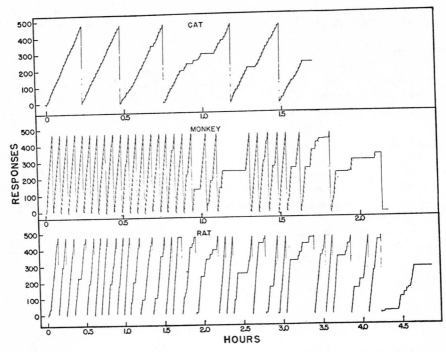

Figure 1. Sample cumulative response records under fixed-ratio schedules of reinforcement. Ratio of responses to reinforcements is 25:1 for the rat and monkey, and 20:1 for the cat. The short diagonal strokes indicate reinforcements.

record. These, however, are independent of the experimental procedure, resulting from a small residue of milk around the rim of the liquid dispenser. Following each reinforcement, the cats spent 5 to 10 sec. licking this residue. With the exception of this artifact, the rates are generally regular at the start of the sessions, with breaks of varying lengths beginning to appear as the period progresses. With few exceptions these breaks appear immediately after a reinforcement. Even at the end of the session, however, when long periods of no responding have become frequent, the same rate is maintained when the animal does respond.

After subtracting the time taken for pauses following reinforcement, the response rate was determined over the first, middle, and last 30 min. of each session at a given schedule. This did not include the first session, during which the animal adjusted its rate from the previous schedule. The initial rate ranged from a low of 51 responses per minute for one of the rats to a high of 167.7 responses per minute for the monkey. No variation greater than 1 percent of the initial rate was observed within or between sessions for a given animal at a given ratio.

Figure 2 shows sample records from the monkey and the same rat as in Figure 1 after they had been prefed. The only effect of the partial satiation appears to be an earlier and more frequent appearance of the periods of no responding. As a consequence, the total number of responses emitted

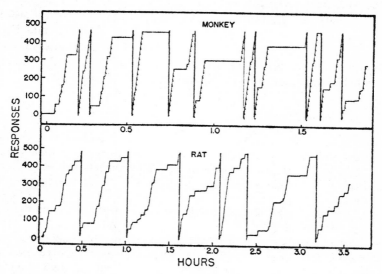

Figure 2. Sample records following prefeeding. Animals and schedules are the same as those in Figure 1.

during the experimental period is less. However, when the animals do respond, their rates are the same (within 1 percent) as those observed at any time during the first phase.

DISCUSSION

The general features of the fixed-ratio curves are in agreement with those previously observed by Ferster and Skinner. With respect to the pauses following reinforcement, they write, "With short enough ratios—under 60 or so for the pigeon—there is no pause following the reinforcement. With larger ratios the pause increases as a function of the size of the ratio" (personal communication). The present findings indicate that these pauses are also under the control of deprivation and satiation operations.

Of greater interest, perhaps, is the independence of the response rate from the feeding operation. If total responses had only been summated with a counter, and then divided by the length of the experimental session, it would have appeared as though feeding produced a lower rate. Examination of the moment-to-moment record, however, indicates that when the animals do respond, their rate is always the same.

Connected with this is the observation that once the animal began to respond, it always continued without a break until the next reinforcement was received. When the animal responded, its own behavior set up a powerful discriminative occasion for reinforcement, each response generating a successor until the reinforcement appeared. Evidence for such a discrimination, or "count," has been presented by Skinner (1953b) and Ferster (1954). The present data indicate that degree of satiation alters only the probability of occurrence of the first response in the run, but has no effect upon the discrimination responsible for the stable rate.

SUMMARY

Four rats, two cats, and one rhesus monkey were trained to press levers under fixed-ratio schedules of reinforcement. The effects of satiation were observed (*a*) after a considerable number of reinforcements had been received in the experimental situation and (*b*) after feeding the animals prior to running them.

Characteristics of the cumulative response curves were similar to those previously obtained by Skinner and Ferster from rats and pigeons.

The effect of satiation was to introduce periods of no responding immediately following reinforcements. However, when the animals did respond, their rates were constant and independent of the degree of satiation. Prefeeding simply produced an earlier and more frequent appearance of the periods of no responding.

REFERENCES

FERSTER, C. B. Use of the blackout in the investigation of temporal discrimination in fixed-interval reinforcement. *J. exp. Psychol.,* 1954, *47,* 69–74.

SKINNER, B. F. *The behavior of organisms.* New York: Appleton-Century-Crofts, 1938.

SKINNER, B. F. *Science and human behavior.* New York: Macmillan, 1953. (a)

SKINNER, B. F. Some contributions of an experimental analysis of behavior to psychology as a whole. *Amer. Psychologist,* 1953, *8,* 69–78. (b)

32

Self-Regulation of Brain-Stimulating Current Intensity in the Rat

Larry Stein and Oakley S. Ray

It is well established that animals will work to stimulate certain portions of the brain electrically (Olds and Milner, 1954). This self-stimulation technique has considerable promise as a tool for investigating the central nervous system actions of many variables. Olds has reported, for example, that food deprivation, castration, or drugs will selectively change the baseline rates of self-stimulation of particular brain structures (1958).

The present report describes an elaboration of the self-stimulation technique in which animals are furnished with the means to regulate the amount of brain-stimulating current they receive as reinforcement. The new method thus permits a continuous determination of the preferred intensity of stimulation, and at the same time gives the rate of self-stimulation as before.

Similar utilizations of operant conditioning techniques have been reported by Blough (1955) for determining visual thresholds in the pigeon and by Weiss and Laties (1958) for measuring tolerance of pain in the rat.

The animals were trained in a small, sound-resistant box with two levers in one wall. Operations of either lever delivered brief brain shocks. A two-way stepping relay provided 24 equal current steps (from 0 to approximately 50 ma., depending on the electrode impedance) by introducing appropriate resistances into the stimulating circuit. Responses at one lever drove the stepper forward, producing brain shock reinforcements of increasing intensity, and responses at the other stepped it back, decreasing the intensity. Any current level, once established, could be maintained by alternating responses between the levers.

Continuous records of the amount of current selected were drawn by a

Adapted from *Science*, 1959, *130*, 3375, 570–572. With permission of the authors and the American Association for the Advancement of Science.

recording potentiometer whose input voltage was controlled by the two-way relay through an auxiliary bank of resistances. A cumulative response recorder and impulse counters simultaneously provided records of the self-stimulation rate.

The stimulating current was supplied from a pulse-pair generator similar to that described by Lilly *et al.* (1955). The relatively noninjurious wave form had positive and negative peaks each 50 μsec. in duration and separated by 200 μsec. A brain-shock reward consisted of a train of pulse-pairs 50 to 100 cy/sec. in frequency and fixed in duration at either 0.25 or 0.5 sec.; the stepper could not be reoperated until a train was delivered. Optimal values of frequency and train duration varied for different animals and were selected experimentally.

The subjects were male albino rats with bipolar electrodes (0.01-in. platinum wires, twisted together and insulated except at the tips) permanently implanted in rhinencephalic, hypothalamic, and midbrain tegmentum sites. All placements specified were verified histologically. In preliminary training, the animals practiced conventional self-stimulation —either lever gave brain shocks of a fixed, moderately reinforcing intensity. After the self-stimulation rates had stabilized, the rats were required to alternate between the levers to obtain the fixed-intensity electrical stimulus (one 2-hour session).

Training in regulating the current followed on the next day. Most animals learned readily how to control the intensity of the stimulation, and variability decreased rapidly with practice. Assistance from the experimenter early in training—for example, raising the current when it was driven down and held at zero, or lowering it when punishing or convulsive levels were approached—greatly facilitated the process.

Sample records of several consecutive hours of current regulation by two well-trained animals are shown in Figure 1. Five-minute periods of self-stimulation were alternated with 5-minute rest periods during which the stimulator and the box lights were turned off. Resetting the current to zero in the rest periods required the animals to recover the preferred intensity at the start of every stimulation period and provided a stringent test of regulating ability.

Current regulation may be observed to be good in both cases, although the levels selected tended to rise somewhat during the experimental sessions. Both the amount of current preferred and the width of the self-selected intensity band were stable for many weeks and, after sufficient "warm-up," even following long breaks in training.

The amount of rest between sequences of brain-stimulation, both during and between experimental sessions, appears to be a critical factor. Rat F–49, for example, on continuous tegmental self-regulation, typically maintained the preferred level of 13 to 15 ma. for about 30 minutes, and then increased the current to the top step, keeping it there by working only

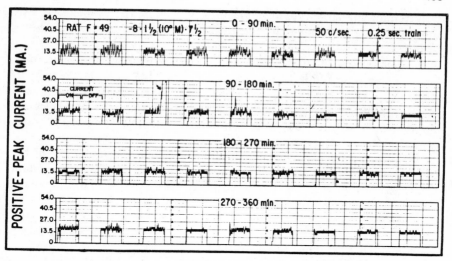

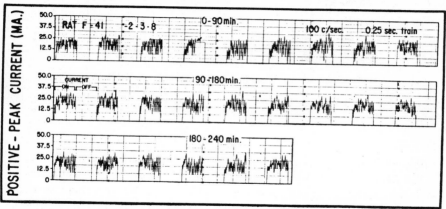

Figure 1. *Current intensities selected throughout an experimental session by two well-trained rats. (Top) Graph for rat F-49, with electrode in midbrain tegmentum. In the 90- to 180-minute segment of the graph, the arrow marks an example of the current-maximizing behavior described in the text. (Bottom) Graph for rat F-41, with electrode in the lateral hypothalamus. The arrow in the 0- to 90-minute segment of the graph indicates a period of no response during which the stimulating leads were untangled. The self-stimulation rates were quite constant throughout the sessions and averaged 34 per minute for rat F-49 and 42 per minute for rat F-41.*

the "up" lever. This current-maximizing behavior was practically elimi-nated by introducing the 5-minute on-off procedure and spacing experi-mental sessions 2 to 3 days apart. Keeping in mind the discussion at the end of the present paper, and assuming with Olds (1958) that positive and negative cell groups are reciprocally inhibitory, one may conclude that these effects may reflect temporary increases in the thresholds of negatively reinforcing structures that are brought about by the intensive self-stimulation of the positive site and which dissipate in time when rest is permitted.

The self-selected intensity level was always well above the reinforcing threshold; usually it was higher than most experimenters would care to assign under the conventional fixed-intensity procedure. Exaggerated and even violent motor activity was often produced by the intensities selected, and after a session of a few hours an animal generally was physically exhausted and wet with saliva.

The effect on intensity regulation of manipulating the frequency of the stimulating current for a rat with an electrode in the midbrain tegmentum is depicted in Figure 2. Similar experiments with other animals employing

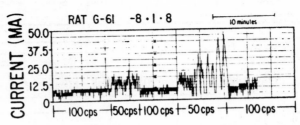

Figure 2.   Changes in the self-selected intensity level induced by manipulation of the frequency (pulse-pair repetition rate) of the stimulating wave form. The data at the end of the experiment are unreliable, owing to the physical exhaustion of the animal.

a limited range of frequencies (25 to 150 cy/sec.) indicate that increases in frequency lead to the selection of smaller intensities, and decreases in frequency lead to higher intensities. The fact that animals tend to compensate for frequency changes in one direction by selecting intensities in the opposite direction suggests that self-regulation is based on a preferred energy of stimulation.

Some of the neural mechanisms that may underlie current-regulating performance may be discussed briefly. Increasing the intensity of the stimulating current train has at least two important effects: (a) the probability or frequency of activation of neurons in the stimulating field is increased; and (b) the effective stimulating field is enlarged to include new elements. On the assumption that animals will work to maximize the firing of positively reinforcing cell groups, it may be expected that, within physiological limits, the greater the current the better. That intermediate intensities are favored may be due, in part, to the spreading of stimulation with large currents to inhibitory or negatively reinforcing regions.

It follows from this that the amount of current selected to stimulate a positively reinforcing site will depend importantly on its proximity to negative cell groups. According to mapping studies of Olds (1956, 1958), negative reinforcing effects are localized caudally in the rat brain; hence, smaller currents should be selected to stimulate caudal rewarding sites (for example, hypothalamus and midbrain tegmentum) than rostral sites (for example, septum and cingulate cortex).

Preliminary findings suggest that this is the case. Electrodes in the region of the septum produced poor regulation—for the most part, the current was increased until convulsions occurred.

Continuous monitoring of the stimulating circuit by means of a cathode-ray oscilloscope and comparison resistances indicated that current increases were actually supplied to the brain and were not the result of artifacts such as polarization of the electrodes.

Even more compelling evidence was provided by an animal (rat F–49) with both an anterior electrode in the cingulate cortex (just rostral to the septum) and a posterior electrode deep in the midbrain tegmentum. Cingulate performance consisted mainly of intensity increases to convulsion-producing levels (usually 40 to 50 ma.), although at the tegmental site the animal self-regulated expertly. Findings related to these have been reported by Roberts (1958) and by Bower and Miller (1958).

It is anticipated that the self-regulation technique will be useful in a variety of situations. Some data have been collected already on the effects of drugs; and to suggest one other example, it seems feasible, by stimulating other brain sites during self-regulation in a particular structure, to obtain information concerning relations of facilitation and inhibition between central structures.

SUMMARY

A modification of the self-stimulation technique of Olds enabled rats to regulate and maintain at a preferred level the amount of brain-stimulating current they received as reinforcement for lever pressing. The method used two levers to deliver brief brain shocks: each response at one lever increased the current intensity a small step and each response at the other lowered it one step.

REFERENCES

BLOUGH, D. S. Method for tracing dark adaptation in the pigeon. *Science*, 1955, *121*, 703–704.

BOWER, G. H., and MILLER, N. E. Rewarding and punishing effects from stimulating the same place in the rat's brain. *J. comp. physiol. Psychol.*, 1958, *51*, 669–674.

LILLY, J. C., *et al.* Brief, noninjurious electric waveform for stimulation of the brain. *Science*, 1955, *121*, 468–469.

OLDS, J. A preliminary mapping of electrical reinforcing effects in the rat brain. *J. comp. physiol. Psychol.*, 1956, *49*, 281–285.

OLDS, J. Self-stimulation of the brain. *Science,* 1958, *127,* 315–324.

OLDS, J., and MILNER, P. Positive reinforcement produced by electrical stimulation of septal area and other regions of rat brain. *J. comp. physiol. Psychol.,*
1954, *47,* 419–427.

ROBERTS, W. W. Both rewarding and punishing effects from stimulation of
posterior hypothalamus of cat with same electrode at same intensity. *J. comp.
physiol. Psychol.,* 1958, *51,* 400–407.

WEISS, B., and LATIES, V. G. Fractional escape and avoidance on a titration
schedule. *Science,* 1958. *128,* 1575–1578.

33

Behavioral Thermoregulation

Bernard Weiss and Victor G. Laties

Behavior is one of the fundamental mechanisms by which organisms regulate body temperature. But, although one can point to numerous illustrations of its importance, quantitative data on the role of behavior in
thermoregulation are rare. Among these are Kinder's findings on nest
building in rats. Employing a technique originally developed by Richter,
she showed that as the ambient temperature fell, rats increased the amount
of paper that they used for nest building (Kinder, 1927; Richter, 1922).

In this article we discuss a recent series of studies on how behavior
contributes to the regulation of body temperature. The major aim of these
studies was to specify the relation between body temperature and a response which provided an exteroceptive source of heat.

The apparatus employed is illustrated in Figure 1. It consists of a Plexiglas cylinder containing a plastic lever attached to a telegraph key. The
red-bulb infrared heat lamp above the chamber goes on for a few seconds
on certain occasions when the rat presses the lever.

The duration of the burst of heat from the lamp is varied by a timer,
and the intensity is varied by a variable transformer. The chambers are
located in a refrigerated room, the temperature of which can be controlled
to within $1°C$. The apparatus that is used to automatically record and
program the relevant events is located in an adjoining room.

Adapted from *Science,* 1961, *133,* 3461, 1338–1344. With permission of the authors. Copyright 1961 by the American Association for the Advancement of Science.

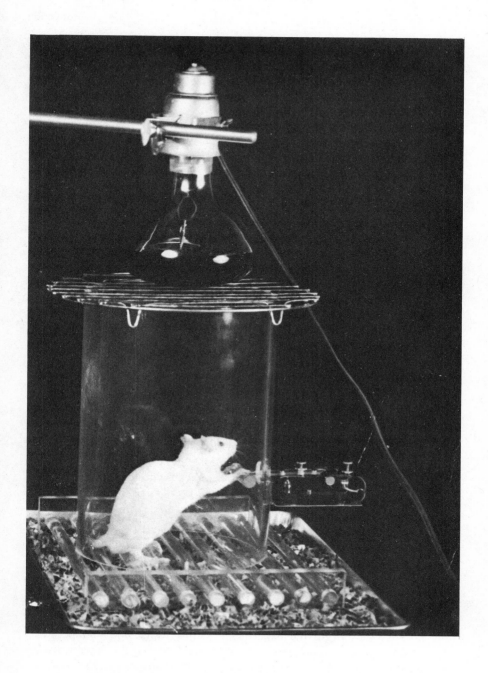

Figure 1. The heat reinforcement apparatus. Depressing the lever closes a switch that activates the heat lamp.

The fur of the rats used in these experiments was removed by clipping before a session. This procedure makes it impossible for the rat to maintain a normal body temperature at the environmental temperatures used in the experiments.

INITIATION

After a rat with no experience in this situation is put into a chamber, it typically spends the first few minutes exploring its surroundings. During this time it occasionally strikes the lever with enough force to close the contacts on the key. This event turns on the heat lamp for several seconds. After this initial flurry of responses the rat usually spends most of the next few hours merely huddling and shivering. Only occasional responses are made during this time. At some point during the session the rat suddenly begins to press the lever at a steady and substantial rate, which it maintains for many hours.

Why does the rat's behavior change so swiftly? It is known that the temperature of a furless rat put into a cold environment undergoes a progressive fall. Perhaps body temperature has to descend to a certain critical point before the burst of heat from the heat lamp becomes reinforcing.

One can test this hypothesis by exposing the rat to cold before putting it into the chamber. Such an experiment was performed with 14 pairs of rats. One member of the pair, randomly selected, was put into a wire-mesh cage in the cold room after being clipped. Its partner was kept at room temperature. Five hours later, both rats were put into test chambers and exposed for 16 hours to a cold-room temperature of 2°C. The heat lamp was set to 250 watts, and each reinforcement (burst of heat) lasted two seconds. This combination produces a transient temperature rise at the skin surface of about 3°C. Each time the lever was pressed while the lamp was off, the lamp came on. Lever presses made while the lamp was on had no effect.

Rats that had been exposed to normal room temperature before being placed in the test chambers waited a mean of 5.16 hours before starting to work for heat at a steady rate. But rats that had spent the immediately preceding 5 hours in the cold waited only a mean of 2.04 hours ($t = 2.40$, $df = 13$, $p < .05$). It appears, therefore, that precooled rats start pressing earlier for heat than rats that have not been precooled, presumably because they begin the experiment with a lower body temperature.

Two other studies supported the hypothesis that the critical variable was a drop in body temperature. In one, the relation between thyroid state and thermoregulatory behavior was examined (Laties and Weiss, 1959). It was found that thyroidectomized rats started to work for heat much earlier during a 16-hour session at 2°C than controls that had undergone a sham operation. This was attributed to the fact that hypothyroid animals lose heat more rapidly in the cold than normal animals (Pichotka, von Kügelen, and Damann, 1953).

The other source of support for the hypothesis came from an experiment on cold acclimatization (Laties and Weiss, 1960). Although animals acclimatized to cold show numerous structural and biochemical changes, perhaps the most dramatic difference between acclimatized and normal rats lies in their resistance to cold after their fur has been removed. Rats that have not been acclimatized die at low temperatures; acclimatized rats survive, presumably because their body temperature does not fall to lethal levels (Sellars, 1957). If the length of the latency (the period before the rats begin to work at a steady rate for heat) is a function of the rate at which body temperature falls in the cold, then acclimatized rats should wait longer than normal rats to begin pressing. They do. There was a considerable difference, with very little overlap, between two groups of eight animals each, one of which had lived about a month at 2°C while the other had been kept at room temperature (25°C).

Despite the evidence favoring the view that a fall in body temperature is the most important factor leading to a steady reinforcement rate, concrete evidence in support of this view was lacking. It was essential to measure body temperature at the same time that the rat was working for heat.

Some preliminary work showed that core temperature changes too slowly, even in an organism as small as the rat, to be sensitive to individual reinforcements. Skin temperature, although quite responsive to individual reinforcements, was rather labile. Subcutaneous temperature also responded to individual reinforcements, but not as transiently as skin temperature. A technique was therefore developed for recording the subcutaneous temperature of a rat moving freely about the experimental chamber. A plastic tube attached to a plastic Luer connector is inserted under the skin on the back and tied to the supraspinous ligament. A purse-string suture is then drawn around a Lucite washer cemented to the tube, and the Luer connector is left projecting from the rat's back. When a rat's temperature is being recorded, a thermocouple (copper-constantan) cemented to a mated Luer connector is inserted in the tube, and the Luer fittings are pressed together. The thermocouple leads to a Minneapolis-Honeywell temperature recorder in another room.

In the next experiment two questions were examined. One was the relation between body temperature and the point at which the rat began to work for heat. The other was the relation between these variables in successive sessions. Each of five rats underwent three 16-hour sessions spaced a week or two apart. The cold room was set at 2°C, and the heat lamp, at 250 watts. Each reinforcement lasted 2 seconds, the heat lamp coming on whenever the lever was pressed while the lamp was off.

The mean subcutaneous temperature at the start of the session was about 35°C for all three sessions. Figure 2 shows records from the first session. For each of the rats except rat NN–N, the figure shows the tem-

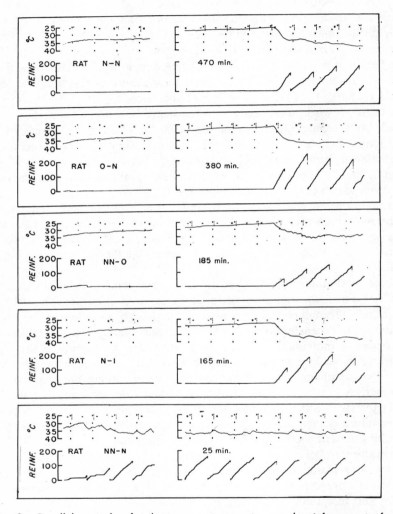

Figure 2. Parallel records of subcutaneous temperature and reinforcements for all five rats on their first session. Records at left, temperature and reinforcements during the first hour in the cold. Top four records at right, temperature and reinforcements during the hour preceding and the hour following the initiation of steady lever pressing. Record at the bottom (rat NN-N), temperature and reinforcements during the entire first three hours, shown because of the short latency. Also shown for each rat in the records at right is the latency (in minutes) to the initiation of steady lever pressing. Reinforcements were recorded cumulatively, the recording pen resetting to the base line every 15 minutes.

perature and reinforcement records for the first hour in the chamber and for the hour before and after the start of consistent responding. The upper tracing represents subcutaneous temperature, and the lower represents reinforcements as recorded on a cumulative recorder. Because the latency for rat NN–N is unusually short, all of the first 180 minutes of the session are shown for this rat. Just why rat NN–N started pressing so early is difficult to say. This may be related to the fact that the rat's initial temperature (33.2°C) was the lowest in the group.

Subcutaneous temperature declines from the time the rat is placed in the chamber until it begins to work steadily for heat. Then, as shown in Figure 2, subcutaneous temperature rises when the rat begins to respond. The transition from a near-zero reinforcement rate to a steady and substantial one occurs so abruptly that it looks practically instantaneous on the records. Once the rat begins to obtain reinforcements at a steady rate, the temperature climbs rapidly to the level that is maintained for the rest of the 16-hour session.

The data in Figure 2 are from experimentally naive rats. Does the same sequence of events appear in rats already experienced in the situation? Figure 3 shows, for the same five rats and for three successive sessions, the amount of fall in subcutaneous temperature between the time the rat was placed in the chamber and the time it began to obtain reinforcements at a steady rate. The mean fall in temperature was 8.20°C for the first session, 3.68°C for the second, and 4.64°C for the third. An analysis of variance showed that differences among sessions were significant at the .05 level; the main contribution to this result is the difference between the first session and the two later sessions. It appears, therefore, that once the rat has had experience in this situation, a fall in temperature considerably less than the fall required in the first session initiates responding. What other factors contribute to the change in latency is a still unanswered question.

MAINTENANCE

The peripheral event that seems most closely related to the initiation of a steady rate of working for heat is a drop in peripheral temperature. Another question is, what keeps a rat working for heat? In particular, what governs the rate at which it obtains reinforcements?

Since the rat survives, the reinforcement rate must be governed in part by the body temperature; otherwise, the rat would succumb to the cold or burn its skin. An interesting deduction follows. If the amount of heat per reinforcement increases, the rate should decrease; if the amount of heat per reinforcement decreases, the rate should increase. In a recent series of studies (Weiss and Laties, 1960) the amount of heat per reinforcement was varied in two ways: by varying the intensity of the heat lamp and by

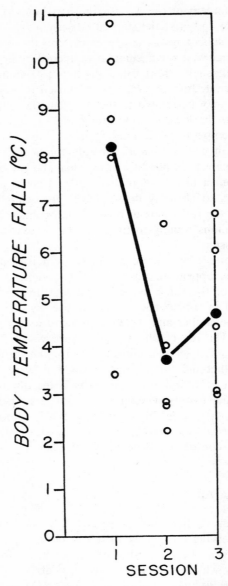

Figure 3. *Amount of fall in subcutaneous temperature before the initiation of a steady rate of working for heat. Data for three successive sessions are shown. Open circles, individual rats; solid circles, the means.*

varying the length of time that it remained on. We discuss here only the data obtained by intensity variation, since both methods of varying the amount of heat per reinforcement give the same results.

Six different intensity settings were selected for the experiment: 125, 175, 225, 275, 325, and 375 watts. Figure 4 shows the transient rises in skin and subcutaneous temperature produced in an anesthetized rat by 2-second bursts of heat with different settings of the lamp. The cold room was maintained at 2°C. After a rat was put into the chamber, we waited

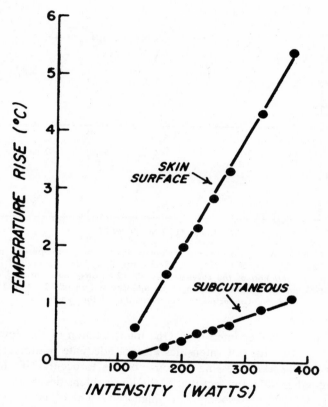

Figure 4. Transient changes in skin temperature and subcutaneous temperature produced by 2-second bursts of heat with the intensities shown. The subject was an anesthetized rat.

until it had been responding steadily for at least 30 minutes. Then, according to a randomly determined sequence, it was switched from one intensity setting to another every 30 minutes. A dozen rats took part in this study.

Pooling the data from all 12 of the rats used in the experiment produced a monotonic function between 125 and 375 watts; the greater the intensity, the lower the reinforcement rate. The cumulative records showed that the change in rate following a change in intensity took place at once. But, as Figure 5 shows, five of the individual curves reverse either at 125 or at 175 watts. Three of the seven rats that did not show a reversal were run at a reinforcement intensity of 75 watts. All three then responded less

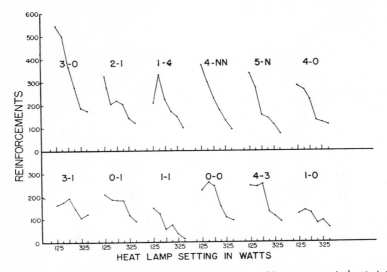

Figure 5. Number of reinforcements obtained in a 30-minute period at intensity settings of 125, 175, 225, 275, 325, and 375 watts. The data are plotted individually for each rat. The left end of the curve represents 125 watts; the right end, 375 watts. Rats 2-1, 4-NN, and O-1 were also run at an intensity setting of 75 watts. These points are not connected to the remainder of the function.

than they had at higher intensities. One interpretation of this lowered rate of response is that the low intensities are not adequate reinforcers, so that extinction of the lever-pressing response begins to occur. This interpretation is strengthened by the fact that at the lower intensities there were often alternating periods of responding at high rates and of no responding at all. Such behavior is also characteristic of inadequate food reinforcement (Ferster and Skinner, 1957).

Once the technique for recording temperature in the freely moving rat had been developed, an obvious application was to perform another experiment on intensity variation. Four intensities were selected: 155, 205, 260, and 310 watts. According to measurements on an anesthetized rat (see Figure 4), single 2-second bursts of heat at these intensities produced transient rises in skin temperature of 1°, 2°, 3°, and 4°C.

The performance of each of eight trained rats was recorded at each intensity for two hours. Figure 6 shows the mean subcutaneous temperature maintained during this 2-hour session. The three highest intensity

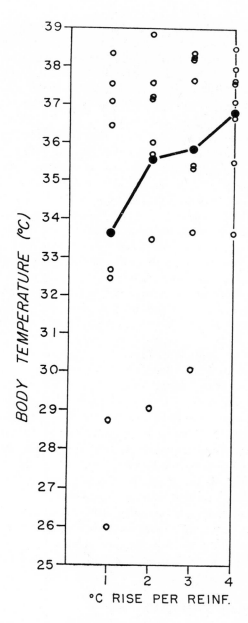

Figure 6. Mean subcutaneous temperature maintained during a 2-hour period as a function of heat-lamp setting. This setting is given in terms of the rise in skin temperature, in degrees centigrade, produced by an individual reinforcement. Open circles, individual rats; solid circles, the means. These data were obtained by calculating the mean temperature during twenty-four 5-minute segments of the 2-hour experimental period. The temperature represented by the open circles is the grand mean for each rat for the entire 2-hour period.

reinforcements led to higher temperatures than the lowest intensity. An analysis of variance indicated that the temperature differences for the four intensities were significant at the .05 level, but only the differences between temperatures at the lowest intensity and temperatures at the other intensities were significant according to t tests.

This finding is similar to that displayed in Figure 5—namely, a disproportionately low increase in reinforcement rate to compensate for the decline in reinforcement intensity when the latter falls below about 175 watts. The function obtained by connecting the mean values, however, does not reflect the performance of all the subjects. Four rats (half the group) showed no temperature difference as a function of heat-lamp setting. The other four showed a considerable dip at the lowest setting. There was a good deal of consistency in the temperature values for individual rats. The animal with the lowest temperature at the lowest intensity setting also had the lowest temperature at the three higher settings. The four rats that maintained the lowest temperatures at the lowest intensity also maintained the lowest temperatures at the next two highest intensities. At the highest intensity there was more overlap, but the two highest temperatures were maintained by rats from the top half of the group, while the two lowest temperatures were maintained by rats from the bottom half of the group.

The temperature records in Figure 7 represent the first hour of each 2-hour session at the four different intensity settings of the heat lamp used in this experiment. Rat A is the animal designated in Figure 6 by the second circle from the bottom at a heat-lamp setting of 1°C rise per reinforcement. This rat maintained a relatively low temperature at this reinforcement setting. At the higher reinforcement settings, however, he maintained a peripheral temperature close to the normal value. Rat B is designated in Figure 6 by the topmost circle at a setting of 1°C rise per reinforcement. That is, he maintained the highest subcutaneous temperature of the group at this heat-lamp setting. Note the stability of the temperature tracing, and note how relatively little variation there is as a function of reinforcement intensity. These records illustrate the main finding of this experiment: that rats adjust reinforcement rate in accordance with reinforcement intensity to produce the end result of a constant peripheral temperature.

METABOLIC VARIABLES

The tendency of rats to compensate for variations in the intensity parameter by variations in reinforcement rate and the stability with which they maintain peripheral temperature by such behavior suggest that the heat-reinforcement technique might be useful for studying metabolic vari-

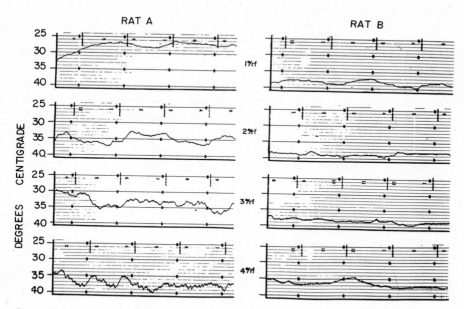

Figure 7.   Records of subcutaneous temperature for two rats at the four different heat-lamp settings noted. Only the record for the first hour of each 2-hour session is shown. These rats belong to the group of Figure 6 (see text).

ables. That is, if we interfere with or enhance the rat's ability to produce heat, would we find compensatory changes in behavior?

In some earlier experiments one of us found that starved and underfed rats responded more often than control rats to obtain heat reinforcement (Weiss, 1957a, 1957b). Hamilton varied the technique by allowing the rats to determine the duration of the reinforcement (1959). He found that food-deprived animals kept the lamp on for a greater portion of a session than controls did. Carlton and Marks (1958) found that cold-exposed rats that had suffered weight loss turned on a hot-air blower in the cold more frequently than control rats did. And, studying a quite different kind of behavior, Kinder (1927) found that rats deprived of food increased their nest-building activity. There seems little doubt that the disturbance of heat balance produced by starvation and weight loss is reflected in compensatory behavior.

A higher proportion of rats fed a diet deficient in the vitamin pantothenic acid die in the cold than rats fed an adequate diet. The former also press a lever at a higher rate for heat reinforcement than the latter (Weiss,

1957a, 1957b). It seems likely that this is another example of how the inability to maintain body temperature in the cold is reflected in overt behavioral thermoregulation.

Our most complete data on metabolic state and thermoregulatory behavior come from a series of studies on thyroid function (Laties and Weiss, 1959). It was stated above that hypothyroid rats begin to respond earlier during a session than euthyroid rats, presumably because their body temperature falls more rapidly. Hypothyroid rats also seek reinforcements at a higher rate than euthyroid rats once they begin to work steadily for heat. Part of the difference, at least, results from the fact that rats with intact thyroids pause more frequently during the session than hypothyroid rats; the hypothyroid rats work at the task with greater constancy.

One can counteract the deficit in heat production that accompanies hypothyroidism by administering a thyroid hormone. In one experiment we were able to produce a fall in the frequency of heat reinforcements sought by thyroidectomized rats by administering the thyroid hormone 3,5,3'–1–triiodothyronine via their drinking water. The fall was great enough, in fact, to carry the rate below that of their intact controls.

With the present system, then, metabolic variables that influence the heat-production capacity of the rat are reflected in the rate at which it works for heat.

BASIS OF THERMOREGULATORY BEHAVIOR

The experiments under discussion were directed toward the question of how behavior contributes to the regulation of body temperature. Two aspects of this question were considered: the factors that lead to the initiation of thermoregulatory behavior and the factors that maintain it.

By correlating subcutaneous temperature with the behavior of pressing a lever for brief bursts of heat, we were able to show that the rat's behavior in the situation we have described results in a fairly constant peripheral temperature. The very precision with which the rat regulates this temperature poses a problem. Why does a large drop in body temperature seem necessary to initiate responding, while much smaller fluctuations govern reinforcement rate once a substantial rate of responding is established?

One reasonable possibility is that when the rat is first placed in the cold, lever pressing must compete with other responses elicited by the cold, such as shivering and huddling. When shivering and huddling can no longer avert a further decline in temperature, they may then be replaced by gross motor activity. When such activity accidentally results in depression of the lever, the burst of heat from the heat lamp produces such a profound change that it is quickly followed by other presses. A sudden onset of responding also appears when food, rather than heat, is the reinforcement (Skinner, 1938).

A more general question may also be asked. What do these data demonstrate about the way in which behavior fits into the pattern of regulatory processes that sustain life?

In most of the experiments set up to answer such questions, factors that control eating and drinking have been studied—to determine, for example, whether an animal can compensate for a diet deficient in a particular substance by the appropriate selection of nutrients. Such studies have demonstrated that under many conditions animals do vary ingestive behavior to compensate for deficiency states. But in numerous instances they do not. Perhaps the reason for the substantial proportion of failures in experiments on eating and drinking is the long chain of processes that intervene between behavior and the ultimate effect. By contrast, the effect of heat is practically instantaneous. This is probably the reason why behavior seems so exquisitely attuned to the regulation of body temperature.

REFERENCES

CARLTON, P. L., and MARKS, R. A. Cold exposure and heat reinforced operant behavior. *Science,* 1958, *128,* 1344.

FERSTER, C. B., and SKINNER, B. F. *Schedules of reinforcement.* New York: Appleton-Century-Crofts, 1957.

HAMILTON, C. L. Effect of food deprivation on thermal behavior of the rat. *Proc. soc. exp. biol. Med.,* 1959, *100,* 354–356.

KINDER, E. F. A study of nest-building activity of the albino rat. *J. exp. Zool.,* 1927, *47,* 117–161.

LATIES, V. G., and WEISS, B. Thyroid state and working for heat in the cold. *Am. J. Physiol.,* 1959, *197,* 1028–1034.

LATIES, V. G., and WEISS, B. Behavior in the cold after acclimatization. *Science,* 1960, *131,* 1891–1892.

PICHOTKA, J., VON KÜGELEN, B., and DAMANN, R. Die Bedeutung der Schilddrüse fur die Temperature-regulation. *Arch. exp. Pathol. Pharmakol. Naunyn-Schmiedeberg's,* 1953, *220,* 398–413.

RICHTER, C. P. A behavioristic study of the activity of the rat. *Comp. psychol. Monogr.,* 1922, *1,* 1–55.

SELLARS, E. A. Adaptive and related phenomena in rats exposed to cold. *Rev. Canad. Biol.,* 1957, *16,* 175–188.

SKINNER, B. F. *The behavior of organisms.* New York: Appleton-Century-Crofts, 1938.

WEISS, B. Pantothenic acid deprivation and thermal behavior of the rat. *Am. J. clin. Nutrition,* 1957, *5,* 125–128. (a)

WEISS, B. Thermal behavior of the subnourished and pantothenic-acid-deprived rat. *J. comp. physiol. Psychol.,* 1957, *50,* 481–485. (b)

WEISS, B., and LATIES, V. G. Magnitude of reinforcement as a variable in thermoregulatory behavior. *J. comp. physiol. Psychol.,* 1960, *53,* 603–608.

34

Preference and Switching Under Concurrent Scheduling

Jack D. Findley

Recent work by Ferster and Skinner (1957) includes several experiments with a type of procedure described as concurrent scheduling. In one variation of this procedure, two operants are separately maintained by primary reinforcement. Reinforcement of these operants is programmed by independent schedules such that the reinforcement of one operant is not directly contingent upon the emission of the other.

The specific behavior resulting from such concurrent scheduling depends upon the nature of the schedules imposed, but is largely characterized by the observed prepotency of first one operant and then the other. This alternation in prepotency, here defined as switching, may be further accompanied by a second characteristic, namely preference. Thus, if a sample of the behavior shows the organism to be emitting one operant to the partial exclusion of the other, then a relative preference is defined for that operant.

The present paper reports a series of experiments concerned with the maintenance of preference and switching under concurrent-type procedures. These experiments originated with the scheduling of primary reinforcement for two operants in a manner similar to that described by Ferster and Skinner (1957). Consideration of this experiment resulted in the development and exploration of a modified procedure in which switching was made more explicit, and in which the behavior receiving primary reinforcement was subject to greater stimulus control.

Adapted from *Journal of the Experimental Analysis of Behavior*, 1958, *1*, 123–144. With permission of the author and publisher.

GENERAL PROCEDURES AND TECHNIQUE

The general technique, common to all of the following experiments, was the training of Utility King pigeons to peck one or more illuminated keys for grain. Delivery of such grain together with the special conditions of a given experiment were programmed by automatic equipment. The birds were typically trained for a given period each day, 7 days a week.

The technical considerations relevant to operant-conditioning experiments with pigeons have been extensively described by Ferster and Skinner (1957), and by Ferster (1953). Since the general procedures and apparatus used in the present experiments follow closely that used by the above investigators, only sufficient detail will be presented with each experiment to clarify the special procedures under consideration. Some departures in general technique, however, are mentioned below.

The grain used as reinforcement of the pecking response was that portion of commercial Purina Pigeon Chow which would pass freely through $\frac{3}{16}$-inch-diameter holes, but not through $\frac{1}{8}$-inch wire mesh. The remainder of this chow was used in nonexperimental feeding, if needed to maintain desired body weights. Vitamins, grit, and mineral supplement were made available to all birds to insure good health.

The experiments were begun with a single experimental unit to which a second and third were subsequently added. Recording of behavior and stimulus conditions from these units was by means of counters, Telechron clocks, and two cumulative recorders.

Partly as a consequence of limitations in recording devices, the general program received an emphasis upon final performance under a given procedure. This emphasis, unfortunately, resulted in the loss of much systematic data on acquisition and transitional effects. In the experiments to follow, therefore, discussion of such effects are minimized.

TWO-KEY CONCURRENT SCHEDULING

The first procedure investigated consisted of training pigeons to peck two illuminated keys for grain. These keys were separated by 6 inches in the front of a conventional pigeon apparatus, and reinforcements were programmed for each key by two continuously moving variable-interval (VI) tapes.[1] The mean interval of these schedules was 4 minutes. A special feature of the programming circuit was a delay contingency such that a reinforcement on one key could not follow a response on the other by less than 5 seconds.

After approximately 30 experimental hours, the behavior had become

---

[1] All programming of interval contingencies reported in this paper were timed from the end of a previous interval, not from a previous reinforcement.

reasonably stable and the birds were observed to work first at one key and then the other, switching keys on the order of 9 times per minute. These switches characteristically followed either the delivery of grain, or a brief period of responding at each key.

The behavior was recorded with separate cumulative recorders, and it was apparent that the responding at each key was a high and sustained rate. However, since the time axis of both recorders ran continuously, the record from one key also included the time devoted to responding on the other. Figure 1 shows the resulting stepwise-type recordings for two birds. In this type of record, switches from one key to another were not difficult to infer, since the birds worked a fairly definite period of time at each key as a consequence of the delay contingency. But when the delay contingency was subsequently removed, the switching rates approximately doubled and consequently removed much of the stepwise character from each record.

In general, the results of these brief experiments were similar to those of Ferster and Skinner in indicating that concurrent scheduling may be

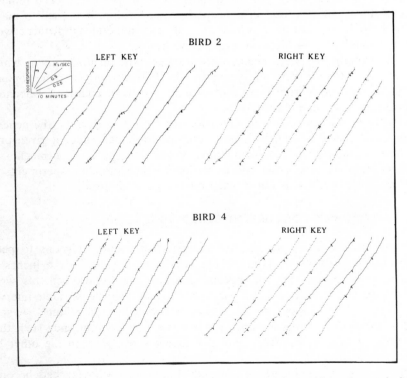

Figure 1. Performance under two-key concurrent scheduling with a 5-second delay contingency.

expected to maintain two operants and generate substantial switching. In the above experiments, however, the exact conditions providing the basis for switching were not clear, and much of the total behavior sequence appeared to be omitted. Two types of procedural modifications were indicated. First, the switching behavior needed to be made explicit; and secondly, the stimulus occasion for each operant reinforced with grain needed to be clearly specified and more subject to the experimenter's control. A procedure was then developed to meet these general demands.

THE SWITCHING-KEY PROCEDURE

In this procedure, pigeons were trained to peck a key which could be illuminated either red or green, and provision was made for associating a given grain schedule with each color. A second key, illuminated white, was located 3 inches to the left and permitted the birds, by a single peck, to switch the color appearing on the first key. This procedure, then, made explicit a switching operant and allowed the behavior reinforced with grain to come under the control of the two colors. Each change in color was defined as a switch.

PREFERENCE AND SWITCHING UNDER VARIABLE-INTERVAL

In the first experiments performed with the newly adopted procedure, VI schedules were also used, programmed as before, but without a delay contingency. They were designed to determine to what extent the rates of response and the percentage time spent in the two colors could be influenced by the mean values of the schedules imposed.

The birds used in the previous experiments were now exposed to the switching-key procedure. The transition was quite rapid and required no special training. Following adaptation, a program was pursued in which the four birds were trained for 4 hours a day for 7 days under a given pair of schedules, and then successively shifted to other pairs of schedules. The means of the schedules were 2, 4, 6, 12, and 20 minutes.[2] From the last 150 minutes of each 4-hour session the following data were obtained: time spent in each color, the rate of response in each color, and the switching rate.

[2] All VI schedules were based upon arithmetical progressions from the expressions:
$$S = N/2(A + L) \quad (1), \text{ and } D = (L - A)/(N - 1) \quad (2), \text{ where}$$
S = the sum, 60 minutes; N = the number of intervals or reinforcements; A = the minimum interval, 0.2 minute; L = the longest interval; and D = the progression constant. Since, for a given mean schedule, S, N, and A were known, solution of (1) gave L. Having obtained L, solution of (2) gave D. Knowing D, the series of intervals were determined and then randomized.

Birds 5 and 6

The procedure followed for Birds 5 and 6 consisted of pairing successively a VI 6-minute schedule in the red with a 2-, 4-, 6-, 12-, and 20-minute VI schedule in the green. (See Table 1.) Figure 2 shows a typical

TABLE 1

Mean VI schedules paired in red and green expressed in minutes.

Birds 5 and 6		Bird 2		Bird 4	
Red	Green	Red	Green	Red	Green
6	2	2	20	2	2
6	4	4	12	4	4
6	6	6	6	6	6
6	12	12	4	12	12
6	20	20	2	20	20

pair of recordings from Bird 6 covering a complete 4-hour session. Each cumulative record sums the responses and time only under a particular color. This pair of records indicates that the rate of response under a given color and the division of time between colors depended upon the mean value of each schedule. These two types of effects were also found in the data obtained from the last 2½ hours under all combinations of schedules. These data are summarized for Birds 5 and 6 in Figure 3. As the mean reinforcement interval in the green was increased, both birds responded at a slower rate in the green, and worked for shorter periods of time in this color. The response rates while in the red showed little change for Bird 5, but showed an increase for Bird 6.

Bird 2

The procedure for Bird 2 was the same as that for Birds 5 and 6 except that as the mean reinforcement interval in the green was increased at successive stages from 2 to 20 minutes, the mean interval in the red was decreased from 20 to 2 minutes. (See Table 1.)

Under this procedure the rate of response in each color and the percentage time in each color were found to be inversely related to the mean reinforcement interval. Figure 4 summarizes these data under the different schedules.

Bird 4

To serve as a control for the effects of differential schedules, Bird 4 was trained under identical mean schedules in red and green, and the

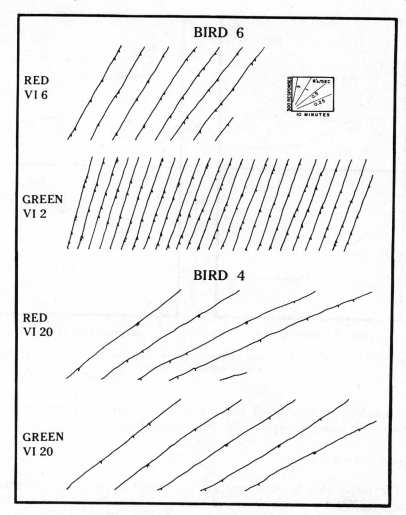

Figure 2. Typical behavior under switching-key procedure with variable-interval schedules associated with each color.

mean of these schedules was varied from 2 to 20 minutes. As the mean reinforcement interval was increased, the rate of response in both colors declined, while the amount of time spent in red and green remained approximately equal. (See Figure 4 and Figure 2.)

The results of the above experiments were clear in indicating that the division of time between the two colors was a function of relative reinforcement conditions. Thus, preference, defined by the relative predominance of one color, was easily manipulated by altering the mean value of

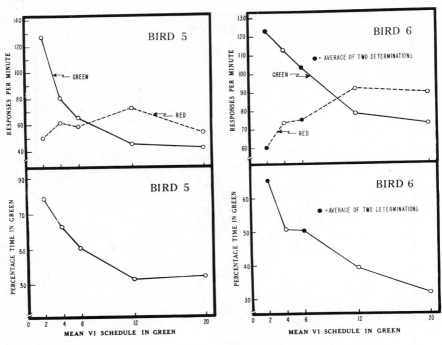

Figure 3. *Rates of response and percentage time in green as a function of mean variable interval in green.*

the schedules. The over-all response rate in each color was generally observed to follow changes in the grain schedules.

Switching Rates

The above data summarizing relative response rates and percentage time in each color were possible, of course, since the birds were switching colors on the order of 12 to 20 times per minute. Changes in the switching rates, however, were generally not found to vary in an orderly fashion with changes in the mean reinforcement schedules. Lack of an orderly relationship between these variables was concluded to result, on the one hand, from the arbitrary length of training under a given pair of schedules, and, on the other hand, from the manner which the schedules provided for the switching. Where two punched tapes are providing the VI schedules, these tapes may run continuously, or they may be set to run only in the presence of each color. If the two tapes run continuously, as in the above procedure, the total reinforcements may be maximized by a given switching rate to an extent determined by the mean values of the schedules. In practice, however, the switching rate may vary considerably

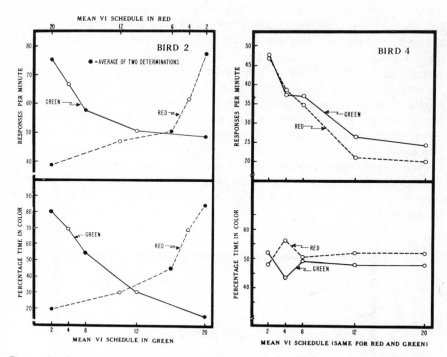

Figure 4. *Response rates and percentage time in each color as a function of mean variable-interval schedules.*

without materially affecting the total reinforcements received. This is possible since a reinforcement can accrue on the tape associated with the absent color. Such an accrued reinforcement would then be delivered with the first response following the reappearance of that color.

The delivery of a reinforcement in one color closely following a switch, either as a result of an accrued reinforcement or as a consequence of the varying intervals of the schedules, would presumably not only strengthen responding in a given color, but would also strengthen switching. Thus, in the above procedures, the maintenance of switching was due in part to the maximizing of total reinforcements, and perhaps to a greater extent due to the occasional delivery of reinforcement closely following a switch in colors. Since under a given pair of schedules the factors affording this maintenance were specified only within rather wide limits, little systematic effect on the switching rate was found when the means of the various schedules were varied.

Observation of the switching rates of birds previously trained under the method of continuously moving tapes when the tapes were set to run independently for each color proved that this method was largely responsible for the maintenance of the switching behavior; i.e., the tape for a given color would run only during the presence of that color. Figure 5 shows the decline of the switching rate in two such cases. For Bird 5, a VI 6-minute schedule in the red was paired with a VI 2-minute schedule in the green; and for Bird 2, the schedules were VI 6 minutes in both colors. An examination of the switching rate during the last hour of each daily session showed in both cases a decline to almost zero by the end of the fourth session. Thus, when each tape was run only in the presence of each color, much of the indirect reinforcement for switching was removed. Consequently, this aspect of the behavior was not maintained. Following the decline in switching rates the birds would occasionally remain in one color throughout the entire session. In the case of Bird 5, where the two schedules differed, the color having the shorter mean interval was found to predominate.

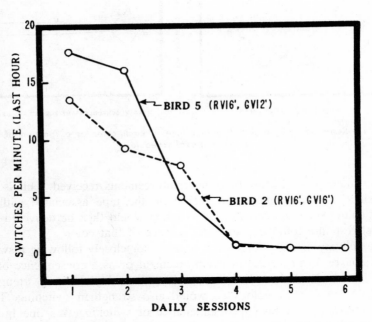

Figure 5. *Showing decline in switching rates when each reinforcement tape ran only in the presence of each color.*

SWITCHING UNDER PROGRESSIVE CONTINGENCIES

In order to examine switching behavior further, reinforcement schedules were sought which would not only give rise to switching, but which would also be better specified and free of the undesirable effects found under VI schedules programmed with continuously moving tapes. After a period of experimentation, schedules were developed in which the contingencies for reinforcement in a given color became progressively altered with successive reinforcements and each switch in color would reinstate the original contingencies.

Thus, as before, birds were reinforced with grain for pecking a key which was illuminated either red or green. Pecking in a given color, however, became less favorable, grain-wise, the longer that color and the associated schedules were in effect. At any time following the first reinforcement in a given color, a peck on the switching key changed the color and reset the schedules to zero. Pecks on the switching key before the first reinforcement were ineffective.

During this period of experimentation, a rather wide variety of schedules were explored and use was made of both ratio and interval contingencies. For a given bird, however, the same set of contingencies prevailed in red and green. Examination of Figure 6 reveals, in general, the type of schedules imposed and the method of recording.

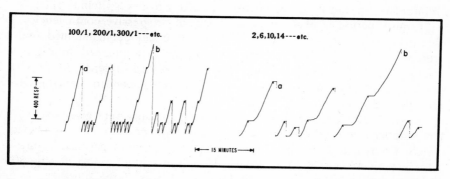

Figure 6. Example of behavior under progressive contingencies showing method of recording.

In Figure 6 the left record was obtained with schedules based upon the following ratio contingencies. The first reinforcement in each color required 100 responses; the second, 200 responses; the third, 300 responses; etc. Thus, the number of responses required for reinforcement increased by 100 responses with each successive reinforcement. The first switch in colors occurs at point a, which is indicated by the recorder returning to the base line and by the delivery of reinforcement following only 100 responses in the new color. The recorder also resets to the base line at point b, after traveling the maximum excursion, but does not indicate a switch in color.

The second record shown in Figure 6 was obtained under interval contingencies. Beginning in a given color, the first interval was 2 minutes; the second, 6 minutes; the third, 10 minutes; etc. Thus, the minimum interval in both colors was 2 minutes and increased by 4 minutes with each successive reinforcement. The reset of the pen at point *a* again indicates a switch in colors, while that at point *b* does not. In practice, these two cases may be easily distinguished by a knowledge of the schedules and by an examination of the record following a reset of the pen.

The type of behavior illustrated in Figure 6 often requires considerable training to establish, and its development varies widely, depending upon the past history of the organism and the values of the schedules. In general, however, the acquisition of such behavior is observed to follow certain stages. Early behavior under such schedules is characterized by extended periods of responding in one color, extinction-like performance, and few pauses following reinforcement. With continued training, the switching response increases in strength and the effect of either ratio or interval contingencies is seen in the over-all response rate and in the development of pauses following reinforcement. A final performance is often indicated by the occurrence of switches primarily following the pause after reinforcement, and by a reasonably stable day-to-day switching rate.

From a period of exploratory treatment of progressive contingencies, it became clear that stable switching behavior could be maintained under certain conditions. Further experiments were then pursued to examine behavior under these schedules in greater detail, and to determine to what extent the maintenance of the switching behavior depended upon the progressive schedules.

Four of the birds used in the previous experiments were given extensive training in which successive comparisons were made between the behavior under fixed- and under progressive-reinforcement contingencies. Figure 7 shows typical records from these comparisons after approximately 500 reinforcements under a given condition. In Figure 7 the schedules were based upon interval contingencies for Bird 10, and upon ratio contingencies for Birds 8 and 5. For a given bird and condition, identical schedules were again used in red and green.

Following a past history of various progressive schedules, Bird 10 was trained under fixed-interval (FI) schedules of 1 minute in both colors. Within 25 experimental sessions the switching rate had declined to almost zero. An example of behavior during the latter days of this condition is that shown in Figure 7. On day 26, the fixed schedules were altered to progressive schedules 1, 9, 17, 25, etc. Under these schedules, the switching behavior reappeared and stabilized at a relatively high rate within 9 additional sessions. Part of a record from the last day under this schedule is that shown in the top record of Figure 7.

In Figure 7 the records for Birds 8 and 5 show comparisons between stable behavior obtained under progressive-ratio and under fixed-ratio

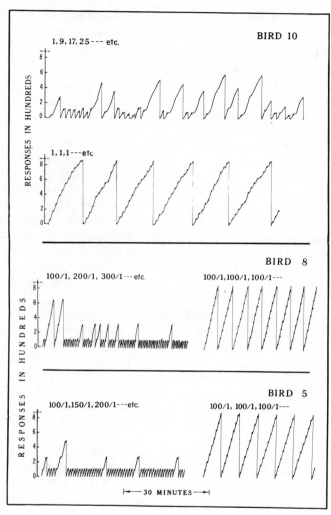

Figure 7. *Sample records comparing behavior under fixed and under progressive contingencies.*

schedules. High switching rates were found under the progressive-ratio schedules, but could not be maintained under the fixed-ratio schedules. This effect was found independent of the order of transition, although, as was found with the interval comparisons, considerably more training was required for the decline of the switching rates than for their establishment.

In general, the results of these comparisons outlined in Figure 7 not only showed that switching behavior could be maintained under progressive contingencies, but also revealed its absence under fixed schedules. This latter finding was consistent with the lack of switching found under VI schedules programmed to run only in the presence of each color, and again suggested that a procedure was being used which gave rise to little spontaneous switching.

Amount of Change with Successive Reinforcements

Early work with progressive contingencies had suggested that the switching rate under a given pair of schedules would in part be determined by the amount of change introduced with successive reinforcements. Such a function seemed even more likely since switching was maintained under progressive schedules, but not under fixed schedules. Thus, a schedule in which the minimum reinforcement contingency increased rapidly with successive reinforcements should result in a high switching rate compared with a schedule whose contingencies increase more slowly. This was found to be the case, both in several instances of shifting schedules to obtain a desired base line, and also from more direct evidence obtained from Bird 7.

Bird 7, which had a substantial past history under interval schedules, was given further training under several progressive-interval schedules, each with different amounts of change. The variable under investigation was the constant with which the minimum interval increased with successive reinforcements. This minimum interval was always 1 minute and the schedules used were based upon a constant increment of 8, 6, 4, 2, or 0 minutes, and presented in that order. The bird was run for at least 500 reinforcements under a given set of schedules and until the switching rate had become reasonably stable.

Sample records from the latter days under each condition are presented in Figure 8. Under the 1, 9, 17, 25, etc., schedules, where each successive interval increases by 8 minutes, a relatively high switching rate was observed of the order of 0.5 per minute. It should be observed that the maximum switching rate would be one per minute, since no peck on the switching key was effective until after the first reinforcement in each color.

Under the schedules with less change, 1, 5, 9, 13, etc., and 1, 3, 5, 7, etc., the pauses following reinforcement grew longer and the bird typically remained in both colors for greater periods of time before switching. These effects resulted in a lower and somewhat more variable switching rate. The introduction of the FI 1-minute schedule was again observed to reduce the switching rate to near zero.

A plot of the data from the last two days under each of the above conditions revealed the switching rate to be an increasing monotonic function of the constant with which successive intervals were increased.

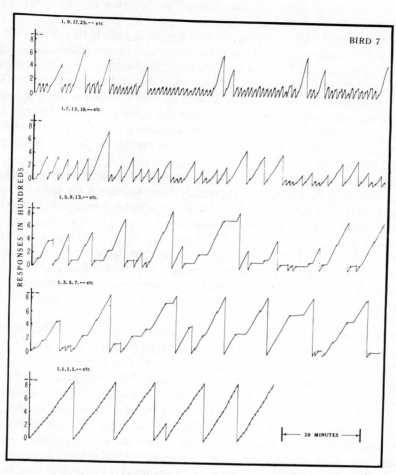

Figure 8. Sample records showing switching rate as a function of the amount of change with successive intervals.

Fixed-ratio Contingencies for Switching

In the experiments discussed thus far, one peck of the switching key was sufficient to reverse the color on the key providing the delivery of grain. This was considered as the simplest contingency that could be imposed. Implied in this contingency, however, is a class of various requirements which might have been used, e.g., higher ratios, higher intervals, and perhaps delayed responding. One such contingency which was treated in some detail was the ratio required to switch colors. This variable, like amount of change with successive reinforcements, was found to have a

pronounced effect upon switching rate. The direction of this effect, however, was opposite.

A given fixed ratio required to accomplish a switch in colors (FR to
SW) was introduced into the general procedure in the following manner.
If, for example, an FR of 10 was required, the first peck on the switching
key would remove the prevailing color from the grain-reinforced key. The
tenth peck on the switching key would then re-illuminate the grain-reinforced key with the new color and reset the schedules. The response and
time components of the recorder were disconnected during the switching
of colors, but indicated the occurrence of a switch, as before, by a reset
of the pen to the base line.

The effects of higher FR's required to switch colors were first examined with Bird 8, which had previously been stabilized on identical progressive-ratio schedules in each color. These schedules were 100/1, 200/1,
300/1, 400/1, etc., and one peck had been required to switch colors and
reset the schedules. When, at this point, an FR of 10 was introduced,
some disruption of the behavior resulted; but within approximately 6
hours of further training, ratio performance was established on the switching key and a switch of colors would be completed within seconds. The
bird was now observed, however, to work for a longer period in each
color before switching.

Following this preliminary training, Bird 8 was given further training
under each of five different FR's required to switch colors. These ratios
were 1, 20, 40, 80, and 100 responses. The bird was run for at least 500
reinforcements and until the behavior had stabilized under each FR.
Figure 9 shows sample records from the latter days under each condition.

An examination of data from these conditions reveals most of the general characteristics which were previously outlined for behavior under
progressive schedules. The effect of increasing the FR required to switch
colors was primarily to drive the organism to higher ratios before the
occurrence of a switch. This effect was obtained without any loss in the
over-all response rate, and the responding which switched the colors was
typical ratio performance and revealed no "breaks."

The average switching rate, obtained from the last 3 days under each
condition, was found to be a decreasing monotonic function of the ratio
required for a switch.

PREFERENCE UNDER PROGRESSIVE CONTINGENCIES

In the previous experiments with progressive schedules, use had been
made of identical schedules in red and green. Under these conditions, no
consistent preferences developed for either color. The introduction, then,
of two different schedules seemed likely to result in a preference for the

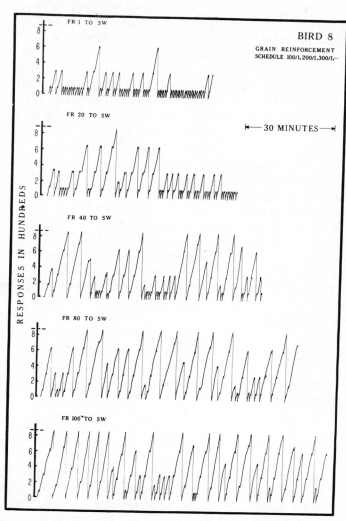

Figure 9. *Sample records showing decline of switching rates with higher fixed ratios required for switching.*

schedule in which the contingencies changed more slowly. Such was found to be the case.

Several exploratory experiments were conducted with Birds 8 and 12 in which various combinations of schedules and FR's required to switch were examined. It immediately became apparent that the behavior was subject to the extremes of high switching rates with no obvious preference on the one hand, and low switching rates with extreme preferences on the other. A combination of conditions was then selected for each bird in which the behavior fell between these extremes.

For Bird 8 the conditions decided upon were as follows. In the red the schedule was 100/1, 200/1, 300/1, etc.; and in the green the schedule was 100/1, 600/1, 1100/1, etc. The FR required to switch was 40 responses. Training was continued for approximately 1000 reinforcements until the preference and over-all behavior had stabilized. The schedules and the colors were then reversed such that in the red the schedule was 100/1, 600/1, 1100/1, etc.; and in the green, 100/1, 200/1, 300/1, etc. Figure 10 shows resulting 2/1 preferences of Bird 8 first for the red and then for the green. The reversal of the preference was obtained within three experimental sessions, although better than 1000 reinforcements were necessary for stable performance.

The same general procedures were followed with Bird 12, except that preferences were obtained under progressive-interval schedules. Bird 12 was trained under the following schedules: 3/4, 1 1/2, 3, 6, 12, etc., in the green; and 3/4, 3, 12, etc., in the red. Thus, in one case the minimum interval of 3/4 minute increased by a factor of 2, and, in the other, by a factor of 4. A stable preference on the order of 3/1 in favor of the green was obtained after approximately 60 experimental hours. The schedules were then reversed and training continued. Reversal of preference was again found to occur within a few experimental sessions. With continued training, however, the behavior stabilized at a somewhat higher switching rate and the final preference was found to be of the order of 2 to 1 in favor of the red. Figure 10 shows portions of cumulative records from the last few days before and after reversal.

Differential Fixed Ratio to Switch

During the above experiments, the importance of the switching requirements for the demonstration of preference suggested a somewhat different means by which preferences might be established. This method was the introduction of differential FR requirements for switching. Thus, under identical progressive schedules in both colors, it was thought possible to establish a preference for red or green by requiring a greater number of pecks to switch colors in one direction than in the other. The effects of such a procedure are outlined below.

Following the termination of the previous experiments with Birds 8 and 12, identical progressive schedules were imposed in both colors. Ratio contingencies were again used with Bird 8 and interval contingencies with Bird 12. As the birds were being stabilized on their respective schedules, it became apparent that under the grain schedules used, rather large differentials were necessary for obvious preferences. Once standard condi-

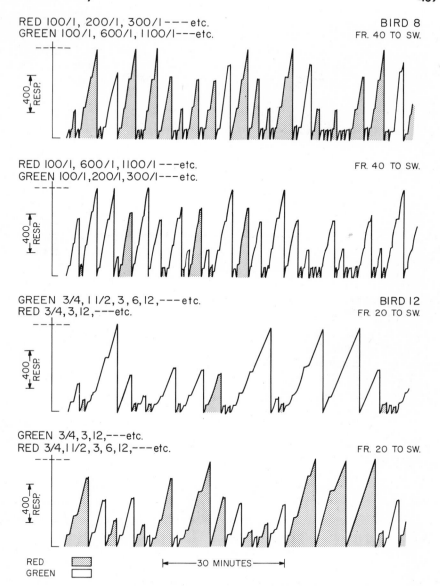

RED 100/1, 200/1, 300/1 ---etc.
GREEN 100/1, 600/1, 1100/1---etc.

BIRD 8
FR. 40 TO SW.

400 RESP.

RED 100/1, 600/1, 1100/1 ---etc.
GREEN 100/1, 200/1, 300/1---etc.

FR. 40 TO SW.

400 RESP.

GREEN 3/4, 1 1/2, 3, 6, 12, ---etc.
RED 3/4, 3, 12, ---etc.

BIRD 12
FR. 20 TO SW.

400 RESP.

GREEN 3/4, 3, 12, ---etc.
RED 3/4, 1 1/2, 3, 6, 12, ---etc.

FR. 20 TO SW.

400 RESP.

RED
GREEN

|←――30 MINUTES――→|

Figure 10.   Preference based upon two different schedules.

tions had been adopted, training was continued until the resulting preferences had stabilized, and then the differentials were reversed.

For Bird 8 the reinforcement schedules were 100/1, 200/1, 300/1,
etc., in both red and green. To switch from red to green, 79 responses
were required on the switching key; and to switch from green to red, only

1 response. Better than 1000 reinforcements were delivered under these conditions, and the resulting preference was on the order of 2 to 1 for the red. The differentials were then reversed for Bird 8 such that only 1 response was required to switch from red to green, and 79 responses from green to red. After about 400 further reinforcements, a preference was obtained now for green, again on the order of 2 to 1. Sample records showing these preferences before and after reversal are found in Figure 11. With the above preferences, the average switching rate was found to be of the same order as found previously with this bird under the same schedules but with a constant requirement to switch of 40 pecks.

The reinforcement schedules used with Bird 12 were 3/4, 1 1/2, 3, 6, etc., in both red and green. The differentials were, first, 39 responses to switch from red to green, and 1 response to switch from green to red. After reversal, they were 1 response to switch from red to green, and 39 responses from green to red. The preferences obtained before and after reversal were of the order of 5 to 1. Typical records showing these preferences are also found in Figure 11.

In general, the results of the above experiments with Birds 8 and 12 not only demonstrated that preferences could be readily established and reversed by the use of two different schedules or by differential FR's required to switch, but also demonstrated how the two variables, amount of change with successive reinforcements, and the FR's required to switch could be played one against the other to obtain a desired effect. This was possible since, as pointed out before, the effects of these two variables were opposite.

SWITCHING BETWEEN RATIO AND INTERVAL CONTINGENCIES

A final complication of the variables outlined thus far was explored briefly by combining both progressive-ratio and progressive-interval contingencies into one experimental procedure. Thus, ratio contingencies were programmed in the red, and interval contingencies in the green. This complication demanded greater stimulus control by each color and provided a further test for the general effects of these schedules.

Bird 17 was given preparatory training under essentially a multiple schedule FR 100 in red and FI 3/4 minute in green. After the behavior had become reasonably appropriate to the two types of contingencies, the switching key was introduced and the schedules altered to progressive ratio and progressive interval. The schedule in the red was now 100/1, 200/1, 600/1, 2400/1, etc.; and in the green, 3/4, 1 1/2, 4 1/2, 18, etc. The FR required to switch colors was at first 2 responses and then raised to 20 responses in a stepwise fashion as the training progressed.

The introduction of the switching key and the progressive schedules disrupted the stimulus control previously obtained and resulted in extinction-like performance. With continued training the switching response gained

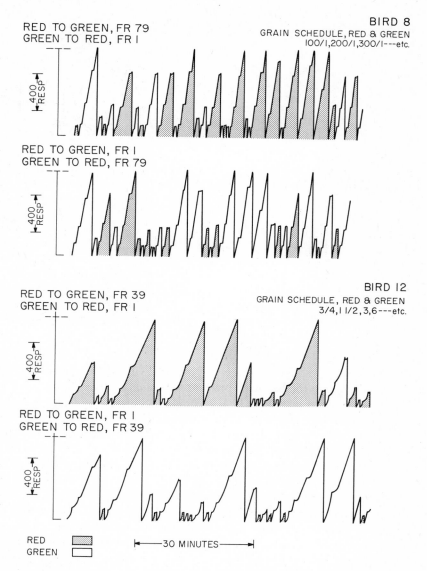

Figure 11. *Preference based upon differential fixed ratios required to switch.*

in strength and the over-all behavior became reasonably stable. Differential effects from the two types of contingencies, however, were observed only after the bird had received more than 2000 reinforcements.

Typical records showing ratio and interval characteristics are found in Figure 12. In these records the onset of responding in the red is usually quite abrupt, with a high sustained rate terminating in reinforcement. The responding in the green, on the other hand, is characterized by more grad-

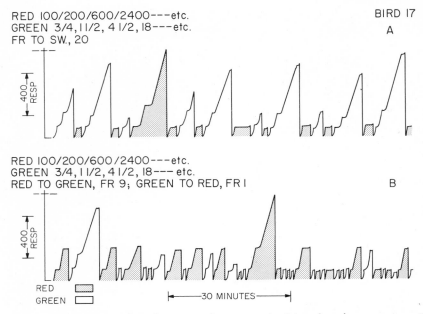

RED 100/200/600/2400---etc.
GREEN 3/4, 1 1/2, 4 1/2, 18---etc.
FR TO SW., 20

BIRD 17

A

RED 100/200/600/2400---etc.
GREEN 3/4, 1 1/2, 4 1/2, 18--- etc.
RED TO GREEN, FR 9; GREEN TO RED, FR 1

B

Figure 12. Switching and preference under progressive-interval and progressive-ratio contingencies.

ual acceleration to a slightly lower terminal rate. These characteristics are most pronounced in the behavior prior to first reinforcement in each color.

The record shown in Figure 12A was obtained after long training under the above conditions, and reveals, in addition to ratio and interval characteristics, a decided preference for the green or interval conditions. This preference is suggested not only from the greater time spent in green, but also from the relative infrequency with which this bird worked beyond the first reinforcement in the red.

In an attempt to improve the ratio and interval characteristics, the FR of 20 responses required to switch colors was altered to a differential of 9/1. Thus, 9 responses were now required to switch from red to green, and only 1 response to switch from green to red. The result of this alteration was an increase in the switching rate and the development of a preference now for the red. A record from the seventh experimental session under these new conditions is that shown in Figure 12B.

In general, these experiments combining progressive-ratio and progressive-interval schedules demonstrated that where switching rates were relatively high these two types of contingencies might be expected to have their characteristic effects. In other respects, the behavior was similar to that obtained under two progressive-ratio or two progressive-interval schedules.

CHAINING AND PROGRESSIVE CONTINGENCIES

In the above experiments in which progressive-reinforcement contingencies were used, both preference and switching rate were found to be under the control of two opposing variables. These variables were amount of change in a given schedule with successive reinforcements, and the FR, or differential FR, required to accomplish a switch in colors. The effects of these variables and the maintenance of preference and switching follow from the chaining nature of the procedures investigated.

Provided the behavior on the key reinforced with grain has been demonstrated to be under the discriminative control of the two colors, two separate operants can be identified. The behavior on the switching key may then be considered a third operant, which mediates, in a chaining fashion, the alternation from the first to the second. Under such an analysis, the sequence would become as follows: responding under one color, for example, results in certain discriminative stimuli which are the occasion for behavior on the switching key. The consequences of pecking the switching key is the production of the new color which in turn is the discriminative stimulus for again pecking on the key reinforced with grain.

Although this sequence is behaviorally identical with that observed in the above experiments, the procedures do not unequivocally specify the discriminative and reinforcing stimuli for the switching behavior. The exact nature of these stimuli, then, is open to some interpretation.

Since the switching response is never followed directly by primary reinforcement, however, the maintenance of this behavior must depend upon secondary reinforcement. This reinforcement would appear most likely to be the onset of a new color, deriving its reinforcing properties from association with the more optimal grain contingencies. The occasion for switching, on the other hand, would arise as the bird experiences higher contingencies with successive reinforcements.

Assuming that the discriminative and reinforcing stimuli for the switching behavior are derived from responding under both optimal and less than optimal grain conditions, it is further apparent that the basis of these stimuli are removed once changes in the grain schedule cease to occur. This latter condition is provided either by nonprogressive schedules, or, under progressive schedules, by continued switching after the first reinforcement in each color. Under progressive contingencies, therefore, the maintenance of switching, and to some extent its variability, develop from a chaining sequence in which the discriminative and reinforcing stimuli for this behavior are afforded by relative changes in the grain contingencies.

The introduction of either high fixed ratios required to switch colors, or progressive schedules which change value slowly, would tend to make the discriminations between relative conditions more difficult, and consequently drive the bird to higher and higher successive contingencies. A given switching rate or preference for one color results, then, from the ease or difficulty of these discriminations provided by a particular arrangement of conditions.

The chaining nature of behavior under progressive contingencies may be further seen when the procedure is reduced to a simpler chain in which the occasion and reinforcement for switching behavior are better specified. This may be done if the delivery of the first reinforcement in each color produces a nonreinforcement, or blackout condition on the grain key. Under this procedure the blackout becomes the discriminative stimulus for switching, and the reinforcement of this behavior, production of the new color. Figure 13 shows several examples of behavior from such an alteration of procedures.

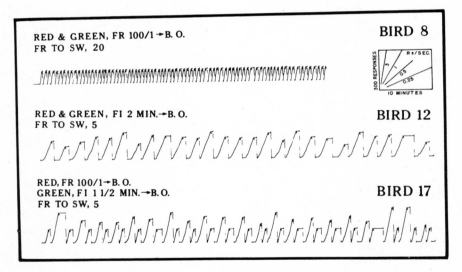

Figure 13.   *Maximum switching rates as a result of blackout procedure.*

Since both the stimulus conditions and the contingencies for reinforcement are now specified within narrow limits in contrast with that under progressive schedules without blackout, the results are maximum switching rates and an obvious chain. Also, when the reinforcement contingencies are identical in red and green, as with Birds 8 and 12, the change in color becomes superfluous and the chain reduces to a sequence of only two operants. On the other hand, provision for discriminative behavior based upon the two colors, as with Bird 17, constitutes a chain composed of three operants.

The general pattern of behavior under progressive schedules, then, while apparently a situation in which the organism is free to choose one color or the other, is, in effect, only a complex sequence where the behavior associated with each color is chained in a not-so-obvious fashion to an intermediate operant.

SUMMARY

A series of experiments is reported in which pigeons were trained to peck an illuminated key for grain. The color of this key was either red or green, and associated with each color was a given reinforcement schedule. Pecking on a second key permitted the birds to switch the color appearing on the first key.

The general behavior resulting from this type of procedure suggested an operant chain in which pecking on the second key was maintained by its consequences for reinforcement on the first key. Preferences for a given color and rate of switching colors were found to be a function of the particular schedules and switching contingencies imposed.

REFERENCES

FERSTER, C. B. The use of the free operant in the analysis of behavior. *Psychol. Bull.*, 1953, *50*, 263–274.

FERSTER, C. B., and SKINNER, B. F. *Schedules of reinforcement.* New York: Appleton-Century-Crofts, 1957.

SUGGESTED READINGS [1]

ATKINSON, J. W. *An introduction to motivation.* Princeton: Van Nostrand, 1964.

BINDRA, D. *Motivation.* New York: Ronald, 1959.

BROWN, J. S. *The motivation of behavior.* New York: McGraw-Hill, 1961.

COFER, C. N., and APPLEY, M. H. *Motivation: theory and research.* New York: Wiley, 1964.

HALL, J. F. *Psychology of motivation.* New York: Lippincott, 1961.

YOUNG, P. T. *Motivation and emotion.* New York: Wiley, 1961.

[1] The most extensive collection of papers under the heading of motivation can be found in the 13 volumes published as the Nebraska Symposia on Motivation (Nebraska University Press, Lincoln, Nebraska, 1953–1965).

Chapter IX

SOCIAL BEHAVIOR

The final selections of this book deal with a topic which has so far been hardly explored by the kind of experimental approach represented by most of the previous articles. As far as this kind of an experimental social psychology is concerned, one might well paraphrase William James' judgment about psychology in general, made in 1892:

A string of raw facts; a little gossip and wrangle about opinion; a little classification and generalization on the mere descriptive level . . . not a single law in the sense in which physics shows us laws, not a single proposition from which any consequences can be causally deduced. We don't even know the terms between which the elementary laws would obtain if we had them. This is no science, it is only the hope of a science (p. 407).

It is to the future development of such an approach, however, that the authors of the articles reproduced here would all enthusiastically subscribe. If they have merely pointed a way, let others improve on their sincere efforts.

REFERENCES

JAMES, W. *Psychology* (1892). Greenwich: Fawcett, 1963.

35

The Contingency as an Independent Variable of Social Interaction

K. Weingarten and F. Mechner

A unique feature of the behavioral sciences is their concern with a special type of independent variable: the contingency. Experimental psychologists use the term "contingency" to refer to the rules that specify what consequences behavior will have for the behaving individual (Skinner, 1953). These rules, which constitute independent variables in experiments, are generally expressed in the form of "if, then" statements, the "if" clause specifying some aspect of behavior, the "then" clause a resulting state of affairs. The contingencies investigated by experimental psychologists range from relatively simple ones (e.g., if the rat presses the bar, a pellet of food is delivered) to complex elaborations involving temporal factors (e.g., if the rat presses the bar, a pellet of food will be delivered after 5 seconds), probabilities (e.g., if the rat presses the bar, there is a probability of .50 that a pellet of food will be delivered), associated stimuli (e.g., a pellet of food will be delivered only if the rat presses the bar in the presence of a light), series or chains of responses (e.g., if a rat presses a bar three times and then turns to the left, a pellet of food will be delivered), and the various permutations of these. However, there is a type of contingency to which experimental psychologists have given relatively little attention: that involved in social interaction. This type of contingency is the main subject of the present paper and will be discussed below.

It should be noted that such "if, then" statements as the above merely define independent variables; they are not empirical propositions (e.g., if a response produces an electric shock, the response will decrease in

Printed with permission of Dr. Kenneth Weingarten, Research Sociologist, National Research and Information Center, National Council on Crime and Delinquency; and Francis Mechner, Ph.D., Basic Systems, Inc.

frequency) where only the "if" clause specifies the independent variable and the "then" clause specifies the dependent variable.

Readers who are unfamiliar with the concept of the contingency may challenge the status of the contingency as an independent variable on the ground that the event specified by the "then" clause can occur only if the subject responds in the designated manner (e.g., the pellet of food will be delivered only if the rat presses the bar). Since the response of the subject is not under the experimenter's control, it may appear that the independent variable is contaminated by the dependent variable, namely, the behavior being studied. This is not so, however, for neither food presentations nor any other actual occurrences function as independent variables. It is rather the contingencies determining the relationship between these occurrences and the subject's behavior that have this function, and these are entirely under the experimenter's control. Even in those experiments where the subject can "select" the contingencies under which he will operate, the rules that allow for this selection are also laid down by the experimenter and are independent of the subject's actual behavior.

The contingencies that are of concern to the psychologist are those that specify the consequences of behavior for the behaving individual. These consequences may be mediated either by electrical and mechanical devices or by the behavior of other individuals; but in every instance the mediating mechanism, whether animate or inanimate, reacts to the behavior of the subject in ways that are predetermined by the experimenter. The contingencies that are of special concern to the sociologist on the other hand, are those that specify the consequences that any individual's behavior, should it occur, will have for others (e.g., rat A's pressing a bar will produce a pellet of food for rat B, and rat B's pressing a bar will produce a pellet of food for rat A). As in the case of psychological experiments, these contingencies are independent of the subjects' actual behavior. In an experiment they would be entirely under the experimenter's control and would be established prior to the experiment's inception. They describe the structural constraints on the subjects' interaction.

This type of contingency bears the same relation to social interaction experiments as the contingencies listed earlier bear to single-subject psychological experiments. Social interaction involves an additional type of contingency, however, which has no obvious counterpart in the psychological experiments. It is the type of contingency produced by the actual behavior of the participants. Each participant's behavior creates contingencies for the other. These contingencies are not under the direct control of the experimenter as are the contingencies discussed above, but are entirely a function of the subjects' interaction. Since these contingencies are dependent on the actual behavior of the participants, they must be distinguished from those established by the experimenter. The contingencies established by the experimenter constitute independent variables. They will, therefore, be referred to as *independent contingencies*. On the other hand, contingencies generated by the interacting participants have the status of dependent variables (in the sense that they are not under experimental control and may be viewed as a consequence of the independent contingencies) and will accordingly be referred to as *dependent contingencies*. The independent contingencies may be viewed as setting bounds upon the dependent contingencies that can emerge during an interaction. A game of poker provides a familiar example of the distinction between independent and dependent contingencies. The rules of play and scoring define the constraints facing the participants and constitute the independent contingencies of the situation. On the other hand, the particular patterns of interaction that might emerge during an evening's play would create the dependent contingencies. For instance, player A's tendency to "bluff" constitutes one of the contingencies that emerge during the course of the game, and might come to affect the behavior of his opponents. In general, the behavior of each participant contributes to the contingencies under which the others must operate. One task of experimental research on social interaction is to determine what, if any, dependent contingencies various types of independent contingencies produce.

There is also an approach to the study of social interaction exemplified by the work of Asch (1952), which regards the individual as functioning in a setting where the actions of others are treated as situational "givens." This approach features experiments that employ "pseudo-subjects" whose behavior in the experimental situation is predetermined by the instructions of the experimenter. The conception of social interaction towards which the present paper is oriented, on the other hand, and the one that sets sociology apart from psychology, focuses on the complex behavioral interplay of two or more individuals. Experimental research within this framework is characterized by situations in which the co-participants are all regarded as subjects with the rules of interaction experimentally fixed (e.g., Azrin and Lindsley, 1956; Bales, 1950; Bavelas, 1950; Calhoun, 1962; Daniel, 1942; Lippitt and White, 1952; Miller and Dollard, 1941; Mintz, 1951; Sherif, 1936; Sidowski, Wykoff, and Tabory, 1956).

Recently, a diagrammatic notation system suitable for representing the contingencies investigated in psychological experiments was proposed (Mechner, 1959). This notation system, which utilizes a set of symbols borrowed from mathematics, logic, electronics, and psychology, was offered as a concise and unambiguous language for making the formal structure of contingencies explicit. The present paper will show how this notation system, originally intended for the description of contingencies involving only a single individual, may be adapted for the description and analysis of contingencies involving more than one individual, i.e., the independent contingencies of social interaction.

Mechner's notation system consists of a set of abbreviations for acts and their consequences and of four symbols that specify the conditional and temporal relations between them. The "acts" of the participants are generally conceptualized as responses, abbreviated by the letter R. When a more general designation standing for long or complex series of responses is desired, the term "behavior," abbreviated B, may be substituted. It is usually necessary to identify these acts, whether designated R or B, according to the subjects who perform them. This is accomplished by the use of a capital letter (A, B, C, . . . N, one letter being assigned to each participant) written as a pre-subscript to the R or B. For instance, $_AR$ would indicate a response made by subject A. To distinguish between different classes or types of acts, lowercase letters written as a post-subscript will be used. Thus, $_AR_c$ is a response of type c made by A (in order to keep the diagram simple, a more thorough specification of the response class in question can be presented in a legend). If a response is to be repeated a specified number of times, this number is represented by the letter N prefixed to the R. For example, N_AR_a would read "N responses of type a made by subject A." If a specific value is assigned to N, the value may be substituted for N (e.g., 8_AR_b or 25_cR_c).

Stimuli, abbreviated by the letter S, require the same set of identifying modifiers as do R and B. Thus, $_AS$ would indicate a stimulus which is directed at or perceived by subject A. Lowercase letters in the post-subscript position designate types of stimuli (further specification again being reserved for an accompanying text). $_BS_a$, for example, represents a stimulus of type a for B. Stimuli may also be classified according to their reinforcing (i.e., rewarding or punishing) properties. This stimulus property is indicated by a sign in the pre-superscript position, plus (^+S) if reinforcement is positive, and minus (^-S) if reinforcement is negative. The magnitude of a stimulus (i.e., any intensive dimension such as brightness, volume, amount of food or money received, etc.) is indicated by the letter M in the post-superscript position. Thus, S^M1 and S^M2 would be read "a stimulus of magnitude $M1$," and "a stimulus of $M2$," respectively. (Magnitude of response may be indicated in the same way.)

The first of the four relational symbols is the horizontal arrow, denoting succession of the events it connects. The expression

$$R_a \longrightarrow S_c$$

for instance, would be read "response a, if it occurs, produces (or is followed by) stimulus c." It is understood that the symbols R and B are always read "R, if it occurs," and "B, if it occurs." The entire notation system deals only with the "if, then" relations between behavior and its consequences. It does not allow for statements that an act *actually* occurs; only the consequences of potential acts can be denoted. This is the essence of the distinction between describing behavior and describing its controlling contingencies. The expression

$$R_a \longrightarrow R_b \longrightarrow S_c$$

for example, would *not* be read "Response *a* occurs and produces response *b,* and response *b* produces stimulus *c,*" but rather, "Response *a,* if it occurs, produces a condition where response *b,* if it occurs, produces stimulus *c.*" In this instance response *a,* if it occurs, produces neither another response nor a stimulus; it produces a contingency, i.e., a condition where another response, if it occurs, will produce a stimulus. It is possible, of course, to surround the contingency with parentheses in order to call attention to its status as a unit—e.g.,

$$R_a \longrightarrow (R_b \longrightarrow S_c)$$

—but if it is remembered that a response cannot be said to produce another response, the unity of the contingency will be apparent, and the parentheses may be omitted without any ambiguities resulting.

The second relational symbol is the letter *T,* which represents a time interval of length *T.* A time interval must always be initiated by a specific event, such as a response—although when this initiating event is irrelevant it may not be necessary to denote it—and its termination always marks the occurrence of some other event, such as a stimulus change or the inception of a contingency. For example,

$$R \longrightarrow T \longrightarrow S$$

would mean that a response initiates a time interval, at the conclusion of which a stimulus appears. If *T* is negligibly short or of no focal significance it may be omitted altogether. Common examples of time delays in behavioral situations are the intervals intervening between placing a bet on a horse race and the actual outcome of the race or between taking an examination and receiving a grade.

A bracket around two or more conditions that are written in vertical relation to one another indicates that these conditions go into effect simultaneously. The expression

$$R \longrightarrow S_b$$
$$T \longrightarrow S_g$$

for example, would indicate that condition

$$R \longrightarrow S_b$$

goes into effect simultaneously with the condition

$$T \longrightarrow S_g.$$

The fourth symbol is the vertical arrow intersecting a horizontal arrow. The event at which the vertical arrow originates prevents the occurrence of the event or condition to which the intersected horizontal arrow leads. In the expression

$$T \longrightarrow\!\!\!\!\!\!\uparrow\; S$$
$$R \;\rule[0pt]{0.5pt}{12pt}$$

for example, the response, if it occurs prior to the termination of the time interval, prevents the occurrence of S at the conclusion of the interval. In the expression

$$R \longrightarrow\!\!\!\!\!\!\uparrow\; S$$
$$T \;\rule[0pt]{0.5pt}{12pt}$$

on the other hand, the response can produce the stimulus only if it occurs prior to the termination of T.

Suppose that two conditions go into effect simultaneously, as in the diagram

$$R_A \longrightarrow S_1$$
$$R_B \longrightarrow S_2$$

and that whichever condition is met first prevents or cancels the other. If R_A occurs first, S_1 is produced and R_B will no longer produce S_2; if, on the other hand, R_B should occur first, then S_2 is produced and R_A can no longer produce S_1. This situation requires reciprocal vertical arrows for its description. The diagram could accordingly be written

$$R_A \longrightarrow\!\!\!\!\!\!\uparrow\; S_1$$
$$R_B \longrightarrow\!\!\!\!\!\!\downarrow\; S_2 .$$

The need for reciprocal vertical arrows arises so frequently that a double-headed vertical arrow has been adopted as a convenient abbreviation:

$$R_A \longrightarrow\!\!\!\!\!\!\updownarrow\; S_1$$
$$R_B \longrightarrow\!\!\!\!\!\!\updownarrow\; S_2 .$$

Any stimulus or stimulus complex S_i is always understood to remain present until it is replaced by a designated successor, perhaps $S_{(i+1)}$. The last indicated stimulus always replaces the current one and remains present until a further stimulus change is specified. No vertical arrow is needed to indicate that a stimulus terminates; all that is needed is the specification of a new stimulus. To show, for instance, that a stimulus change occurs every 5 seconds, a diagram of the form

$$\boxed{\begin{array}{c}5 \text{ sec.} \\ S_1\end{array}} \longrightarrow \boxed{\begin{array}{c}5 \text{ sec.} \\ S_2\end{array}} \longrightarrow \boxed{\begin{array}{c}5 \text{ sec.} \\ S_3\end{array}} \longrightarrow$$

would be used. The horizontal arrows lead away from the time intervals rather than from the stimuli. Similarly, to show that stimulus changes depend upon the occurrence of responses, the diagram would read

$$\begin{bmatrix} R \\ S_1 \end{bmatrix} \longrightarrow \begin{bmatrix} R \\ S_2 \end{bmatrix} \longrightarrow \begin{bmatrix} R \\ S_3 \end{bmatrix} \longrightarrow .$$

In practice it is frequently not important or even desirable to specify the precise duration and termination point of every stimulus. Accordingly, these specifications may be omitted for purposes of abbreviation. This will be done in most of the examples given in the present paper. Also, strictly speaking, there always has to be *some* stimulus present. When the reinforcing stimulus ends, some other stimulus complex replaces it, and when a light goes out it must be replaced by other visual stimuli. Since this alternative stimulus is frequently of no focal significance, however, it too may be left unspecified. Such abbreviations as these are often convenient ways of simplifying the diagrams to emphasize the relations that are of primary concern.

The illustrations thus far presented are non-repetitive; that is, the sequences, as described, may occur only once. In order to represent repetitive conditions no additional symbol is required. A horizontal arrow which recycles the sequence fulfills this function. For example, if a response is to produce a positive reinforcer (e.g., a pellet of food), and if this contingency is to go into effect repeatedly, rather than writing

$$R \longrightarrow \begin{bmatrix} {}^+S \\ R \longrightarrow \begin{bmatrix} {}^+S \\ R \end{bmatrix} \end{bmatrix} \ldots$$

which entails a separate representation for each occurrence, a recycling arrow may be employed:

$$\hookrightarrow R \rightleftharpoons \longrightarrow {}^+S.$$

There are situations where a quantity, such as a required number of responses or a time interval, varies from trial to trial. This may be indicated by prefixing a v to the term—either N or T—that stands for the quantity in question. For example,

$$\hookrightarrow vNR \rightleftharpoons {}^+S$$

would mean that the number of responses required to produce the reinforcing stimulus varies from trial to trial. In

$$\hookrightarrow vT \rightleftharpoons {}^+S$$

it is the time interval that varies. When actual values are substituted for these symbols, T and N can be replaced by the mean of the varying quantity. Thus $v3$sec. would indicate that the mean interval is 3 seconds, and $v10R$ would indicate that the mean number of responses is ten. Additional information as to the nature of this variation would be given outside the diagram.

These are the basic features of the notation system.

The conditions of social interaction may be said to exist whenever an act of one individual, should it occur, will alter either stimulus conditions or contingencies for others. The case where stimulus conditions are altered may be notated as follows:

$$\left[\begin{array}{l} {}_{B}S_a \\ {}_{A}R \longrightarrow {}_{B}S_b \,. \end{array} \right.$$

Here A's response will change B's stimulus conditions from S_a to S_b. If it were desired to specify that the stimulus change involves an alteration from a negative to a positive reinforcer, ${}_{B}^{-}S$ would be substituted for ${}_{B}S_a$, and ${}_{B}^{+}S$ for ${}_{B}S_b$. We would then say that A has the power to reward B. The other case where one individual can alter the contingencies for others involves either the creation or the termination of contingencies or a combination of these. An example of the latter is

$$\left[\begin{array}{l} {}_{B}R \longrightarrow {}_{B}^{+}S \\ {}_{A}R \Longrightarrow {}_{B}R \qquad {}_{B}^{-}S. \end{array} \right.$$

Here A's response terminates the contingency under which B's response will produce a positive reinforcer and substitutes one where the same response will produce a negative reinforcer.

The above are instances of "one way" interaction. In mutual interaction the participants' ability to alter one another's stimulus conditions or contingencies is reciprocal (though not necessarily symmetrical). A relatively simple example of this is the situation in which two subjects have the power to reward or to punish one another:

$$\left[\begin{array}{l} {}_{A}R_a \longrightarrow {}_{B}^{+}S^{M1} \\ {}_{A}R_b \longrightarrow {}_{B}^{-}S^{M2} \\ {}_{B}R_a \longrightarrow {}_{A}^{+}S^{M3} \\ {}_{B}R_b \longrightarrow {}_{A}^{-}S^{M4}. \end{array} \right.$$

These conditions frequently hold in normal face-to-face interaction; each participant usually has both flattery and insult at his disposal. Differentials in power between the two participants can be indicated by making use of the symbol for stimulus magnitude. For example, if M_1 is greater than M_3 and M_2 is greater than M_4, then A could be said to be more powerful than B.

The independent contingencies of social interaction vary from the relatively simple to the extremely complex. The systematic analysis of these contingencies, and their consequences is beyond the scope of the present paper, but constitutes a challenging problem for future research. It would be impossible at this point to give an adequate sampling of the full range of these contingencies. The remaining portion of this paper will accordingly be restricted to a consideration of those relating to competition and cooperation.

COMPETITION

The independent contingencies that describe one simple type of competition specify that reinforcement is "scarce," so that the obtaining of reinforcement by one participant prevents others from obtaining it:

$$\left[\begin{array}{c} {}_AR \longrightarrow {}_A^+S \\ {}_BR \longrightarrow {}_B^+S \end{array}\right.$$

A and B cannot both be reinforced. Whichever participant responds first obtains reinforcement and prevents the other from doing so. (If we wished to represent a situation in which these conditions are repetitive, recycling arrows would be added to the diagram.) The behavior involved might be a series or chain of responses:

$$\left[\begin{array}{c} {}_AR_a \longrightarrow {}_AR_b \longrightarrow {}_A^+S \\ {}_BR_a \longrightarrow {}_BR_b \longrightarrow {}_B^+S. \end{array}\right.$$

It could also involve repeated responses, where the rate of emission determines which participant will be reinforced:

$$\left[\begin{array}{c} N_{1A}R \longrightarrow {}_A^+S \\ N_{2B}R \longrightarrow {}_B^+S. \end{array}\right.$$

If N_1 does not equal N_2, the participant with the larger quota is laboring under a handicap.

Comparable diagrams may be elaborated for competitive avoidance, i.e., contingencies where the participants are competing, not to obtain positive reinforcers, but to avoid negative reinforcers, for instance:

$$\left[\begin{array}{c} T_1 \longrightarrow {}_A^-S \\ N_{1A}R \\ N_{2B}R \\ T_2 \longrightarrow {}_B^-S. \end{array}\right.$$

Punishment is impending for both participants (at the termination of interval T_1 for A and of T_2 for B). Either can avoid punishment by completing his quota of responses before the termination of the relevant time interval *and* before his competitor's quota is completed. The winner avoids punishment for himself and prevents his opponent from doing the same. Where T_1 is not equal to T_2 a burden is placed upon the participant who must complete his quota within the shorter interval. Again the numbers of responses required of the competitors may be equal or unequal.

COOPERATION

The independent contingencies of cooperation are exemplified by the extremely wide variety of situations in which the behavior of more than one participant is required for the reinforcement of any. The simplest instance involves only two participants.

$$\begin{bmatrix} {}_AR \longrightarrow {}_BR \\ {}_BR \longrightarrow {}_AR \end{bmatrix} \xrightarrow{(A,B)} {}^+S$$

Here A's response produces a condition such that B's response will produce a positive reinforcement for both. This information is contained in the first line of the diagram. The second line indicates that these responses in the opposite sequence will have the same consequence. A simplification of this diagram is possible with the symbol " "—the logical product sign—which implies that the events which it connects must both occur (the sequence being irrelevant) in order to produce the indicated result. Utilizing this symbol the above diagram would be rewritten:

$$_AR \cap {}_BR \longrightarrow {}_{(A,B)}{}^+S.$$

The case where more than one response is required from each participant would be diagrammed:

$$N_{1A}R \cap N_{2B}R \longrightarrow {}_{(A,B)}{}^+S.$$

N_1 and N_2 may be individually specified so that each participant must fulfill a designated quota; or, alternatively $N_1 + N_2$ may be set equal to a fixed number. In this case the individual frequencies are allowed to assume a variety of values, so long as their sum equals $N_1 + N_2$. This would be an example of a group quota.

It should be noted that certain independent contingencies which do not fall within the category of cooperation as it was defined above, may nevertheless produce behavior resembling that generated under a cooperation contingency. The condition

$$\begin{bmatrix} {}_AR \longrightarrow {}_B^+S \\ {}_BR \longrightarrow {}_A^+S \end{bmatrix}$$

for instance, may produce a pattern of interaction where each participant reinforces his partner only if his partner reinforces him. In that case, each is operating under the dependent contingency

$$\boxed{\;}\;R\longrightarrow T\rightrightarrows\;{}^+S$$

where T is the latency of the other participant's response. But the independent contingencies do not specify this behavior; they permit the frequent reinforcement of one participant together with complete absence of reinforcement for the other.

INTER-GROUP COMPETITION

Another interesting situation is that where a group of cooperating individuals competes against another similar group. The independent contingencies of such a situation are built up from contingencies that have already been described. The following diagram, for instance, shows competition between two dyads:

$$N_{1A}R\frown N_{2B}R\longrightarrow {}_{(A,B)}{}^+S$$
$$N_{3C}R\frown N_{4D}R\longrightarrow {}_{(C,D)}{}^+S$$

Each line comprises a cooperative dyad. The contingencies allow for the reinforcement of only one of them—whichever fulfills its quota first. This diagram as well as those above may be modified to include more subjects (e.g., $_AR\frown {}_BR\frown {}_cR\frown \ldots \frown {}_NR$ would indicate a cooperative group with N members), although in the interests of simplicity interaction situations with only two subjects have been selected.

Inter-group competition of this sort may also be analyzed from the point of view of one of the competing groups, the rate of performance of the opposing group being represented by the time limit which the latter's performance sets for the former.

$$\begin{bmatrix} N_{1A}R\frown N_{2B}R\longrightarrow {}_{(A,B)}{}^+S \\ T \end{bmatrix}$$

Here the quota must be met before the conclusion of the time interval if the subjects within that dyad are to be reinforced. They are, in a sense, "competing against the clock." In the laboratory the experimenter could manipulate this time interval systematically in order to establish the effects of various deadlines on cooperative behavior. For example, what are the effects upon performance rates of ample as against minimal time allowances? What happens when the time allowance is varied from trial to trial rather than held constant? (This would be indicated by substituting vT for T in the diagram and adding a recycling arrow.)

CONCLUSION

It should be emphasized that the notation system was used as a purely descriptive and analytical tool, and not as a theory or calculus of propositions. The entire paper was concerned only with the analysis of the special contingencies which function as independent variables of social interaction. The actual effects of such contingencies upon interaction processes must be determined by empirical research. Only such research can give rise to viable theories.

Psychologists may be tempted to suggest that the ultimate analysis of social interaction will be carried out in the psychological laboratory, on the grounds that since all social interactions involve individual organisms responding to "complex and changing" contingencies, we need only investigate how these individual organisms behave under such conditions. (This is the reductionist argument.) The answer to this argument is that we do not know how to generate the relevant "complex and changing" contingencies in the laboratory except by actually introducing the second subject. To simulate this second subject realistically would require an exhaustive understanding of the laws of individual behavior. This answer is the same one that the psychologist gives when he is told that physiology is the key to understanding behavior and that the physiologist gives when chemistry is held up to him as the true path. In the light of our present limited knowledge of individual behavior, the soundest, and most expedient, way to develop a science of social interaction is to treat interaction as a subject of scientific investigation in its own right. It is even possible that dyads, triads, tetrads, and larger groups constitute different levels of analysis and will come to be regarded as separate major provinces of behavioral science. This is not to say that there are no unifying laws cutting across them all. Such laws will undoubtedly be uncovered, though this may take a great deal of empirical research. Psychologists have till now largely confined their attention to one of these levels: the monad. The reasons for this are probably historic rather than strategic. An understanding of social interaction is surely as important as an understanding of individual behavior, and our technological and conceptual resources are now adequate for the development of a fruitful methodology. Here too, the reductionist fallacy of insisting that dyads must receive attention before triads, and triads before tetrads will have to be avoided. Since these provinces are all of equally pressing concern, their investigation must proceed concurrently.

REFERENCES

Asch, S. E. *Social psychology*. New York: Prentice-Hall, 1952.

Azrin, N. H., and Lindsley, O. R. The reinforcement of cooperation between children. *J. abnorm. soc. Psychol.*, 1956, *52*, 100–102.

Bales, R. F. *Interaction process analysis*. Cambridge, Mass.: Addison-Wesley, 1950.

Bavelas, A. Communication patterns in task-oriented groups. *J. accoust. Soc. Amer.*, 1950, *22*, 725–730.

Calhoun, J. B. A "behavioral sink." In E. L. Bliss (Ed.), *Roots of behavior*. New York: Harper & Row, 1962.

Daniel, W. J. Cooperative problem solving in rats. *J. comp. physiol. Psychol.*, 1942, *34*, 361–368.

Lippitt, R., and White, R. K. An experimental study of leadership and group life. In G. E. Swanson, T. M. Newcomb, and E. L. Hartley (Eds.), *Readings in social psychology*. New York: Holt, Rinehart and Winston, 1952.

Mechner, F. A notation system for the description of behavioral procedures. *J. exp. Anal. Behav.*, 1959, *2*, 133–150.

Miller, N. E., and Dollard, J. *Social learning and imitation*. New Haven: Yale University Press, 1941.

Mintz, A. Non-adaptive group behavior. *J. abnorm. soc. Psychol.*, 1951, *46*, 150–159.

Sherif, M. *The psychology of social norms*. New York: Harper & Row, 1936.

Sidowski, J. B., Wyckoff, L. B., and Tabory, L. The influence of reinforcement and punishment in a minimal social situation. *J. abnorm. soc. Psychol.*, 1956, *52*, 115–119.

Skinner, B. F. *Science and human behavior*. New York: Macmillan, 1953.

Other notation systems for describing social interaction can be found in the following (Ed.):

Heider, F. *The psychology of interpersonal relations*. New York: Wiley, 1958.

Hoffman, H. Symbolic logic and the analysis of social organization. *Behavioral Science*, 1959, *4*, 288–298.

36

The Effect of a Verbal Stimulus as a Reinforcement

Joel Greenspoon

The purpose of this research was to determine the effect of a verbal reinforcement introduced immediately following a plural noun response on the frequency of plural noun responses. Twelve college students were randomly assigned to the experimental and control groups. The experiment was conducted in a soundproof room and was recorded on a wire recorder. A chronoscope was used to record the time.

The subjects were instructed to say all the words that they could think of, but were not to use sentences, phrases, or to count. In the case of the experimental group, immediately after each plural noun response the verbal reinforcement, "Mmm-hmm," was introduced by the experimenter. No reinforcement was introduced for the control group. The subjects responded for a period of 25 minutes. At the end of the experimental session each subject was asked if he knew what had been transpiring in order to determine if he could verbalize any changes that may have occurred in his behavior.

The results were computed on the basis of 5 minute periods. The percentage of plural noun responses to the total number of responses was computed for each period and for the total experimental session. It was found that the experimental group gave a significantly larger number of plural nouns than the control group. None of the experimental subjects was able to verbalize any changes in his behavior.

It can be concluded that "Mmm-hmm" is a reinforcement in this type of training and changes in verbal behavior can occur without the subjects' being able to verbalize them.[1]

Adapted from *Proceedings of the Indiana Academy of Science*, 1949, *59*, 287. With permission of the author and publisher.

[1] J. Greenspoon, "The Reinforcing Effect of Two Spoken Sounds on the Frequency of Two Responses," *Am. J. Psychol.*, 1955, *60*, 409–416, is a better known reference to the type of research described in the paper reprinted here (Ed.).

37

Cooperative Problem Solving in Rats

William J. Daniel

INTRODUCTION

Several experiments (Crawford, 1935, 1936, 1938; Crawford and Nissen, 1937) have been presented which have more or less successfully demonstrated cooperative behavior in the higher apes. A few experiments (Berne, 1930; Lewin and Lippitt, 1938; Moore, 1931), observational in character, have indicated this behavior in children. Only one experiment, that of Wolfle and Wolfle (1939) has attempted to study cooperative behavior genetically by comparing the behavior of apes and children in nearly identical experimental situations.

It has generally been believed that a study of cooperative behavior in animals as far down the evolutionary scale as the rat is rather fruitless. Only one such experiment (Winslow, 1940) has come to the writer's attention. One of the three experiments which constitutes that monograph was designed to test for cooperative behavior in the rat. This experiment was negative; and aside from the films of Mowrer, no other attempt to obtain cooperative behavior in rats has been reported. The experiment reported here represents an apparently successful attempt at obtaining cooperation and one which relies primarily on quantitative data.

PROBLEM

In the experiment described below we wanted to know if it is possible to arrange an experimental situation in such a manner that two animals can assist one another in obtaining food and at the same time escape electric shock.

The experimental situation consisted of a grid box with an electrically insulated platform at one end which, when a rat stepped on it, would re-

Adapted from *Journal of Comparative Psychology,* Vol. 34, pp. 361–369. Copyright ©, 1942. The Williams & Wilkins Co., Baltimore 2, Md. U.S.A.

move the charge from the grid. There was also a food crock flush with the grid and beyond the reach of a rat on the platform. This situation is represented schematically in Figure 1.

Our problem is concerned with the behavior of *two* rats in this situation. Will one rat go to the platform and remain on it, thus enabling the other rat to feed? Will the feeding rat leave the food crock and go to the platform, enabling the rat to leave the platform and feed? Finally, will they exchange positions in such a manner that both are adequately fed and both escape or minimize shock? In short, will cooperative behavior be obtained when two rats are put into a double motive situation if the satisfaction of both of these motives is contingent upon the behavior of both animals?

ANIMALS

Heterozygous albino rats were used, ten males and two females ranging from 90 to 107 days of age at the start of the experiment.

APPARATUS

The Experimental Situation (Figure 1)

The experimental situation consisted of a paraffined wood cage 22½" long x 12" wide x 4½" high with a grid floor and a glass top. In the center of the cage a food crock, flush with the grid, was placed 8" from the edge of the platform thus making it impossible for a rat to feed from the platform.

This grid cage was mounted on a set of stilts thus facilitating the replenishing and replacing of the food crock. A small wooden wall stop was mounted over the platform at the end of the cage forcing all rats to remain beyond its center of gravity and making it impossible for a rat to administer shock without leaving the platform. The tilting of the platform also completed a light circuit so that a 40 watt bulb flashed whenever a rat received a shock. This facilitated an objective counting of the number of shocks administered by each rat.

The rats were dropped onto the grid through a small glass door on the top of the apparatus. Directly beneath this door a small entrance alley 6" long and 4½" wide served to orient the animals in the proper direction, that is, facing directly towards the food crock and platform.

The Shocking Circuit

The grid was wired in series with a high resistance shocking circuit and the platform automatically shorted out the grid when a rat stepped on it.

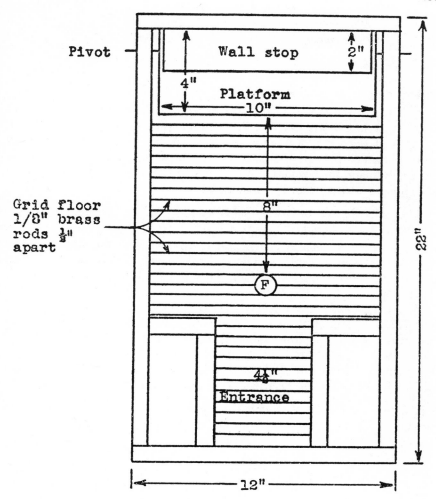

Figure 1. Diagram of apparatus.
F = Food crock
Scale—1/4 inch = 1 inch

The essential problem here was to apply an electrical stimulus to·the rats, the physical constancy of which we could be reasonably assured. Our circuit was of such a high external resistance that the added resistance of one or two rats gave the same meter reading as when a copper wire was placed across the grid. The transformer of this shocking circuit applied 3,750 volts to the rectifier tube and the current at the shock grid terminals could be varied from 100 microamps to 5 milliamps. The average shock intensity of 250 microamps required a circuit resistance of 3,400,000 ohms.

PROCEDURE

The Preliminary Training

The aims of the preliminary training were three-fold:

1. To train the rats to feed in the experimental situation.
2. To train the rats to go to the platform when the grid was electrified.
3. To develop this discrimination, basic to the solution of the problem to be presented in the social situation, to the point at which the rats immediately made the response appropriate to the situation when the situations were varied in an irregular order.

The following schedule was maintained:

1. The rats were unfed for 24 hours.
2. One rat was placed in the grid cage alone with the shock off and the food crock in place. It remained there for two 450-second trials, and was weighed before and after each day's trials. This procedure was continued through the 8th day for each rat.
3. At the end of the 8th day's run the sated rat was put in the grid cage with the grid electrified at 100 microamps. It was not removed until it had reached the platform and remained on it for 30 seconds. This procedure was repeated for 20 trials on this day.
4. From the 9th through the 13th day the rat was run for 20 irregularly mixed trials with electrified and non-electrified grid.

On the shock trials the rat had to learn to go to the platform and to remain on it for 30 seconds. The time it took the rat to make the appropriate response, i.e., going to the platform, was recorded.

On the food trials the grid was not electrified and the rat was left in the apparatus for 100 seconds. If by the end of this time it had not made the appropriate response (feeding) it was removed from the apparatus and given the next trial. The time it took the rat to commence feeding was recorded and if the rat did feed it was allowed to do so for 30 seconds so long as it started sometime within this 100 second interval.

By the end of the 13th day of the preliminary training the rats had mastered this discrimination. When dropped on a cold grid the rat immediately went to the food crock and fed; when dropped on a hot grid the rat immediately went to the platform and remained on it for 30 seconds. It made this discrimination in less than a second or before the experimenter could get to his stopwatch to start timing the rat.

Thus at the conclusion of the preliminary training each animal had learned to escape from shock or to feed in the apparatus depending upon the situation and it had learned this individually and in isolation.

The Experimental Trials

At the end of the preliminary training the rats were divided into pairs of as nearly equal weight as possible.

In the experimental trials *two* rats were put into the cage with the grid electrified and the food crock in place. They remained in the experimental cage for one trial of 120 seconds duration. They were run 12 trials a day, a total of 1,440 seconds, which, on the basis of preliminary experimentation, was adequate for the hunger satiation of both animals. The trial was timed by an electric stopclock and the individual feeding times by a manually operated stopwatch.

Throughout the experimental trials the apparatus operated automatically. With one or both rats on the platform the shock was off. With the grid not charged, a rat could feed at the food crock. Thus at least *one* rat had *always* to be on the platform if the other was to get to the food crock. Occasionally both rats would leave the platform and attempt to feed and take shock simultaneously. If this behavior persisted for 5 consecutive times the shock was increased 50 microamps, and this "double feeding" stopped.

The rats were fed pulverized Purina dog chow mixed with water in the ratio of 5:6 respectively. At no time did the rats receive food other than that obtained in the experimental situation. This procedure was continued for 40 days at which time it appeared that the rats were doing as well as they ever would.

RESULTS

The most significant fact in the data is that the rats exchanged positions from food crock to platform and from platform to food crock. Many of these exchanges were accompanied by shock and many shocks were administered in between these exchanges. It will be remembered that whenever there was any shock both rats received it, but it was administered only by one rat (the platform rat) stepping off the platform and thus electrifying the entire grid. As the experiment progressed more and more of the position shifts were accomplished without shock. Also fewer and fewer shocks were administered which did not result in an alternation. This data for 6 pairs of rats are presented in Table 1. Since we are most interested in the final stage of this behavior the data are given in terms of the mean performances for the last 5 days of the experiment as compared with the mean performances for the first 5 days of the experiment.

Notice that with the exception of pairs 1–2 and 9–10 the critical ratios indicate that there is a marked and statistically significant decrease in the

TABLE 1

Pair	Mean Shifts for Last 5 Days	Percent of Total Shifts Without Shock	C.R.
1–2	18	14	−1.33
3–4	15	68	4.64
5–6	92	89	8.92
7–8	14	92	6.04
9–10	25	89	1.29
11–12	95	93	8.89

number of shocks not resulting in an alternation. The shock seems to have been quite effectively reduced.

The nature of the alternations is also important. Let us call one of these rats A and the other B. Now if rat A is feeding at the food crock he may return to the platform and then again return immediately to the food crock. We shall call this exchange in position an "individual" alternation since it is accomplished only by one rat. When rat B exhibits this behavior we shall also call this exchange in position an individual alternation. When rat A is at the food crock and returns to the platform and rat B comes off the platform and goes to the food crock we refer to this

TABLE 2

	Pairs					
	1–2	3–4	5–6	7–8	9–10	11–12
Total number of alternations	947	863	3748	957	1201	3271
Percentage which the mutual alternations are of the total	97	94	97	94	95	99

kind of a shift as a "mutual" exchange in position. The question is, then, what percentage of the total exchanges in position is mutual and what percentage is individual? These data are presented in Table 2.

These data support the conclusion that for the entire group the rats alternate in a *mutual* manner in at least 94 percent of the total alternations. We can say then that they are "taking turns" 94 to 99 percent of the time.

Our next question is, how well do these rats get fed while they are eliminating shock and exchanging positions in the experimental situation? Table 3 gives the mean weights for the first 5 days and the last 5 days of the experiment.

It is clear from this table that every rat gained weight during the experiment and these gains ranged from 24 to 140 grams. This, along with the fact of their general healthy and vigorous appearance, further support the conclusion that the rats were adequately fed throughout the experiment.

Another factor of importance is the extent to which the animals use the total available time in the apparatus. Means of this data for the entire

TABLE 3

Rat	Grams Eaten per Day	Weight before the Experiment	Weight after the Experiment	Weight Gained
1	21	96	153	57
2	21	113	253	140
3	25	109	144	35
4	20	121	179	58
5	25	118	205	87
6	27	126	189	24
7	27	127	170	43
8	23	140	211	71
9	30	121	160	39
10	21	158	230	72
11	32	182	250	68
12	31	161	231	70

TABLE 4

Pair	Mean Feeding Time	Mean Time Together on the Platform
		(sec.)
1–2	1425	15
3–4	1410	30
5–6	1358	82
7–8	1407	33
9–10	1407	33
11–12	1397	43

experiment are given in Table 4. Since they were run for 12 2-minute trials a day the total available feeding time for each pair of rats is 1440 seconds a day. Occasionally both rats would go to the platform and remain on it together. This is considered time wasted in as much as it is time during which food was available for one or the other animal but was taken by neither. We can see that the rats used practically all of the available feeding time. This speaks well for our final choice of time interval and also indicates that the rats were actively working on the problem set by the experimental situation practically all of the time that they were in the apparatus.

DISCUSSION AND INTERPRETATION

First of all let us re-emphasize the fact that this was a double motive situation. Our original intention was to arrange these motives in an experimental situation in such a manner that neither of them could be satisfied without the co-ordinated efforts of *both* animals.

Rather than put the organism into an experimental situation and observe if it exhibits "cooperative behavior" we attempt to put the animal through a procedure which will train it to be cooperative. Next we put it into a situation which is a cooperative one and quantify the extent to which it exhibits the behavior. In short, we train the behavior into, rather than draw it out of, the animal.

At the end of the preliminary training the rats have mastered a discrimination basic to the satisfactory solution of the problem presented in the test situation. First they shocked each other a great deal as they exchanged positions from food crock to platform. They received many shocks and they did not get as much food as they did later. But very soon they shifted more frequently and received more food. They shocked each other less and less in between the shifts in position. They accomplished a greater and greater number of shifts without getting any shock. In doing this they fed more and escaped more shock. They satisfied both of the motives in the situation.

There are, finally, several observations that throw light on the nature of the behavior of the animals. As the experiment progressed the rats directed their behavior more and more towards each other rather than towards the food crock or the platform. The rat on the platform would reach off holding the platform down with only one foot, and nudge the feeding animal. It would sometimes crawl up on the latter's back and paw it. This frequently resulted in the feeding rat's return to the platform. Sometimes it would hoist the feeding animal up on its shoulders. It might even bite and pull on the feeding rat's tail. These are overt responses directed towards the other animal.

It would seem, then, that the platform rat's leaving the platform is conditional and dependent upon the movements of the other animal. The rat keeps at least one foot on the platform until the other animal is on the platform, or until the feeding rat goes by the platform rat towards the platform, or at any rate until the feeding animal has completed its return. In short, the rat has apparently learned that it or the other rat must be on the platform if it is to escape shock. The feeding rat, which has returned to the platform, remains there as the platform rat leaves. Then it exhibits the behavior typical of the platform rat. They "take turns" and thus they both get adequately fed and they both eliminate shock.

In all the other animal experiments on cooperation both animals do the same thing; i.e., they pull ropes, punch stimulus cards, operate levers, etc. In this experiment the cooperative aspect of the situation rests on the animals' doing distinctly *different* things; i.e., one feeds and the other turns off the shock. They synchronize their activity on *two* different tasks. The products of this solution are mutually shared. There is no simultaneous sharing of the goal achieved and thus there is no chance for competition. There is also an element of inhibition in the shape of delaying of responses since one animal waits on the platform while the other eats and they take turns doing this.

Since the animals do respond in the experimental situation in a manner consistent with the preliminary training, since they do distinctly different things in the cooperation testing situation, and since some of their behavior has the characteristics of synchronization, restraint, and differentiation of response, it would seem that their behavior may fairly be called cooperative.

SUMMARY AND CONCLUSIONS

To investigate the development of cooperative behavior in rats 6 pairs of rats were put into a double motive problem situation (feeding and avoiding shock) requiring the co-ordinated efforts of both animals for its adequate solution.

Each rat was individually trained to feed when the grid floor was not electrified, and when it was charged to go to a platform which shorted out the grid floor when a rat stepped on it. The rats were then paired, and the problem was to discover if cooperative behavior would be obtained when two rats were put into a double motive situation in which the satisfaction of both of these motives is contingent upon the behavior of both animals. One rat of a pair had to run to a platform which shorted out the electrified floor grid of a feeding box in order that a second rat might feed.

From the data obtained in this situation we might draw the following conclusions:

1. The rats learned to exchange positions in this situation and at the same time allow sufficient feeding time for each rat to become adequately fed in the course of the experimental session.

2. They showed marked improvement in alternating without shock and in eliminating the shocks which did not result in an alternation.

3. They learned to take turns at the food crock and platform so that by the end of the experiment they spent almost all of the available time in the apparatus working on the problem and very little time together on the platform.

4. And finally, in this situation, cooperative behavior has been apparently established. In a food-shock situation both animals exchange positions so that both are adequately fed. Furthermore, they exchange positions with sufficient care and speed that they avoid shock. They satisfy both conditions of the experiment in a situation in which the satisfaction of *both* conditions was contingent upon the behavior of *both* animals.

REFERENCES

BERNE, E. VAN C. An experimental investigation of social behavior patterns in young children. *Univ. Ia. Stud. Child Welf.*, 1930, 4, 1–61.

CRAWFORD, M. P. Cooperative behavior in chimpanzee. *Psychol. Bull.*, 1935, *32*, 714.

CRAWFORD, M. P. Further study of cooperative behavior in chimpanzee. *Psychol. Bull.*, 1936, *33*, 809.

CRAWFORD, M. P. Cooperative solution by chimpanzees of a problem requiring serial responses to color cues. *Psychol. Bull.*, 1938, *35*, 705.

CRAWFORD, M. P., and NISSEN, H. W. Gestures used by chimpanzees in cooperative problem solving. (Silent film.) New York: Instructional Films, Inc., 30 Rockefeller Plaza, 1937.

LEWIN, K., and LIPPITT, R. An experimental approach to the study of autocracy and democracy: A preliminary note. *Sociometry*, 1938, *1*, 292–300.

MOORE, E. S. The development of mental health in a group of young children: An analysis of factors in purposeful activity. *Univ. Ia. Stud. Child Welf.*, 1931, *4*, 1–128.

WINSLOW, C. N. A study of experimentally induced competitive behavior in the white rat. *Comp. psychol. Monogr.*, 1940, *15*, 1–35.

WOLFLE, D. L., and WOLFLE, H. M. The development of cooperative behavior in monkeys and young children. *J. genet. Psychol.*, 1939, *55*, 137–175.

38

Experimental Analysis of Cooperation and Competition

Ogden R. Lindsley

BACKGROUND AND CONCEPTS

The behavior of living organisms with respect to their environments has been most successfully described for experimental purposes in terms of stimuli and their associated responses. The most useful definitions of

Read in part in a symposium on S–R Modes of Social Interaction, Eastern Psychological Association, Philadelphia, April 8, 1961.

Research was supported by grants G–9516 and G–19608 from the Division of Social Sciences, National Science Foundation, and was conducted in the Behavior Research Laboratory, Harvard Medical School, located at Metropolitan State Hospital, Waltham, Massachusetts.

The energetic and extremely able collaboration of Donald J. Cohen, Yale Medical School, is sincerely appreciated. Using this method introduced him to free-operant conditioning and produced his Brandeis University honors thesis (Cohen, 1962). Special thanks also to Judy Rosenberg for editorial assistance.

these stimuli and responses have been found to be both operational and functional.

Operational and Functional Definitions

By *operational* we mean that the stimuli and responses are described in terms of the actual operations involved in physically recording these energy changes. Operationally defined terms describe experimental plans, procedures, and results more accurately than interpretive or mentalistic terms based on how the stimuli and responses look to us, what we think they mean to the subjects, or how the subjects verbally describe them.

By *functional* we mean that the stimulus is designated as some reliably measured event that is regularly followed by some reliably measured change in the organism's position in time and space (response). The stimulus and response are defined by their relationship to each other, or their function. The gradual development of functional behavioral description and measurement can be seen in the writings of Dewey (1896), Kantor (1924), and Skinner (1935). But it was left to Skinner (1938) to develop the most useful method for the experimental manipulation of these functional relationships, with both full environmental control and sensitive, continuous, objective measurement. This method of studying behavior has been termed free-operant conditioning and, with little modification, has proved successful in the measurement and control of a wide variety of behaviors.

Free-Operant Conditioning

A brief, general description of the method of free-operant conditioning follows. An animal is placed unfettered and alone in a small experimental enclosure which isolates him from those events in the environment which might elicit responses that could interfere with the responses under observation. In the enclosure he is *free* to make any response at any time—hence the term *free*. If the animal *operates* a small lever, wheel, key, plunger, or some similar device, he is promptly reinforced (rewarded) with some agent appropriate to his deprivation—hence the term *operant*.

Typical procedure involves directly recording the *rate of responding* as the slope of a cumulative response record and reinforcing only a small percentage of the responses (Skinner, 1938). Skinner and his co-workers found that various arrangements of intermittent reinforcement produce responding which (1) occurs at a wide range of rates, (2) is less dependent upon deprivation and satiation, (3) is more resistant to experimental extinction, and (4) is more sensitive to the effects of independent variables (e.g., drugs) than is possible by the reinforcement of *each* response (Ferster and Skinner, 1957). The *free* aspect of the method dispensed with the "trials" often used in behavioral experimentation. Using trials was cumbersome, prevented fine-grain time-analysis, and often reduced the sensitivity of measurement by adding sources of variability between trials. Further, the free-operant method is completely automated with electromechanical devices which present stimuli and record responses. Thus, problems of observer bias and memory bias are eliminated—a requirement for accurate human research.

Experimental, Statistical, and Interpretive Analyses

Generally speaking, statistical and interpretive analyses dominate experimental analysis in behavioral investigation. In the purest case of experimental analysis, a single organism-environment system is used to determine the effect of a number of independent variables. These variables are systematically presented, one at a time, until suitable controls allow a definite conclusion concerning their effects upon and interactions with the behavior of the single organism. Scientists using statistical analyses generally pay less attention to careful environmental control, since separate observations are grouped and the conclusions arrived at by some form of averaging. A statistical analysis yields less specific information, as averaging makes it impossible to predict exactly the behavior of any given single organism. Conclusions from interpretive analyses are even more readily biased by uncontrolled variables than are conclusions from statistical analyses, since they are based upon conclusions drawn from separate organisms, in separate experiments, and conducted by different experimenters who, in some cases, used different statistics.

Experimental analyses are the rule in laboratory biology, chemistry, and physics where fine experimental control is possible. The relatively recent development of the method of free-operant conditioning has brought equivalent control to the study of the behavior of single individuals, thus permitting the experimental analysis of human behavior. Bernard (1865), Kraepelin (1896), Pavlov (1899), and Skinner (1938) independently referred to the superiority of experimental analysis in research design. They appealed for its use in exploratory research where uncontrolled variables are frequently unknown and in human and medical research where individual differences are the rule rather than the exception.

The key to the superiority of experimental over statistical and interpretive analyses is control, for only by modifying experimental procedures on a single organism as an experiment progresses can control be achieved over the process under study. That control is the final criterion of knowledge is demonstrated by the fact that complete social acceptance of a new method occurs only when society can be shown that the method controls a particular subject matter. A method that produces control over a subject matter replaces one that only predicts the occurrence of the subject matter or merely integrates it with other disciplines, no matter how refined and sophisticated the prediction or integration may be.

Since the free-operant method produces relatively complete control over the behavior of single individuals and achieves a gain in the sensitivity of measurement, it is the best single method available for experimental analysis of both individual and social behavior. Sidman (1960) has written an excellent, detailed description of the tactics involved in this application.

Experimental Analysis of Social Behavior

Social behavior is the term used to describe the large class of behavioral interactions between two or more individuals or between two or more individuals and their physical environment. A great deal of significant and interesting work has been done in this area, but little of this work has met the standards of an experimental analysis. The interests and needs of society have forced the majority of social research to approximate as rapidly as possible the answers to certain pressing questions. This is one reason that statistical and interpretive analyses have been favored.

In an experimental analysis of social behavior, it is necessary to compare directly social and nonsocial situations, preferably on the same individuals. Only in this way can the social and nonsocial properties of the behavior be parceled out and the contribution of individual performance variables (such as motivation and discriminative ability) be separated from the emergent social variables. Unless individual behavior and social behavior have been measured by minor variants of the same basic method, such a comparison is difficult at best.

To make matters even more difficult, in a true functional analysis of social behavior, even though the experimental situation is arranged so that social variables can emerge, one or both of the individuals may not be responding to the *social* aspects of the situation. That is, one or both of the individual subjects may be responding as if his teammate were a functioning machine rather than another person. In other words, the stimuli cannot be functionally defined as social unless the subject responds to them differently from the way he would respond if they were mechanical. Unless the behavior of each individual in the experiment can be shown to change when a machine is substituted for and performs the function of the teammate, with all other variables held constant, it is only a topographical "pun" to invoke the term *social* to describe the behavioral transaction with the other teammate.

Social Emergents

It clearly follows that a nonsocial (or mechanical) control must be run for each stimulus and response in an experimental analysis of social behavior in order to insure that the stimuli and responses are functioning socially. If social interaction does not produce emergent properties over and above similarly complex transactions with non-living systems, we have no need to generate a special class of terms to describe social behavior, since we can consider it merely a part of the field of complicated discriminations. If, however, appropriate controls have been run and the social emergents clearly defined, then the field of social behavior can be simplified and separated from the field of complicated individual behavior. Such simplification and clarification of social behavior, as distinct from individual behavior, has yet to be provided for the field of experimental social psychology.

Furthermore, in measuring social deficits in neurotic, psychotic, and developmentally retarded persons, it is essential to have a method that clearly controls for the patient's ability to engage in the nonsocial aspects of the task. That is, it is necessary to show that a patient can engage in equally complicated transactions with the physical environment before his inability to engage in a transaction with another individual can be considered a *social* deficit. It may well be that many so-called social deficits are merely deficiencies in the ability to make complicated discriminations. In non-experimental settings, these inabilities may be erroneously interpreted as social deficits simply because the most complicated discriminations demanded of an individual tend to be social. Steinbeck's (1937) character Lennie, in the novel *Of Mice and Men,* is a fictional example of an individual who was punished for sexual aggression but whose problem was, in fact, retardation and the consequent inability to distinguish his victim's teasing from a sincere demonstration of desire for him.

If true social emergents can be measured directly, and if reversible social aspects of the situation can be presented and withdrawn in an experimental session, the social factors, abilities, and deficiencies in a relationship between any particular pair of subjects can be determined in a single experimental session. Moreover, with continuous direct measurement, it is possible to determine the nature and duration of action of other agents (e.g., a drug given only to the uncooperative or hostile member of a team) on the social behavior of a single team within a single session.

Extension of Free-Operant Method to Experimental Analysis of Cooperation

Miller and Dollard (1941), Keller and Schoenfeld (1950, pp. 352–397), and Skinner (1953, pp. 297–312) have suggested that the principles which govern the behavior of single individuals with respect to their physical environments also govern their behavior with respect to other organisms. Others feel that some of the phenomena which emerge in social behavior are governed by principles which cannot be determined from studying the behavior of isolated individuals (Hunter, 1919; Köhler,

1947). This problem of emergent social phenomena has not been subjected to careful experimental analysis.

It is apparent that the method of free-operant conditioning will be useful in comparing the behavior of individuals in similar isolated and social situations. Skinner (1953, p. 306) has extended his own method to the study of social behavior in lower animals. In classroom demonstrations, he showed that two pigeons could be trained to cooperate by reinforcing each pigeon whenever they cooperated in making a joint response. Later, Azrin and Lindsley (1956) extended the method to the human case by performing a similar experiment on nursery school children. They demonstrated the differential reinforcement and extinction of cooperative responses and by using only one reinforcer which was available to both subjects, showed that a cooperative response could be treated exactly as an individual response and that no new principles were involved in this simple cooperative situation.

In these two experiments it was insured that the joint responses had to be made by responding to the behavior of the other teammate. The possibility of a high rate of joint responses occurring by chance was eliminated by the use of three manipulanda for each subject. The individuals faced each other, with a set of three manipulanda arranged in front of each of them (Figure 1). Since each subject had only one stylus, he could operate only one manipulandum at a time. (In effect, the stylus served the subject as the pigeon's beak served the pigeon in Skinner's study.) At any given time, only one pair of opposing manipulanda was effective in producing the next reinforcement. The particular pair effective at any time was randomized, so that the subjects had to explore the three pairs to discover which was at that moment effective and in exploring had to insert their styli into opposite holes at the same instant.

In order to produce a moderate rate of cooperative responding, one individual (the leader) explored the holes with his stylus. The other individual (the follower) placed his stylus into the hole opposite the one to which the leader had just responded within 0.04 second of the leader's response. Such leader-follower relationships were observed, and in some cases these roles were alternated between teammates as higher rates of cooperation developed. These interesting relationships were not experimentally controllable by differential reinforcement nor were they objectively recorded, but their high importance compelled Skinner (1953, p. 306) to report them.

Although useful for demonstrating the development and maintenance of cooperation solely by differential reinforcement, the use of three manipulanda for each subject was not appropriate for an experimental analysis of cooperation and leader-follower emergents. The three responses (1) added complicating multiple-response variables when the cooperative responses were to be compared with the single responses of the individuals behaving

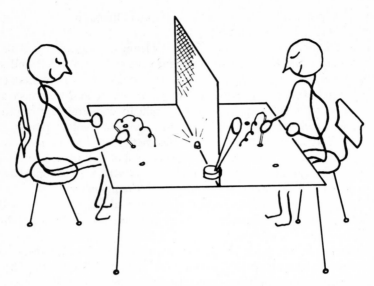

Figure 1. Apparatus used by Azrin and Lindsley (1956) to demonstrate reinforcement of cooperation between children. Interesting emergent leader-follower relationships were not differentially recorded or experimentally controlled; they were merely reported as field observations. The method demanded three separate responses by each individual, thus unnecessarily complicating the experiment and confounding variables when social data were compared with data from isolated individuals responding on a single manipulandum.

in isolation, (2) made the recording of competitive responding and its control by differential reinforcement very difficult to program, and (3) made the recording and the differential control of leader-follower relationships in both cooperation and competition even more difficult to program.

Point of Departure of this Research

The purpose of the present research was to develop a free-operant method for experimentally analyzing leader-follower relationships in human cooperation and competition without the limitations of the Azrin-Lindsley experiment. The method had to meet three requirements. (1) The physical properties of the apparatus must be no different for the measurement of individual behavior than they would be for the measurement of a wide variety of social behavior (except for adding the necessary social stimuli and rearranging the reinforcement contingencies). (2) The refined procedure must include direct recording and experimental control of leader-follower relationships. (3) The method must permit measurement and control of both cooperation and competition without any apparatus changes which would confound variables. Ideally, cooperation and competition should be capable of alternate study, under otherwise equivalent conditions, by changing reinforcement contingencies only.

Apparatus permitting intrasession alternation between study of individual behavior and study of cooperation and competition, by changing only the value of the discriminative stimuli and the programming of the reinforcing stimuli, would have analytical superiority over the majority of previously used techniques. In his preliminary analysis of social behavior, Skinner (1953) was aware of the importance of developing procedures of this sort. Although he did not know how to demonstrate it experimentally, he suggested that competition was not an exact complement of cooperation (Skinner, 1953, p. 311). The method reported here clearly shows that both cooperation and competition can be generated in the same experimental situation simply by changing the reinforcement contingencies so that the participants work with or against each other. In this general sense they are complements of each other. However, the required change in reinforcement contingencies is not a complementary change, so in this finer sense, cooperation and competition are *not exact* complements of each other.

METHOD

Social Teams

The individuals composing the experimental social teams were pairs of students of both sexes from the fifth through ninth grades, with ages ranging from 10 to 14 years.[1] Normal, highly motivated subjects were selected so that the method and procedural values could be standardized before searching for social deficits in abnormal subjects.

Experimental Rooms

The basic apparatus consists of two indestructible 6 by 6 foot rooms, each equipped with a standard operant conditioning panel on one wall (Figure 2). The rooms are the same as those used for the past eleven years in the operant conditioning of normal and psychotic individuals (Lindsley, 1956b). On each panel is a plunger that can be pulled and an opening into which the reinforcers (pennies) are dispensed. Between the two rooms a sliding partition can be opened to reveal a transparent plexiglass window, which permits teammates to observe each other, but prevents their physical contact and insures against one individual operating both manipulanda.

[1] The kind cooperation of the Sisters of St. Joseph's School, Waltham, Massachusetts, Sister Superior Ursula Marie, S.N.D., the students, and their parents in offering the behavior for our experimental analysis is greatly appreciated.

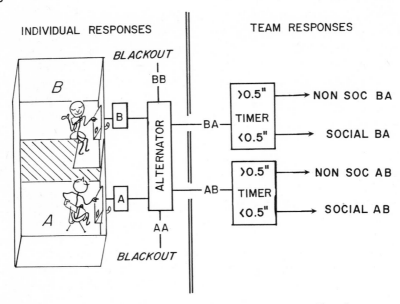

Figure 2. Apparatus and team response definition schema used in the present experiment. Emergent leadership—experimentally controlled by differential reinforcement—was directly, automatically, and continuously recorded. The apparatus provided only one manipulandum for each individual, so that response topography variables would not be confounded in comparing social data with data from isolated individuals responding on a single manipulandum. Team response definition is described in the text.

Automatic controlling and recording apparatus is located in an adjoining area, along with hidden periscopes for observing the rooms. Speakers in each room deliver white noise to mask the sound of the apparatus and the responding and talking of the subject in the next room. When the "social window" is closed, each room represents one of the simplest and most controlled experimental situations yet developed for investigating the behavior of isolated single individuals ranging from normal persons to severely disturbed psychotics.

Team Response Definition

Team responses were defined by an electrical circuit (Figure 2). An impulse shortener (box labeled "A" in Figure 2) converted each of A's individual plunger pulls into an electrical pulse of 0.04 second duration. Similarly, when individual B pulled his plunger, an impulse shortener (box labeled "B" in Figure 2) converted the response to an electrical pulse of 0.04 second duration. These impulses were fed into a sequence alternator (labeled "alternator" in Figure 2) which separated each pair of incoming pulses into four sequential categories: A followed by A (AA),

A followed by B (AB), B followed by A (BA), and B followed by B (BB).[2]

Since AA and BB pairs were individual responses which did not require the response of the other teammate, they were mildly punished. Immediately after each AA sequence, individual *A* was given a 2.5-second period of darkness, while a 500 cycle tone sounded over his speaker. During this period (labeled "blackout" in Figure 2) his and his teammate's responses did not enter the sequence alternator. Individual *B* was blacked out for BB sequences in the same manner. These blackouts, which mildly punished the nonsocial, individual response sequences, are more fully described elsewhere as time-outs (Ferster and Skinner, 1957).

The sequential pairs AB and BA were team responses, since they demanded the response of both individuals for their occurrence. These team responses were further classified by two timers (shown in Figure 2). A followed by B within 0.5 second was called a Social AB, since it was improbable that the follower would respond that quickly merely by chance.[3] Similarly, B followed by A within 0.5 second was called a Social BA. A followed by B over 0.5 second later was called a Nonsocial AB; and B followed by A over 0.5 second later, a Nonsocial BA.

Differential Reinforcement Contingencies

Uncontrolled and controlled leadership in both cooperation and competition were experimentally generated and maintained by selective reinforcement of different combinations of the four team responses. These contingency arrangements are diagrammed in Figure 3. The rows in this contingency table represent the four team responses that were differentially reinforced. The columns represent the types of social behavior and leadership that can be differentially reinforced. The italicized entries in the table indicate which individual is reinforced for each team response in order to generate the type of social behavior abbreviated in the column

[2] It is important to note that each A and B response was *used only once* in a sequential pair. That is, once an AB sequence had occurred, the entire analysis was reset so that if the next response was a B, it was not recorded as a BB sequence but was stored as the initial member of the next response pair. This is different from the more common Markovian type of sequential analysis in which each response is used more than once (i.e., an ABB sequence includes AB and BB pairs). The non-Markovian sequential pairs used in this experiment seem more appropriate for behavioral analysis since we have found them easier for human subjects to discriminate than the Markovian sequential analysis.

[3] Intermittently over a period of six years, various devices using response topographical and counting dimensions were tried in unsuccessful attempts to define team responses without the limitations of the multiple response devices used by Skinner (1953) and Azrin and Lindsley (1956). It may be that since we do not sense time directly, we explored it last. Our successful use of the temporal dimension for defining social responses suggests that it should not be overlooked in developing behavioral research methods.

heading. A single entry indicates that only one individual is reinforced for that team response. A double entry indicates that both are reinforced. No entry indicates that the team response is extinguished.

TEAM–RESPONSE REINFORCEMENT CONTINGENCIES

	UNCONTROLLED LEADERSHIP		CONTROLLED LEADERSHIP			
	COOPERATION	COMPETITION	A LEADS COOP.	B LEADS COOP.	A LEADS COMP.	B LEADS COMP.
SOCIAL AB	*AB*	*B*	*AB*		*B*	
SOCIAL BA	*AB*	*A*		*AB*		*A*
NON-SOC AB		*A*			*A*	
NON-SOC BA		*B*				*B*

INDIVIDUALS REINFORCED

Figure 3. Contingencies used to reinforce differentially the four team responses. These produce and maintain different patterns of leadership in cooperation or competition. In cooperation both teammates were jointly reinforced for team responses; in competition they competed for individual reinforcement.

The first and second columns include the contingency arrangements for *uncontrolled leadership*. For example, when both teammates are reinforced for the occurrence of a Social AB pair (A followed by B within 0.5 second, *cooperation* is generated. However, since either teammate may lead, leadership is not differentially reinforced and is experimentally uncontrolled. In this situation, emergent leadership relations are a function of previous history variables and can be used to diagnose or predict leadership.

When only one of the teammates is reinforced for each team response, the situation is *competitive*. Only individual B is reinforced for Social AB pairs (A does not "catch B asleep"); A is reinforced for Nonsocial AB pairs (A "catches B asleep"); A is reinforced for Social BA pairs; and, finally, B is reinforced for Nonsocial BA pairs. The teammates thus have a situation in which they can compete for reinforcement. Since either individual can lead, the situation can be described as uncontrolled leadership in competition.

The third through sixth columns include the contingency arrangements for experimentally *controlled leadership*. For example (in the third column), when both individuals are reinforced for the occurrence of a Social AB pair, and all other team responses are extinguished, cooperation is generated. However, since they are only reinforced when A leads, cooperation with A leading is generated. Similarly, when both are reinforced only for Social BA responses, cooperation with B leading is generated. The contingency arrangements used for differential reinforcement of leadership in competition are shown in the fifth and sixth columns.

Reinforcement of AA and BB sequences could be used to generate, rather than discourage, individual behavior. By applying an intermittent schedule of reinforcement to some combination of team responses and also to individual responses, an index of the reinforcing properties of the social aspect of the behavior could be obtained. Furthermore, it would be possible to arrange more complicated leadership contingencies requiring alternation of leadership, different combinations of positive and negative reinforcement, and different schedules of positive reinforcement. These possibilities are left to the reader's imaginative skill and to further research.

Nature and Schedule of Reinforcement

Since reinforcement should be maximized in procedural standardization, pennies were used as reinforcers.[4] Differential reinforcement of a selected team response was programmed for each emission of that response. This continuous reinforcement schedule was used because it is the schedule on which discriminations are most easily formed (Ferster and Skinner, 1957). The method was designed, however, to permit the use of intermittent schedules of reinforcement. In further research, fixed-ratio schedules of reinforcement could be used, once the discriminations are acquired, to conserve reinforcement and to permit long experimental sessions without satiation. Furthermore, the difficulty of acquiring these social responses could be increased for use with highly skilled subjects merely by altering the value of the fixed-ratio schedule.

When a penny was presented to a team member, the overhead light in his experimental room was dimmed and a light in his reinforcement bin went on for 5 seconds. This change in illumination was designed as conditioned reinforcement to accentuate the presentation of the penny. Dur-

---

[4] Each subject obtained approximately $5.00 in pennies for each 2-hour experimental session. Although this may seem a lot to pay grammar school children for participation in experiments, there are several good reasons for using such strong reinforcement. (1) When the entire cost of the experiment is considered, the cost of reinforcers represents only 10 percent of the total. (2) Experience with human subjects suggests that a very strong reinforcer must be programmed in order to collect reliable and sensitive data under high environmental control, because unprogrammed reinforcement (music, a pleasant surrounding, neighbors, etc.) is eliminated. (3) Strong reinforcers markedly reduce acquisition time and thus save costly experimental time. (4) Strong reinforcers generate frequent and prompt subject attendance, which greatly decreases the amount of time and money otherwise spent in locating subjects. (5) Strong reinforcers eliminate low motivation as a possible source of variability.

ing this 5-second conditioned reinforcement period, no responses entered the recording and programming apparatus.

When the window between the rooms was open, there was probably additional conditioned reinforcement in observing the other individual acquire a reinforcer. Presentation of a reinforcer to another individual can serve as a social reinforcer, as was demonstrated in a study with chronic psychotics who were given an opportunity to feed milk to a hungry kitten (Lindsley, 1956a). However, the act of presenting reinforcement to another individual can be positively reinforcing to some persons (charitable individuals) but negatively reinforcing to others (greedy individuals). Therefore, the sign of the social reinforcement available through the window probably varied with the team constitution and previous experimental history.

Manipulation of Nature of Discriminative Stimuli

Two types of discriminative stimuli were necessary to perform the team responses reinforced in this experiment: (1) stimuli produced by response of the other teammate and (2) stimuli involved in the reinforcement of the other teammate. In order for the task to be presented as nonsocial, the human or social property of these stimuli must be removed.

When the window between the experimental rooms was open, both discriminative stimuli, for both individuals, were *human* (condition "H" in Figure 4). In this condition each individual directly observed the response and reinforcement of his teammate. An opaque slide could be placed between the sheets of plexiglass to mask the visual human stimuli. On each side of this slide were two lights, mechanical stimuli which substituted for the human stimuli necessary to team responding. A response (plunger pull) by one teammate was indicated to the other by the flash of a red light ("B resp. red" in Figure 4), and the presentation of reinforcement to a teammate was indicated to the other by the 5-second illumination of a white light (labeled "B reinf. white" in Figure 4). The condition in which only *mechanical* stimuli were used is labeled "L^2" (two lights) in Figure 4.

Two intermediate conditions were also possible. In the first intermediate condition, both the human stimuli and the mechanical response stimulus could be presented simultaneously ("HL" in Figure 4). In the second intermediate condition, both the human stimuli and the two mechanical stimuli could be presented ("HL^2" in Figure 4). These intermediate conditions were useful in experimentally analyzing for interaction between the variables.

The mechanical stimuli were located on the slide so that when viewed by each teammate they were in the same position as were the human stimuli when the window was open. This precaution was taken to control

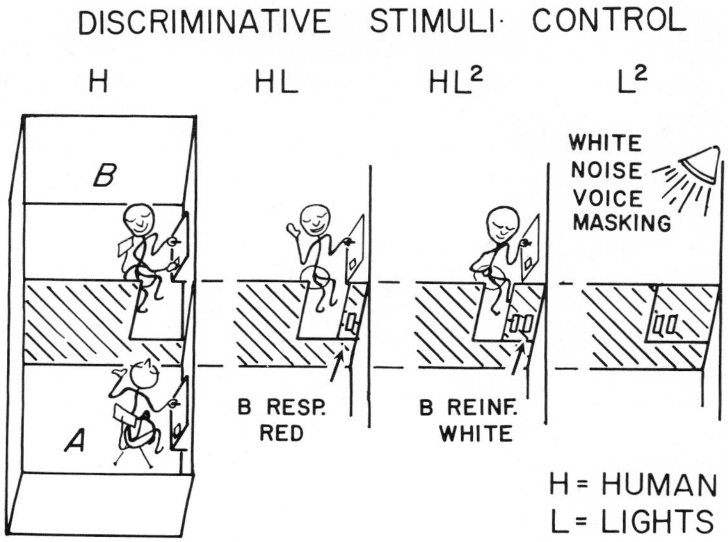

DISCRIMINATIVE STIMULI· CONTROL

Figure 4. Method of experimentally manipulating the nature of the discriminative stimuli required for cooperation and competition. Each teammate could directly observe the responding and reinforcement of the other through a plexiglass window (human stimulation: H). With the window closed by an opaque slide, each teammate could observe a red light flash when the other teammate responded and a white light flash when the other was reinforced (lights only: L^2). Two intermediate conditions (HL and HL^2 were possible. Conversation between teammates could be masked by white noise.

for viewing position and possible response interference from tonic neck reflexes.

All four of the stimulus conditions (H, HL, HL^2, and L^2) provided two-way, or bidirectional, discriminative stimulation between teammates. In more refined experimental analyses using closed-circuit television for unidirectional manipulation of the human stimulation,[5] we could determine which teammate—leader or follower—was most affected by human stimulation, since one individual could be responding to human stimuli while the other responded to mechanical stimuli.

It is important to note that the procedures described above permitted manipulating the *nature* of the discriminative stimuli independently of the *programming* of the stimuli. With the window fully closed (L^2), the discriminative stimuli were of a mechanical nature, but they were still programmed socially by the responding and reinforcement of the other teammate. If differences in the rate of social behavior were to be attributed to the nature of the discriminative stimuli involved, we had to insure that

[5] Closed-circuit television permits, for the first time, the unidirectional manipulation of visual communication between two people. Since unidirectional control of social stimulation greatly facilitates experimental analysis, this new tool will prove invaluable in future social research.

the programming of these stimuli was the same in both the social (H) and mechanical (L²) conditions. Limitations of our present knowledge precluded construction of a machine capable of simulating the programming of the discriminative stimuli by the other teammate. Therefore, it was necessary to leave the programming of both the human (H) and mechanical (L²) discriminative stimuli to the other teammate.

Manipulation of Social Connotation

It was possible to study cooperation and competition with mechanical stimuli which, although socially scheduled, were without social connotation. This was done by bringing the members of a team to the laboratory separately and by starting the experimental session under the L² condition. However, it was not possible to reverse this variable. Once the human discriminative stimuli were used, the individuals responded to the task socially, even when the currently available stimuli were solely mechanical.

Experimental Sessions, Instructions, and Conditions

Most experimental sessions were of 2 hours' duration. Subjects were brought to the laboratory two at a time (except when studied without social connotation as described immediately above). The subjects were told only to pull the lever, start when the overhead light went on, and that they could keep all the pennies they got. Since most subjects came from the same school, many learned from their schoolmates that they would play a game in which they could make a lot of money by "figuring out the combinations." However, subjects did not tell each other what the "combinations" were; instead, they competitively tried to keep other subjects from finding out in advance and to make them learn on their own.

Experimental conditions (viz., human vs. mechanical discriminative stimuli, differentially reinforced leadership, cooperation, and competition) were usually changed several times during each experimental session. To insure meaningful analysis without statistical treatment of the data, conditions were changed when the rates of the emergent team responses had stabilized rather than at predetermined intervals of time.

Recording of Responses

Responses by each individual (A and B in Figure 2), individual response pairs (AA and BB in Figure 2), and reinforcers presented to each individual were separately recorded on electrical counters for each experimental session. Individual response pairs (AA and BB) were also recorded as pips on a polygraphic record that ran throughout the experimental session except during blackouts and conditioned reinforcement periods. Team responses (SOC AB, SOC BA, NON-SOC AB, and NON-SOC BA) were functionally recorded on separate cumulative recorders that were reset at the end of each segment of an experimental session (i.e., when experimental conditions were changed). Reinforcement of either or both individuals was marked as a pip on the appropriate team response cumulative recording. The cumulative response recorders operated continuously throughout each experimental session, except during blackout and conditioned reinforcement periods.

DEMONSTRATIVE RESULTS

Since this paper is primarily methodological, data were selected to demonstrate the power and utility of the method, rather than to report parametrically the effects of a single social variable. The data which are presented here demonstrate: (1) acquisition of social responses in cooperation, (2) emergence of initial leadership in cooperation, (3) reversal of initial leadership by differential reinforcement, (4) acquisition of competition, and (5) effects of human stimulation.

The emergence and reversal of leadership in cooperation show that leader-follower relationships can be directly recorded and experimentally manipulated by differential reinforcement contingencies. The recordings of acquisition and effects of human stimulation show that social variables clearly emerge and can be functionally measured independently of the mechanical requirements of the method.

I. Acquisition of Social Responses in Cooperation

In order to simplify our exploratory interpretations, all teams to date have been started on uncontrolled leadership in cooperation. Two stages of acquisition can be discerned. First acquired is rapid social responding using the other teammate's response as the discriminative stimulus (Social AB and Social BA responding). This is accompanied by extinction of Nonsocial AB and BA responding and a decrease in the frequency of punished AA and BB individual response pairs. Second, and usually some minutes after full acquisition of social responding, some stable pattern of initial leadership emerges.

Slow Acquisition Without Social Connotation. When subjects were brought to the laboratory and into the experimental rooms alone, with no knowledge of the presence of another subject, with no instructions implying the social nature of the task, and with the lights alone serving as discriminative stimuli, they took an extremely long time to acquire social responding. One team of graduate students showed no acquisition in two sessions involving over 4 hours of experimental time. However, when social connotation was given prior to the first experimental session, most teams of normal individuals acquired cooperative responding within 30 minutes. Social connotation was given either by conducting teammates to the laboratory and experimental rooms together or by opening the social window in the middle of a session that had begun without joint conduct to the laboratory. This marked effect of social connotation in facilitating acquisition of social responses, without specific instructions about the nature of the discriminations involved, demonstrates the method's sensitivity to emergent social variables.

The extremely slow acquisition of social responding with only mechanical stimulation and without social connotation is probably due to inappropriate mechanical sets that most subjects have when responding without social connotation. This is suggested by the fact that children acquire social responses more rapidly under these conditions than do intelligent adults, who often test many erroneous mechanical hypotheses in attempts to determine the relationship between their responding and the lights.

Rapid Acquisition with Social Connotation. Figure 5 is the record of the first experimental session of cooperation between two 18-year-old boys. Neither had previous experimental experience, and both were ignorant of the nature of the experiment. They knew each other from high school and were graduated in the same class, but they were not close friends. They were quite surprised to meet at the laboratory prior to this session.

Segment 5–1.[6] During the first 8 minutes, social responding (SOC AB and SOC BA) occurred at low irregular rates and nonsocial responding (NON-SOC AB and NON-SOC BA) extinguished. After 8 minutes, individual *A* emerged as the initial leader (increase in SOC AB, decrease in SOC BA).

Figure 6 is the record of the first experimental session of cooperation between two 12-year-old boys who were strangers. Individual *A,* a seventh grader, had never been to the laboratory before. This was the seventh experimental session for individual *B,* who was in the eighth grade. At this time, *A* was receiving psychological counseling for his hostility and aggressiveness.

Segment 6–1. Acquisition of social responding was immediate in this team. There is reason to believe that the experimentally skilled subject (*B*) signaled his teammate (*A*) through the open social window how to respond appropriately.

---

[6] The vertical lines drawn through the cumulative response records in Figures 5 through 11 indicate the points in the continuous experimental sessions at which an experimental condition was changed. These successive segments within each experimental session will be described in temporal order moving from left to right across each record. The segment numbers are circled at the bottom of each figure. In Figure 5, the first segment will be referred to as "Segment 5–1," segment 2 of Figure 5 as "Segment 5–2," etc.

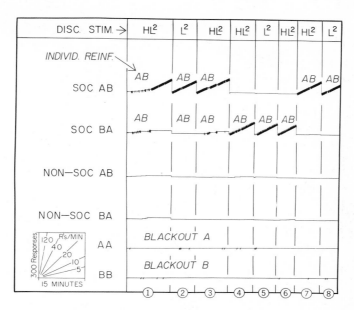

Figure 5. Rapid acquisition of social responding and emergence of A as initial leader in the first session of cooperation between two 18-year-old, experimentally naive acquaintances. There are six continuous, simultaneous tracings. The four team response tracings are cumulative (SOC AB, SOC BA, NON-SOC AB, and NON-SOC BA), and the two individual response tracings are non-cumulative (AA and BB). Figures 6 through 11 are similar records of controlled social interaction between other individuals under different experimental conditions.

Acquisition of social responses can be made more difficult by a shorter time definition for the social responses. For example, decreasing the social time limit from 0.50 to 0.25 second would require more accurate responding. Conversely, in teams showing slow acquisition or under experimental conditions in which acquisition is difficult, social responding can be shaped up by starting with a long, easy social response time (about 0.75 second) and gradually working up to a very short time (0.10 second). Ideally, the time definition of a social response should be functionally determined for each team so as to produce an equal rate of social and nonsocial responding prior to conditioning.

II. Emergence of Initial Leadership in Cooperation

In uncontrolled leadership in cooperation (both individuals are reinforced for social responses regardless of who leads, as shown in the first column of Figure 3), the immediate experimental environment does not

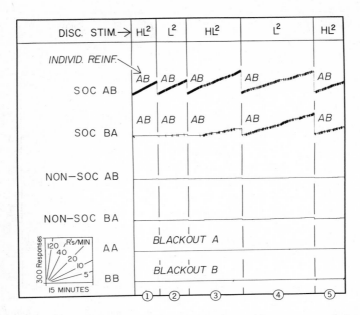

Figure 6. *Immediate acquisition of social responding and emergence of A as initial leader in first session of cooperation between two 12-year-old strangers. A, a hostile youngster, was experimentally naive. This was the seventh session for B.*

bias leadership. Therefore, if there is no previous experimental history, the emergence of high and stable differential leadership indicates a previous extra-experimental history of leadership, or relative leadership potential.

In order to validate the experimentally determined leadership by comparing it with extra-experimental indications of leadership and leadership potential, each team started its first experimental session together under the reinforcement contingency of uncontrolled leadership in cooperation. This insured that no specific experimental histories could bias the recorded leadership. Such unbiased leadership appears as a stable and significantly higher rate of either Social AB or Social BA responding during the first experimental segment and hence is termed *initial leadership*. If Social AB and Social BA responses occur at stable and approximately equivalent rates, then *balanced leadership* is recorded. If the rates are equivalent but erratic, with leadership shifting back and forth from *A* to *B, unstable leadership* is recorded.

If teammates have had an extra-experimental history together long enough to obtain evidence of leadership at work or in play by one teammate, he is called the *natural leader*. If there was no mutual extra-experimental history, but one teammate was older, more skillful, or more of a leader among his peers, he is called the *potential leader*.

The method is validated when natural leaders and potential leaders are found to be initial leaders. Differential reinforcement and experimental control of leadership are shown most dramatically when we can experimentally reverse strong initial leadership. For these two reasons it was important to demonstrate early in the standardization of this new method the emergence of strong initial leadership in cooperation.

Rapid Emergence of Initial Leadership.

Segment 5–1.   After 8 minutes of unstable leadership, individual *A* of this naive team of young adults took over full initial leadership. Although the teammates knew each other from school, and were the same age, there was no evidence of natural leadership. However, *A* was certainly the potential leader, having been one of the school's leading athletes, a top student, and a very active and aggressive person. *B* had also been a good student, but was more reserved, a little shy, and surely not a "leader among men." *B*'s high school yearbook gave him the attributes "generosity, conscientiousness, and dependability. . . ."

Segment 6–1.   Individual *A,* the experimentally naive member of this team of strangers, emerged immediately as the initial leader. Although *A*'s overly aggressive nature made him the potential leader, it is more probable that *B,* with seven sessions of situational skill, gave *A* the leadership rather than lose reinforcement opportunities while *A* was learning the task.

Gradual Loss of Initial Leadership.

Segments 6–2 through 6–5.   Throughout the remaining 45 minutes of this session, *B* gradually took over leadership until the leadership was fairly well balanced at the end of the experimental session (increase in rate of SOC BA). The leadership was little changed by removing the human stimuli.

This gradual loss of initial leadership—most often seen when one teammember is situationally naive and the other experienced—adds credibility to our interpretation that experienced *B* gave initial leadership to naive *A*. Therefore, when predicting potential and natural leadership from experimentally measured initial leadership, it is best to have both teammates experimentally naive, or at least with nearly equal situational experience.

III. Reversal of Initial Leadership by Differential Reinforcement

Rapid Reversal of Initial Leadership.

Segments 5–1 through 5–3.   After a few minutes of unstable leadership, individual *A* emerged as the stable initial leader. Under conditions of both human (HL^2) and mechanical (L^2) stimulation, he continued to lead the cooperative responding, with only a few attempts at leadership by *B* (SOC BA) in segment 5–3.

Segments 5–4 through 5–6. In order to reverse the leadership from *A* to *B*, reinforcement was programmed only for SOC BA responding. *A* almost immediately relinquished leadership to *B*, showing the immediate control of leadership in cooperation by differential reinforcement. Removing the human stimuli (L^2) in segment 5–5 produced inappropriate social responding for only 1 minute, as the team adjusted to using the lights for discriminative stimuli.

Segments 5–7 and 5–8. Reinforcement was again programmed only for SOC AB responding and leadership was immediately reversed back to *A*, the initial leader.

Segments 8–2, 8–3, 8–4, and 8–9. Similar immediate, complete, and reversible control of leadership in cooperation by differential reinforcement is seen in Figure 8. However, this is not initial leadership because it is the team's third session together.

Slow Reversal of Initial Leadership. Figure 7 is the record of the second session of a team of "best friends" who had a long history of extra-experimental cooperation. During their first experimental session, these two boys acquired the cooperative response. After the first 15 minutes of their first session, *A*, the natural leader and the older and bigger of the two, emerged as a strong initial leader and continued to lead the cooperative responding, using both human and mechanical stimuli, throughout the session of uncontrolled leadership.

Segment 7–1. With only human stimuli present (H), *A* immediately began to lead this second session of cooperative responding at a high, stable rate (SOC AB). *B* occasionally followed after the 0.5 second time limit (NON-SOC AB) but made no attempts at leadership.

Segment 7–2. Reinforcement was then programmed only for social responses led by *B* (SOC BA). The rate of Social BA responding gradually increased to a high, stable rate, as *A* very slowly relinquished leadership. Such extremely slow reversal of initial leadership is rare and occurs only when opposing very strong natural leadership.

The exponential decrease in the rate of SOC AB responding shows the extinction of a team response. The shape of this curve is similar to many individual extinction curves and suggests that the basic laws of behavior operate at the social as well as individual level.

IV. Acquisition of Competition

So far, we have had little experience with the competition contingency. No team has been started on competition. Six teams with situational histories of cooperation have responded on the competitive schedule, and all have resolved it by a complex form of cooperation. They have done this by alternating their leadership, thus giving each other equal opportunities for individual reinforcement.

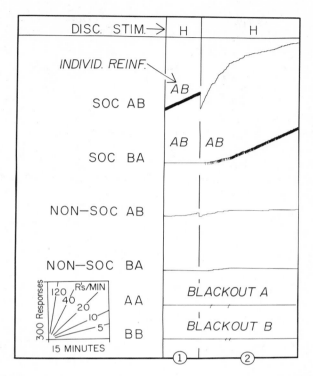

Figure 7. *Slow reversal of initial leadership in second session of cooperation between two young boys who were "best friends." A was one year older and the natural leader outside the laboratory as well as the initial leader in our experiment.*

Further research is required to determine why our teams do not readily compete. We will attempt to produce competitive behavior under the competition contingency by:

1. Selecting subjects who are more competitive than middle-class grammar school children,
2. Using much stronger reinforcement,
3. Starting out the teams on the competitive rather than the cooperative contingency,
4. Experimentally creating inequality of reinforcement between the teammates by using altruistic reinforcement contingencies.

The demonstrative data on competition included here show (a) cooperative resolution of competition and (b) generation of competition by a segment of altruism.

Cooperative Resolution of Competition. Figure 8 is the record of the third session of a team of brothers, 13-year-old *A* and 14-year-old *B*. Both brothers were in the eighth grade. *A,* the more alert and aggressive of the two, led *B* in school and social activities. *A*'s natural leadership of *B* validated his initial and continuing leadership throughout their first two experimental sessions.

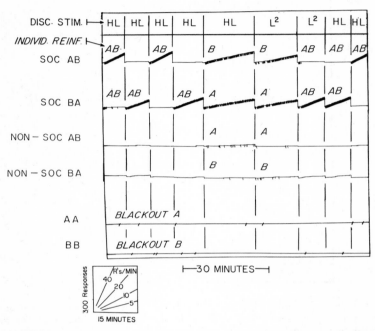

Figure 8. *Cooperative resolution of competition contingency by two brothers. Although A was the natural leader in school and at home and the initial leader in our experiment, leadership was easily reversed to B by differential reinforcement. By alternating their leadership and opportunities for reinforcement, they converted the competitive program to a cooperative task (segments 5 and 6).*

Segment 8–1.   *B* struggled briefly for initial leadership but again yielded to *A*'s dominance. Since this was the team's third session together, and *A*'s seventh experimental session, acquisition of the cooperative response is not seen.

Segments 8–2 through 8–4.   *A*'s strong initial leadership was successfully reversed to *B* by differential reinforcement in the second segment (high rate of SOC BA responding). In the third segment, reinforcement was programmed for SOC AB responses and *A* immediately led. Leadership was switched back to *B* in the fourth segment. Note that more NON-SOC AB and NON-SOC BA responses occurred when *B*-leading was re-inforced than when *A*, the strong initial leader, had to lead for reinforcement. These nonreinforced team responses were soon called "mistakes" by experienced teammates and usually occurred when strong initial leadership was counter-conditioned by differential reinforcement. These erroneous responses represent the difficulty that a strong natural and initial leader experiences in learning to be a follower.

Segment 8–5. Team response contingencies were changed to produce *uncontrolled leadership in competition.* However, these two brothers did not compete: they cooperatively resolved the competitive contingencies by alternating their leadership and thus their individual reinforcement. The higher rate of NON-SOC AB over NON-SOC BA responses suggests that *A,* the initial leader, was somewhat more competitive than *B.*

Segment 8–6. The human stimuli were removed (L^2) but the cooperative resolution of the competitive task persisted, though with slightly less stability.

Segment 8–7. The contingencies were again reversed to uncontrolled leadership in cooperation. This time, individual *B* emerged as the leader, after a few leadership attempts by *A.* This reversal in uncontrolled cooperative leadership may have been due to *B*'s anger because in segments 8–5 and 8–6 *A* had taken more reinforcements than he had "given" *B.* This apparent anger had been observed through the periscopes.

Segments 8–8 and 8–9. When the human stimuli were replaced (HL), there was no change in the uncontrolled cooperative leadership. In the final segment of this session, leadership was again restored to *A* by differential reinforcement.

Competition Generated by Altruism. Figure 9 is the record of the sixth session of the "best friends" team. In their first experimental session, *A,* the natural leader, emerged immediately as the initial leader. In their second session (Figure 7), *A* continued to lead and only very slowly relinquished leadership when they were reinforced only when *B* led. In their immediately preceding fifth experimental session, they had cooperatively resolved the competitive contingency by alternating leadership as did the team of Figure 8.

Segment 9–1. For approximately 4 minutes, *B* led the cooperative social responding. After this warm-up, leadership spontaneously shifted to *A,* who again exerted his natural leadership.

Segment 9–2. In an attempt to produce competition in this highly cooperative team, we created an unequal distribution of reinforcement between the individuals. An *altruistic* reinforcement contingency was programmed—*B* received a reinforcement for every SOC AB response, but there was no way for *A* to be reinforced. *A* was simply permitted to provide his friend with the *opportunity to get reinforcement.* During this segment, there was an increase in the rate of leadership attempts by *B* (SOC BA, NON-SOC BA, and BB individual response pairs) as *B* tried to give *A* some reinforcement. However, toward the end of the segment these

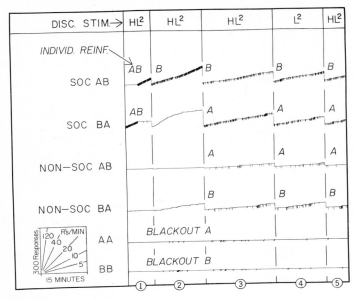

Figure 9. Competition generated in a previously cooperative team by an altruistic period (A sets up B's reinforcement). These two "best friends" had cooperated for several years outside the laboratory, for five sessions within the laboratory (second session shown in Figure 7), and had previously resolved the competitive program by cooperatively alternating leadership. The extra reinforcement altruistically given to B in segment 2 catalyzed the competition recorded in segments 3, 4, and 5.

responses extinguished. *A* set up 110 reinforcements for *B* during this altruism segment and received only smiles for his labor.

Segments 9–3 through 9–5. The competition contingency was presented, and this time it produced competition. Although *A* (the recipient of the altruism) did "offer" *B* (the donor) some reinforcement, it amounted to only 30 more pennies during all three segments. The rest of the reinforcement was fought over, as *A* tried to catch up with *B*'s total "take."

The competition is seen in the record by the increase in NON-SOC AB and NON-SOC BA response rates, wherein they "caught their opponent asleep." The removal of the human stimuli (L^2) in segment 9–4 did not change their competitive behavior.

When the intensity of the white noise was briefly reduced, interesting and validating competitive dialogue occurred:

A: "C'mon, you had 10,000. Keep it up. Give me some."
B: "Yeah, but you couldn't help it."
A: "Go ahead, come on! You got all the money, didn't ya? So, shut up!"

> *B:* "You couldn't help it!"
>
> *A:* "Do it!" (Meaning "Respond first so I can get some pennies and catch up.")
>
> *B:* "Take turns!" (Meaning "Take turns, so I can stay ahead from the altruism segment.")

This dialogue shows how competitive the team had been made by the altruistic contingency. *B*'s statements, "You couldn't help it!", and his refusal to let *A* catch up suggest that altruistic gifts are not accepted as debts unless the donor provided the gifts by sacrificing reinforcement to himself. In other words, an unavoidable "gift," one with no other alternative, is not responded to as a gift. (This method might provide a way of experimentally determining the response to tax-deductible "gifts.")

The competitive behavior seen in Figure 9, clearly proves that our method can generate and measure competition. The failure to get competitive behavior from the other teams under the competitive schedule is not a fault of the method. Rather, it is due to our ignorance of the nature of competition and how to generate it for laboratory analysis. The altruistic contingency is only one of many procedures that should be tried in attempting to generate competition.

V. Effects of Human Stimuli

Decreased Control of Leadership in Cooperation Between Strangers by Adding Human Stimuli. Figure 10 is the record of the second experimental session of cooperation between relative strangers. Neither individual had participated in any other session. Both boys were of the same age and school grade and seemed to have equal poise, skill, and leadership in school and at play. The team's cooperative and leadership behavior had stabilized during the previous experimental session.

Segment 10–1. Uncontrolled leadership in cooperation was programmed, with both the human stimuli and the two lights present (HL^2). Under these conditions, leadership was almost balanced between these two boys with approximately the same leadership potential and with minimal previous extra-experimental social interaction.

Segment 10–2. Leadership was controlled by reinforcing both teammates only when *A* led (SOC AB). However, *B* led more (SOC BA) when his leadership was extinguished than when it had been reinforced in segment 10–1. *B*'s unreinforced attempts to lead cost both teammates many reinforcers.

Segment 10–3. When the human stimuli were removed (L^2), *B*'s inefficient attempts at leadership (SOC BA) rapidly extinguished.

Segment 10–4. When the human stimuli were replaced (HL^2), *B* again led about half the time (high SOC BA rate), at the expense of reinforcement to both teammates.

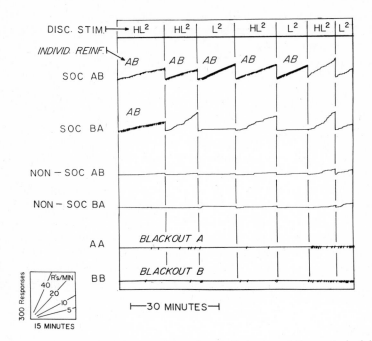

Figure 10. *Human stimuli (HL² in segments 2 and 4) decreased the control of leader-ship from that developed with the lights alone (L² in segments 3 and 5) in cooperation between strangers. B could follow A's lights but not A's movements. This team had minimal previous social interaction.*

Segment 10–5. Leadership was again brought under the control of differential reinforcement by removing the human stimuli (L²). In other words, *B* could follow *A*'s lights, but he could not follow *A*. Segments 10–2 through 10–5 demonstrate the reversible effect of the human stimuli in decreasing the control by differential reinforcement of leadership between strangers.

Segments 10–6 and 10–7. All responses were extinguished with the human stimuli present (segment 10–6) and with the human stimuli absent (segment 10–7). Note the increase in the rate of previously extinguished team responses (NON-SOC AB and NON-SOC BA) and individual response pairs (AA and BB). During this extinction period, the rate of individual response pairs increased despite continued punishment with blackouts.

Increased Control of Leadership in Cooperation Between Siblings by Adding Human Stimuli. Figure 11 is the record of the first experimental session of a brother and sister team. Since the brother (*A*) had participated in three previous sessions with a different teammate, and the sister (*B*) had one previous session with another teammate, situational team acquisition is not present in these records. This team thus had maximal previous extra-experimental experience together, at least one session of previous individual situational experience, but no previous situational experience together.

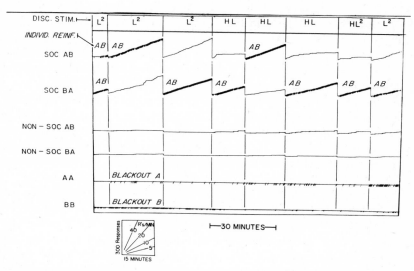

Figure 11. *Human stimuli (HL in segments 4, 5, and 6 and HL² in segment 7) increased the control of leadership over that developed with the lights alone (L² in segments 1, 2, 3, and 8) in cooperation between a brother and sister. A could follow his sister but could not follow her lights. This team had maximal previous social interaction.*

Brother (*A*) was 13 years old, an "A" student in the ninth grade, and frequently dominated by his bigger, 2-year-older sister, who was a "B+" student in the tenth grade. Thus, sister (*B*) was the natural leader of this team.

Segment 11–1. In uncontrolled leadership in cooperation with human stimuli absent (L²), sister emerged as the initial leader, but not without some argument from brother (*A*) as shown by the intermittent bursts of SOC AB responses toward the end of the segment.

Segment 11–2. Attempting to reverse initial leadership, we reinforced both teammates only when brother led (SOC AB). Sister did not relinquish her initial leadership, at a loss of reinforcement to them both. Note the high frequency of individual responses (AA and BB), suggesting an unstable social relationship.

Segment 11–3. With the human stimuli still absent, both individuals were reinforced only when sister led (SOC BA). Brother would not now relinquish his unreinforced leadership, even though initially he followed sister when his leadership was reinforced (Segment 11–1).

Segment 11–4. When the human discriminative stimuli were added (HL), brother (*A*) did relinquish unreinforced leadership, as shown by the extinction of SOC AB responses. In other words, brother could follow sister, but he could not follow her lights.

Segment 11–5. With the human stimuli still present, leadership was successfully reversed when the team was again reinforced only when brother led (SOC AB). Note that sister's rate of unreinforced leadership attempts (SOC BA), although they did not completely extinguish, occurred at a much lower rate than they did in segment 11–2 with the human stimuli absent. In other words, sister could follow brother, but she could not follow his lights.

Segments 11–6 and 11–7. With human stimuli still present (HL), leadership was successfully reversed back to sister (SOC BA) by differential reinforcement. Brother's unreinforced leadership attempts (SOC AB) gradually extinguished, as they had done in segment 11–4. In segment 11–7 the reinforcement lights were added (HL^2) with no discernible effect.

Segment 11–8. The human stimuli were removed (L^2) while the team continued to be reinforced only when sister led (SOC BA), and the control of leadership was lost. Unreinforced leadership by the brother (SOC AB) increased to a rate equal to that previously emitted under the same conditions in segment 11–3. The experimental analysis recorded in Figure 11 shows that the control of cooperative leadership between these siblings was more readily achieved with human discriminative stimuli present than with only mechanical discriminative stimuli present.

Emergent Property of Human Discriminative Stimulation. In these two demonstrations of the effects of human stimulation on control of cooperative leadership by differential reinforcement, provision was made for experimental control of social connotation, previous situational and extra-experimental teammate experience, and teammate constitution. The use of the lights as discriminative stimuli controlled for the mechanical, discriminative, and neuromuscular aspects of the cooperative task. Therefore, human discriminative stimulation emerges as an important social variable.

In the team composed of relative strangers with minimal teammate experience, the human stimuli *decreased* control of cooperative leadership (Figure 10). In the brother and sister team with maximal previous extra-experimental experience, human stimuli *increased* control of cooperative leadership (Figure 11). This happy result eliminated the need to run a complicated series of controls to show that the differences between the effects of the human and mechanical stimuli were not due to differential reaction times or other nonsocial properties. If the different effects of the human and mechanical stimuli were due to their nonsocial properties, their effects on leadership control would be in the same direction regardless of extra-experimental teammate experience.

In retrospect, it is not surprising that the human nature of immediate discriminative stimulation is important. My secretary, for example, is less apt to linger in gossip when the door between our offices is open than when it is shut—even though she knows I can hear her through the closed door. Evidently my immediate human stimulation is more effective than my mechanical directives and instruction. As another example, the face of Hitler on World War II Allied propaganda posters was more effective in suppressing gossip than was the name "Hitler" or the sign of the swastika. Still again, the psychoanalyst's couch may make the flow of socially disturbing material easier for a patient to emit because it removes the analyst's immediate visual presence as the patient closes his eyes or looks at the wall when he speaks his socially embarrassing words. These extrapolations, admittedly examples of *post hoc ergo propter hoc* reasoning, are included only to point out that the immediate effect of human stimulation, with all other factors held constant, may have important implications far beyond the laboratory.

Differential Sensitivity of Teams to Human Stimuli. In four of the five previously described teams, human stimuli were added with little or no effect on cooperative (Figures 5, 6, and 8) or competitive (Figures 8 and 9) team responses. This shows that human stimuli are sensitive variables which do not operate on all teams and that we must learn more about them before we can insure their operation under specified conditions. The secrets may lie in team constitution (individual susceptibility), team experimental or extra-experimental history, or team stability.

Because of the only occasional operation of human stimuli, a method that does not require statistical analysis for conclusive statements was necessary to discover their operation on single teams. The highly significant effects of human stimuli shown in Figures 10 and 11 prove that these effects exist. Until more is learned about these effects, they must be obtained for experimental analysis by using individually sensitive experimental methods in conjunction with team screening and selection.

SUMMARY

A single method for investigating both individual behavior and cooperative and competitive social behavior was developed and standardized. The objective measurement and control of these different behaviors was effected merely by adding the relevant social stimuli and altering the opportunities for reinforcement. This method simplifies the experimental analysis of social behavior by helping to eliminate confounded variables and permitting the laboratory analysis of social behavior with all the rigor and control of laboratory natural science.

This and other similarly controlled methods will qualify sociology as a natural science.

Acquisition of complicated discriminations involved in cooperation and competition was more rapid with social connotation than without. This was probably due to joint problem solving ("two heads are better than one") or the effect of social set ("people don't expect machines to act like people").

An added advantage of the method is that important leader-follower relationships, which are clear social emergents, were directly recorded and were experimentally manipulated by differential reinforcement. This control facilitated studying their characteristics.

Human discriminative stimuli were shown to have different effects from mechanical stimuli on the differential control of leadership, even when social connotation, social programming, and other aspects of the situation were the same. The direction of the effect of human stimuli differed with the degree of previous teammate experience. This effect of the human nature of discriminative stimuli is a social emergent with important implications for social research and its application.

The method has been standardized in the investigation of leadership relations in cooperation between normal grammar and high school students. Further investigations currently under way have uncovered deficits in cooperative and competitive ability between couples in marital difficulty and severe social deficits in a few acute psychotics. Accurate measurement of such deficits will add much to our basic knowledge of social behavior.

Social psychology is necessary as a separate and higher order discipline above individual psychology. The social emergents—social connotation, differential leadership, and human stimuli—experimentally demonstrated in this article, require special methods and treatment. The degree and direction of action of these social emergents could not have been accurately predicted by studying individuals in isolation. However, the methods used for objectively measuring and precisely controlling these emergents must include all the controls and variables used in the study of individuals. Individual psychology and social psychology are overlapping portions of a natural continuum extending from the behavior of single reflexes in single individuals to communal responses in large groups. Since it is folly to expect high objectivity at the complex social end of the continuum without the controls required at the simpler individual end, I suggest that social psychology will profit from using the skills and precision of the individual psychologist. By using these skills, the social psychologist can demonstrate precisely the emergence of his variables, the boundaries of his field, and his place on the natural science continuum.

REFERENCES

AZRIN, N. H., and LINDSLEY, O. R. The reinforcement of cooperation between children. *J. abnorm. soc. Psychol.*, 1956, *52*, 100–102.

BERNARD, C. *An introduction to the study of experimental medicine* (1865). New York: Dover, 1957.

COHEN, D. J. Justin and his peers: An experimental analysis of a child's social world. *Child Developm.*, 1962, *33*, 697–717.

DEWEY, J. The reflex arc concept in psychology. *Psychol. Rev.*, 1896, *3*, 357–370.

FERSTER, C. B., and SKINNER, B. F. *Schedules of reinforcement.* New York: Appleton-Century-Crofts, 1957.

HUNTER, W. S. *Human behavior* (1919). Chicago: University of Chicago Press, 1928 (Rev. ed.).

KANTOR, J. R. *Principles of psychology.* New York: Knopf, 1924.

KELLER, F. S., and SCHOENFELD, W. N. *Principles of psychology.* New York: Appleton-Century-Crofts, 1950.

KÖHLER, W. *Gestalt psychology: An introduction to new concepts in modern psychology.* New York: Liveright, 1947.

KRAEPELIN, E. The psychological experiment in psychiatry. *Psychol. Arbeit.*, Leipzig: Engelmann, 1896.

LINDSLEY, O. R. Feeding a kitten—a social reinforcer. In Annu. Tech. Rep. #3, Contract N5–Ori–07662, Office of Naval Research. Waltham, Mass.: Harvard Medical School, Behavior Research Laboratory, November, 1956. (a)

LINDSLEY, O. R. Operant conditioning methods applied to research in chronic schizophrenia. *Psychiat. Res. Rep.*, 1956, *5*, 118–139. (b)

MILLER, N. E., and DOLLARD, J. *Social learning and imitation.* New Haven: Yale University Press, 1941.

PAVLOV, I. P. *Experimental psychology and other essays.* New York: Philosophical Library, 1957. (P. 35, excerpt from speech, 1899).

SIDMAN, M. *Tactics of scientific research.* New York: Basic Books, Inc., 1960.

SKINNER, B. F. The generic nature of the concepts stimulus and response. *J. gen. Psychol.*, 1935, *12*, 40–65.

SKINNER, B. F. *The behavior of organisms.* New York: Appleton-Century-Crofts, 1938.

SKINNER, B. F. *Science and human behavior.* New York: Macmillan, 1953.

STEINBECK, J. *Of mice and men.* New York: Covici, 1937.

39

Reflexive Fighting in Response
to Aversive Stimulation

R. E. Ulrich and N. H. Azrin

When electric foot-shock is delivered to paired rats, a stereotyped fighting reaction results (O'Kelly and Steckle, 1939; Daniel, 1943; Richter, 1950). The present investigation studies several possible determinants of this fighting reaction.

METHOD

Subjects

Male Sprague-Dawley rats of the Holtzman strain were used because rats of this strain were found to be very docile and nonaggressive in the absence of electric shock. At the beginning of the experiment the subjects were approximately 100 days old and weighed between 295–335 g. None of the rats had prior experience with the apparatus.

Apparatus

The experimental compartment measured 12 in. by 9 in. by 8 in., two sides of which were constructed of sheet metal and the other two of clear plastic. The floor consisted of steel rods, $\frac{3}{32}$ in. in diameter and spaced 0.5 in. apart. An open chest contained the experimental chamber, thereby permitting a clear view through the transparent door of the chamber. A shielded, 10-watt bulb at the top provided illumination, and a speaker produced a "white" masking noise. An exhaust fan provided additional masking noise as well as ventilation. The temperature was maintained at

Adapted from *Journal of the Experimental Analysis of Behavior,* 1962, *5,* 511–520. With permission of the authors and publisher.

about 75° F. The various stimulus conditions used were programmed by electrical apparatus located in a room separate from the experimental chamber. A cumulative recorder, counters, and timers provided a record of the responses. Shock was delivered to the subjects through the grid floor for 0.5 sec. duration from an Applegate constant current stimulator. A shock scrambler provided a changing pattern of polarities so that any two of the floor grids would be opposite polarity during a major part of each presentation of shock.

PROCEDURE AND RESULTS

Definition of the Fighting Response

When two Sprague-Dawley rats were first placed in the experimental chamber, they moved about slowly, sniffing the walls, the grid, and occasionally each other. At no time did any fighting behavior appear in the absence of shock. Soon after shock was delivered, a drastic change in the rats' behavior took place. They would suddenly face each other in an upright position, and with the head thrust forward and the mouth open they would strike vigorously at each other assuming the stereotyped posture shown in Figure 1.

This behavior has typically been referred to as fighting (Scott and Fredericson, 1951), and it was found to be readily identifiable provided that the topography of the response was well specified. For this experiment, a fighting response was recorded by an observer who depressed a microswitch for any striking or biting movement of either or both animals toward the other while in the stereotyped fighting posture. Once a shock was delivered, the subjects would typically assume and maintain this posture for brief periods during which several striking movements might be made. A new response was recorded only for those striking movements which were separated from previous striking movements by approximately 1 sec. Typically, rats struck at each other for only a brief duration (less than 1 sec.) following a delivery of shock; therefore, the number of fighting episodes was more easily recorded than the duration of fighting. The duration for which the rats maintained the stereotyped fighting posture could not be reliably measured since this posture often blended imperceptibly in time into a more normal posture.

A measure of the reliability of recording was obtained by having two observers simultaneously score the fighting behavior. Figure 2 shows the cumulative records of the fighting responses which occurred during a 10-min. period in which shock was presented at a frequency of 20 shocks per min. The number of fighting responses recorded by each observer agreed within 5 percent. The parallel slopes of the two lines indicate that there

Figure 1. Example of the stereotype fighting posture.

was close agreement between the two observers on both the total number of responses and also on the momentary changes in the rate of fighting.

Frequency of Shock Presentation

Six rats were divided into three pairs, and each pair was exposed to electric foot-shock (2 ma.) delivered at frequencies of 0.1, 0.6, 2, 20, and 38 shocks per min. Each of these frequencies was administered during each of three different sessions (10 min. per session) with a 24-hr. interval usu-

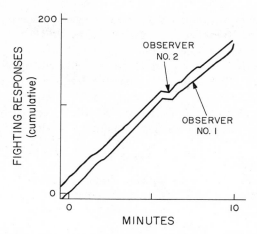

Figure 2.   *Agreement between observers in the simultaneous recording of fighting responses.*

ally allowed after each session. The order of presentation of frequencies was irregular. Figure 3 is the rate of fighting for each of the three pairs of subjects as a function of the frequency of shock presentation. The frequency of fighting for each pair of subjects increased from zero responses in the absence of shock to 33 fighting responses per min. at a frequency

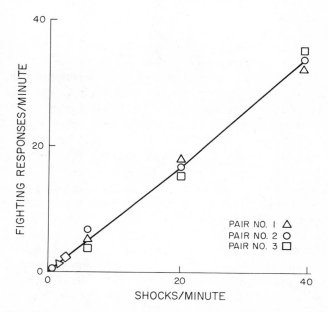

Figure 3.   *The elicitation of fighting responses as a function of the frequency of presentation of foot-shock for each of three pairs of rats.*

of 38 shocks per min. Individual differences between the pairs of rats were largely absent; the frequency of fighting of the different pairs of subjects was almost identical at each of the shock frequencies.

If each delivery of shock produced a fighting response, the rate of fighting would be directly known from the frequency of shock presentation. Indeed, the higher frequencies of shock presentation did result in a relationship of this sort. Shock frequencies in excess of 6 per min. produced fighting in response to 82–93 percent of the shocks (Table 1).

TABLE I

Examples of the consistency of fighting elicited by shock from three pairs of subjects during two sessions at each of the different shock frequencies. The consistency of the fighting reflex is expressed as the percentage of shocks that resulted in a fighting response.

Frequency of Shocks (Shocks/Min.)	Consistency of Fighting Reflex (Responses) (Shocks)		
	Pair No. 1	Pair No. 2	Pair No. 3
0.1	0.33	0.66	0.66
0.6	0.61	0.55	0.61
2.0	0.83	0.58	0.58
6.0	0.83	0.94	0.77
20.0	0.92	0.91	0.82
38.0	0.85	0.89	0.93

Lower frequencies of shock (less than 1 per min.) produced fighting in response to no more than 66 percent of the shocks. Visual observation of the rats revealed that shortly after a shock was presented, the subjects slipped out of the fighting posture and assumed other positions. It was also apparent that fighting in response to shock was more likely if the animals were facing each other at the moment of shock-delivery. Thus, the probability of fighting appeared to be lower at the lower frequencies of shock presentation because of the likelihood that the rats were at some distance from each other. This direct relationship between rate of shock presentation and rate of fighting reversed at very high frequencies. In an additional study with two pairs of rats, the shock was made so frequent as to be continuous. Although occasional fighting responses occurred, much of the behavior of the rats appeared directed toward escape from the experimental chamber. This "escape" behavior appeared to interfere somewhat with the usual reflexive fighting. Such behavior was also noted during the early part of the initial session when the subjects were first presented with shock. However, in this case the escape behavior did not persist.

Intrasession changes in fighting behavior were conspicuously absent (Figure 4). The bottom curve is the cumulative record of the fighting for a 10-min. session in which only one shock was delivered at the middle of the session. This single shock produced an immediate fighting response. At a shock frequency of 0.6 shocks per min. (second curve from bottom) the rats did not fight after all of the six shock deliveries, but observation revealed that the four fighting responses which did occur were immediately preceded by the presentation of a shock. At no time did fighting occur during the interval between shock presentation although the stereotyped fighting posture was often maintained during that time. No warm-up period appeared at the beginning of the session; nor did the frequency of fighting decrease toward the end of the session.

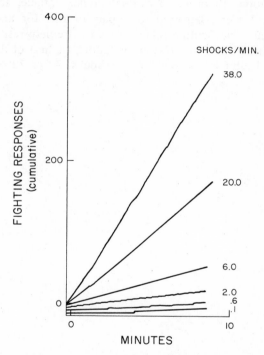

Figure 4. Typical curves for one pair of rats of the fighting responses at various frequencies of presentation of shock.

Sequential Effects

Elicitation of the fighting reflex on a given day was virtually independent of the shock frequency used on preceding days or even on the same day. As a rule, the number of fighting responses at a given shock frequency varied less than 10 percent, irrespective of the preceding shock frequency. On several occasions, the sessions followed within 10 min. of each other in order to determine the effects of a shorter interval between sessions.

At a frequency of 2 shocks per min., 68 percent of the shocks were effective when 24 hr. were allowed between sessions; 63 percent of the shocks were effective when only 10 min. were allowed between sessions. This small difference in responding as a function of the interval between sessions was typical. The strength of the fighting reflex appears to be fairly independent of its history of elicitation.

Reflex Fatigue

Figure 2 revealed little change in the consistency with which the fighting reflex was elicited, even after 300 elicitations at the higher rates of shock presentation. In order to evaluate reflex fatigue, frequent shocks (every 1.5 sec.) were delivered to a pair of rats for an uninterrupted period of 7.5 hr. The fighting reflex proved extremely resistant to fatigue (Figure 5). During the first 2400 presentations (1 hr.) of the shock, fighting was elicited after 82 percent of the shocks. After 7200 presentations

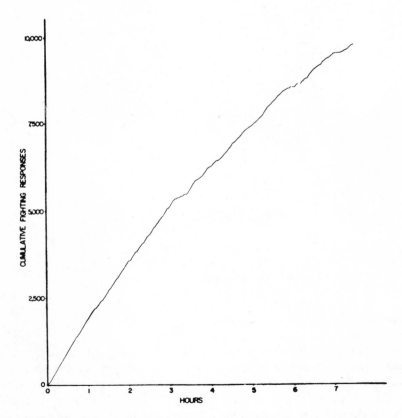

Figure 5. Cumulative record of the fighting responses that were elicited from a pair of rats during a long period (7.5 hr.) of frequent (every 1.5 sec.) shock presentation.

of shock (third hour), fighting still occurred after 70 percent of the shocks. Only during the last 1.5 hr., after 6 hr. and nearly 15,000 shocks, did the consistency of elicitation drop below 40 percent. By this time the rats were damp with perspiration and appeared to be weakened physically. By the end of the 7.5 hr., approximately 10,000 fighting responses had been elicited. Several observers were required because of the extended observation period.

Intensity of Shock Presentation

Three pairs of rats were exposed to various intensities of shock at a fixed frequency of 20 shocks per min. Each intensity was presented for at least 10 min. The sequence of intensities was varied and several 10-min. periods were given at each intensity. The cumulative-response curves of Figure 6 for one pair of rats were typical of those obtained with all three

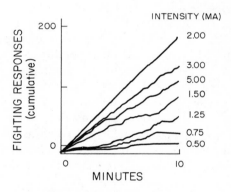

Figure 6. Typical cumulative records of the fighting responses that were elicited from one pair of rats at various intensities of foot-shock.

pairs of rats. Increasing the shock intensity from 0–2 ma. produced an increased frequency of fighting; at still higher intensities (3–5 ma.), the rate of fighting was somewhat reduced. Visual observations indicated that lower intensities produced a fighting response of less vigor and longer latency. Also, at the lower intensities, chance factors, such as the orientation of the rats relative to each other and to the grid floor, appeared to influence greatly the likelihood of a fighting response. If the rats were making good contact across several of the floor grids, and were also oriented toward each other, a fighting response was likely to result. Even so, this response was relatively short in duration, slow in onset, less vigorous, and less likely to result in a maintained fighting posture than the responses elicited by the higher current intensities. At these lower intensities, the definition of a movement as a fighting response often became arbitrary. At the higher intensities, the attack movement was unmistakable.

The slight decrease in fighting behavior at the highest intensity (5 ma.) appeared to be partly a consequence of the debilitating effects of the shock. Prolonged exposure to this intensity often resulted in a complete loss of fighting because of the paralysis of one or both of the subjects. Even during the initial exposure to this very high intensity, fighting behavior appeared to be reduced by the strong tendency of the rats to engage in other shock-induced behavior, such as biting the grids, jumping, running, or pushing on the walls.

Thus, the optimal current intensity for eliciting fighting was approximately 2 ma. At lower intensities, the shock did not appear to be sufficiently aversive, while at higher intensities, the shock appeared to be debilitating and generated competing behavior. Tedeschi (1959) also found that 2- to 3-ma. intensity is optimal for producing fighting between mice.

Uniformity of Shock Presentation

All previous investigations of shock-produced fighting appear to have used the same type of shock circuit. Alternate bars of the floor grid have been wired in parallel so that adjacent bars were of opposite polarity, but many nonadjacent bars were of the same polarity. Such a design permits the rat to avoid the scheduled shocks by standing on bars of the same polarity. Skinner and Campbell (1947) found that this unauthorized avoidance could be eliminated by a scrambling circuit which insured that any two bars would be of opposite polarity during a major part of each shock delivery. A scrambling circuit of this sort was used throughout the present investigation. Three pairs of rats were now studied to determine the effects of omitting this scrambling circuit. An hour-long period of shock (2-ma. intensity at a rate of 20 per min.) was given to each pair of rats on each of three successive days. On one or two of these days, the scrambler was omitted. For all three pairs of rats, the omission of the scrambler produced less than half as many fighting responses as were obtained with the scrambler. The curves in Figure 7 for one pair of rats reveal great variability in the frequency of fighting; periods of frequent fighting alternate with periods or little or no fighting. Visual observation revealed that one or both rats often avoided shocks by standing on bars of like-polarity. This safe posture was often maintained for several minutes during which no fighting was produced. When a part of the rat happened to contact a bar of different polarity, the resulting shock usually jolted the rat out of this safe posture. For the next few minutes, the rat was likely to receive the scheduled shocks and fighting resumed until once again a safe position was discovered. When the scrambler was in use, no safe position was possible and the rats typically fought immediately fol-

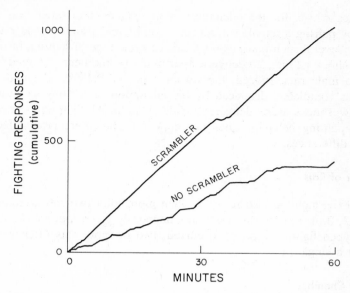

Figure 7. The elicitation of fighting responses by foot-shocks that were delivered with or without a polarity scrambler for the floor grids.

lowing each scheduled shock. The omission of a polarity scrambler in past studies may account for the frequent failure of shock to elicit fighting behavior (Miller, 1948; Richter, 1950).

Previous Experience

In this study, each rat had been housed individually and had no prior contact with his fighting-mate. This general unfamiliarity of the rats with each other might have been a factor in obtaining the fighting response to shock. This possibility was evaluated by housing two rats together in a single cage for several weeks. Subsequent exposure to foot-shock in the experimental chamber produced the same degree of fighting that had been obtained when the same rats had been housed separately. These results were replicated with 24 other animals. It appears, therefore, that previous familiarity of rats with each other does not appreciably effect the elicitation of fighting through foot-shock. On the other hand, non-reflexive fighting behavior has been found to be affected by previous familiarity (Seward, 1945).

Sex

Male rats are known to fight more often than female rats in a natural (no-shock) situation (Beeman, 1947; Scott and Fredericson, 1951). The relevance of sex for the elicitation of fighting by foot-shock was investigated by pairing a female rat with a second female, and a male rat with a female. Several such pairings revealed the same type of fighting in response to foot-shock (2 ma., 20 deliveries per min.) as had been obtained between the two male rats. Indeed, the sexual behavior between the male-female pair was completely displaced by the elicitation of fighting soon after the first few shocks were delivered. Unlike "natural" fighting behavior, reflexive fighting behavior does not appear to be appreciably affected by sexual differences.

Number of Rats

Reflexive fighting also resulted when more than two rats were shocked. When 2, 3, 4, 6, or 8 rats were simultaneously given foot-shock, the same stereotyped fighting reaction occurred, two or more rats often aggressing against a single rat.

Size of Chamber

Throughout the present study the size of the experimental chamber was 12 by 9 by 8 in. In this phase a pair of rats was given shock (2 ma.) for 10 min. (20 shocks per min.) in a square chamber having an adjustable floor area. The height was held constant at 17 in. Figure 8 shows the number of fighting responses as a function of the floor area at each of the different floor sizes. With only a very small amount of floor space (6 by 6 in.) the fighting response was elicited by approximately 90 percent of the shocks. At the larger floor areas, the number of fighting responses decreased; with the largest floor space (24 by 24 in.), only 2 percent of the shocks elicited fighting. The amount of fighting between rats in response to shock appears to depend critically upon the amount of floor space in the fighting chamber. When the rats were only a few inches apart, the shock was likely to cause them to turn and lunge at each other. At the larger distances, the rats largely ignored each other.

Strain

As mentioned above, the Holtzman Sprague-Dawley rats are unusually docile in the absence of shock. Additional study revealed that other less docile strains of rats also exhibited this shock-elicited fighting. Two pairs of mature male rats from four other strains (Long-Evans hooded, Wistar, General Biological hooded, Charles River Sprague-Dawley) were exposed to the optimal shock conditions (2 ma. at 20 shocks per min.) in the same experimental chamber (12 by 9 by 8 in.) as had been used for the Holtzman strain. In all of the strains the same stereotyped fighting reaction oc-

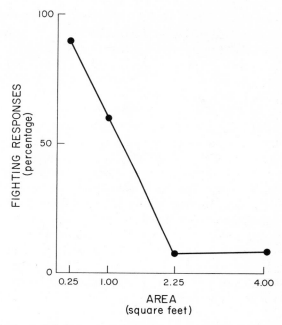

Figure 8. *Elicitation of fighting responses from two rats by foot-shock in a square chamber of constant height and variable floor area.*

curred following the presentations of shock. However, less than 50 percent of the shocks produced fighting between rats of the Wistar strain, whereas over 70 percent of the shocks produced fighting between rats in each of the other strains. The Wistar rats appeared to be more sensitive to the shock since much competing behavior was generated by shocks of 2-ma. intensity, and two out of the four Wistar rats died after exposure to these shocks. Apart from this seemingly greater sensitivity of the Wistar-strain rats, all of the strains showed the same stereotyped fighting response to foot-shock.

Species

Mature guinea pigs and hamsters were studied under the same conditions of shock presentation and in the same experimental chamber to ascertain the existence of reflexive fighting in other species. Delivery of shock to a pair of hamsters produced a similar type of stereotyped fighting posture and attack as was seen with rats. These fighting responses could be consistently elicited at lower intensities of shock (0.75 ma.) than was required with the rats. Also, the hamsters persisted longer in their fighting, often biting and rolling over each other. Tedeschi (1959) found that paired mice also fought vigorously in response to foot-shock. In contrast, the paired guinea pigs never showed the fighting posture or any attack movements in response to shock. Variations in the intensity and frequency of shock presentation, as well as food deprivation up to 72 hr., did not alter this failure to fight.

Interspecies Fighting

When a Sprague-Dawley rat was paired with a hamster, shock produced the same fighting reaction by both animals. However, when a rat was paired with a guinea pig, all of the attacking was done by the rat. The guinea pig reacted only by withdrawing from the rat's biting attacks following the shock delivery. The rat attacked only the head of the guinea pig. During this attack, the rat assumed a semi-crouching position with the forepaws raised only slightly off the floor, a posture which differed from the upright position assumed by rats in fighting each other. Since the guinea pig never stood upright, the crouching position of the rat brought its head to the level of the guinea pig's head. The otherwise inflexible and stereotyped fighting posture of the rat appeared to be modified by the position of the guinea pig. No fighting occurred in the absence of shock.

Inanimate Objects

When an insulated doll was placed into the experimental chamber while a rat was being shocked, no attack was attempted. Similarly, no attack movements were made toward either a conducting doll or a recently deceased rat. Dolls moved rapidly about the cage also failed to produce fighting. Fighting responses were elicited only when the dead rat was moved about the cage on a stick.

Electrode Shock

In using foot-shock, both rats are shocked simultaneously since they are standing on the same grid floor. Does the elicitation of fighting require that both rats be shocked? This question might be investigated by electrifying only that section of the grid under one of the rats. However, the rat quickly learns to stand on a nonelectrified section. A second solution is to shock the rats through implanted electrodes. The two rats were placed in an experimental chamber, and electrodes were implanted beneath a fold of skin on the back of one rat. A harness and swivel arrangement allowed the rat complete freedom in moving about. When a 0.5 sec. shock was delivered at an intensity of 2 ma., only a spasmodic movement of the rat resulted if no other rat were present. When the shock was delivered in the presence of a second rat, the stimulated rat usually assumed the stereotyped fighting position and attacked the unstimulated rat. Upon being attacked, the unstimulated rat in turn often assumed the stereotyped posture and returned the attack. Once the attack was initiated by the shock, the continuance of the fighting appeared to be partly under social control. Fighting was elicited, then, even when only one member of the pair of rats was stimulated. Somewhat the same result was seen above when the foot-shock elicited fighting in a rat paired with a guinea pig, in spite of the failure of the guinea pig to reciprocate. Similarly, in the course of delivering foot-shock to a pair of rats, occasionally a rat would learn to eliminate the shock by lying motionless on its back, thereby producing a situation in which only one rat was being stimulated. Under these circumstances, the rat stimulated by foot-shock often attacked the supine rat in the same way that the rat stimulated by electrode-shock attacked the unstimulated rat. It should be noted that in each of these situations where only one rat was being stimulated, the full-blown fighting response was elicited less frequently than when both rats were stimulated. Stimulation of a second rat is not a necessary condition for producing the fighting reaction but does, nevertheless, increase the likelihood of its occurrence.

Intense Heat

The elicitation of the fighting reflex through electrode-shock as well as foot-shock suggested that other aversive stimulation also might elicit fighting. A pair of rats was placed in an experimental chamber with a thin metal floor that could be heated from below by a heating coil. After the heating coil was energized, the metal floor became progressively hotter and the two rats began jumping about and licking their feet. No fighting was produced in spite of the agitated movements of both rats. However, when the same pair later was placed on a preheated floor, fighting consistently resulted. The same results were obtained with additional rats. The rats scrambled about the chamber, interrupting their movements frequently to assume a fixed position and attack each other before resuming their running about. It is very likely that the rats received more painful heat stimulation during the fighting episodes than they would have received if they had jumped about. No more than 2 min. of exposure to the heated floor was given because of the possibility of tissue damage. Nevertheless, the heated floor appeared to elicit fighting in much the same manner as a continuously electrified floor grid. It is probable that the gradual heating of the floor grid allowed the reinforcement of competing behavior, especially licking of the forepaws. This wetting the paws appeared to be effective in cooling the animal at the initially lower temperature of the gradually heated floor but not at the high temperature of the preheated floor. Once fighting was elicited by a preheated floor, subsequent exposure to a gradually heated floor did elicit some fighting, and the competing licking behaviors were reduced.

Cold and Intense Noise

In spite of the effectiveness of intense heat in eliciting fighting behavior, no fighting was elicited by placing rats on a sheet metal floor precooled by dry ice. It is possible that the temperature induced by the dry ice was not sufficiently aversive; no pain was felt by a human observer upon touching the cooled floor for periods less than 2 sec. Since the rats were consistently moving about, it is quite likely that they did not allow a given paw to remain in contact with the cold floor for a sufficient period of time. Since the cool floor did not produce pain upon immediate contact, unlike electric shock and heat, the rat probably could eliminate pain completely in much the same manner as the rat lying upon its insulated back can completely eliminate painful foot-shock.

Intense noise was similarly ineffective in producing fighting behavior between paired rats. The noise was at an intensity of 135 db (re 0.0002 dyne/cm^2) and enclosed a band from 200-1500 cps. The delivery of noise was varied from brief bursts of less than 1 sec. to periods of more than 1 min. No fighting resulted. A pair of guinea pigs was subjected to the same treatment in the expectation that guinea pigs might be more reactive to intense noise. No fighting resulted.

Fighting appears to be elicited by foot-shock, electrode-shock, and intense heat, but not by intense noise or moderate cold.

DISCUSSION

The present investigation found that fighting behavior could be elicited from several paired species by several different types of aversive stimulation. The elicitation of this fighting occurred in almost a one-to-one relationship to the aversive stimulus when the optimal value of the aversive stimulus was used. When a response, such as salivation, is consistently made to a stimulus, such as meat powder, with no previous training, that response is referred to as an unconditioned response (Pavlov, 1927; Sherrington, 1947) or as a respondent (Skinner, 1938). Physiologists have supplied us with the term reflex to designate such specific stimulus-response relationships and in fact have extended the term to denote responses for which related stimuli are not always clearly observable (Keller and Schoenfeld, 1950). The consistent elicitation of the fighting response by aversive stimulation without prior conditioning appears to be best defined as an unconditional reflex. Miller (1948), however, has taken a different approach in the study of fighting behavior. He reports that he trained his subjects to fight by removing the shock each time the animals approximated the fighting position. In this case fighting is presumed to be an escape reaction that is reinforced by the termination of electric shock. In spite of the virtual one-to-one relationship between shock and fighting observed in the present study, it is possible that this apparently reflexive fighting was maintained by some unsuspected and perhaps subtle operant reinforcement. Several possible sources of operant reinforcement seem apparent. First, it is possible that the rats were simply attempting to stand on each other in order to eliminate the aversive stimulation. Several observations made during the course of these experiments bear upon this interpretation: (1) When one of a pair of rats was lying on its back and effectively avoiding all shock, the shocked rat, rather than attempting to climb upon the other rat, often directed an attack specifically at the other rat's head. (2) Fighting was maintained by electrode-shock even though no escape was available to the rat stimulated through the electrodes. (3) Leaning against the other rat eliminated the shock no more than simply leaning against one of the insulating plastic walls of the experimental chamber. (4) On the heated floor, the fighting behavior served to increase rather than decrease the amount of aversive stimulation. (5) When an insulated doll was placed in the experimental chamber while a rat was given foot-shock, no attempt was made by the rat to jump upon the doll until several minutes of stimulation had elapsed.

A second possible source of operant reinforcement of fighting is that the fixed-duration shock delivery happened to terminate at the moment that the rats moved toward each other; thus, superstitious reinforcement of these movements would have resulted (Skinner, 1948). Again, several observations indicated that reinforcement of this sort was not operative in producing fighting: (1) Fighting often occurred with the onset of the first shock delivery when prior reinforcement through shock reduction was necessarily impossible. (2) Continuous and uninterrupted delivery of either foot-shock or severe heat produced fighting. Of course, no reinforcement through the termination of the stimulus can result if the stimulus is not terminated.

A plausible interpretation of the fighting reflex is that a rat will attack any nearby object or organism upon being aversively stimulated. However, rats did not attack a nearby doll, either insulating or conducting, upon being shocked. Nor was the movement of an inanimate object in the presence of a shocked rat a sufficient condition for eliciting fighting. No fighting resulted when the dolls were moved about the cage at the end of a stick during and between shock presentations. Additional experiments revealed that even a recently deceased rat would not be attacked by a second rat that was given foot-shock, unless the dead rat was moved about the cage on a stick. It would seem, therefore, that a second moving animal either rat, guinea pig, or hamster is a necessary condition for eliciting the fighting response from a rat stimulated by foot-shock.

SUMMARY

Reflexive fighting was elicited between paired rats as a reflex reaction to electric shock prior to any specific conditioning. Such fighting was fairly stereotyped and easily differentiated from the rats' usual behavior. The strength of this reflex was not attributable to any apparent operant reinforcement. Elicitation of fighting was a direct function of the enclosed floor area and a nonmonotonic function of the shock intensity.

Failure to scramble the polarity of the electrified grid produced inconsistent fighting. Under optimal conditions fighting was consistently elicited by shock regardless of the rat's sex, strain, previous familiarity with each other, or the number present during shock. Repeated shock presentations did not produce an appreciable decrease in fighting until signs of physical debility appeared. Although shock did not cause a rat to attack inanimate objects, it did produce attack movements toward other small animals. Failure of guinea pigs to defend themselves revealed that the elicitation of fighting from the rat does not require reciprocal attack. Paired hamsters showed fighting reactions similar to those of the rats, whereas guinea pigs failed to fight. Electrode shock and a heated floor elicited fighting between the rats, but intense noise and a cooled floor did not.

REFERENCES

BEEMAN, E. A. The effect of male hormone on aggressive behavior in mice. *Physiol. Zool.*, 1947, *20*, 373–405.

DANIEL, W. J. An experimental note on the O'Kelly-Steckle reaction. *J. comp. Psychol.*, 1943, *35*, 267–268.

KELLER, F. S., and SCHOENFELD, W. N. *Principles of psychology.* New York: Appleton-Century-Crofts, 1950.

MILLER, N. E. Theory and experiment relating psychoanalytic displacement to stimulus-response generalization. *J. abnorm. soc. Psychol.*, 1948, *43*, 155–178.

O'KELLY, L. I., and STECKLE, L. C. A note on long enduring emotional responses in the rat. *J. Psychol.*, 1939, *8*, 125–131.

PAVLOV, I. P. *Conditioned reflexes: An investigation of the physiological activity of the cerebral cortex.* London: Oxford University Press, 1927.

RICHTER, C. P. Domestication of the Norway rat and its implications for the problem of stress. *Ass. Res. in Nerv. and ment. dis. Proc.*, 1950, *29*, 19.

SCOTT, J. P., and FREDERICSON, E. The causes of fighting in mice and rats. *Physiol. Zool.*, 1951, *24*, 273–309.

SEWARD, J. P. Aggressive behavior in the rat. I. General characteristics: age and sex differences; II. An attempt to establish a dominance hierarchy; III. The role of frustration; IV. Submission as determined by conditioning, extinction, and disuse. *J. comp. Psychol.*, 1945, *38*, 175–197, 213–224, 225–238; *39*, 51–76.

Sherrington, C. *The integrative action of the nervous system.* New Haven: Yale University Press, 1947.

Skinner, B. F. *The behavior of organisms.* New York: Appleton-Century-Crofts, 1938.

Skinner, B. F. "Superstition" in the pigeons. *J. exp. Psychol.,* 1948, *38,* 168–172.

Skinner, B. F., and Campbell, S. L. An automatic shocking grid apparatus for continuous use. *J. comp. physiol. Psychol.,* 1947, *40,* 305–307.

Tedeschi, R. E. Effects of various centrally acting drugs on fighting behavior of mice. *J. pharmacol. exp. Ther.,* 1959, *125,* 28.

SUGGESTED READINGS

Bandura, A., and Walters, R. *Social learning and personality development.* New York: Holt, Rinehart and Winston, 1963.

Brown, R. *Social psychology.* New York: Free Press, 1965.

Homans, G. C. *Social behavior.* New York: Harcourt, Brace & World, 1961.

Kuhn, A. *The study of society: A unified approach.* Homewood, Ill.: Irwin, 1963.

Miller, N. E., and Dollard, J. *Social learning and imitation.* New Haven: Yale, 1941.

Newcomb, T. M., Turner, R. H., and Converse, P. E. *Social psychology: The study of human interaction.* New York: Holt, Rinehart and Winston, 1965.

GLOSSARY

accidental chaining A process in which a response which frequently precedes a reinforced response shares in the effect of the reinforcement in such a way that the whole sequence becomes a stable part of the organism's behavior. A form of superstitious behavior (q.v.).

accidental (or incidental or spurious) reinforcement A coincidence of a response and a reinforcing event (e.g., in certain programs designed to establish a discrimination, the appearance of the discriminative stimulus may coincide with a response in its absence).

adaptation (1) As operation: exposing an organism to a stimulus. (2) As process: a change in the extent of the reaction of the organism to the stimulus.

ad lib body-weight The weight approached or reached by a mature organism under continuous access to food.

ad-lib feeding Providing continuous access to food.

adjusting schedule A form of schedule in which a value (e.g., of interval or ratio) is changed in some systematic way from reinforcement to reinforcement as a function of the performance (e.g., a fixed ratio is adjusted after each reinforcement according to some measured aspect of the performance in the preceding session, such as the length of the pause before the first response).

alternative schedule A response is reinforced on whichever of two schedules is satisfied first (e.g., after 5 minutes has elapsed or after 50 responses have been emitted, whichever occurs first).

anxiety, see conditioned suppression.

aversive stimulus A stimulus, the removal of which is reinforcing, or which may produce a low rate in the presence of a stimulus which frequently precedes it (which thus becomes a conditioned aversive stimulus).

avoidance behavior Behavior which postpones an aversive event and thus provides escape from conditioned aversive stimuli. Avoid RS 10 SS 10 is a notation for the avoidance procedure of Sidman; the numbers represent seconds, and RS stands for response-shock interval (q.v.) and SS for shock-shock interval (q.v.)

behavior   (1) Broadly speaking, any activity of the organism; more particularly any activity which changes the position of the organism or any
part thereof in space. The dependent variable in a science of behavior.
(2) The events of (1) as they affect the organism as stimuli (traditionally called proprioceptive stimulation, feed-back, etc.).

bite   A deviation from a smooth curve consisting of a period of relatively
slow responding followed more or less abruptly by a compensatory increase in rate which restores the curve to the extrapolation of the
earlier portion. Opposite of knee (q.v.).

body-weight (in control of level of deprivation)   A collateral effect of a
schedule of food deprivation used as a check upon such a schedule. It
is usually measured immediately prior to an experimental session. A
fairly constant body-weight from day to day is maintained by feeding
the organism up to a given weight after completion of each session.

box   An experimental chamber containing the organism during an experiment, usually with some degree of sound and light shielding, and
containing one or more manipulanda, reinforcing devices, and manipulable stimuli.

chained responses   A sequence of responses in which one response produces conditions essential to the next, as in making the next response
possible or more likely to be reinforced. Successive responses may or
may not have the same topography.

chained schedules (chain)   A schedule in which responding under one
stimulus on a given schedule is reinforced by the production of a second stimulus in the presence of which a response is reinforced on a second schedule with food, water, etc. Resembles a multiple schedule
(q.v.) except that the reinforcement of the first component is simply
the production of the stimulus of the second component.

clock   A stimulus some dimension of which varies systematically with
time, usually measured from the preceding reinforcement but possibly
from some other point. (E.g., FI + clock means reinforcement on FI
in the presence of such a stimulus.)

compensatory rate   A higher than normal rate following one lower than
normal, tending to restore the over-all rate to an earlier value. Also a
lower than normal rate following a higher than normal one with the
same result.

concurrent operants   Two or more responses, of different topography at
least with respect to locus, capable of being executed with little mutual
interference at the same time or in rapid alternation, under the control
of separate programming devices (e.g., responses to two keys present
at the same time under separate schedules).

concurrent schedules (conc)   Two or more schedules independently arranged but operating at the same time, reinforcements being set up by both.

conditioned reinforcer A stimulus having the effect of a reinforcer because of its relation to a stimulus already having that effect.

conditioned suppression A reduction in rate in the presence of a previously neutral stimulus which has characteristically preceded an aversive event. (E.g., a 3-minute tone which has repeatedly been followed by a strong shock will eventually suppress operant behavior in progress when the tone is introduced.) Sometimes equated with anxiety.

conditioned stimulus A stimulus which evokes a response or alters some other condition of behavior only because of a history in which it has been paired with a stimulus (often unconditioned) having the same effect.

conditioning, see **operant conditioning, respondent conditioning.**

conjunctive schedule (conj) A schedule in which two contingencies must be met to achieve reinforcement. (E.g., a response is reinforced after 10 minutes and after 100 responses have been emitted, both of these since the preceding reinforcement.)

contingency (of reinforcement or punishment) (1) In operant conditioning: the temporal, intensive, and topographical conditions under which a response is followed by a positive or negative reinforcing stimulus or the removal of either of these. (2) In respondent conditioning: the conditions under which unconditioned and conditioned stimuli are paired.

continuous reinforcement (crf) Reinforcement of every response. Sometimes called "regular" reinforcement. Nonintermittent reinforcement.

control (as in "stimulus control") An observed tendency for a probability or rate of responding to vary with the presence and absence of a variable (e.g. a stimulus).

counter A stimulus some dimension of which varies systematically with number of responses emitted, counted from the preceding reinforcement or some other marking event. FR + counter means reinforcement on FR in the presence of such a stimulus.

crf Continuous reinforcement (q.v.).

cumulative curve A curve showing the number of responses emitted plotted against time. Such a curve is conveniently recorded while the behavior is in progress. Rate of responding can be read from it as the slope at any given point, and compensatory changes in rate can be estimated from inspection.

curve Used in referring to the present figures to refer to any unitary portion of a recorded performance.

deprivation (1) As operation: withholding food, water, sexual contact, etc. Any given program establishes a "level" of deprivation. (2) As process: resulting changes in behavior, usually spoken of as an increasing "state" of deprivation. Any given state is a given "level" of deprivation.

deviation   A change in rate against an established baseline, often followed by compensatory changes in rate.

differential rate reinforcement   Reinforcement (continuous or intermittent) which depends upon the immediately preceding rate of responding. This may be the reciprocal either of the time elapsing between the reinforced response and the immediately preceding response or of the time required to execute three or more responses. See also **differential reinforcement** of high rates, of low rates, and of paced responses.

differential reinforcement   Reinforcement which is contingent upon (1) the presence of a given property of a stimulus, in which case the resulting process is discrimination, (2) the presence of a given intensive, durational, or topographical property of a response, in which case the resulting process is differentiation, or (3) a given rate of responding. See also **differential rate reinforcement**.

differential reinforcement of high rates (drh)   Reinforcements occur only when the rate is above some specified value.

differential reinforcement of low rates (drl)   Reinforcements occur only when the rate is below some specified value.

differential reinforcement of paced responses (drp) or (pacing)   Time between the preceding response and the reinforced response is specified more narrowly as falling between certain limits.

differentiation   (1) As operation: the differential reinforcement of responses which satisfy some formal specification with respect to intensity, duration, or topography. (2) As process: the resulting change in relative frequency of responses showing the specified property.

disk, see key.

discrimination

    operant discrimination: (1) As operation: the differential reinforcement of a response with respect to a property of a stimulus (e.g., responses to a red key are reinforced; responses to a green key are not). (2) As process: the resulting change in rate as a function of the properties of the stimuli, observed either concurrently or under later conditions. The organism "shows a discrimination" by responding more rapidly in the presence of the property correlated with reinforcement.

    respondent discrimination: (1) As operation: arranging a third stimulus in respondent conditioning in the presence of which unconditioned and conditioned stimuli are paired and in the absence of which they are not (e.g., a tone is paired with food in the presence of a flashing light). (2) As process: the resulting change in behavior by virtue of which a conditioned response is elicited (by the tone) only in the presence of the

stimulus present when the conditioned stimulus is paired with a reinforcing stimulus (the flashing light).

discriminative stimulus (1) In operant discrimination: a stimulus in the
presence of which a response is reinforced and in the absence of which
it goes unreinforced. (2) In respondent discrimination: a stimulus in
the presence of which an unconditioned and conditioned stimulus are
paired, and in the absence of which they go unpaired.

drh Differential reinforcement of high rates (q.v.).

drl Differential reinforcement of low rates (q.v.).

drp Differential reinforcement of paced responses (q.v.).

escape behavior (esc) Behavior which terminates an aversive stimulus
(e.g., esc RS 10 designating a contingency in which a response produces
the cessation of an aversive stimulus for 10 seconds).

excursion On the standard recorder the pen returns to a baseline after
cumulating a block of responses of the order of 800 to 1000. In describing the present figures, each crossing of the paper by the pen is referred to as an excursion.

extinction (ext)
operant extinction: (1) As operation: the withholding of a reinforcement
previously contingent upon a response. (2) As process: the resulting
decrease in probability or rate.
respondent extinction: (1) As operation: the presentation of a conditioned stimulus occurring without the unconditioned or reinforcing
stimulus. (2) As process: the resulting reduction in the magnitude or
other dimension of the response elicited by the conditioned stimulus.

fine grain, see grain.

fixed-interval schedule (FI) A schedule of intermittent reinforcement in
which the first response occurring after a given interval of time, measured from the preceding reinforcement, is reinforced. A given interval
schedule is designated by adding a number to the letters FI to indicate
minutes. (E.g., FI 5 is a schedule in which the first response which occurs
5 minutes or more after the preceding reinforcement is reinforced.)

fixed-ratio schedule (FR) A schedule of intermittent reinforcement in which
a response is reinforced upon completion of a fixed number of responses
counted from the preceding reinforcement. ("Ratio" refers to the ratio:
responses/reinforcement.) A given ratio schedule is designated by adding a number to the letters FR to indicate the ratio. (E.g., FR 100 is a
schedule of reinforcement in which the 100th response after the preceding reinforcement is reinforced.)

food magazine, see magazine.

FR   Fixed-ratio schedule (q.v.).

generalization, see induction.

gradient   A related set of values on a dimension of a stimulus, along which stimulus induction has occurred.

grain   The character of the recorded cumulative curve arising from variability in inter-response times. Responses equally spaced regardless of rate produce a "smooth" grain. Groups of responses with pauses interspersed produce a "rough" grain. The term usually applies to short intervals of time and hence only to local rates (q.v.). Occasionally, it is useful to distinguish between "fine" grain and somewhat larger irregularities in the local rates.

hold, see limited hold.

"house light"   The light responsible for the general illumination in the experimental box.

incidental reinforcement, see accidental reinforcement.

induction   Often called generalization.

stimulus induction: a process through which a stimulus acquires or loses the capacity to elicit a response, control a discriminative response, set up an emotional "state," etc., because of its similarity to a stimulus which has acquired or lost such a capacity through other means. (E.g., if a red light is established as a discriminative stimulus, an orange [or even yellow] light may be found to share the same function, though in lesser degree.)

response induction: a process through which a response changes its probability or rate because it shares properties with another response which has changed its probability or rate through other means.

interlocking schedule (interlock)   A schedule of intermittent reinforcement in which the reinforcement is determined by two schedules, where the setting of one schedule is altered by progress made in the other. (E.g., in the schedule interlock FI 5 FR 250, the organism is reinforced at a ratio which is slowly reduced from 250 to 1 during 5 minutes. If responding is rapid, reinforcement occurs only after a large ratio has been completed; if responding is slow, reinforcement occurs at a much lower ratio; if no response occurs within 5 minutes, the first response is reinforced.)

intermittent reinforcement   Noncontinuous reinforcement. A schedule according to which not every response is reinforced. See entries listed under schedules of reinforcement.

intermittent schedule A schedule involving intermittent reinforcement as contrasted with continuous reinforcement and extinction.

interpolated schedule (inter) A single block of reinforcements in one schedule is interpolated into a sustained period of responding on a different background schedule. (E.g., on FR 20 inter FI 15, several reinforcements on FR 20 are inserted into an experimental period in which the organism is otherwise reinforced on FI 15.)

inter-response time (IRT) Time elapsing between two successive responses; response-response interval.

interval schedules Schedules of intermittent reinforcement in which reinforcements are programmed by a clock.

IRT Inter-response time (q.v.).

key Any manipulable object, the movement of which closes or breaks an electrical circuit. In experiments with pigeons, a useful key is a translucent disk at a convenient height on the wall of the experimental box. When the pigeon pecks this disk, a circuit is made or broken. In experiments with rats, a horizontal bar parallel to and approximately ½ inch from the wall of the experimental box can be pressed downward against a light spring to close or break the circuit.

key light Light projected upon the translucent pigeon key, used as a stimulus. Lights of different colors or patterns may be used.

knee A deviation from a smooth curve, often seen in the early acceleration of interval or ratio segments, consisting of a brief period of rapid responding followed more or less abruptly by a compensatory low rate which restores the curve to an extrapolation of the earlier portion. Opposite of bite (q.v.).

lever, see key.

limited hold A short period during which a reinforcement arranged by an interval schedule is held available. At the end of the limited hold, a response will not be reinforced until another reinforcement has been set up.

local rate Rate of responding in some small region of a curve. Contrasted with overall rate. See also rate of responding.

magazine A mechanical device which makes food, water, etc., available to the organism, usually in reinforcement.

manipulandum Any movable object serving as a key (q.v.).

mean rate, see rate of responding.

mediating behavior Behavior occurring between two instances of the response being studied (or between some other event and such an instance) which is used by the organism as a controlling stimulus in subsequent behavior. (E.g., under drl the necessary delay in responding is often produced by the incidental reinforcement of mediating behavior which might be called "marking time.") A time out between response and reinforcement may not greatly reduce the effectiveness of the reinforcement if mediating behavior has been acquired during the TO.

mixed schedule (mix) Reinforcement is programmed by two or more schedules alternating usually at random. No stimuli are correlated with the schedules as in multiple schedules. (E.g., mix FI 5 FR 50 represents a schedule in which a reinforcement sometimes occurs after an interval of 5 minutes and sometimes after a "ratio" of 50 responses, the possibilities occurring either at random or according to a program in any determined proportion.)

multiple schedule (mult) Reinforcement is programmed by two or more schedules alternating, usually at random, each schedule being accompanied by an appropriate stimulus as long as the schedule is in force. Differs from mixed schedule simply in the presence of controlling stimuli. (E.g., mult FI 5 FR 100 represents a schedule under which reinforcement sometimes occurs after an interval of 5 minutes and sometimes after 100 responses, the possibilities occurring either at random or according to some program in any determined proportion, when an appropriate stimulus accompanies each schedule.)

negative reinforcer An aversive stimulus (q.v.).

nonintermittent schedules Continuous reinforcement (q.v.) and extinction (q.v.).

number Brief expression for the number of responses already emitted in executing a ratio, especially as these function as stimuli. (E.g., "number as reinforcer" means that the accumulation of a number of responses in the course of emitting a ratio acts as a conditioned reinforcer.) See counter.

operant A unit of behavior defined by a contingency of reinforcement. Pecking a key is an operant if instances are reinforced in a given situation. A class of responses, all members of which are equally effective in achieving reinforcement under a given set of conditions.

operant conditioning (1) As operation: arranging the reinforcement of a response possessing specified properties, or, more specifically, arranging that a given reinforcer follow the emission of a given response. (2) As process: the resulting increase in the rate of occurrence of responses possessing these properties.

operation   Arranging or altering some condition in an experiment (e.g., arranging or changing a contingency of reinforcement, depriving an animal of food on a given schedule, introducing a conditioned aversive stimulus, etc.).

over-all rate   The mean rate over a fairly large segment of behavior. See also rate of responding.

pacing, see differential reinforcement of paced responses.

pause   A period of no responding, contrasted with neighboring fairly high rates, as after reinforcement at high ratios.

Pavlovian conditioning   Respondent conditioning (q.v.).

percentage reinforcement   On any given schedule, including continuous reinforcement, a certain percentage of reinforcements may be replaced by some other event, such as a time out. [E.g., FR 50 (20%) means that the completion of 50 responses is followed by reinforcement 20% of the time and by a time out 80% of the time, the order of reinforcements and time outs being random.]

performance   Behavior characteristically observed under a given schedule (e.g., FI performance).

pre-aversive stimulus   A stimulus repeatedly preceding an aversive stimulus.

prime   In a multiple schedule a stimulus under which the organism embarks upon a schedule performance which usually sustains itself when the prime is withdrawn.

probability of response   The probability that a response will be emitted within a specified interval, inferred from its observed frequency under comparable conditions.

probe   A change in conditions at some arbitrary point in an experiment made to evaluate or test for the conditions currently in control. May be a TO, a discriminative stimulus, a schedule-controlling stimulus, etc.

process   Any change in rate of responding, specifically as the result of an experimental operation.

programming   Arranging a set of reinforcing contingencies, including schedules, stimuli, etc.

punishment   An operation in which an aversive or conditioned aversive stimulus is made contingent upon a response.

rate of responding   Responses per unit time, usually responses per second. It is convenient to distinguish between different rates according to the interval of time covered.

  fine grain: rate distribution among smallest clusters of responses.

  local rate: rate measured over a short time. The tangent of the cumulative curve at any given point, ignoring the fine grain.

mean rate: responses per unit time calculated for an interval during which changes in local rate have occurred.

over-all rate: mean rate for a still longer period of time (of the order of minutes or hours). Frequently applying to the rate between successive reinforcements, without respect to segment curvature.

running rate: sustained constant rate, often the only important single rate except for zero observed under a given schedule (as in some ratio performances).

terminal rate: the rate reached on the fixed schedules at the moment of reinforcement.

ratio schedules Reinforcements are programmed according to the number of responses emitted by the organism.

record Used in speaking of the present figures to identify a portion representing either a whole session or part of a session, as distinct from curve, excursion, etc.

recorder Device for obtaining a cumulative record of the responses of an organism.

"regular" reinforcement, see continuous reinforcement.

reinforcement

operant reinforcement: presenting a reinforcing stimulus when a response occurs, or arranging such presentation.

respondent reinforcement: presenting a conditioned and an unconditioned stimulus at approximately the same time. See also **contingency, differential reinforcement, intermittent reinforcement, continuous reinforcement,** etc.

reinforcer Any event which, when used in the temporal relations specified in reinforcement, is found to produce the process of conditioning.

respondent An unconditioned or conditioned reflex in the sense of a response elicited by a particular stimulus.

respondent conditioning The establishment and strengthening of a conditioned reflex through the roughly simultaneous presentation of unconditioned and conditioned stimuli, as in the Pavlovian experiment.

response (1) An instance of an identifiable part of behavior. (2) A class of such instances. In this sense, response is equivalent to operant (q.v.). See also **behavior.**

response-response interval (RR) Time elapsing between two successive responses. Inter-response time.

response-shock interval (RS) In avoidance conditioning the time elapsing between the last response and occurrence of a shock as an aversive stimulus. See also **avoidance behavior.**

RR Response-response interval (q.v.).

RS Response-shock interval (q.v.).

running rate, see rate of responding.

running weight A given body-weight, selected as an indicator of a schedule of deprivation, at which the organism is held from day to day during an experiment.

satiation (1) As operation: making food available to an organism, possibly until it stops eating. (2) As process: the resulting change in rate, usually a reduction.

schedules of reinforcement, see the following:

nonintermittent: continuous reinforcement (crf)
                  extinction (ext)

intermittent: fixed ratio (FR)
                  variable ratio (VR)
                  fixed interval (FI)
                  variable interval (VI)
                  tandem (tand)
                  multiple (mult)
                  mixed (mix)
                  interlocking (interlock)
                  alternative (alt)
                  concurrent (conc)
                  conjunctive (conj)
                  interpolated (inter)
                  chained (chain)

scallop Postively accelerated portion of the cumulative record, usually used in speaking of interval or ratio segments.

second-order effect A relation between the numbers of responses emitted in two or more successive intervals on FI in which an over-all acceleration may be observed throughout all segments.

segment Part of the record of an experimental session, usually between two reinforcements.

session Experimental period. The period during which an organism is exposed to experimental conditions, usually once per day.

set up To set up a reinforcement is to close a circuit so that the next response will be reinforced whenever it occurs.

shock-shock interval (SS) In avoidance conditioning, the interval between successive shocks when no response has been made in that interval. See also avoidance behavior.

speedometer A stimulus, some dimension of which changes as a function of the rate of responding measured over some arbitrary period of time.

spontaneous recovery A temporarily higher rate sometimes observed at the beginning of an experimental session, following a session in which the rate has declined (e.g., in extinction). This traditional term suggests that the earlier rate has "recovered" during the intervening time.

A more plausible explanation is that stimuli closely associated with the beginning of the session control a higher rate because of earlier conditions of reinforcement and because there has not yet been an opportunity for this effect to be changed by the experimental changes made during the bulk of the preceding session.

spurious reinforcement, see accidental reinforcement.

SS Shock-shock interval (q.v.).

stimulus Any physical event or condition in the experimental situation including the organism's own behavior. Not to be confined, as it sometimes is, to those events or conditions which have a demonstrable effect on the organism. See particular names for different types of stimuli.

strength of response Sometimes used to designate probability or rate of responding.

superstitious behavior Behavior strengthened through reinforcing contingencies not explicitly arranged and possibly not frequent or permanent, but nevertheless effective in increasing the strength of the operant.

tandem schedule (tand) A schedule of intermittent reinforcement in which a single reinforcement is programmed by two schedules acting in succession without correlated stimuli. E.g., in tand FI 10 FR 5 a reinforcement occurs when 5 responses have been executed after a 10-minute interval has elapsed. In tand FRFI, a (usually) short interval must elapse after the completion of a ratio before a response is reinforced. It is often important to specify which of the two schedules composes the more substantial part of the schedule. This can be done by italicizing the important member.

terminal rate, see rate of responding.

time out (TO) Time (in minutes unless otherwise specified) during which the organism characteristically does not engage in the behavior being studied. With pigeons a convenient TO is arranged by turning off all lights in the apparatus. In the rat, a TO can be achieved through the use of a previously developed discriminative stimulus. TOs are used as probes, markers in a series of events, a method of eliminating effects of earlier behavior, etc.

unconditioned stimulus A stimulus, the capacity of which to elicit a response does not depend upon its having been paired with another stimulus possessing this capacity.

variable Any condition in an experiment, whether manipulable or merely observed, which can be changed or changes.

dependent variable: in these experiments, the behavior of the organism, or more specifically the rate of emission of a given type of response.

independent variable: any condition which is varied systematically in studying a change in the dependent variable (e.g., a stimulus, a reinforcing contingency, a schedule of deprivation, etc.).

variable-interval schedule (VI) A schedule of intermittent reinforcement in which reinforcements are programmed according to a random series of intervals having a given mean and lying between arbitrary extreme values.

variable-ratio schedule (VR) A schedule of intermittent reinforcement under which reinforcements are programmed according to a random series of ratios having a given mean and lying between arbitrary extreme values.

warm up Acceleration at the start of a session leading to the level of performance characteristic of the bulk of the session.

water magazine, see magazine.

weight The body-weight of the animal usually measured at the beginning of the daily experiment.

yoked boxes A system of controlling frequency of reinforcement as one variable in experiments on ratio schedules. Reinforcements are "set up" in one box whenever they are set up in another on a ratio schedule. The schedule in the yoked box is, nevertheless, an interval schedule.